Welding Know-How

The Tips & Techniques of Master Welders

First Edition

Frank M. Marlow, PE

with

P.J. Tallman

Metal Arts Press
Huntington Beach

Metal Arts Press

MetalArtsPress.com
8461 Valencia Drive
Huntington Beach, CA 92647-6033
USA

Welding Know-How
The Tips & Techniques of Master Welders
First Edition
ISBN-13 978-0-975-9963-6-2
Copyright © 2012 by
Frank M. Marlow & Pamela J. Tallman
All rights reserved.

Other books by Frank M. Marlow
Machine Shop Essentials: Questions & Answers
Machine Shop Know-How: The Tips & Techniques of Master Machinists

Cover design by Stephanie Starr

10 9 8 7 6 5 4 3 2 1

To David Randal
for his friendship and his knowledge

Contents

Preface

Most people don't read prefaces, but I encourage you to make this one the exception. I guarantee that it has no highfalutin' philosophy or history that no one cares about. This preface is actually useful.

What This Book Is About

This book is about welding, cutting, and brazing.

Welding Know-How takes an in-depth look at the four most common welding processes—oxyacetylene, stick, wire-feed and TIG—and describes how each process works, its equipment, applications, advantages, start-up and shutdown procedures, along with welding techniques and troubleshooting.

The book also covers the five most used metal cutting processes—oxyacetylene, plasma arc, shielded metal arc cutting, air carbon arc, burning bar and oxygen lance cutting—including their equipment, applications and techniques.

In addition, the book features the equipment, materials, and processes for brazing and soldering, including brazing methods for steel, aluminum, stainless steel, cast iron and tungsten carbide. *Welding Know-How* compares the advantages of silver brazing, bronze brazing and several solder alloys. Step-by-step brazing and soldering instructions for sweating copper tubing are there too.

Welding Know-How features dozens of helpful projects, repair techniques and solutions to common welding problems. This book will teach you how to make special-purpose tools, improve commercial tools, and build welding fixtures.

Who This Book Is For

This book is for anyone who desires a basic knowledge of welding and wants to use its equipment with safety and confidence. Even experienced welders will find useful tips they've never seen before. The list of who could benefit from this book includes machinists, industrial welders, industrial model makers, R&D lab technicians, home shop machinists, scientific instrument makers, prototype designers, custom motorcycle and car builders, gunsmiths, hobbyist, farmers, teachers, and students.

Welding Know-How contains more information than is presented in three semesters of junior college welding courses and in considerably more depth, yet it can be read in less than a day. While many junior college courses focus on training "rod burners," this book will show you how to fabricate *useful* items and repair broken ones. It will not teach you how to make lawn ornaments, decorative mailboxes, or utility trailers. There are already too many books doing this.

Why Learn to Weld?

Who doesn't want to do their own repairs, to not be at the mercy of repairmen? The ability to weld gives you unique capabilities and alternative solutions to tricky problems, whether the problem involves a leaky pipe, a damaged injection mold, race car parts, jet engines, firearms, product prototypes, model trains or scientific instruments, welding and brazing play a critical role in their fabrication and repair.

Welding is a vital part of most machine shops, repair facilities, and one-of-a-kind fabrication workshops because it can make very strong joints, replace worn away metal, or improve the hardness and wear properties on critical areas of parts. Though the actual volume of weld metal added is quite small, the value added by restoring a part to service is quite large.

Welding Equipment

Although the most common welding processes have seen few changes in the last twenty years, the welding industry has changed immensely because the price of equipment has dramatically fallen and its availability and selection has improved. Big box home improvement stores carry stick and wire feed welding machines and budget import tool stores stock a good selection of TIG welding machines and plasma arc cutters. People now have access to affordable welding equipment, and this book supplies the knowledge needed to use this equipment.

Illustrations

This book contains over 500 line drawings, most of which were created specifically for *Welding Know-How*. Although not the easier or cheaper path, I chose to use drawings instead of photographs because of the focus, detail, and clear explanations they provide. No other welding book has as many original illustrations. Most use manufacturer-supplied stock photos, which many times are not helpful.

Glossary

The glossary—usually 30 pages of filler—does not take up space in this book. The glossary is on the Internet at: www.MetalArtsPress.com.

Note From the Author

I am thankful for the generous help of the many individuals and companies who contributed their time and knowledge to this book. The greatest care has been taken to be precise and accurate, but naturally, I remain responsible for any errors.

HUNTINGTON BEACH, CALIFORNIA   FRANK MARLOW
MARCH 2012

Acknowledgements

Aladdin Welding Products, Inc.
American Beauty – Assembly Technologies International, Inc.
American Welding Society
Applied Home Healthcare Equipment, LLC
John Carleo
Copper Development Association, Inc.
Prof. Robert J. DeVoe, PE
Di-Acro, Incorporated
The Do-All Company
ESAB Welding & Cutting Products, Inc.
Industrial Press Inc.
The James F. Lincoln Welding Foundation
The L.S. Starrett Company
Joe Martin
The M.K. Morse Company
Mathey Dearman, Inc.
Victoria Marquard
Miller Electric Mfg. Co.
Oxylance Corporation
David Randal
Sherline Products Inc.
Don Tallman
Van Sant Enterprises Inc.
Vise-Grip – American Tool Companies, Inc.
Bernie Wasinger
Weldsale Company

Chapter 1

Welding Overview

*Working in a welding supply store and not knowing how to weld
is like working in a bookstore and not knowing how to read.*

—Sheldon at V.B. Anderson Company

Introduction

This overview chapter introduces many new terms and procedures, so don't
worry if you don't understand all of if it now. You *will* understand it when you
finish the book.

With the first read you might feel overwhelmed by the number of welding
processes this chapter introduces. When re-read, though, after you finish the
rest of the book, you will understand the advantages and disadvantages of the
various welding processes and how to troubleshoot common problems.

Welding Functions

Welding is used to perform one or more of these functions:

- Joining together two or more workpieces. This is by far the most common
  welding function.

- Changing the surface contour on a workpiece. This is often done to hide a
  seam or joint.

- Adding filler metal to the workpiece surface falls into two categories:

  - In a process called *hardfacing,* a special alloy is applied to increase
    surface hardness, to add wear resistance, or to replace metal that has
    been worn away. Hardfacing is most commonly performed on earth
    moving equipment, chutes and rock breakers. Applying this metal can
    indefinitely prolong the useful life of this heavy equipment.

  - Very often only a small amount of weld metal is added to high-value
    parts like jet turbine blades, gear teeth and plastic injection molds to
    replace worn or eroded metal and restore the part to service. These
    repairs represent a small percentage of welding activity, but a good
    repair can mean high-dollar cost savings.

Major Welding Processes

This book concentrates on the four most important welding processes:

- *Shielded Metal Arc Welding* (American Welding Association designation SMAW), also called *stick welding,* accounts for the majority of filler metal usage. Shielded metal arc welding is commonly used for structural steel, shipbuilding, pipelining, tank building and general metal fabrication. SMAW can weld most metals including cast iron and aluminum. A wide variety of SMAW electrodes with different alloys and coverings provide a range of handling characteristics to solve many welding problems. In fact, there are more types of electrodes available for SMAW than for any other process. Many of these electrode-alloy and covering combinations cannot be used with *gas tungsten arc welding* (GTAW) because, during welding, the important properties of the final filler metal result from the interaction between both the electrode and its covering. Electrode-wire diameter ranges from $^3/_{32}$–$^1/_4$", making SMAW suitable for relatively rough tasks.

  SMAW power supplies are the simplest and least expensive of all the major welding power supplies. A few hundred dollars—the cost of the transformer-based *buzz box*—puts SMAW on farms and in garages. Based on the equipment needed to weld $^1/_4$" steel plate, SMAW is the most economical of all the major welding processes, followed closely by oxyacetylene. Although the necessary skill level varies with the task, generally SMAW requires an intermediate skill level, somewhere between that of wire feed welding and gas tungsten arc welding. Though SMAW produces smoke, particulates, and spatter, it provides excellent penetration. See Figure 1-1.

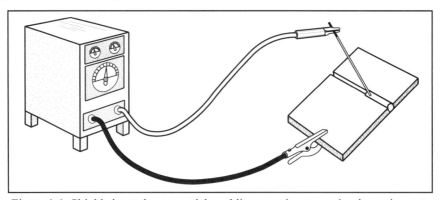

Figure 1-1. Shielded metal arc, or stick welding, requires very simple equipment.

- *Wire Feed Welding* is a blanket term that refers to both *Metal Inert Gas Welding* (commonly called MIG), *Gas Metal Arc Welding* (AWS designation GMAW) and *Flux Core Arc Welding* (AWS designation FCAW). Wire feed welding is used in the same applications as SMAW, but this process applies filler metal at a much higher rate. This is possible because wire feed welding is a continuous feed process without the need to stop to replace burned out electrodes. The ability to weld continuously makes wire feed welding ideal for robotic welding. The continuous feed ability also makes it the easiest and fastest process to learn because it has the fewest variables that the welder needs to control. The simplest tasks can be mastered in a few hours. Wire feed welding requires a DC power supply, which is slightly more complex and more expensive than a basic SMAW power supply. Unlike SMAW power supplies that can be located hundreds of feet away from the weld, wire feed welding machines (and the wire feed mechanism, if separate from the power supply) must be within 15–20' of the weld because, due to friction, the wire feed mechanism cannot force the electrode wire through longer cables. GMAW produces some smoke, but is nearly spatter-free, while FCAW produces more smoke, about the same volume as SMAW, and produces considerable spatter. See Figure 1-2.

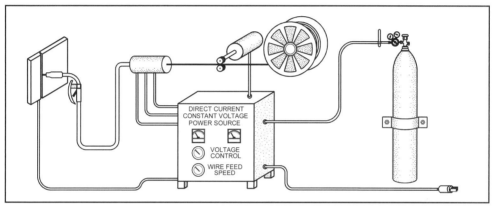

Figure 1-2. Commonly called MIG, wire feed welding equipment is more complex than stick welding equipment, but applies metal faster.

- *Gas Tungsten Arc Welding* (AWS designation GTAW) was refined during WWII in the Southern California aircraft industry for welding aluminum. GTAW (commonly called TIG for Tungsten Inert Gas) has two important advantages over stick and wire feed welding: First, it welds nearly all metals, and second, it offers the most control of all the processes. With GTAW the welder controls the position of the welding rod, the amount of metal added, the torch position, the travel speed, and the heat input. GTAW—with its foot-control torch heat—allows precise arc current adjustments, giving the welder heat-input control otherwise only available with an oxyacetylene torch. However, GTAW requires more welder skill than other wire-feed processes and has a much lower metal deposition rate. In most cases, though, it is the best way to weld aluminum. Nearly all GTAW welding adds filler metal, but *autogenous welds* can also be made by fusing parts together without added metal. The combination of inverter technology and microprocessor control has produced high-end GTAW power supplies capable of making welds that were once impossible. GTAW produces a smooth weld with little smoke and no spatter. See Figure 1-3.

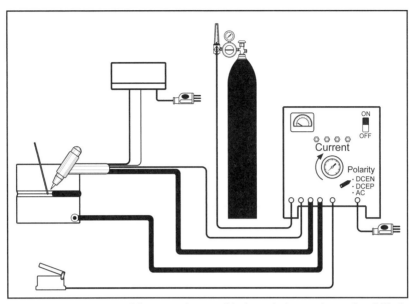

Figure 1-3. GTAW, or TIG welding, requires sophisticated electronics and a skilled welder.

- *Oxyacetylene Welding* (AWS designation OAW) is tied with GTAW for the number of different metals it can join, but oxyacetylene has several advantages. OAW equipment can also braze, braze weld, preheat, anneal, harden, bend, solder, and shrink panels. Because OAW is a relatively slow process with a low deposition rate, many other processes have replaced it in production. Despite this disadvantage, OAW is excellent for many critical repairs. Oxyacetylene equipment requires no electrical power, just the basic cylinders, regulators, hoses and a torch. However, it does require considerable practice to get good results. See Figure 1-4.

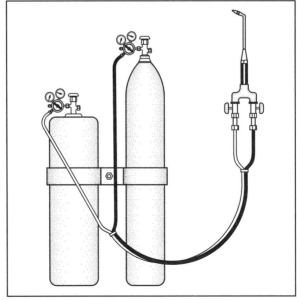

Figure 1-4. Oxyacetylene equipment is much less complex than that of other welding processes, but it requires considerably more skill to achieve good welds.

Table 1-1 compares these four welding processes.

Process	Ease of Learning (1=Easiest)	Metal Deposition Rate (1=Highest)	Precise Weld Control (1=Best)	Cost of Equipment (1=Highest)	Number of Metals Welded (1=Most)
SMAW	2	2	3	1	2
GMAW/FCAW	1	1	4	3	3
GTAW	3	4	1	4	1
OAW	4	3	2	2	1

Table 1-1. Comparison of the four most common welding processes.

How Welds Are Made

Every welding process makes welds by:

- Providing enough heat to melt both the workpiece base metal and the welding rod (or electrode wire) in the weld pool to fuse the joint.

- Protecting the molten metal in the weld pool from oxygen and nitrogen in the atmosphere until the metal cools and solidifies.

- Regulating the heat input so there is neither too much, nor too little.

- If filler metal is used, adding more welding rod or electrode wire to the molten joint as the joint progresses.

Because these four major welding processes perform these actions in different ways, they require different equipment, consumables, and welding skills. Also, these four processes have great differences in their penetration and metal deposition rates.

Factors Affecting the Metal Transfer Process

In each welding process the welding arc and the transfer of filler metal from the rod or electrode to the work is affected by the following factors:

- *Gravity* assists the welder by attracting weld metal to workpieces held in the flat position, but retards the deposition of metal to joints in the overhead position.

- *Magnetic fields* are created by the flow of welding current both through the arc itself and as it flows through the work to the ground lead. When these magnetic fields distort the arc, they create an effect called *arc blow*. The magnetic fields at the end of the electrode and inside the arc affect how molten filler metal forms drops as it leaves the electrode. This is called *pinch-off*.

- *Capillary attraction* is the inter-atomic force between individual atoms that affects how weld metal particles are pulled toward each other and to the work metal.

- *Heat transfer* occurs by *conduction, radiation* and *convection*. All three of these mechanisms play important roles in welding. They determine how fast the work heats and cools as well as the arc properties.

- *Arc properties* determine how easily the arc can be struck and maintained.

Welding is a complex process with many physical and chemical interactions going on at once. Because this complexity makes it difficult to analyze and mathematically predict welding processes, trial and error and experimentation are more commonly used than engineering analysis and computer modeling.

Factors Affecting Weld Quality

Several factors impact weld quality:

- *Workpiece surface cleanliness* – To insure a quality weld, the metal on and around the weld must be free of dirt, rust, paint, plating and other contaminants. Surface scale—which is principally iron oxide that forms on hot-rolled steel—is a common problem and must be removed by grinding. Although there are some stick welding rods which will burn through dirt and paint, many rods and electrodes will not. Grinding, wire brushing, sandblasting, glass-bead blasting, and filing will expose bare, clean metal. On smaller, critical TIG welds, a careful acetone or alcohol wipedown insures that no grease remains to add carbon to the weld. This cleaning is important because the additional carbon weakens welds. Even the carbon in black markers and Sharpies contaminates and weakens welds. To avoid this, many welders use pencils like the Blackstone #753 Silver Pencil, which leaves visible pencil lines, but no carbon.

  Be aware that welding over plating vaporizes the plating and exposes the welder to its toxic fumes. The fumes of heavy metals like cadmium, zinc and chromium are distinctly unhealthful.

- *Fit-up* – Poor fit-up means that the gap between the workpieces is too large to weld across and achieve adequate fusion on both sides and to the bottom of the weld. This is particularly true in thin plates, pipe and tubing where a single-pass weld is applied. Generally, gaps must be smaller than the diameter of the electrode or welding wire being used. In most cases, a tighter fit-up produces a stronger weld.

- *Edge preparation* – Beveling or shaping the sides of the weld provides welding access to the entire joint face of the workpiece. Usually, the thicker the work, the more edge preparation needed. In contrast, thin work often requires no edge prep.

- *Workpiece positioning* and *clamping* – These are two different steps, but many times both are achieved by the same means. The following positioning and clamping methods go from the least to the most complex:

  - *Tack welds* are small preliminary welds which are important aids in workpiece positioning and are discussed in *Chapter 3 – Terms, Joints & Edge Preparation.*

- *Existing structures* sometimes make it possible to perform a weld because two sides of the work are already supported. By applying a few tack welds the work is held rigidly enough to make the final, larger weld. With this simple support method no clamping is needed.

- *Clamps* are used to achieve precise alignment between weld parts. Clamps hold the two sides of a joint in place and are common in pipe and tubing welding where the work must be welded in coaxial alignment. Clamps are a critical factor in controlling weld-induced distortion, and in bending and forming operations.

- *Welding fixtures* are the next step in complexity. They not only position the work, they restrain it from moving under the forces of expansion and contraction caused by welding heat. See the fixture in Figure 1-5. Some fixtures in non-critical applications insure that a series of welded parts have *nearly* the same dimensions, but with a carefully designed fixture, critical parts can be made to precise dimensions—plus or minus a few thousandths of an inch—and will require little or no additional machining.

While soldering and brazing are not welding processes and differ in how they form a joint, welders often perform these tasks, and all of the factors that affect the quality of welding also affect the quality of soldering and brazing.

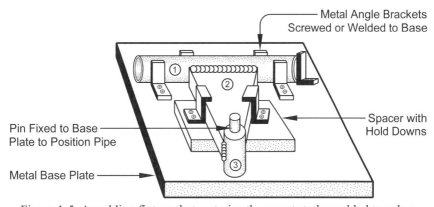

Figure 1-5. A welding fixture that restrains three parts to be welded together.

Filler Metal

Filler metal is the pure metal or metal alloy that is added to complete a welded or brazed joint. Filler metal can be in *rod* or *wire* form. Though rods and wires take two different forms, in the electrically-based welding processes of SMAW, GMAW, FCAW and GTAW, both rods and wires are commonly called *electrodes*. Filler metal may be solid metal, have an internal flux, as with FCAW electrodes, or an external flux, as with most SMAW rods. Brazing rods may be solid, have internal flux or an external flux coating. When two or more filler metal wires of different alloys are twisted together to form a single rod or electrode and melted together in the weld, they form *point-of-melt alloys*. Often these point-of-melt alloys cannot be created from a single rod and are real problem solvers. In general, each welding rod or electrode wire design works best with particular workpiece metals and a specific power supply polarity.

Welding Polarity

The choice of welding polarity is governed by the heat input requirements of the process and depends on the ability of the workpiece metal to conduct heat away from the joint fusion line. There are three types of polarity:

- *DC Electrode Negative (DCEN)* – With this polarity the work is positive with respect to the welding rod, electrode wire or tungsten electrode. This makes the end of the electrode an *electron emitter* which causes electrons to flow away from the rod or wire and down to the work. DCEN puts two-thirds of the welding heat into the work and leads to deep weld penetration.

- *DC Electrode Positive (DCEP)* – Here the welding rod or electrode wire is positive and the work negative. The result is that the electrons leave the workpiece and impact the rod or electrode. This puts two-thirds of the welding energy on the rod or electrode side of the arc. An obsolete term for DCEP is *DC Reverse Polarity (DCRP)*.

- *Alternating Current (AC)* – This polarity distributes the welding heat evenly between the work and the rod. There are two other factors which influence the use of AC:

  - *Arc Wander* – Using DC sets up strong magnetic fields that make control of the arc difficult. This is called *arc wander* and using AC avoids this problem. However, using AC may cause other problems because the arc is extinguished and then restarted every half cycle.

  - *Cleaning Effect* – AC has an important cleaning effect on refractive metals such as aluminum, magnesium and titanium because it disrupts the surface oxide that instantly forms on these metals from atmospheric oxygen. Without this cleaning effect these metals could not be welded.

Selecting Electrode Wire or Rod & Welding Amperage

For a sound weld, these five variables must be balanced against each other:

- *Electrode or Rod Diameter* – When selecting welding rod, the diameter must be compatible with the required welding current. Too small a welding rod diameter vaporizes the rod before it can join the weld pool, and too large a diameter will not get enough heat energy to melt, heat and penetrate the work. In general, the welding rod diameter is matched to the work metal thickness and then the welding current is adjusted to the combination of the two. Sometimes on a thick workpiece, a thin electrode wire is used to achieve better penetration even though the weld metal deposition rate is lower than the rate of a large diameter electrode. On thin work like sheet metal, a large diameter rod is often chosen to prevent burn-through. This approach works on thin metals because more welding energy goes into melting the filler metal which reduces the heat available to melt the workpiece.

- *Chemistry* – Welding rod and wire chemistry must be compatible with the workpiece metallurgy. While all pure solid metallic elements can be welded with rods or electrodes of the same element, alloys—which include most metals in commercial use—require a rod with a *different* chemistry from the base metal to make the strongest weld. This lack of compatibility—not to mention contaminating paint coatings—is one of many reasons why coat hangers make very poor welding rods.

- *Thermal Conductivity of the Workpiece Metal* – In welding, thermal conductivity is a metal's ability to conduct heat from a hot area to a cooler one. The higher the thermal conductivity, the more rapidly heat is conducted away from the weld zone, and the more welding current—or heat energy—is needed to maintain the workpiece temperature for proper fusion. Table 1-2 shows that aluminum conducts heat nine times better than stainless steel. This explains why it is hard to get enough heat into aluminum and easy to get too much into stainless steel. Carbon steel falls between stainless steel and aluminum as a heat conductor.

Metal	Conductivity (W/m-C)	Conductivity Relative to SAE 1010 Steel
Aluminum, 6061-T6	167	2.8
Cast Iron	55	0.9
Magnesium	171	2.9
Stainless Steel, Type 316	16.3	0.3
Carbon Steel, SAE 1010	59	1.0

Table 1-2. The heat conductivity of common metals.
Thermal conductivity is measured in Watts per meter per degree C.

- *Thickness* – With regard to workpiece thickness, the thicker the workpiece, the more welding current, or heat energy, is needed to melt the metal into the weld pool and complete the weld.

- *Weld Position on the Part* – The greater the volume of workpiece metal in proximity to the weld bead, the more heat is needed to bring the weld up to temperature. The converse is also true, so welding amperage must be reduced on edges, outside corners, and on the edges of holes compared with the current required for an inside fillet or groove weld. See the welding positions in Figure 1-6. Too little heat will fail to produce complete fusion, too much heat will melt the part. The foot pedal, or torch-mounted knob on TIG welders, enables the welder to adjust the welding current to compensate for these variations in heat needed.

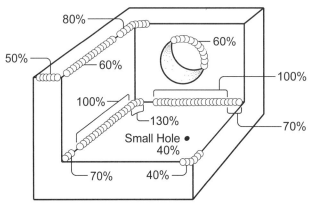

Figure 1-6. The welding current and the amount of heat it produces must be adjusted to the position of the weld on the part. The proximity of the volume of metal near the weld bead determines how much and how fast heat is removed from the fusion zone. The percentages in this figure are the approximate welding current required to add metal to various positions on the workpiece relative to that needed for an inside fillet weld.

Other Weld Heat Variables

- *Air Temperature and Wind Speed* – The colder the air and the higher the wind speed, the more rapidly heat leaves the work. Under cold and windy conditions more amperage is needed to maintain welding fusion temperatures.

- *Recent Welding Passes* – If the weld bead area has been heated by one or more previous welding passes, the workpiece temperature is already hot before subsequent welding passes. This means that less welding heat is needed.

- *Volume-Specific Heat Capacity of the Work Metal* – This means the quantity of heat required to raise the temperature of the same volume of metal one degree. The higher the volume-specific heat capacity, the more welding heat needed.

- *Current and Travel Speed* – Welding current and welding speed are adjusted to match all of the other variables.

Weld Degradation

Any pure metal, such as Series 1100 aluminum, can be successfully welded with rods or filler metal of itself, but most commercial metals today are not pure; they are alloys. Welding subjects the base alloy to high temperatures which adversely affects its metallurgy. Alloy components come out of suspension and different materials come to the surface of the weld where they crystallize. Grain size is affected, and oxygen and nitrogen combine with some of the alloy components. All of these changes weaken the weld and base metal in the heat-affected zone. These deleterious effects are collectively called *weld degradation*.

Using a welding rod with the same chemistry as the base alloy will not fix this problem, but using a welding rod with the proper chemistry to compensate for these changes does. Using the correct rod produces a weld that is actually stronger than the base metal itself. Remember that the more sophisticated or complicated an alloy, the easier it is to disturb its chemistry and strength.

Welding in the Machine Shop

Welding is often used in machine shops because it is versatile and cost-effective. In fact, welding can solve many machine and repair shop problems that steel fabrication alone cannot. Here are some examples:

- *Gang Machining* – Welding can assist in machining parts by tack welding stacks of identical plates together so they can be machined simultaneously and then breaking the welds apart when the machining is completed.

- *Hardfacing & Padding* – Welding can be the key part of the machining process when welding *adds metal to a part* which is then machined or ground to size. Because there are welding rods that are *hard as welded*, many parts that require areas of high hardness can be made or repaired by adding this special weld metal without further heat treating.

- *Replacing Castings* – This saves the time and cost of mold making and allows rapid part delivery. Replacing castings with welded parts also permits later modification and repairs. See the part in Figure 1-7.

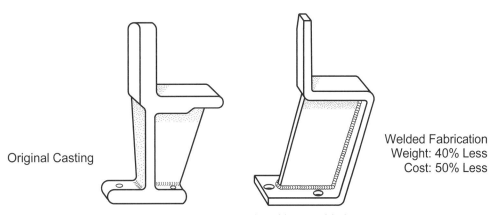

Original Casting

Welded Fabrication
Weight: 40% Less
Cost: 50% Less

Figure 1-7. A casting replaced by a welded part.

- *Steel, Cast Iron & Aluminum Castings Repair* – Defects in new castings, as well as cracks in older ones, can often be corrected by welding.

- *Replacing Forgings* – Welded assemblies can replace many forgings. This saves on expensive forging costs, delivery time, and allows rapid, low-cost modifications. See Figure 1-8.

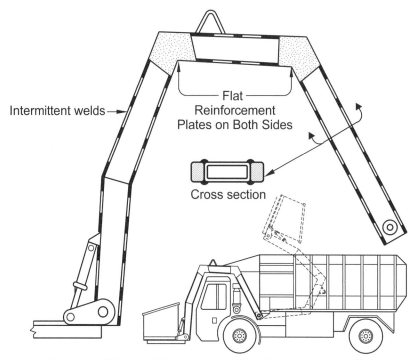

Figure 1-8. Fabricated boom on a trash truck replaces a forging
which greatly reduces the cost of the part and the delivery time.

- *Repairing Molds & Dies* – Welding can repair cracks and replace worn and eroded areas in molds and dies which are usually made of special tool steel alloys that are difficult to machine.

- *Fabricating Parts* – Often welding components together instead of machining them from a single piece of stock saves time and money.

- *Auto Body & Truck Frames* – Auto body sheet metal and truck frames are repaired by welding, and some repairs can only be made by welding.

Overwelding

A properly made weld is very strong, generally having more than 60,000 psi tensile strength. Each $1/4$" tack weld can be compared to the strength of a $1/4$-20 SHCS. Many weld applications do not require weld beads to be the full length of the joint. While a full-length bead may add strength, it will cost more, weigh more, take more welding time, and increase weld-induced distortion. A knowledgeable welder adds only enough weld metal to safely hold parts together plus a reasonable safety margin, but no more. Adding more is called *overwelding*. In this case, more is definitely *not* better. The converse is also true. You cannot make a secure weld in 1" thick plate with a $1/8$" groove weld. The proper weld size matches the workpiece thickness.

Standard vs. Super Premium Welding Rods

Most welding operations require only standard welding rods or electrode wire. While an experienced welder will notice a subtle difference between these widely-available, competitively-priced commodity products and prefer one brand over another, they contain similar metallurgy and have the same capabilities. The standard welding rods meet AWS, trade association, and government specifications.

However, there is an entirely different class of welding rods for both SMAW, GTAW and brazing—the *super premiums* or *maintenance and repair rods*.

Here are some of the problems these rods can solve:

- Welding cast iron and cast steel, which are sometimes difficult to wet.
- Hardfacing on conveyors, chutes and earth moving equipment.
- Welding high-alloy steels or steels of unknown composition.
- Adding impact and chemical corrosion resistance.
- Renewing bearing surfaces.
- Cutting and gouging high-alloy welds which are resistant to mechanical and oxyacetylene flame cutting.

Some of the major suppliers of these specialty welding rods are:

- Stoody/Thermadyne
- Eutectic/Castolin
- Haynes International/Hastelloy

Many of these super-premium welding rods do not meet AWS, military or other international specifications—they exceed them. Super premium rods do not meet these standards because these rods are formulated to solve tough welding problems, and they need the freedom to incorporate the ingredients that give them their special properties. These rods are ten times more expensive than standard rods and cannot be purchased individually, but are furnished in sealed ten-pound containers. The high cost is easily justified by the value of quickly getting critical equipment back in service.

Although these rods are real problem solvers, remember that it may be very difficult to later remove their welds. Some of these welds are so hard they cannot be ground or sawed and can only be removed with a plasma torch. Because of their cost, they are not often used in production.

Manufacturers of these rods provide some guidance on their use, but for liability reasons they are often deliberately sketchy on their contents and precise applications. Yet, despite the fact that these rod manufacturers do not reveal the magic ingredients of their products, when other rods fail to work, these are the rods to use.

There are several heavily-advertised specialty welding rod supply companies that do not manufacture, but merely purchase rods and repackage them. Their prices may be attractive, but their technical support and product consistency are shaky. Avoid them.

Product Mix-Ups & Labeling

There are two situations where the product you ordered is not the one you get:

- *The Rod Switch* – When you order fewer welding rods than a sealed box or tube, the clerk in the welding supply store reaches into the proper box and pulls out the rods you ordered. The problem is that the last time he reached into the box, he withdrew too many rods and when he put them back, they went into the wrong box. Those misplaced rods are the ones you get. Surprise!

- *The Mystery Package* – Figure 1-9 shows a snap-together, resealable package of expensive coiled silver braze wire. It is packaged by the original manufacturer, but carries uninformative labels that include only the reseller's name and part numbers. The hand-written alloy contents were added by the purchaser with data from catalogues. Despite the fancy-looking bar codes and the ominous cadmium warning, the alloy contents are not shown on the original labels, and because the packages have no seal, they can be popped open and reclosed so there is no way to be certain what's inside.

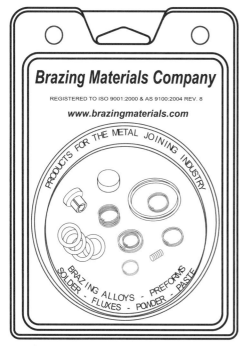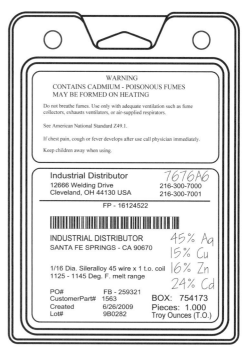

Figure 1-9. The front and back of a snap-together container of a silver braze filler wire. The hand-written information on the right of the label should appear on the packages, but does not. Only the manufacturer's and reseller's names have been changed.

The lesson is: Buy only *sealed containers* of filler metal, preferably from the OEM and never buy loose pieces of rod or filler. For critical applications—life-safety, medical, nuclear or flight applications—purchase materials with a *certificate of inspection* from the manufacturer. This will add to the cost, but increase the chances of getting what you ordered.

Welding Supply Companies

Welding supply customers should be aware of the practices of this industry and its distribution chain:

- *Lack of Pricing Transparency* – In brick-and-mortar stores prices are often coded, and on their websites prices are often replaced with the phrase "call for prices." You would think that a company which has sold acetylene for over 100 years would know the price of this product. The truth is, prices are flexible and depend entirely on which customer is buying and how foolish the seller believes you are. Except for purchasing compressed gases, which cannot be shipped long distances, the Internet offers customers a more competitive marketplace than bricks-and-mortar stores because the prices are known before you reach the "buy" button.

- *Bogus MSDS Surcharges* – Some stores add several dollars to each item as an "MSDS surcharge." Even if you're buying welding gloves, a helmet or a chipping hammer, you receive a 2–3 page printout of the Material Safety Data Sheet, as if you need instructions on how to wear gloves. Ridiculous, but they've got you. You may try to protest, but usually to little avail. Internet sales often do not carry this extra charge.

- *Spare Parts & Service Manuals* – These are often not available even for the most popular products. The most helpful welding equipment supplier or dealer suddenly goes deaf on hearing a request for repair service manuals. Also, if you try to purchase rebuild kits for oxyacetylene regulators, the major companies will tell you to send the regulators in for service and refuse to sell just the parts themselves despite the simplicity of the repair. This can easily double the repair cost of the regulators and often makes it more desirable to buy a new imported regulator. Take your business elsewhere.

- *Cylinder Hydro Testing & Cylinder Condition* – You don't have to wait for a traveling carnival with sticky-fingered barkers to come to town. There's already one here; so hold onto your wallet.

  Here are some ways to reduce or avoid problems with gas cylinders:

  - Comparison shop at local welding supply stores because prices can vary widely.

  - Use the Internet to buy supplies that can be shipped. Compressed gases have to be purchased locally and trucked under special regulations.

  - If a cylinder is in poor shape or has a hydro testing date that expires sooner than the one you turned in, insist on another cylinder.

  - Have spare cylinders so their replacement is not under a time constraint. Having spares allows you to reject sub-optimal cylinders.

- Try to develop a relationship with a good supplier and the people who work the sales counter because in many cases it leads to better service.

These issues are covered in detail in *Chapter 8 – Oxyacetylene*.

A Special Word on Overwelding

Overwelding is often inadvertently caused by the following chain of events: The designer may specify the next larger weld size because of a lack of confidence in welding. When the part reaches the shop floor, the shop foreman, wishing to play it safe, marks the piece up for the next weld size. The welder, having just been criticized for making under-size welds, makes very sure that these welds are still larger. The result—a $^1/_4$" fillet weld has become a $^1/_2$" weld. The people in this chain usually do not realize that the weld metal increases as the square of the leg size. The apparently harmless $^1/_4$" increase in the leg size has increased the amount of weld metal deposited, increased the weld shrinkage, and increased the weld cost by four times. As shown in Figure 1-10, more weld filler metal is not necessarily better.

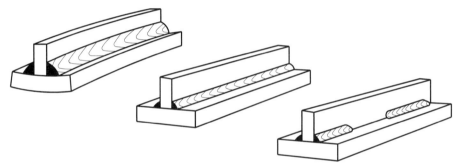

Figure 1-10. Overwelding increases the shrinkage force which leads to distortion (left), small leg size decreases distortion forces (center), and using intermittent welds further reduces shrinkage and distortion (right).

Chapter 2

Safety

*Experience is the name everyone
gives to their mistakes.*

—Oscar Wilde

Section I – The Welding Work Environment

The Welding Work Area

Like playing with fire, welding is inherently dangerous. The goal of this chapter is not to scare you with the list of possible hazards: the goal is to equip you with the knowledge to avoid these hazards. To begin, the right work environment is critical for welding safely.

A good welding area should:

- Be clean and comfortable to work in.

- Allow you to position the work to avoid welding on the floor unless absolutely necessary. You will not do you best work there.

- Be free of drafts on the work from fans, wind, windows, and doors, yet still have adequate ventilation to reduce the inhalation of welding fumes.

- Provide bright light: welding in sunlight is better than in dim light because the non-glowing parts of the weld show up better.

- Be maintained at 70–80°F because better welds will result at these temperatures than welds made in cold temperatures. However, acceptable welds can be made at ambient temperatures in the 40–50°F range except where the weld specifications call for preheating.

- Have tools positioned within easy reach of the welder.

- Be free of combustibles, puddles and tripping hazards.

- Be outfitted with all the necessary personal safety equipment for the processes to be used.

Section II – Eye, Face & Skin Protection

Welding Hazards

Welding and cutting operations produce many hazards. These include ultraviolet, infrared and visible radiation, flying metal particles, sparks, chipping slag, and grinding particles. Because these hazards are ever present in the welding environment, proper selection and consistent use of appropriate eye, face and skin protection is vital.

Prescription Glasses & Safety Glasses

If you're now wearing bifocal lenses, you should know that Varilux-type progressive lenses are a big improvement over traditional bifocals. When the wearer looks straight ahead, these lenses focus at long distances, and when the wearer looks down at an angle, the lenses focus at a normal distance for reading. This arrangement works well for most situations, but for some shop projects—welding and layout work are good examples—the wearer needs to see close work at a *straight-ahead* angle. In this case, the lenses are set for a long-distance focus and the work is blurry. For most people the solution is to purchase a pair of inexpensive, drug-store reading glasses for close work. These readers are adequate for some close-up shop work if worn under safety goggles, but prescription safety glasses made specifically for the welding work environment are the proper solution. *Remember: Safety glasses with side shields should be worn at all times in the welding shop.*

Welding Helmets

Welding helmets protect the eyes and face from radiation and mechanical injury. Helmets are made of fiberboard or fiberglass and have a tinted plate or window for viewing. These tinted glass plates are available in a series of shades or densities so visibility and protection at a range of arc currents, or light levels, is possible. In general, the higher the welding current, the higher the radiation level, and the higher the shade of the protective lens required. Table 2-1 shows the recommended shade numbers for common processes and current levels. Today, in addition to the traditional welding helmets with glass plates, welding helmets with electronic faceplates, sometimes called *auto-darkening filters (ADFs),* are very popular because they have become inexpensive and offer these advantages:

- The welder does not need to raise and lower his helmet when performing a series of welds. He can always see where he is with the helmet down.

- The beginner does not have to master holding his electrode steady when he drops his helmet. This permits beginners to perform better welds earlier in their training.

- Electronic faceplates offer continuous eye protection from infrared radiation coming off red-hot metal even when they are *not* in the darkened mode. Electronic faceplates are just easier on the eyes.

Operation	Steel Plate Thickness (inches)	Welding Current (A)	Lowest Shade Number	Comfort Shade Number
Arc Welding (Shielded Metal Arc Welding)	—	>60 60–160 160–250 250–550	7 7 10 11	– 10 12 14
Wire Feed Welding (Gas Metal Arc Welding & Flux Core Arc Welding)	—	>60 60–160 160–250 250–500	7 10 10 10	– 11 12 14
TIG (Gas Tungsten Arc Welding)	—	>50 50–150 150–200	8 8 10	10 12 14
Oxyfuel Gas Welding (Steel)	$> \frac{1}{8}$ $\frac{1}{8} - \frac{1}{2}$ $< \frac{1}{2}$	— — —	— — —	4, 5 5, 6 6, 8
Plasma Arc Cutting	—	>300 300–400 400–800	8 9 10	9 12 14
Air-Carbon Arc Cutting	—	>500 500–1000	10 11	12 14
Oxyfuel Gas Cutting (Steel)	> 1 1–6 < 6	— — —	— — —	3, 4 4, 5 5, 6
Torch Brazing	—	—	—	3, 4
Torch Soldering	—	—	—	2

Table 2-1. Suggested viewing plate shades. To select the best shade for the application, start with the highest shade number and, if it is difficult to see the operation, reduce the shade number until the operation is sufficiently visible. Do not go below the lowest given shade number. Lighter shades may be used where the arc is hidden by the work.

Tip: Choose a welding helmet with an adjustment knob to control the size of its headband, not the notch-in-hole designs that have fixed diameter increments. These rarely fit properly and are either too tight or too loose.

Goggles & Face Shields

Tinted goggles are suitable for many oxyfuel gas welding and brazing operations which require a lower level of skin protection. Tinted goggles may be appropriate for some oxyfuel cutting work as well.

Goggles and face shields are essential during grinding operations that produce sparks and abrasive particles, and when wire brushing, which can release wheel wires that fly at high speeds.

Welding Gloves

Welding gloves are the first line of defense against electric shock, flames, hot parts, sharp or flying metal and arc rays. Different types of gloves are required for different processes and hazards. The thin and flexible deerskin or goatskin gloves which are suitable for low-current GTAW precision welding, would offer insufficient protection for air-carbon cutting where insulated, tough and durable cowhide gloves are essential.

Protective Clothing

Long sleeve cotton or wool shirts are suitable for many processes. The weave of the fabric must be dense enough to stop arc radiation from reaching the skin. Be sure to button the top shirt button to protect the upper chest and neck area from arc rays. Synthetic fabrics tend to melt when burned and must be avoided. For overhead work, leather shirts, commonly called *leathers*, are essential for protection against falling sparks and molten metal. Cloth caps are helpful to protect the head from being burned by direct, indirect or reflected light. Wearing a headband under your welding helmet helps prevent sweat from getting into your eyes. See Figure 2-1.

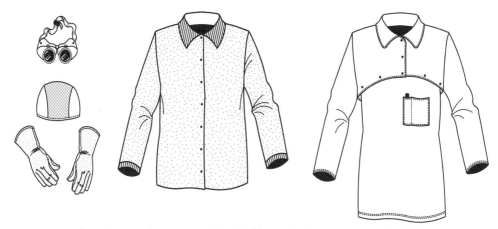

Figure 2-1. Welders protective clothing. The leathers are on the right.

Arc Radiation

There are three types of arc radiation: *infrared*, or heat, *visible light*, and *ultraviolet light*. All of these rays are capable of both temporary and permanent eye and skin damage.

Ultraviolet, in addition to creating an immediate painful sunburn, is carcinogenic and, over time, a real life-threatening danger. Although arc brightness or luminance increases slowly with increasing arc current, ultraviolet radiation increases as the square of the arc current, meaning twice the current produces four times the radiation. Since UV is invisible, large increases are not detectible visually and may cause major injury before these high levels are detected. Welding processes that use argon shielding gas are usually intense UV sources.

In addition to direct exposure to arc rays, reflected radiation can cause injury to other workers and to the public. Personnel in the welding area must be protected from the welding arc and sparks by protective screens.

Arc Flash

Arc flash, also called *photokeratitis*, *arc eye*, *welder's flash*, *bake eyes*, or *ultraviolet keratitis,* is a painful eye condition caused by exposure to the welding arc. It is a sunburn of the cornea and whites of the eyes, and is not usually noticed until several hours after exposure. The eye lids moving against the eyes cause irritation, tearing and pain likened to having sand in the eyes. Eyes suffering from this condition will also be sensitive to bright light. In extreme cases, blindness can occur for two or three days. Arc flash usually occurs when welders raise their hoods and forget to lower them before striking an arc.

This condition is usually treated by wearing dark glasses and avoiding welding for several days. Over the counter pain medications are often helpful.

Section III – Electric Shock

Shock Hazards

Contact with electrical conductors can cause:

- Sudden death or injury from electric shock. This hazard is especially dangerous to the heart.

- Death or injury from involuntary muscle contractions that cause the victim to suffer falls and head injuries.

- Serious burns as a result of body contact with power lines, and severe thermal damage to the skin and eyes as a result of arcs produced by short circuits across power lines.

Sources of Electrical Shock

The three most common sources of electric shock while welding are:

- Contact with 110/220/480 VAC utility lines.

- Internal short circuits which electrify the housing of the electrical equipment that should be at ground potential with utility voltages.

- Open-circuit welding power supply output voltage on welding electrodes, plasma torches, welding equipment or poorly grounded workpieces.

Shock Prevention

Here are the most basic steps:

- Turn off all power to equipment before attempting to work on it, and do not touch live electrical parts.

- Do not work in water or wet areas unless insulated from the workpiece by standing on dry insulating mats or covers big enough to prevent any physical contact with the work or ground.

- Wear dry, hole-free insulating gloves when welding. *Never* weld barehanded.

- Be aware that under unfavorable conditions the open-circuit voltages of many welding power supplies can be lethal. Do not touch an energized electrode while you are in contact with the work.

- Follow all national and local electrical codes and properly ground all equipment.

- Know where the electrical safety switch for the welding machine is located.

- Never dip the electrode holder in water or lay it on a conductive surface.

- Welding machines must be turned off when not attended and should be disconnected from their power source.

- Do not work alone in hazardous conditions.

- Have all installation, maintenance and repair performed by qualified people.

- Inspect frequently for power cord damage and replace cords immediately if they are damaged.

Section IV – Air Contamination

Welding & Cutting Particulates

Because both welding and cutting processes raise workpiece temperatures well above their melting points, some metal particles are vaporized, condense into solids, and become particulates or fumes—tiny pieces of metal or metal oxides that float in the air. Welding fume particulates are usually under one micron—one-millionth of a meter—in diameter. When breathed in as dust, fumes or vapors, they enter the lungs and penetrate into the *alveoli*—the tiny, thin-walled air sacs in the lungs where carbon dioxide is transferred from the blood into the lungs and oxygen in the air into the blood. There these particulates cause both short-term and long-term health effects. Although there are several different mechanisms by which metals can damage the human body, mostly it attacks the lungs and central nervous system.

Electrode metal, workpiece metal, flux materials and coatings, oils, rust inhibitors, paints, and primers on the work are the main sources of particulates. Some of these are heavy metals which can have toxic levels just above the concentrations naturally found in nature. Small quantities of these metals—iron, copper, manganese, and zinc—are essential for good health, but at higher, toxic levels they are not metabolized and accumulate in the body.

Fourteen days or less of exposure to toxic heavy metal is considered *acute* as well as a sudden, unexpected exposure to high levels. Acute exposure has rapid-onset symptoms that include: cramping, nausea, vomiting, pain, sweating, headaches, difficulty breathing, impaired motor, cognitive and language skills and convulsions. Chronic exposure develops slowly—over months or years—with symptoms that include: impaired motor, cognitive and language skills, learning difficulties, nervousness, emotional instability, insomnia, nausea, fatigue, and feeling just plain ill.

Toxic Metals & Their Symptoms

Here is a list of the most dangerous metals and the health problems they can cause:

- *Manganese* fumes from welding filler metal and base metal alloys can cause an array of psychiatric and motor-skill disturbances known as *manganism, manganese poisoning,* or colloquially known as *welder's disease.* Symptoms in the initial stages of exposure are irritability, mood changes, compulsive behaviors, and reduced response time. With longer exposure the symptoms worsen and resemble a form of Parkinson's disease. Exposure to this heavy metal is serious stuff.

- *Zinc oxide* fumes, which are released when welding or cutting zinc-coated metals like galvanized steel, and when brazing brass and bronze, can lead to what's known as *metal fume fever.* Though necessary in small quantities for good health, overexposure to this heavy metal causes flu-like symptoms that include fever, chills, nausea, dry throat, fatigue, general weakness, cough, and head and body aches. The symptoms rarely last more than 24 hours.

- *Cadmium* is an extremely toxic heavy metal which is commonly used as a rust-preventative coating on steel and as an alloying element often added to brazing filler metals—especially silver solder—because it promotes wetting of the base metal. Cadmium and its oxides are usually released when cadmium-plated articles are brazed and welded.

  Acute exposure to high levels of cadmium fumes can cause everything from lung irritation to pulmonary edema to death. Chronic low-level, long-term exposure can cause emphysema and kidney damage. Cadmium is also a carcinogen; so keep your head out of the weld plume.

The National Institute for Occupational Health recommends a limit of one microgram per cubic meter for safe breathing. But be warned, this level is 500 times lower than the current OSHA limit of 5 milligrams per cubic meter.

- *Lead and its oxides* are toxic in all forms. The melting, cutting, or welding of lead releases fumes, vapors, and dust. Lead accumulates in the bones and organs and exposure can cause a metallic taste, loss of appetite, nausea, cramps, and insomnia. Chronic long-term exposure can cause central nervous system damage such as mental retardation, psychosis, muscular weakness, and paralysis. Lead also attacks the kidneys and the circulatory and reproductive systems. This heavy metal damage may be irreversible. It's really bad stuff.

- *Chromium* from chromium-based metal primers is particularly hazardous, causing emphysema, kidney failure, and possibly cancer.

- *Nickel, especially nickel carbonyl fumes and dust*, are highly hazardous. Nickel is used in plating and as an alloy material. Early symptoms from inhaling nickel include nausea, vomiting, headaches, and sleeplessness. The symptoms worsen 12–24 hours after exposure and include rapid pulse, difficulty breathing, chest pains, and extreme fatigue. Chronic exposure may cause cancer of the lungs or nasal sinuses. Because nickel carbonyl is so toxic, some labs used to keep a canary as an early warning system. Recovery from nickel poisoning takes a long time, but if caught early, damage is usually not permanent.

- *Beryllium fumes and grindings* are both toxic. Beryllium is alloyed with copper to make springs and is used in plastic injection molds for rapid heating and cooling. If beryllium concentrations in the air are high enough, it can lead to *acute beryllium disease*, which resembles pneumonia. Prolonged exposure to beryllium results in *chronic beryllium disease (CBD)*, which causes fatigue, weakness, night sweats, dry cough and breathing difficulties, some extremely severe. CBD is treatable, but not curable. Beryllium exposure also increases the risk of lung cancer.

- *Fluoride compounds*, while not metallic, are toxic and frequently found in brazing fluxes and metal cleaners. Good for you in very small amounts, if large amounts of fluoride compounds are ingested they, among other things, form hydrofluoric acid in the stomach. Short-term exposure causes irritation of eyes, nose, and throat, abdominal pain, diarrhea, nausea and vomiting. Long-term exposure can lead to neurological symptoms such as headaches, muscle weakness, muscular spasms, and tremors. Sever cases can result in multi-organ failure. Not nice.

- *Iron and iron oxide fumes* cause *siderosis*, sometimes called *welder's lung*, which is a chronic inflammation of the lungs. Though previously considered a benign condition, a statistical correlation has been established between working with iron and death from lung cancer and other respiratory diseases. Iron is the principal alloying element in steel making. During welding, exposure to iron oxide fumes arise from both the base metal and the electrode. So again, keep your face out of the plume.

To avoid these potentially serious health problems:

- Read the MSDSs of the materials you are working with.
- Keep your head out of the welding, cutting, or brazing plume.
- Work in a well-ventilated area. Working with forced ventilation is good and working outside upwind of the work area is even better.
- In confined spaces, where ventilation is inadequate, wear an approved air-supplied respirator.

Toxic Gases

The intense UV of the welding arc produces:

- *Ozone and carbon monoxide,* which are both harmful gases. Exposure causes headaches, chest pain, and dryness of the upper respiratory tract. Excessive exposure causes fluid in the lungs. These risks are easily avoided by working in a well-ventilated area and keeping your head out of the plume.

- *Hydrogen chloride (hydrochloric acid) and phosgene,* which occur when there is a residue of chlorinated cleaning agents left on the work surface, are both irritating and toxic chemicals.

Grinding Hazards

Grinding operations produce small particles of base metal, filler metal, grinding wheel materials and weld slag. Wear a respirator or work in a position where you do not inhale grinding dust.

Suffocation Hazards

Whenever confined spaces, such as small rooms, pits, vats, storage tanks, silos, utility vaults or ship compartments, contain compressed gases, there is a suffocation hazard. Any gas that can displace oxygen either by being heavier than air or by reducing the oxygen content by an overwhelming volume presents a suffocation hazard. Argon, helium, nitrogen, and carbon dioxide, which are frequently used in welding operations, can be dangerous if they leak into a confined space. Even natural gas can suffocate. Testing for hazards inside confined spaces requires special training and equipment and is not a job for amateurs.

Radiation Hazards

Thoriated tungsten electrodes are naturally mildly radioactive and a source of alpha particles. These electrodes present little hazard while welding, but avoid inhaling the grinding dust when sharpening them. To decrease the risk of exposure, the grinder should have a mechanical exhaust system that safely vents the grindings outside. If the electrodes must be sharpened in a confined area, use a respirator to avoid inhaling the grinding dust.

Section V – Fire & Explosion

Fire Hazards

- When cutting near materials that will burn, make sure that flame, sparks, hot slag, and hot metal are not allowed reach them. Cutting creates more sparks than OAW.

- If the work to be cut can be moved, bring it to a safe location before cutting.

- When flammable materials around the cutting site cannot be moved, use sheet metal shields or guards to keep the sparks away from combustibles.

- Prevent sparks from falling into holes or cracks in wooden buildings.

- If cutting on a wooden floor, first sweep it clean, then wet it down before starting cutting. If using a plasma torch, stand on a dry mat when cutting.

- Do not use tarps or fabric covers to protect other materials from sparks as the covers themselves will catch fire.

- Avoid using excessive oxygen pressure while cutting as this will propel sparks farther and make more of them.

- Plan ahead where hot metal will fall when cut; be especially careful so that hot metal does not touch your legs, feet, gas hoses, cylinders and regulators.

- Make sure jacketed or hollow parts are vented before beginning cutting operations.

- Have fire extinguishers, buckets of sand, or water on hand should a fire start.

- Do not leave hot pieces of metal unattended without posting a sign over them.

- SMAW welders must plan for the disposal of electrode stubs. They are hot enough to cause burns and to start fires and must not be dropped from heights because of the hazard to others.

Container Explosion Hazards

Never weld on a sealed container regardless of its size. Even if the vessel is clean and empty, penetration of the shell could release hot gases from the interior. These gases could also drive the torch flame back toward the welder. If the cylinder is empty and contains no residual vapors, vent it to atmosphere by opening a valve, hatch, bung, or by drilling a hole. This hole may be welded shut later when all other welding is complete.

An even more dangerous situation results when the container holds residual flammable vapors whether it is vented to atmosphere or not. This will almost certainly result in an explosion. Few people survive explosions from welding on gasoline tanks.

Here are several methods to prevent container explosions:

- If the container is relatively small and can be moved, have it "hot tanked" —cleaned in warm caustic—to remove all traces of hazardous materials.

- Live steam can be used to purge a tank or container of fumes.

- Larger containers can be filled with water before welding or soldering. See Figure 2-2. The air space above the water must be small or the explosion danger will still be present.

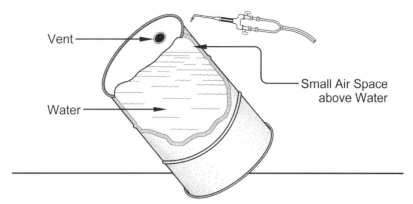

Figure 2-2. Filling a container with water before welding or cutting
can prevent an explosion. Remember that a vent is still required.

- Oxygen and explosive fumes that are lighter than air can be purged by filling the container with an inert gas such as argon, helium or carbon dioxide which are often found in the welding shop. See Figure 2-3. Another solution is to fill the container with carbon dioxide by pouring dry ice pellets into it. As the dry ice warms and releases carbon dioxide, the remaining oxygen, which is heavier than carbon dioxide, will be purged from the container. A more expensive but effective alternative is to discharge a carbon dioxide fire extinguisher into the container. Be sure to have the container checked by a qualified person to insure no hazardous fumes remain.

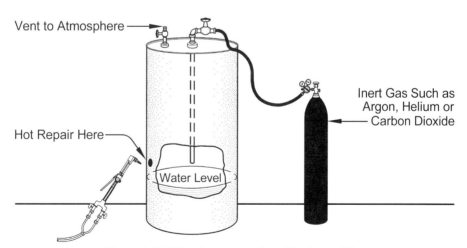

Figure 2-3. Using inert gases found in the welding
shop to purge a container of explosive fumes.

Section VI – Compressed Gas Hazards

- Secure cylinders to prevent them from being knocked over in use. High-pressure compressed gas cylinders, if not properly secured, can become lethal projectiles capable of breaching brick and cinder block walls.

- Use valve protection caps on cylinders while moving them.
- Never leave a lighted torch unattended.
- When a cylinder is empty, close the valve and mark the cylinder *EMPTY.*
- Do not attempt to repair cylinder valves or regulators; send them to a qualified repair shop.
- Never use compressed gas cylinders as rollers.
- Never weld on a compressed gas cylinder.
- Keep power and welding cables away from compressed gas cylinders.
- Prevent sparks from falling on cylinder hoses.
- On old-style acetylene cylinders with a removable valve wrench, always leave the wrench on the cylinder so the gas can be shut off quickly in an emergency.
- When transporting compressed gas cylinders by truck, have the cylinder caps in place and secure the cylinders so they will not move around or tip as the vehicle starts and stops. Never transport cylinders with the regulators in place.
- Never use oxygen in place of compressed air.
- Never use oxygen for starting engines or cleaning clothing.
- Never carry compressed gas cylinders inside a car or car trunk.
- Store and use acetylene and propane cylinders valve end up.
- Inspect all oxygen handling equipment to insure it is free from grease, because oxygen coming in contact with grease may cause an explosion. All oxygen handling equipment should be supplied by the manufacturer with tags indicating it has been *cleaned for oxygen service.* Do not use pipe dope on oxygen equipment threads; use PTFE tape. A particularly dangerous situation occurs when removing a bolt or pin from a blind hole and the lance or burning bar reaches a pocket of grease. The resulting explosion will blow back towards the operator with substantial force, so a strong splatter shield is essential.
- Store all oxygen handling equipment in a clean area away from oil and grease.
- Plug or tape shut oxygen equipment fittings when not in use to keep out dirt and insects. Spiders often make webs inside hoses and fittings.

Section VII – Hearing Hazards

High noise levels cause full or partial hearing loss which can be either temporary or permanent. When noise levels averaged over 8 hours exceed 85 dbA, OSHA requires hearing protection devices. Today, if employees are required to work in noise levels over this threshold, employers must provide the protection devices free of charge to the employees.

Hearing loss can be very gradual and nearly imperceptible, but its long-term effects are usually irreversible.

To avoid hearing loss:

- Reduce the intensity of the noise by shielding the source, if possible, with barriers and screens. Loud mechanical equipment such as air compressors can be put into a separate room or enclosure.

- Wear approved personal protective devices: ear plugs or ear muffs.

- Attach mufflers to compressed air exhausts.

The loudest welding processes are air carbon arc-cutting, oxygen lances and burning bars, GMAW, FCAW MCAW and plasma cutting. But welders are usually also exposed to air-driven grinders, chippers and needle guns which emit high-sound levels from their exhausts. Even electric grinders and edge prep millers are noisy. Hammering on steel plates is another dangerous noise source.

Section VIII – Material Safety Data Sheets (MSDSs)

By U.S. Federal law, suppliers of potentially hazardous industrial products are required to supply MSDSs to their customers. The law also requires ready access to these data sheets by all users in their work area. Sometimes these sheets are posted; sometimes they are in a binder or a computer file. MSDSs for virtually all materials can be easily found with an Internet search. Also, many state governments and university websites offer MSDSs.

MSDSs are designed to provide both workers and emergency personnel with the proper procedures for handling or working with a particular substance. MSDS requirements apply to products found in the workplace, but not to consumer products.

MSDSs are required for all hazardous materials used in industry whether they are chemicals, solvents, adhesives, elements, gases, or metals. Even products which contain no hazardous materials or components must have MSDSs.

Even seemingly harmless products such as the Silver-Streak Welder's Pencil has an MSDS because someone *could* inhale the aluminum fumes or ingest the pencil lead—though you would have to work hard to attain a toxic level.

Primary Welding Safety Standards

For more information on welding safety, check the American National Standards Institute (ANSI) document *Safety in Welding, Cutting and Allied Processes, Z49.1.* This is the primary standard for welding safety and is available as a pdf from the American Welding Society at AWS.org.

General Shop Safety Precautions

Although the welding shop has its own set of dangers, the hazards of the machine shop are also usually present. Here are some steps to avoid them:

- Know where the first aid kit is kept and how to call emergency services.
- Keep an ice substitute like Igloo Ice or Blue Ice in the freezer. Apply it to burns to bring down skin temperature and reduce the size of a burn.
- Because the bandages in the first aid kit are too small for serious trauma, store several clean fabric towels in a plastic Ziploc bag near the first aid kit to use as a pressure bandage until the paramedics arrive.
- Never attempt to operate a machine until you understand how to use it properly and learn how to stop all machines quickly and the location of the emergency stop button, if any.
- Do not stand under or near suspended loads. They can fall and crush you.
- Listen to your machine; if it sounds like something is wrong, it probably is. Stop the machine and find out what is wrong.
- Make sure the workpiece and tool are securely mounted or clamped *before* turning on the machine.
- Rotate lathe work manually before applying power to make sure the tool is not touching the work and the work rotates freely. On larger lathes, use the jog button to make sure the work turns freely before applying full motor power.
- Lock out machinery so someone else cannot turn on the machine while you are working on it; this is especially important if you are not in full view when working.
- Avoid eating and drinking in the work area. However, if you must, keep food in distinctive containers reserved for food and drink alone to avoid accidental ingestion of oils, solvents and chemicals.
- It is bad practice to talk with someone while operating machinery because your attention is distracted.
- Do not walk away and leave a machine running.
- Some tasks require wearing gloves and other tasks become hazardous when wearing them. Be sure to know the difference.
- Never use a rag near rotating machinery or grinders; it can be pulled into the machine and draw you in too.
- After a workpiece has been cut, remove all burrs and sharp edges with a file, belt sander or grinder.
- Store pointed and bladed tools in boxes or with protective covers.
- Lay tools out in an orderly fashion; do not heap them in a tangled pile.
- Wear nitrile gloves, a special kind of rubber glove, when handling degreasing solvents.
- Report and get immediate medical attention for cuts, burns, scrapes, pinches or any other injury no matter how minor.

Chapter 3

Terms, Joints
& Edge Preparation

The more original a discovery,
the more obvious it seems afterwards.

—Arthur Koestler

Weld Bead Terms

- *Parts of the Weld* – The two most common welds are the *groove* and the *fillet* weld. Figure 3-1 shows the parts of these welds.

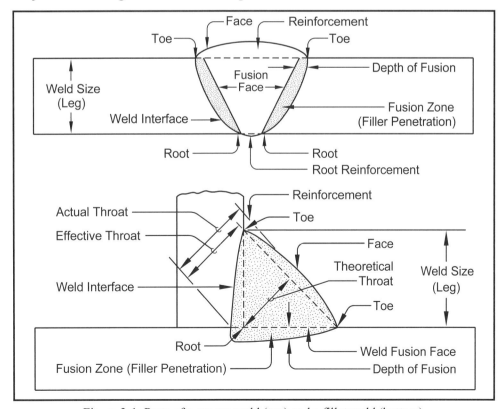

Figure 3-1. Parts of a groove weld (top) and a fillet weld (bottom).

- *Slag,* though technically not part of the weld, is created along with the weld bead. Slag is deposited by the welding electrode to protect the weld metal while it cools. Slag must be completely removed between passes because it will form inclusions *within* the weld metal and weaken the weld. Slag is usually removed with a slag hammer and a wire brush, and sometimes a wire wheel. Some welders prefer a claw hammer instead of a slag hammer. On pipe welding, grinders and power wheels are used between each welding pass to assure a slag-free surface for the next pass.

Weld Axes & Weld Angles

- *Weld axis* is an imaginary line drawn parallel to the weld bead through the center of the weld. Weld angles are measured from the weld axis.

- *Travel angle* is the smallest angle formed between the electrode axis and the weld axis. See Figure 3-2 (top).

- *Work angle* is the angle of less than 90° between a line perpendicular to the major workpiece surface and the plane determined by the electrode axis and the weld axis. See Figure 3-2 (bottom).

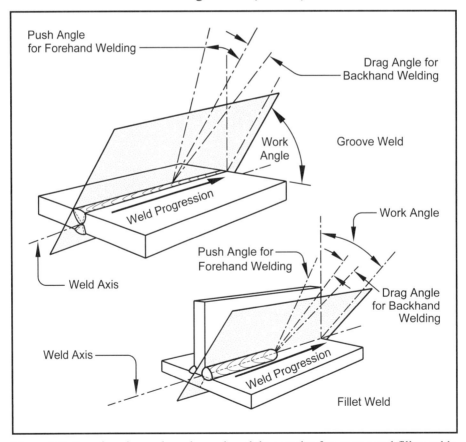

Figure 3-2. Travel angle, work angle, push and drag angles for groove and fillet welds.

- *Push angle for forehand welding* is the travel angle during push welding when the electrode is pointing *toward* the direction of welding.

- *Travel speed* is the velocity of the electrode rod or wire as it moves along the travel axis. Travel speed is usually measured in inches per minute.

- *Drag angle for backhand welding* is the travel angle during welding when the electrode is pointing *away* from the direction of welding.

Types of Welds

- A *stringer bead* is a weld which is deposited when the path of the electrode is *straight and parallel* to the axis of the weld.

- A *weave bead* is created when the welding rod or electrode is used in a *side-to-side motion* to make the weld. See Figure 3-3 for weave bead patterns. Weaving applies heat directly to the edges of the weld puddle. This insures that the puddle fully wets the edges of the joint and reduces the chances of a cold joint. The force of the arc is alternately directed to the sides of the weld because the axis of the electrode points from side to side of the joint as the weaving progresses. This arc-force churns the weld puddle and brings trash to the weld surface, a desirable effect.

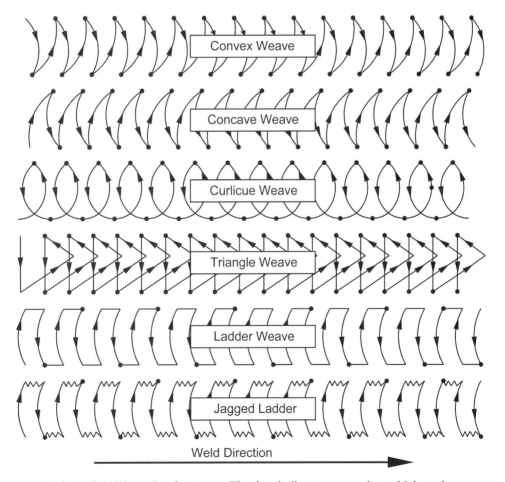

Figure 3-3. Weave bead patterns. The dots indicate pause points which apply additional heat and metal at the edge of the bead where it is most needed.

In general, the width of the weave pattern should not exceed twice the electrode diameter. Weaving makes the weld bead wider and the heat-affected zone larger than that of a stringer bead. Weaving also reduces the height of the weld bead by "spreading it out" which allows the metal to cool more rapidly than if the heat were concentrated in a straight-line stringer bead. If the arc stays in the middle of the weld puddle as it does with stringer beads, all the welding heat has to pass through the molten weld metal before heating the base metal. The spreading out of weave beads is particularly helpful in out-of-position welds where too large a weld puddle can sag due to gravity.

The dots in the weave patterns of Figure 3-3 represent *dwell* or pause points which applies heat to the edges of the puddle where it is needed. No dwell is needed in the center of the puddle because it is already hot and does not require additional heat input.

Weaving is often used on the final, or *cover pass*, of a weld. Figure 3-4 shows how the cover pass weld bead on a pipe weld can be widened to stretch completely across the joint.

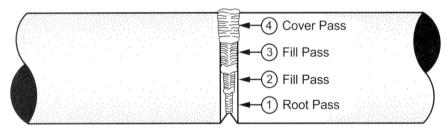

Figure 3-4. The four passes needed to complete this welded pipe joint.
The cover pass is a weave bead. More on pipe welding in *Chapter 16 – Pipe & Tubing*.

Some weaving applications are:

- *Single-pass welding* – A weave bead can be used to complete a joint with a single pass when the available electrode is too small to deposit enough filler metal in a single pass with a stringer bead. This may occur because the available welding power supply is too small to run a large electrode that would make the bead in a single pass, and several passes with a smaller rod or electrode would be needed. On SMAW, weaving not only increases the width of the filler metal deposit, weaving decreases overlap, and assists in slag formation.

- *Open root-pass welding* – Weaving is necessary to draw the weld puddle onto *both* sides of the open root and apply enough heat for complete fusion or "wetting."

• *Multiple-pass welding* is used when a large weld must be made, but the electrode deposition is much smaller than the weld width. This weld is made with multiple passes of parallel weld beads as show in Figure 3-5.

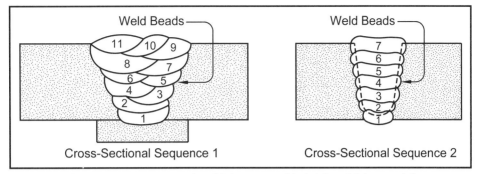

Figure 3-5. Two types of multiple-pass welds joining thick material.

- A *root-pass weld* uses filler metal to close the root space between the weld faces. See Figure 3-6. Root-pass welds are necessary when welding pipe and thick plates where only one side of the weld is accessible and no backing material is used. The root pass also serves to keep oxygen away from the main weld when there is no backing plate to protect it.

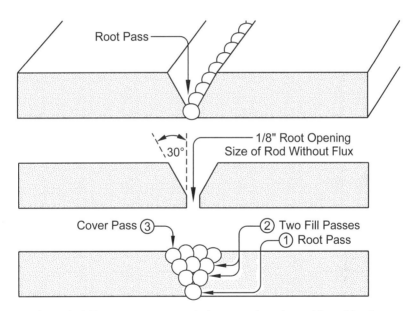

Figure 3-6. Four passes are needed to complete the weld on this plate.

- *Padding* is when weld filler metal is added to make a plate thicker or to increase the diameter of a shaft. It is used either to restore a dimension on a worn part or to apply an extra-hard wear surface. See Figure 3-7 (left).

- *Boxing* is a fillet weld continued *around* a corner. See Figure 3-7 (right).

- *Surfacing*, also called *hard surfacing* or *hard facing*, is the application of *extra-hard* weld metal in a padding process. This is done on surfaces subject to severe wear and abrasion such as the teeth, buckets and blades of earth moving equipment and the interior chutes of rock crushers. When using the proper filler metal, SMAW, GTAW, FCAW and GMAW processes can all perform surfacing.

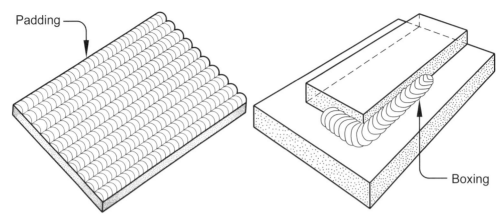

Figure 3-7. Padding on a plate (left) and boxing (right).

- *Plug & slot welds* – These join two or more parts by welding them at a point *other* than their edges. Plug and slot welds are used to secure workpieces subjected to shearing forces. These welds are particularly useful in sheet metal and auto body work where welds can be completely concealed by grinding and painting. To make a plug or slot weld, a hole is usually made in the upper workpiece and the weld made inside it. Filler metal completely fills the hole or slot and penetrates into the metal of the lower workpiece. See Figure 3-8.

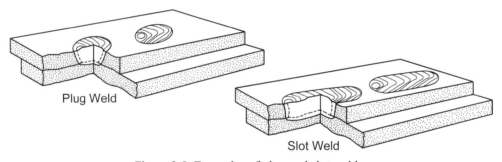

Figure 3-8. Examples of plug and slot welds.

- *Intermittent Welds* fall into two categories: *chain intermittent* and *staggered intermittent*. These welds are used to reduce distortion, weight, and the cost of materials. See Figure 3-9.

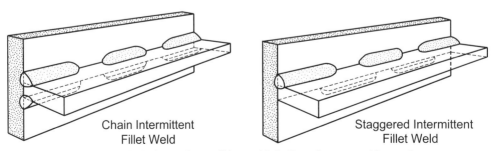

Figure 3-9. Chain intermittent fillet weld (left) and staggered intermittent fillet weld (right). Intermittent welds can also be used on groove welds.

- *Tack welds* are short preliminary weld beads applied before the main welds are made, and may be made with any welding, brazing or soldering process. The size of the tack weld is smaller than the size of the finished weld bead so it is possible for the tack on a large joint to be the size of the completed weld bead on a smaller joint.

Normally, tack welds are made using the same welding process as the process used to make the final weld, but tack welds are short, typically $^1/_4$–$^1/_2$" in length and 4–6" apart depending on the thickness of the part and its tendency to move out of alignment. See Figure 3-10. Tack welds can:

- Hold workpieces in the proper location and alignment until the final welding is completed.

- Provide a way to see how components fit up before placing the final welds. If repositioning is necessary, tack weld are easily removed by snapping or grinding them off.

- Control distortion caused by welding heat by holding the components in place as the main welds are made.

- Set and maintain the root gap.

- Temporarily maintain the fabrication's mechanical strength as it is hoisted, moved or turned up-side down.

- Complement the function of a welding fixture because after tack welds have been applied with the work in the fixture, the work can be removed from its fixture for better welding access.

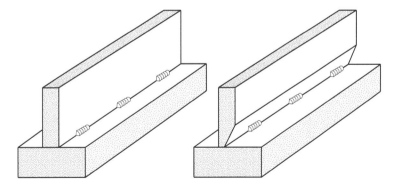

Figure 3-10. Tack welds.

To avoid stress buildup and plate deformation on a long seam, place the first tack in the middle and then along the joint length in both directions in proper back or skip sequence. If tack welds are placed progressively from one end of the joint to the other, welding heat-induced stresses can close the gap at the opposite end and might even cause one sheet end to overlap the other.

Alternatively, tacks can be placed at the ends of the joint and then more added starting with the center tack. On very long joints, such as those on truck bodies or petroleum storage tanks, many tacks may be needed to control distortion and insure plates stay in alignment. In fact, there can be so many tacks that the joint weld looks almost complete. More tacks at shorter intervals are needed on austenitic stainless steel than on mild steel because of stainless steel's greater coefficient of expansion.

When the final weld is made, the tacks are completely or partially remelted into the final weld bead and disappear. Tack welds are often ground down to improve remelting into the final weld. Figure 3-11 shows this grinding for flat plate and Figure 3-12 shows tapering, often called *feathering*, of the beginning and the end of a root-pass weld on pipe. Incomplete remelting of the tack into the final weld leaves discontinuities which create stress points that can cause weld cracking and possibly weld failure. Grinding and feathering help avoid this situation.

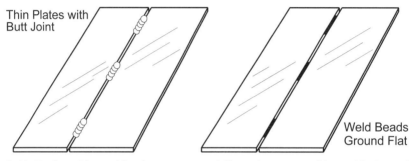

Figure 3-11. Tack welds on thin plate are ground flat to insure remelting with the main bead.

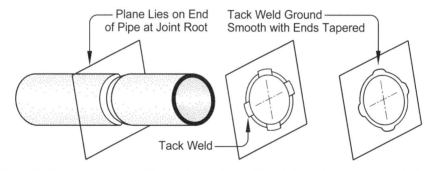

Figure 3-12. Feather tack welds on pipe so they will melt into the root-pass weld bead.

On short production runs tacks can replace fixtures. Even when fixtures are available, once tacks are placed on the components, the parts can be removed from the fixtures. This allows more welder access to the parts. Similarly, clamps can initially position the parts and be moved out of the way after tacks are placed. Usually tack welds do a better job than clamps for holding seams in alignment and controlling root spacing.

While tack welds may seem only of temporary importance during fabrication, they should be applied with the same care and quality as the main welds. This is particularly true when the fabrication will be subject to cyclic loads. Too short a tack weld can result in inadequate heat input, leading to incomplete fusion and weld failure. Also, small tacks cool much more rapidly than larger ones and this rapid cooling can cause hardening on some heat-sensitive alloys, leaving stress—and potential failure points. With tack welds, better too large than too small.

There are three rules for tack welds. They must be:

- Strong enough to control welding distortion forces and also maintain root spacing and plate alignment.

- Able to withstand the stresses imposed on the workpiece when being moved, lifted and turned during welding.

- Applied and prepared so they can be remelted or incorporated into the final weld.

• *Bridge Tacks* provide a pivot point or "wiggle room" to allow the welder to move or pull parts into position and then hold them there while the final weld is made. See Figure 3-13.

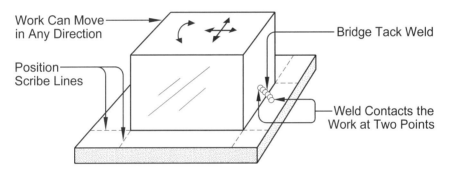

Figure 3-13. Bridge tacks hold work in place and allow adjustment before the final welds are applied. Make beads at each end, then going from end bead to end bead, fill in until bridge is complete.

Welding Aids

• *Backing Plates* are used to contain the large weld pool when joining two thick sections that are accessible from only one side. As in Figure 3-14, a backing plate takes the place of a root-pass weld and also shields the weld pool from atmospheric contamination entering from the back of the weld. Steel backing plates are usually tack welded to the two pieces to be welded, but there are also proprietary ceramic tapes and metal-glass tapes that perform the same function and do not need to be tacked into place.

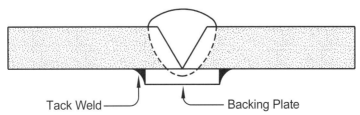

Figure 3-14. A backing plate tack welded into position on a large groove weld.

- *Runoff Plates* are plates made of the same material as the workpieces being joined. Tack welded to the joint at the start or the end of a weld groove, the runoff plate prevents discontinuities caused by the starting and stopping of the welding process. The starts and stops are done on the runoff plate, not on the workpiece. See Figure 3-15. A runoff plate also prevents three things: arc wander, too high heat at the end of the weld, and the wash-out of corners.

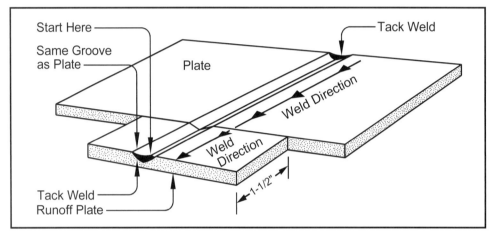

Figure 3-15. A runoff plate allows discontinuities to occur off the workpiece.

Plate Preparation

There are many methods for producing weldment blanks from plate:

- Flame cutting
- Plasma cutting
- Shearing
- Sawing
- Punch press blanking
- Nibbling
- Lathe cut-off
- Carbon air-arc cutting

The accuracy and edge quality obtainable and the extra stock needed to allow for the later application of edge or groove preparation are important factors in selecting a method to produce weldment blanks. Thick plates are sometimes prepared with a J- or U-groove because these edge treatments require less weld metal than a double V-groove.

Types of Joints

Figure 3-16 shows the five basic joint types: butt, corner, lap, T-joint and edge joint.

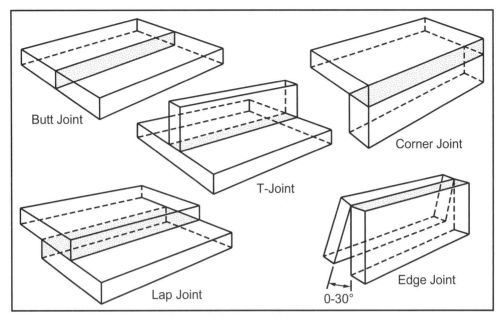

Figure 3-16. Five basic joint types.

- A *joggle joint* is a weld which is used where a strong joint and a flat surface are needed to join two pieces of sheet metal or light plate. Joggle joints provide a finished surface which conceals the weld, and they work on thin sheet metal where butt joints do not. See Figure 3-17. There are hand tools available to put the joggle into sheet metal.

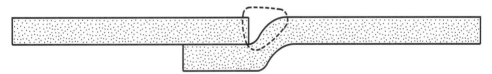

Figure 3-17. A joggle joint weld.

Joint Edge Preparation

Joint edge preparation, often called *edge prep*, provides access to the joint interior. Figure 3-18 shows the typical shapes used for joint edge preparation.

Without edge preparation the entire internal portion of the joint would not be fused or melted together, weakening the joint. Remember that a properly made, full-penetration joint can carry as much load as the base metal itself, but full penetration will only occur with the correct joint prep.

The choice of joint preparation depends on the following factors:

- Size of the weld.
- Conditions under which the weld will be made.
- Type of equipment used for welding.
- Type of joint loads (tension, compression, shear, or torsion).
- Level of joint loading.
- Static or dynamic loading and vibration.

- Thickness and type of the metals joined.
- Welding position.
- Access to the weld; one or both sides.
- Skills of the welder.
- Trade-offs between joint preparation costs, filler metal costs, and welding labor costs also must be considered. Each joint type carries its own combination of total costs.

The most common methods of applying a joint preparation are:

- Forming the edge with an oxyacetylene or plasma torch.

- Cutting the edge with an electrically- or air-driven motor.

- Grinding the edge with an abrasive wheel.

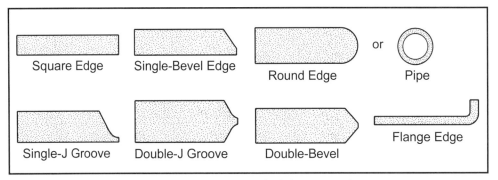

Figure 3-18. Edge shapes for joint preparation.

Edge Preparation Terminology

Figure 3-19 outlines the terms used in edge preparation for V-groove and U-groove joints.

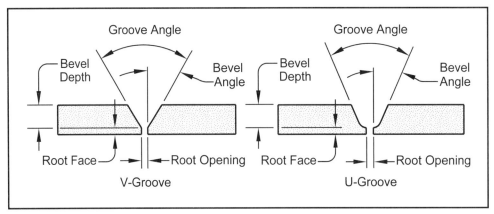

Figure 3-19. Terms for V- and U-groove edge preparations.

Edge shapes can be applied to each side of the joint using the same method, or a combination of joint prep methods can be used. Figures 3-20 and 3-21 show the edge preparations used on the most common types of joints.

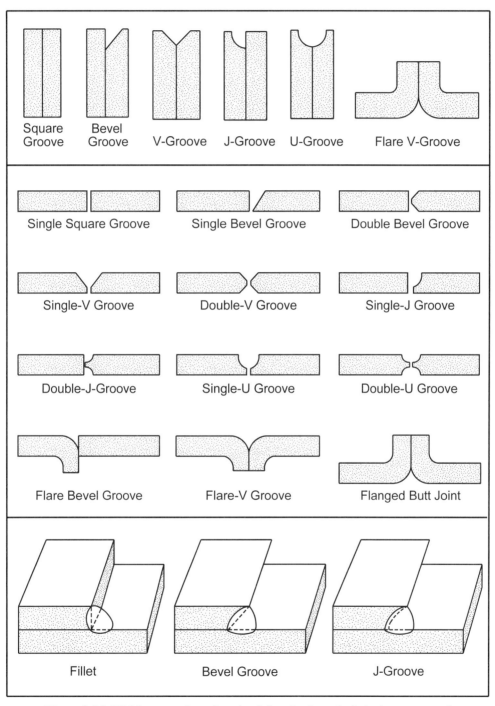

Figure 3-20. Weld preparations for edge joints (top), typical single-groove and double-groove butt joints (center) and lap joints (bottom).

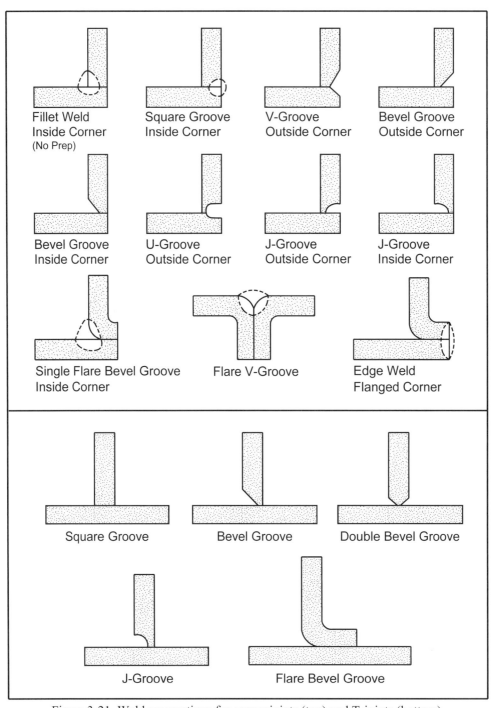

Figure 3-21. Weld preparations for corner joints (top) and T-joints (bottom).

Weld-Size Guidelines

A conservative rule of thumb for determining the size of fillet welds in order
to develop the full strength of the plates they join is that the leg size of the
fillet should be $^3/_4$ of the plate thickness of the thinner plate. This assumes that

the fillet weld is on both sides of the plate, the fillet weld is on the full length of the plate, and if two plates of different thickness are being joined, the thickness of the thinner plate is used. See Figure 3-22.

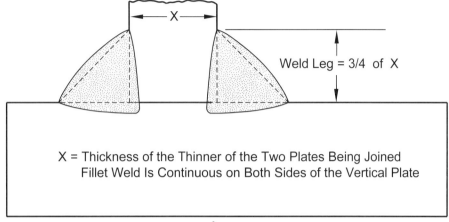

Figure 3-22. Fillet should be $^3/_4$ the thickness of the thinner plate.

Weld Strength

Welds have a great reserve of strength over that required by codes and in service. In many cases this reserve is not recognized by the code bodies. For example, the *minimum* strength of ordinary E60XX electrodes is about 50% higher than the structural steels they join. In fact, as welded, many of the E60XX electrodes have about a 75% higher yield strength than the structural steel itself.

Welded structural steel joints are stronger than the base metal alloys because:

• The core wire used in the electrode is of premium steel and held to a closer specification than the plate.
• There is complete shielding of the molten metal during welding. This, plus the scavenging and deoxidizing agents and other ingredients in the electrode coating, produce a uniformity of crystal structure and physical properties on a par with electric furnace steel.

Figure 3-23 shows the effect of reducing the fillet weld size on a T-joint. Figure 3-24 shows the AWS and AISC weld-size guidelines for structures and bridges.

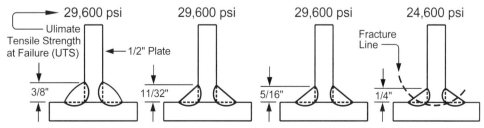

Figure 3-23. Ultimate tensile strength is reduced as the fillet weld size is reduced. A $^3/_8$" fillet weld on a $^1/_2$" plate has such a reserve of strength that only when the fillet size is reduced to $^1/_4$" does the strength of the joint decrease.

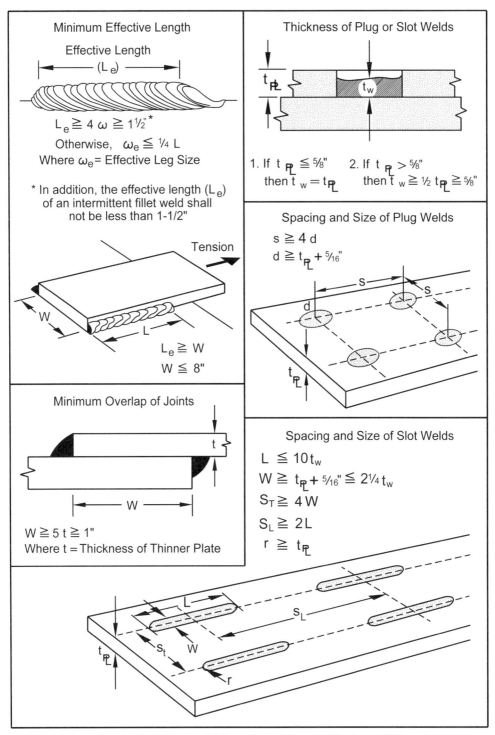

Figure 3-24. AWS/AISC guidelines for minimum effective weld length.

Welding Positions

Welding positions are designated G for groove welds and F for fillet welds. They are divided by the position of the weld axis with respect to the horizontal and whether the welds are on plate or pipe. See Figure 3-25.

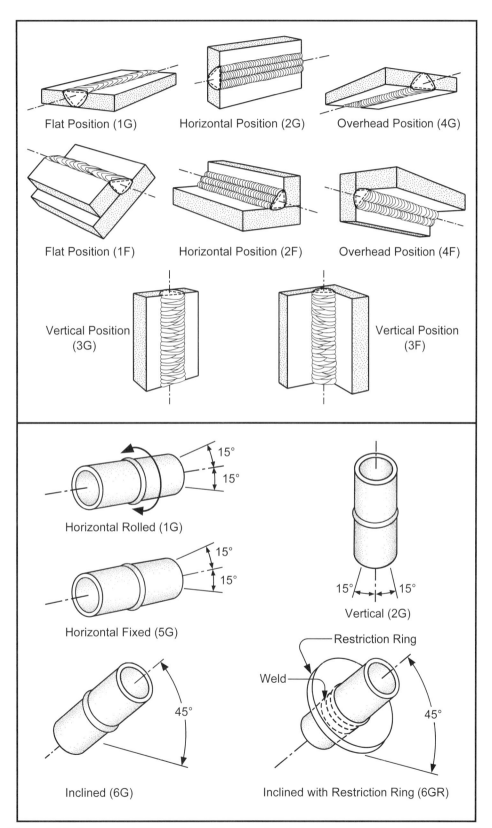

Figure 3-25. Groove and fillet weld positions (top) and pipe groove-weld positions (bottom).

Basic Welding Symbols

Welding symbols graphically convey complete information about a welded or brazed joint—where it goes, how it's made, and how it's tested—in a standardized and abbreviated format. The complete symbol system is described in *ANSI/AWS A2.4, Standard Symbols for Welding, Brazing, and Nondestructive Testing*. While symbols may contain a lot of information and be quite complicated, in practice most weld designers use only a few of the many symbols available. This is because on welded machinery 80% of the welds used are fillet welds, 15% are groove welds and only 5% are special welds. See Figure 3-26.

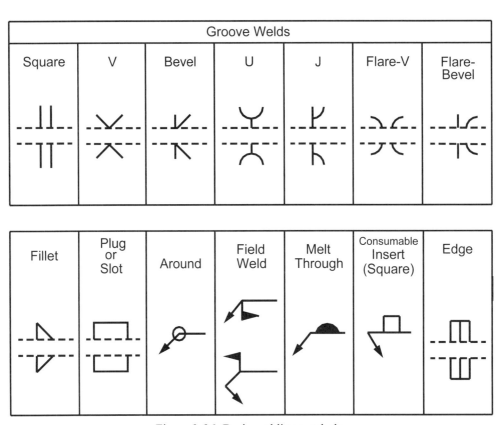

Figure 3-26. Basic welding symbols.

The top half of Figure 3-27 shows three common groove welds and the welding symbols for them. The arrows pointing to the welds provide a reference point that indicates which side of the plate contains the weld. If the weld symbol is on the side of the horizontal or reference line, the weld is on the side of the work facing the observer. If the symbol is on the side away from the arrow, the weld is on the other or far side of the work. The bottom half of Figure 3-27 shows how to indicate the desired root-gap size.

Figure 3-28 shows the symbols for location and dimensioning of fillet welds.

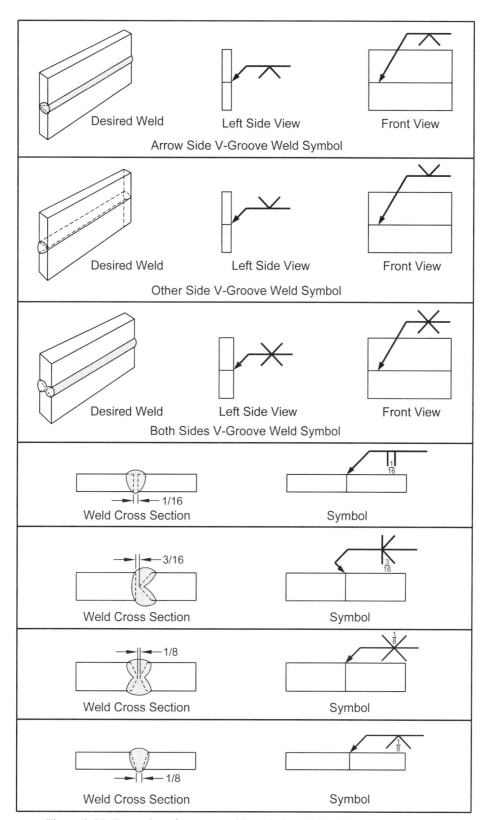

Figure 3-27. Examples of groove weld symbols and the joints they represent.

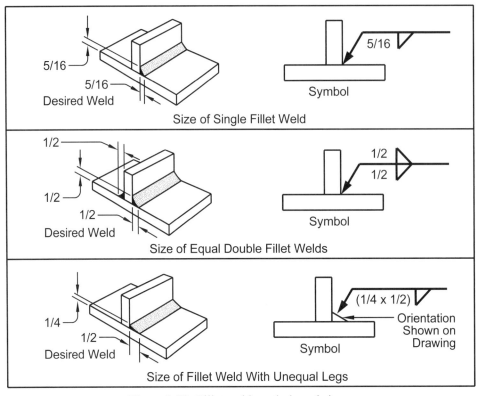

Figure 3-28. Fillet weld symbols and sizes.

All Around Symbol

The all around symbol is a circle around the junction of the reference line and the arrow. This symbol indicates a weld that is continuous around the joint, even though there may be a change in welding direction. See Figure 3-29.

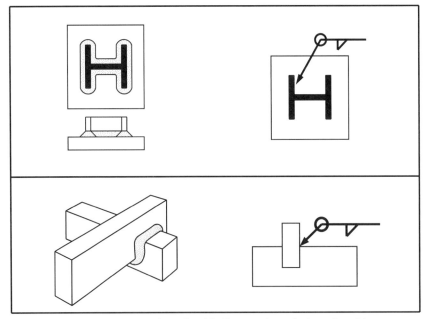

Figure 3-29. Examples of weld all around symbols and welds.

Chapter 4

Tools & Welding Tables

Education is learning to use the tools humanity has found indispensable.
—Josiah Royce

Introduction

To know what tools and equipment are needed for a welding job, you need to understand the steps required in the fabrication process:

1. Get or make a fabrication sketch or drawing.
2. Develop a well thought out welding procedure.
3. Gather all necessary welding equipment including measuring tools.
4. Assemble all materials to be welded.
5. Make patterns, jigs, templates and fixtures, if needed.
6. Put together a cut list.
7. Lay out and cut materials.
8. Clean metal areas to be welded and make the edge preparations.
9. Position and clamp materials prior to welding.
10. Tack weld assemblies, check dimensions, setup and squareness.
11. Place the final welds and assemble the fabrication.
12. Paint the fabrication promptly to avoid rust formation.

Section I – Hand Tools

Measuring Tools

- *Framing, carpenter's, cabinetmaker's and combination squares* – Use the largest square that fits the work. The combination square is convenient for the layout of 45° corner cuts and short, parallel lines. Grind the outside corners off the carpenter's and cabinetmaker's squares to allow them to fit snugly into work corners that have a fillet weld in place. See Figure 4-1 (A, B, C & D).

- *Builder's and torpedo levels* – Use the larger builder's level whenever possible because it is more accurate and measures over a longer span. Use the torpedo level wherever the builder's level won't fit. See Figure 4-1 (E & F).

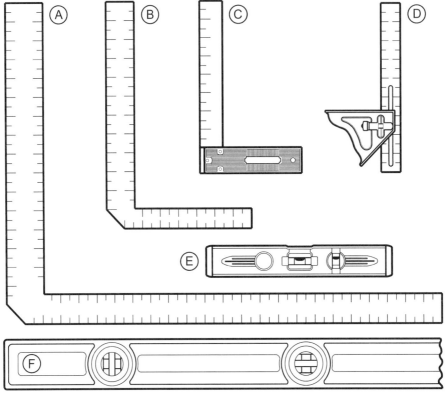

Figure 4-1. Common measuring and leveling tools for welders: (A) framing square, (B) carpenter's square, (C) cabinet maker's square, (D) combination square, (E) torpedo level and (F) builder's level.

- *Compass and dividers* – For scribing circles or stepping off a series of equal intervals.

- *Steel measuring tape* – The most convenient sizes are the 16' and 24' tapes. These are also useful for measuring curved surfaces.

- *Precision steel rules* – Available in lengths from 6–72", these steel rules are for measuring along or drawing a straight line.

Metal Marking Tools

The following items will mark metal:

- Snapped chalk lines, which use a mason's string.

- Welder's chalk, also called *soapstone*.

- Ball point metal marking pen.

- Single center-punch mark or a line of center-punch marks.

- Silver Streak welder's pencil.

- Felt-tip pen, such as a Sharpie.
- Aerosol spray paint.
- Scribed lines either on bare metal or on layout fluid.

Use welder's soapstone for marking rough dimensions, bend lines, and to indicate cutting lines that need to hold up under cutting torch heat. A line of center-punch marks can be more accurate and will also withstand torch heat. For very accurate layout lines, spray paint the metal in the area of the layout lines and use a scriber to scratch through the paint to make the lines. Alternatively, machinist's layout fluid—available in red or blue—can be used to make the scribed lines visible. Although these lines will not hold up under torch heat, they can be essential to laying out non-torch cutting lines. Felt-tip pens can be used in place of layout fluid to darken the metal to better show scribed lines. Do not use scribe marks to designate bend or fold lines since they are stress raisers and the part will eventually fail along the scribed line.

Welding Hand Tools

- Chipping hammer to remove welding slag, particularly for SMAW.
- Files for bringing an oversized part down to exact dimensions, removing a hazardous razor edge or burr, and smoothing the ends of wire-feed electrodes before feeding them through the torch liner.
- Ball pein hammer and cold chisel to break tack welds.
- Pliers, such as Channel Locks, for moving hot metal safely.
- Wire cutters to trim electrode wire (GMAW and FCAW only).
- Hack saws for slow, but accurate metal cutting.
- Wire brush for cleaning welds. See all these tools in Figure 4-2.

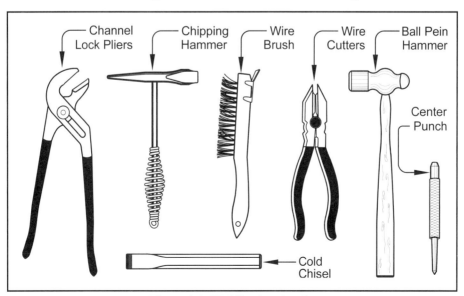

Figure 4-2. Welding hand tools.

Clamps

Figure 4-3 shows general purpose clamps for welding. These clamps include:

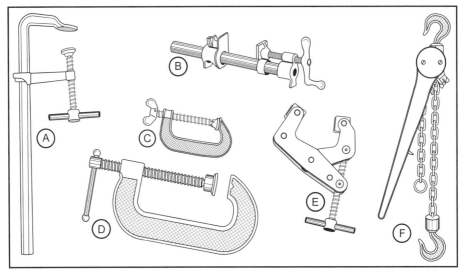

Figure 4-3. A selection of general purpose clamps used in welding: (A) bar clamp,
(B) pipe clamp, (C & D) C-clamps, (E) Kant-Twist clamp and (F) come-along.

- *C-clamps.*

- *Bar clamps* and *pipe clamps* are used to clamp across long spans.

- *Come-alongs*, also called *cable pullers*, are used to pull large, long or stiff parts into position. These are particularly good on structural steel for pulling frames into square.

- *Kant-Twist heavy-duty clamps.* Figure 4-4 shows how to tighten Kant-Twist clamps using a wrench. Pulling them up without a wrench does not take full advantage of their clamping power.

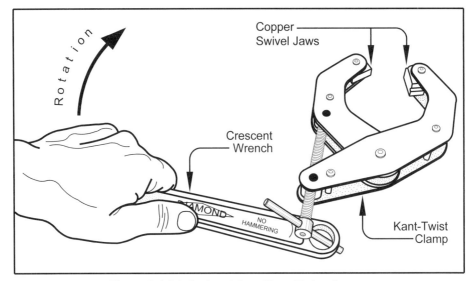

Figure 4-4. Method to tighten Kant-Twist clamps.

- *Bessey welding clamps* are heavier and stronger than general-purpose welding clamps, and more expensive, but usually worth it. See Figure 4-5.

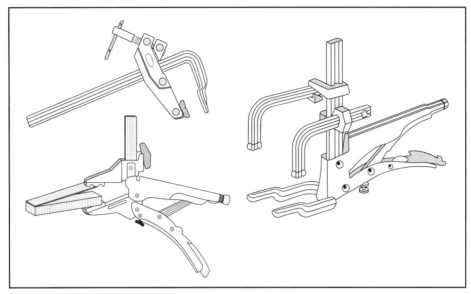

Figure 4-5. Several designs of Bessey heavy-duty welding clamps.

- *Corner-clamping fixtures*, such as the Bessy corner clamp in Figure 4-6, make getting accurate right-angle joints easier. Although these clamps are most often used sequentially to weld up corner joints, sometimes four or more are positioned on a rigid base to form a fixture for production work. These clamps have aluminum bases and copper-plated screws so welding spatter does not stick to them.

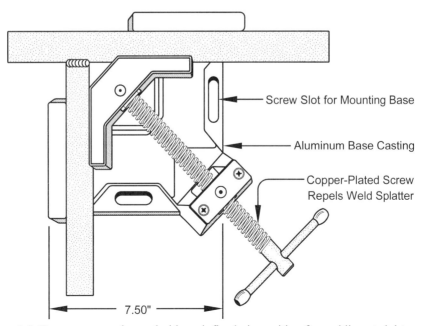

Figure 4-6. Bessey corner clamps hold work firmly in position for welding at right angles.

- *Angle clamps* for tubing are inexpensive, commercially available and can produce excellent results on light tubing, but are not rigid enough to be used on pipe. The angle clamp in Figure 4-7 is simple enough to be made in the shop using short lengths of angle iron with bolt adjustment bars and simple clamps welded to the angle iron.

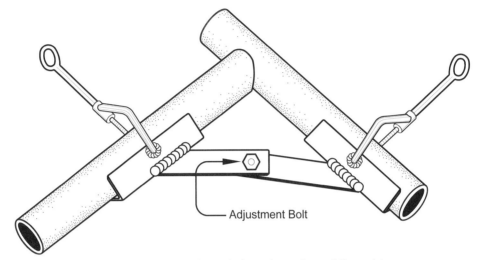

— Adjustment Bolt

Figure 4-7. Shop-made angle iron clamp for welding tubing.

- *Vise-Grip-style welding clamps* and *pliers* have many applications. Some pin two pieces of metal together, some hold a small part such as a washer to a larger part, some hold two pipes in alignment, and others have a deep throat for an extra-long reach from the edges of the clamped material. Vice-Grip chain pliers hold irregular parts. Figures 4-8 through 4-10 show a selection of the many clamp styles available. When Vise-Grip-style clamps are held so that the handle containing the screw is on top, the screw threads are protected from weld spatter by the metal handle.

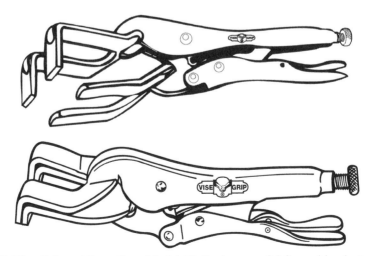

Figure 4-8. Vise-Grip welding pliers, Model 9R (top) are useful for making butt welds, and Model 9AC (bottom) holds thin strips of material together for edge welds.

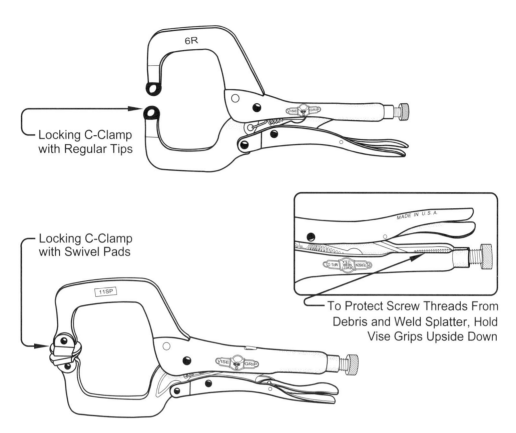

Figure 4-9. Vise-Grip welding clamps (top) with regular tips, and (bottom) with swivel pads. The inset on the right shows how the clamp handle can protect the screw threads from weld spatter.

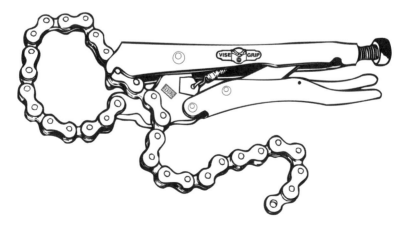

Figure 4-10. Vise-Grip chain pliers, Model 20R, hold irregularly shaped objects firmly against a pipe or tube. This tool can hold more than two objects together and add-ons to extend the length of the chain are available.

- *Magnetic clamping blocks* are useful for lightly holding work in place for tacking, but they are not strong enough to control distortion. Figure 4-11 shows four different magnetic clamp designs.

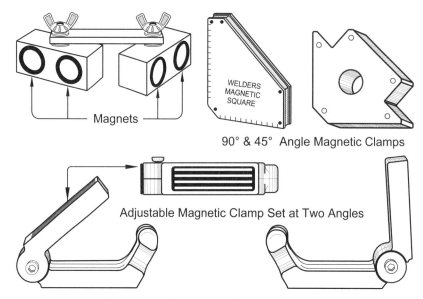

Figure 4-11. Four magnetic clamp designs.

- *Puller clips* are for aligning and holding plates and panels in position when considerable force is required. Because the steel plates are rigid, forcing them to conform to the desired shape and weld-induced distortion together produce very large forces. Puller clips are widely used in shipyards, petroleum and chemical tank construction, and truck building to pull plates into place. A series of clips welded along a seam—sometimes twenty or more for long seams—are needed to overcome the forces preventing alignment. When final welding is completed, the clips are easily snapped, chiseled or ground off. A little touch-up with a grinder will hide that they were ever used. See Figure 4-12.

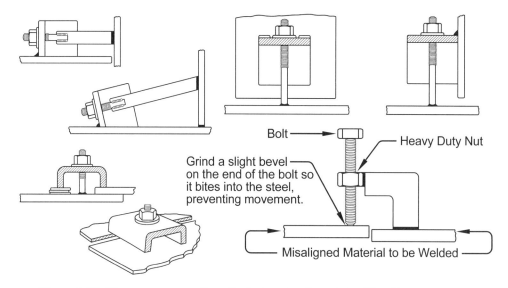

Figure 4-12. There are many puller clip designs to align plates. Usually two or more clips are needed to apply enough force to move plates into position.

- *Bridge clamps* are used to pull plate seams together. They are often used in rows of twenty or more to bring heavy, large plate edges into perfect alignment. See Figure 4-13.

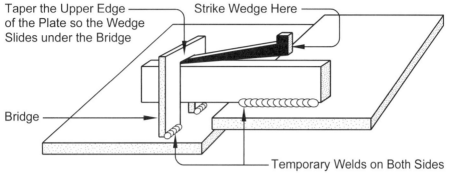

Figure 4-13. Bridge clamps are often used to bring long seams between plates together.

Section II – Power Tools

Hand-Held Power Tools

- *Electric drills* and *twist drill bits* are good for making starter holes to begin oxyfuel cutting.

- *Abrasive cutoff saws* work well on rebar, bar stock and pipe. These are not good for rolled shapes and for thin tubing because it is difficult to make accurate cuts and thin-walled tubing is easily flattened. See Figure 4-14.

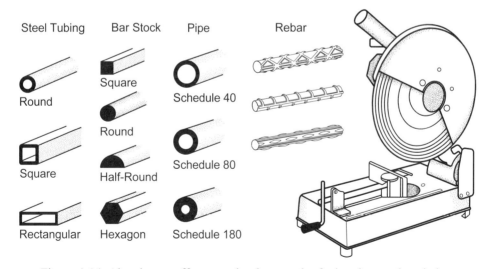

Figure 4-14. Abrasive cutoff saws make short work of rebar, bar stock and pipe.

- *Portable grinders*, as in Figure 4-15 (top), use abrasive wheels for removing mill scale, rust and paint before welding, for edge preparation, for smoothing rough edges, and for removing bad welds. Wire wheels remove paint and light rust, flap wheels smooth welds and blend curves. See Figure 4-15 (bottom).

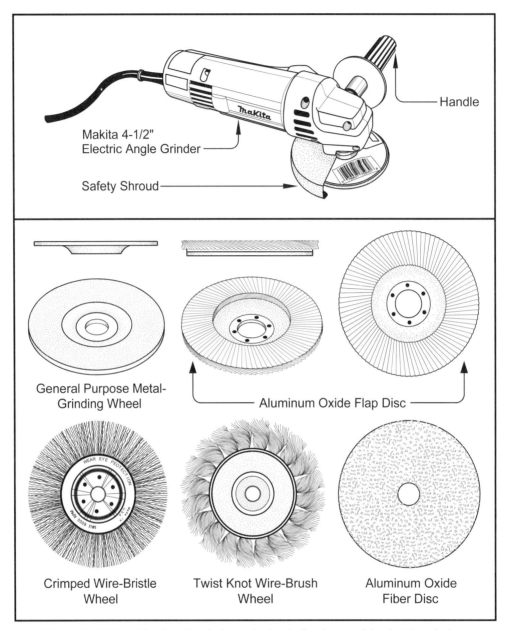

Figure 4-15. Portable electric grinder and wheels for the portable electric grinder.

Cutoff Bandsaw

Bandsaws of the design shown in Figure 4-16 have been available for the last 40 years. Many of these machines have been at work for years with only the replacement of bearings, motors and drive gears. These bandsaws are inexpensive and durable. In a non-production setting, they are capable of quickly and accurately performing thousands of cuts in ferrous and non-ferrous metal. Although mainly used as cutoff saws for preparing raw metal stock for machining, they can also be used like a vertical bandsaw. Most models automatically turn off the motor power when the cut is finished.

There are heavier production versions of the cutoff bandsaw which have pumps to apply a continuous stream of cutting fluid for faster cuts and longer blade life. Also, many of these machines have provisions for angled cuts.

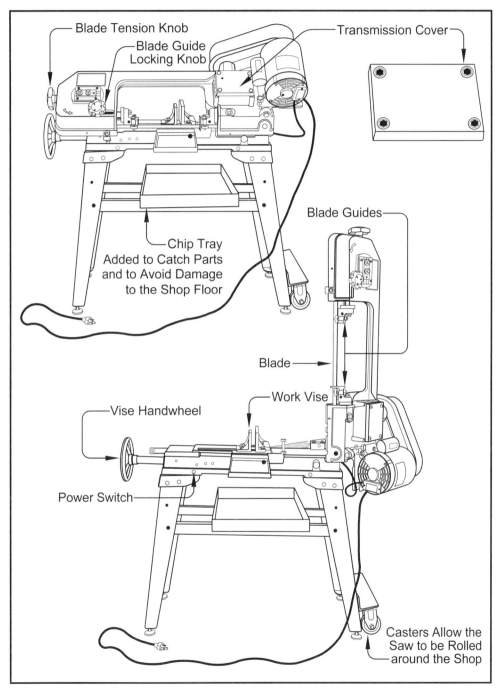

Figure 4-16. Budget cutoff bandsaws can perform thousands of cuts. Note the addition of the chip tray which not only makes cleanup easier, it catches small parts.

Disc & Belt Grinders

Both disc and belt grinders can:

- Square up smaller workpieces.

- Remove burrs and jagged edges.

- Add rounded corners to flat stock.

- Smooth welds.

- Grind parts to size from oversized rough cuts.

See the combination disc and belt grinder in Figure 4-17.

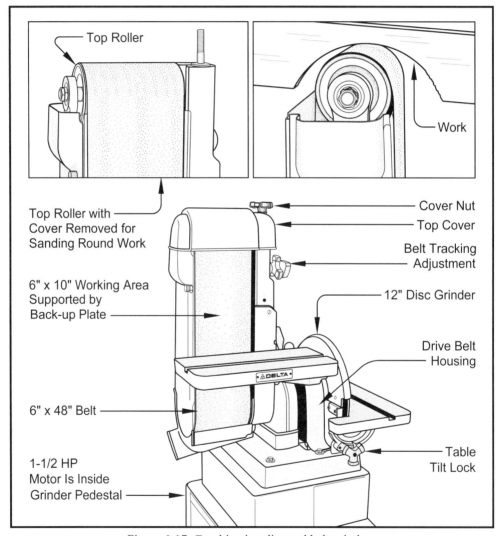

Figure 4-17. Combination disc and belt grinder.

Shears

There are many large commercial power shears available, but their size and cost make them impractical for most welding shops. The shears in Figure 4-18 are small bench-top models. They are used for precise cuts of rod and bar stock, but these shears cannot cut curves in heavy stock. The Beverly Shear in Figure 4-18 (left) is especially useful for cutting curves and irregular shapes in thin plate stock. A disadvantage of shears is that the *fall-off*, the section of the raw stock that is cut away to get the desired part, is usually badly bent.

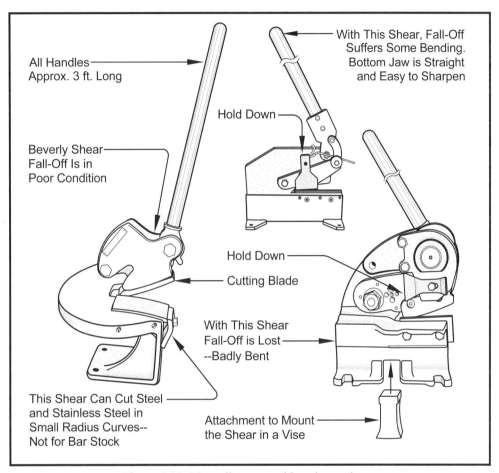

Figure 4-18. Manually operated bench-top shears.

Section III – Welding Tables

Steel Tables

Welding tables are commercially available, but are most often shop-made, as is the one in Figure 4-19.

A good welding table offers the following advantages:

- Positions work at a comfortable working height for the welder.
- Offers a conductive return path to the ground lead so the ground lead does not have to be attached to the work itself.
- Supports the work on a flat surface so parts can be properly aligned.
- Provides a work surface for clamping or tack welding work to the table.

- Holds smaller gas cylinders and tools on the steel shelf below the table top. The cylinders should be clamped to the welding table shelf or to one of the legs so they do not tip over or fall off.

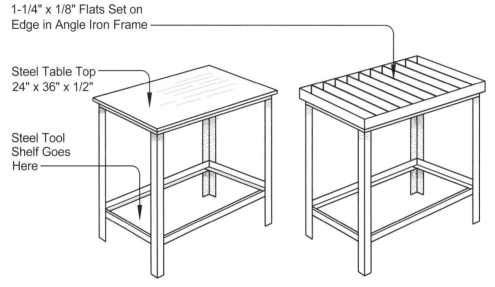

1-1/4" x 1/8" Flats Set on
Edge in Angle Iron Frame

Steel Table Top
24" x 36" x 1/2"

Steel Tool
Shelf Goes
Here

Figure 4-19. Shop-made welding table (left) and cutting table (right).

Welding Platens

Welding platens are an improvement over the basic welding table because they have Blanchard-ground cast iron surfaces with a grid of clamping holes as shown in Figure 4-20. Platens can be of any size, but typically range in size from one foot square to five feet square.

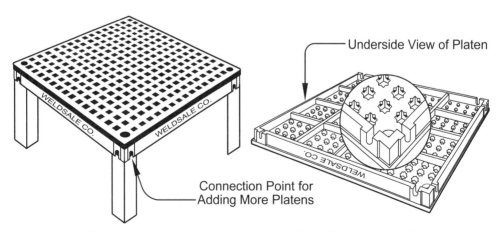

Underside View of Platen

Connection Point for
Adding More Platens

Figure 4-20. Welding platen supported on legs and a view of its underside. The notches on the sides of the tabletop provide a means of bolting two or more platens together.

Platens have provisions so several of them can be fastened together to support large fabrications. A variety of clamps, like the ones shown in Figure 4-21, fit into these holes to position and support the welding workpieces and to control weld-induced distortion.

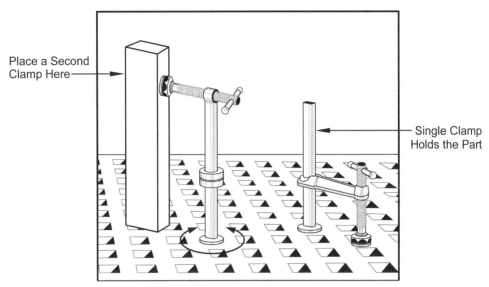

Place a Second Clamp Here

Single Clamp Holds the Part

Figure 4-21. Two clamps secured in welding platen holes.

In addition to the basic cast iron or cast steel welding platen system which is adequate for most industrial welding, DEMMELER Maschinenbau GmbH & Co. KG, Heimertingen, Germany, offers multi-component, modular fixturing systems that allow the fabrication of high-precision parts that need little additional machining. A complete fixturing system that constrains the part, holds it in precise location with respect to the other parts and controls distortion is the solution to precise assembly. You can see more about these high-end products at: www.BLUCO.com.

Cutting Pyramids

Cast iron cutting pyramids, typically about 3" tall, are a valuable addition to the cutting table. Slots in their bases fit over the bars of a cutting table. Cutting pyramids provide additional flame protection to the table, and can be positioned so the work is completely supported and does not shift as pieces are cut from it. See Figure 4-22.

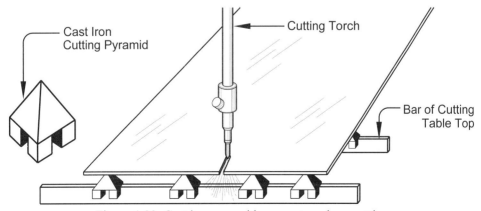

Cast Iron Cutting Pyramid

Cutting Torch

Bar of Cutting Table Top

Figure 4-22. Cast iron pyramids support work on cutting tables to minimize torch damage to the table.

Rotary Tables

Rotary tables permit the welder and his torch to remain stationary while the work turns to make a circumferential weld. This relieves the welder of constantly repositioning the torch and makes a much smoother and continuous weld bead. For hands-free operation, many tables have foot-operated speed controls. The table in Figure 4-23 can support workpieces up to 35 pounds, but larger table designs can handle work weighing several tons. The rotary table is an essential tool if many circular weld beads must be made. The large-capacity rotary tables often have the ability to tilt the work on several axes as well as rotate in both directions. Workpieces can be clamped to the table or a three- or four-jaw chuck can be secured to the table and the part welded while held in the chuck. Old chucks are usually used for this job because welding heat damages them.

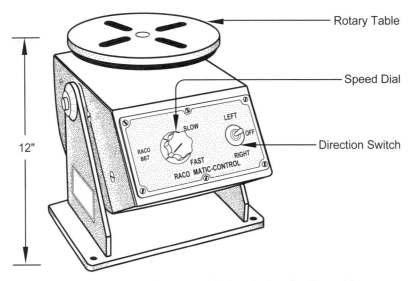

Figure 4-23. Small rotary table for placing circular welds.

Cooling Plates

Cooling plates consist of a $^3/_4$–1" aluminum plate and a fan which blows air over the part and the plate. They cool the workpiece quickly, but gradually enough to prevent thermal shock, unlike the shock resulting from quenching in water. Plunging a welded or brazed part in water is almost always a poor practice. On small parts, where weld-induced distortion and overheating must be avoided, a cooling plate can provide the solution. Welding is interrupted only for a short time with a trip to the cooling plate.

Tooling Plates

Tooling plates are very much like a miniature welding platen. Although they can be purchased commercially, most are shop-made. They can hold small, irregularly shaped parts in position that would otherwise be difficult or impossible to secure with welding clamps. Any number of tooling plate clamps can be used. These plates are especially useful when repair welding or brazing cracked castings which have broken into several pieces. Tooling plates can also be used on a lathe faceplate or in a mill to machine the repaired part when the welding is completed. See Figure 4-24.

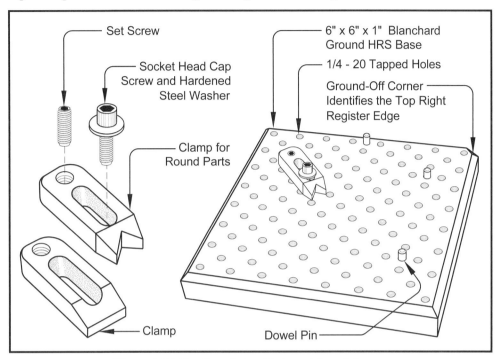

Figure 4-24. Tooling plate with two styles of clamps.

Section IV – Grounding Clamps

Grounding Clamps

Grounding clamps connect the return lead from the work back to the welding power supply. There are several types of grounding clamps:

• Spring-loaded clamps are the least expensive and the most common.

• Screw-clamps are secure, yet easily removed.

• Magnetic attachments are very convenient and often offer a handy swivel feature.

• Tack welded attachments are the most secure and take the most time to install and remove.

A good connection to ground is essential because a poor ground connection will generate heat between the connection and the work. It is best to make a solid connection on freshly cleaned base metal. To reach the base metal, use a grinder or wire wheel to get through rust, paint and mill scale. One of the most common causes of poor ground connections is the oxide scale on hot rolled steel which must be ground away to reach bare steel to make a solid connection. See four types of grounding clamps in Figure 4-25.

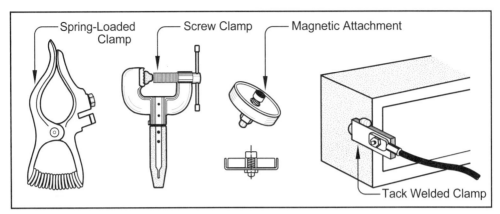

Figure 4-25. Four types of grounding clamps: spring-loaded,
screw-type, magnetic attachment and tack-welded ground clamps.

Chapter 5

Shielded Metal Arc Welding

The brain that contains the problem
probably also contains the solution.

—Nancy Kline

Introduction

Shielded metal arc welding, AWS designation *SMAW*, is also commonly called *arc welding*, *stick welding* and *stick electrode welding*.

Although there had been initial work on arc welding in the 1700s using carbon electrodes powered by batteries, development intensified between 1880 and 1900 when electric generators replaced batteries. By the early 1900s Lincoln Electric offered the first arc welding machine, and by 1912 covered electrodes were patented. Arc welding remains an important process for structural steel and pipeline construction because decision makers in these critical industries choose it for its reliability. Today, arc welding is also popular for industrial, automotive and farm repair because the equipment is relatively inexpensive and can be made portable. Although more welders have learned this process than any other, and its annual filler metal poundage continues to grow, lately it is declining in importance as the wire feed welding processes continue to gain popularity and market share.

During WWII many shipyard workers and servicemen were trained to use shielded metal arc welding. After the war the popularity of low-cost transformer welding power supplies like the Lincoln Electric Company's "tombstone" enabled these newly trained welders to bring their skills to the farm, the garage, and to factories.

SMAW Equipment

As shown in Figure 5-1, an SMAW outfit requires:

- Constant-current welding power supply.
- Electrode holder, electrode lead and its terminals.

- Ground clamp, work lead and its terminals.
- Welding electrodes.

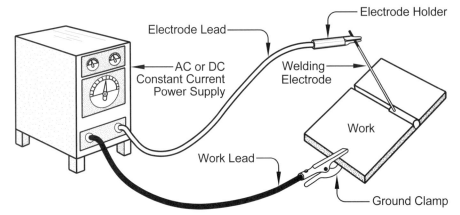

Figure 5-1. Shielded metal arc welding outfit.

SMAW Process

SMAW is usually a manual process, but it can be automated. During welding, an electric current flows between the welding power supply, the electrode, the welding arc, the work, the ground clamp, the work lead and back to the welding power supply. Electrons flowing through the gap between the electrode and the work produce an arc, or plasma, that furnishes heat to melt both the electrode metal and the workpiece metal.

Because temperatures within the arc exceed 6000°F, tiny globules of metal form at the tip of the electrode, then transfer to the molten weld pool on the work. As the electrode moves away from the weld pool, the molten mixture of electrode and base metal solidifies, completing the weld.

In the flat or horizontal position, gravity aids electrode metal transfer by gas expansion from the electrode coating materials, electromagnetic forces and surface tension. In other positions, gravity opposes these forces.

The electrode is coated with a flux, and heat from the arc causes this flux coating to burn and decompose. This creates a gaseous shield that protects the electrode tip, the work, and the molten weld pool from atmospheric contamination. The flux contains materials that coat the molten steel droplets as they transfer to the weld and become slag after cooling. This slag floats on the weld pool surface before it solidifies over the weld bead, where it protects the molten metal from exposure to atmosphere and slows the cooling rate. See Figure 5-2.

Some electrode-flux coatings contain metal powder to provide additional metal filler to increase the deposition rate.

The electrode flux and metal electrode determine the chemical, electrical, mechanical and metallurgical properties of the weld as well as the electrode handling characteristics. Only 50% of the heat furnished by the power supply enters the weld; the rest is lost to radiation, the surrounding base metal, and to the weld plume.

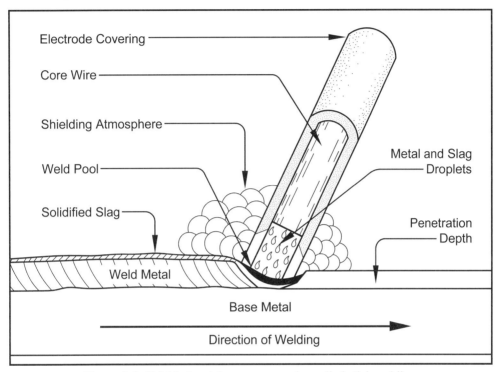

Figure 5-2. Shielded metal arc process, also called stick welding.

Applications
SMAW can weld the following metals:

- Aluminum
- Bronze
- Carbon steel
- Cast iron
- Hardfacing alloys

- High-strength steels
- Low-alloy steels
- Malleable iron
- Nickel
- Stainless steel

Some metals require preheat, postheat, or both to prevent weld bead cracking. Since better processes exist, not much aluminum welding is done by SMAW.

SMAW welds from $^1/_{16}$" to unlimited thicknesses are possible. Thicknesses less than $^1/_8$" can be joined but require much greater skill to prevent the weld from burning through the metal. Thicknesses over $^3/_4$" are more economically welded by other methods such as FCAW, which deposits metal faster.

SMAW Advantages

- Low cost equipment.

- Welds many different metals and alloys, including the most commonly used.

- Relatively portable and can be used in confined spaces.

- With different current settings and rod diameters, the same equipment can weld metals from $^1/_8$" (16 gauge) to metals several feet thick. There is no upper limit on the thickness of metal that can be welded with SMAW.

- Welds can be performed in any position.

- SMAW is less affected by wind and drafts than gas-shielded processes like GMAW and GTAW.

SMAW Disadvantages

- Not suitable for metal sheets under $^1/_8$" thick.

- Operator duty cycle and overall deposition rate are usually lower with SMAW than with wire-fed processes because, with SMAW, welding must be stopped when the electrode is consumed and needs to be replaced.

- Not all of the electrode can be used. The remaining stub in the electrode holder must be discarded, wasting 1–2" of every electrode.

- The frequent stops and starts caused by changing electrodes can result in weld defects.

Weather Restrictions

SMAW is not permitted in rain, snow or blowing sand, and when the base metal is below 0°F. But during these adverse weather conditions, temporary shelters known as *dog houses* can be erected around the weld site to allow the welding to proceed. Preheating the weld base metal to 70°F with rosebud tips permits welding when the outside temperature is below 0°F.

Welding Power Supplies

SMAW uses constant current welding power supplies because their output characteristics give the welder control over the weld pool size and still limits maximum arc current. The shape of the voltage-versus-current curve indicates that increasing the arc length reduces the welding current—and the size of the weld pool.

Because there is some variation in arc length as the welder moves the electrode along the weldment, the constant-current welding power supply insures a stable arc during these variations. For more on constant-current power characteristics, see *Chapter 18 – Power Supplies & Electrical Safety*.

Typical SMAW welding current is 25–600 amperes. With these power supplies the open-circuit voltage—the voltage when no welding is being done and the arc is off—runs from 50–100 volts, but drops to 17–40 volts during welding. The higher the open-circuit voltage, the easier it is to strike an arc, but the greater the risk of electric shock.

AC vs. DC Power Supplies

DC power always provides a more stable arc and more even metal transfer than AC power. Once struck, the DC arc remains continuous. When welding with AC, the arc extinguishes and restrikes 120 times a second as the current and voltage reverse direction. A DC arc has good wetting action of the molten weld metal and uniform weld bead size at low welding currents. For this reason, DC is excellent for welding thin sections. DC is also preferred to AC on overhead and vertical welding jobs because of its shorter arc and dramatically better weld pool control.

When DC welding power supplies are run on three-phase power they provide an even smoother arc than DC welding power supplies run on single-phase power. This is because the three-phase wave forms, when combined by the rectifier, are much smoother—and closer—to pure DC. See *Chapter 18 – Power Supplies & Electrical Safety*, Figure 18-15 for more details.

Welding Polarities & Characteristics

All three types of polarities are used for SMAW:

- Alternating current (AC).

- Direct current electrode negative (DCEN), also called *DCSP* for DC-straight polarity, produces less penetration than DCEP but has a higher electrode burn-off rate. See the DCEN setup in Figure 5-3.

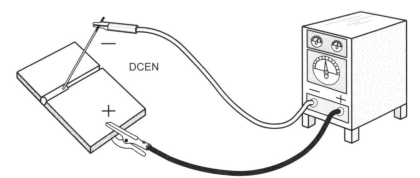

Figure 5-3. DC-Electrode Negative now replaces the term DC-Straight Polarity.

- Direct current electrode positive (DCEP), also called *DCRP* for DC-reverse polarity, is especially useful for welding aluminum, beryllium-copper, and magnesium because of its surface cleaning action which permits welding these metals without using a flux. DCEP produces better penetration than DCEN, but has a lower electrode burn-off rate. Most combination electrodes designed for AC *or* DC operation work better on DC. See the DCEP setup in Figure 5-4.

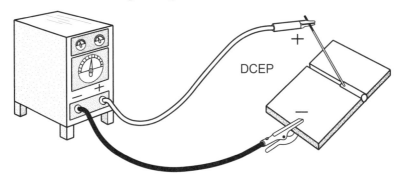

Figure 5-4. DC-Electrode Positive (DCEP) is also known as DC-Reverse Polarity (DCRP).

Penetration & Heat of the Three Polarities

Weld penetration changes with different power supply polarities. Figure 5-5 shows weld penetration going from the lowest, DCEN, to the intermediate penetration with AC, to the highest penetration with DCEP.

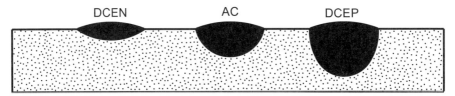

Figure 5-5. At the same welding current, weld bead penetration
changes with DCEN, AC and DCEP power supply polarity.

Equipment cost aside, AC has no great advantages over DC for SMAW, but there are many more AC rods available because they were developed when DC machines were considerably more expensive and much less common than AC machines. But, any AC rod will run on DC, and sometimes these AC rods can solve difficult welding problems that other rods cannot.

Arc Blow

Arc blow is the twisting, turning or distortion of the welding arc caused by the magnetic field of the welding current flowing in the base metal. See the examples in Figure 5-6. Whenever current flows, it creates a magnetic field around its conductor. Any shape of wire other than a straight line will produce an asymmetrical field causing the arc to be drawn in a particular direction like smoke in the wind. At currents above 600 amperes, the force created by the unevenness of the field may even cause the wire to move.

To reduce the effects of arc blow:

• Use AC, not DC welding current.

- Move the welding work lead so you weld away from the ground lead.
- Use a shorter arc length.
- Tack or weld along the weldment to alter return-current flow paths.
- Clamp a steel block over the unfinished end of the weld.
- Keep magnetic clamps and grounds away from the weld area.
- Change welding direction.

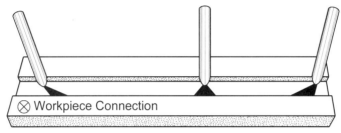

Figure 5-6. Arc blow on left and right arc, normal arc, center.

Amperage Setting

Once an electrode class and diameter is selected, use Table 5-1 to determine the manufacturer's recommended amperage range. Between manufacturers there will be some differences in recommended ranges for the same electrode class and diameter, so consult their specification sheets.

Lincoln Electric Product Name	AWS Class	Electrode Polarity	Sizes & Current Ranges (Amperes)					
			3/32"	1/8"	5/32"	3/16"	7/32"	1/4"
Fleetweld 5P	E6010	DCEP	40–70	75–130	90–175	140–225	200–275	220–325
Fleetweld 35	E6011	AC DC±	50–85 40–75	75–120 70–110	90–160 80–145	120–200 110–180	150–260 135–235	190–300 170–270
Fleetweld 7	E6012	DC-AC	— —	80–135 90–150	110–180 120–200	155–250 170–270	225–295 250–325	245–325 275–360
Fleetweld 37	E6013	AC DC±	75–105 70–95	110–150 100–135	160–200 145–180	205–260 190–235	— —	— —
Fleetweld 47	E7014	AC DCEN	80–100 75–95	110–160 100–145	150–225 135–200	200–280 185–235	260–340 235–305	280–425 260–380
Jetweld LH–70	E7018	DC+ AC	70–100 80–120	90–150 110–170	120 190 135–225	170 280 200–300	210 330 260–380	290–430 325–530
Jetweld 3	E7024	AC DC±	— —	115–175 100–160	180–240 160–215	240–315 215–285	300–380 270–340	350–450 315–405
Jetweld 2	E6027	AC DC±	— —	— —	190–240 175–215	250–300 230–270	300–380 270–340	350–450 315–405
Jetweld LH–3800	E7028	AC DC+	— —	— —	180–270 170–240	240–330 210–300	275–410 260–380	360–520 —

Table 5-1. Recommended polarity and current ranges for various diameter electrodes.

Choosing the Better Current Range Setting

When there are overlapping current ranges on your welding machine, such as 25–150 A and 60–260 A, to get a current setting of 80 A, the lower current range would be the better choice. It is better to use the *lower* current range setting because the top of a current range is likely to have less *current ripple*—AC riding on the top of the DC—than the same current output setting from a higher current range, and will provide a smoother arc. The ripple effect leads to arc instability which results in inconsistent weld beads.

Determining Arc Length

Although the correct arc length is usually equal to the diameter of the electrode, the sound of the arc is an excellent indicator of arc length. The proper arc length sounds like the crackling of bacon and eggs frying. Too short an arc makes a sputtering sound, while too long an arc makes a humming sound.

Electrode Holders

The function of the electrode holder is to:

- Electrically insulate the welder from the welding power supply voltage.

- Thermally insulate the welder from the conducted heat of the electrode.

- Make a secure electrical connection between the welding cable and the electrode with a minimum of voltage drop.

It is important to keep electrode holders in good condition. Poor gripping of the electrode by the jaws of the electrode holder will cause poor conduction of electricity, and power intended for the weld will be lost in the holder. The holder will become so hot that the operator cannot hold it. If not corrected, the heat will deteriorate the electrical insulation properties of the electrode holder, eventually exposing the welder to electric shock. When choosing an electrode holder, the smallest size holder that can be used without overheating is the best one to use because it will be the lightest weight and the least tiring for the welder.

SMAW Electrodes

SMAW electrodes contain a solid or cast-metal core wire covered by a thick flux coating. Every change of flux composition and thickness alters the electrode's welding characteristics. These changes, plus current type and polarity, determine how the rod will perform and what type of weld bead it will deposit. SMAW electrodes are made in lengths of 9–18 inches. The coating on SMAW rods performs the following functions:

- Provides a gas stream to shield the molten weld pool from atmospheric oxygen, hydrogen and nitrogen contamination until the weld solidifies.

- Supplies scavengers, deoxidizers and fluxing agents to clean the weld and prevent excessive grain growth in the weld material.

- Adds chemicals to the arc that control the electrical characteristics of the electrode: current type, polarity and current level.

- Covers the finished weld with slag, a protective covering that controls weld cooling rate, protects the cooling materials of the weld from the atmosphere, and controls bead shape.

- The coating also adds alloying materials to enhance weld properties.

- Iron powder added to the coating increases the weld temperature and the deposition rate.

- Potassium in the coating makes the gases of the plasma readily ionize, which improves the smoothness of AC operation when the arc extinguishes and re-ignites 120 times a second. Without this additive, AC operation would not be possible.

- The shielding gas generated by the burning electrode and the deoxidizers in the rod coating prevent the pickup of oxygen and nitrogen by the filler metal and molten weld pool. Oxygen and nitrogen contamination would lead to the weakening and possible cracking of the weld.

SMAW Electrode Classification

There are two common systems for classifying welding electrodes:

- The *ANSI/AWS Carbon and Low Alloy Steel Electrode Classification System*, based on ANSI/AWS A5.1, is the most popular specification used by welders today. Table 5-2 explains the AWS electrode coding system for low-carbon and low-alloy steel electrodes and Table 5-3 describes the electrodes in each classification.

- *Section IX of the ASME Pressure Vessel Boiler Code* provides another way to classify the same group of electrodes.

While the AWS system provides 16 classification groups, the ASME boiler code has only four. Both systems provide convenient and effective ways of comparing the qualities of the welding electrodes used for low-carbon and low-alloy steel.

Most of these electrodes have the ANSI/AWS classification number printed on their flux coating. The color coding of SMAW *coated* electrodes, which used to be popular, is now obsolete, but *uncoated* electrodes used for surfacing are still color coded. Some manufacturers use their own color codes to identify their electrodes and they are explained in their manufacturer's data sheets.

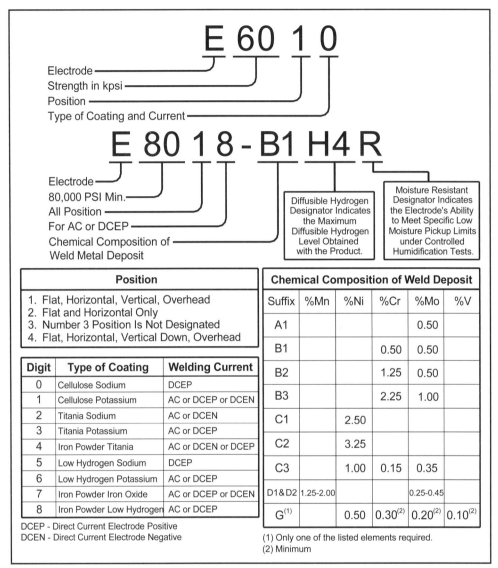

Table 5-2. The AWS electrode classification system for low-carbon and low-alloy steel electrodes. The abbreviation *kpsi* stands for thousands of pounds per square inch.

ASME System for Classifying Coated Electrodes

This system applies to carbon and mild steel only and enables selection of the proper electrode based on the welding position. The ASME system works by classifying electrodes into four main groups:

- F-1 – High-Deposition Group, also called *Fast-Fill.*

- F-2 – Mild-Penetration Group, also called *Fill-Freeze.*

- F-3 – Deep-Penetration Group, also called *Fast-Freeze.*

- F-4 – Low-Hydrogen Group.

AWS Class	ASME System	Current and Polarity	Welding Positions	Type of Covering	Type of Arc	Degree of Penetration	Surface Appearance	Type of Slag	Character of Slag
EXX10	F-3	DC, electrode positive	All	High-cellulose, sodium	Digging	Deep	Flat, wavy	Organic	Thin
EXX11	F-3	AC or DC, electrode positive	All	High-cellulose, potassium	Digging	Deep	Flat, wavy	Organic	Thin
EXX12	F-2	Ac or DC, electrode negative	All	High-titania, sodium	Medium	Medium	Convex, rippled	Rutile	Thick
EXX13	F-2	AC or DC, either polarity	All	High-titania, potassium	Soft	Shallow	Flat or concave, smooth ripple	Rutile	Medium
EXX14	F-2	DC, either polarity or AC	All	Iron-powder, titania	Soft	Medium	Flat, slightly convex, smooth ripple	Rutile	Easily removed
EXX15	F-4	DC, electrode positive	All	Low-hydrogen, sodium	Medium	Medium	Flat, wavy	Low-hydrogen	Medium
EXX16	F-4	AC or DC, electrode positive	All	Low-hydrogen, potassium	Medium	Medium	Flat, wavy	Low-hydrogen	Medium
EXX18	F-4	DC, electrode positive or AC	All	Low-hydrogen, potassium, iron powder	Medium	Shallow	Flat, smooth, fine ripple	Low-hydrogen	Medium
EXX20	F-1	DCEN or AC for horizontal fillets; DC, either polarity, or AC for flat work	Horizontal fillets & flat	High-iron oxide	Digging	Medium	Flat or concave, smooth	Mineral	Thick
EXX22	F-1	DC, either polarity or AC	Horizontal, flat	High-iron oxide	Soft, smooth	Medium	Flat or slightly convex	Mineral	Medium
EXX24	F-1	AC or DC, either polarity	Horizontal fillets and flat	Iron powder, titania	Soft	Shallow	Slightly convex, very smooth, fine ripple	Rutile	Thick
EXX27	F-1	AC or DC, electrode negative	Horizontal fillets and flat	High-iron oxide, iron powder	Soft	Medium	Flat to slightly concave, smooth fine ripple	Mineral	Thick
EXX28	F-1	AC or DC, electrode positive	Horizontal fillets and flat	Low-hydrogen, potassium, iron powder	Medium	Shallow	Flat, smooth, fine ripple	Low-hydrogen	Medium
EXX48	F-4	AC or DC, electrode positive	Flat, horizontal, vertical-down, overhead	Low-hydrogen, potassium, iron powder	Soft	Shallow	Concave. Smooth	Low-hydrogen	Thin

Table 5–3. The AWS electrode classification system for carbon and low alloy steel electrodes.

The *F* numbers come from the classification system used in Section IX of the *ASME Pressure Vessel Boiler Code* and in the *AWS Code, Section A5.1 or A5.5*. Class SFA means that the specification has been developed and adopted by AWS.

Properties of the High-Deposition Group – (Fast-Fill) F-1:

- F-1 electrodes have coatings that contain 50% iron powder by weight, so they produce a higher weld deposition per electrode than the electrodes of any other group.

- Produces a smooth, ripple-free bead with little spatter.

- Heavy, dense slag that is easily removed.

- Dense slag and slow cooling make this group useful only for flat and horizontal fillet welds.

Properties of the Mild-Penetration Group – (Fill-Freeze) F-2:

- F-2 electrodes have a titania, rutile, or lime-based coating.

- They are excellent for welding sheet steel under $^3/_{16}$" thick where high-speed travel with minimum skips, slag entrapment and undercut are required. These electrodes are often used with DCEN.

Properties of the Deep-Penetration Group – (Fast-Freeze) F-3:

- F-3 electrodes have a high cellulose coating that produces deep penetration and a forceful arc. They may also contain iron powder, rutile and potassium.

- The weld solidifies rapidly for use in all positions.

- Excellent for welding mild steel in fabrication and maintenance work.

- Best choice on dirty, painted, or greasy metal.

- Produces light slag that is easily removed.

- Especially good for vertical-up, vertical-down and overhead welds.

- Good for open root passes.

Properties of the Low-Hydrogen Group – F-4:

- F-4 electrodes are resistant to hydrogen inclusions and underbead cracking in medium- to high-carbon steels, hot cracking in phosphorus-bearing steels, and porosity in sulfur-bearing steels.

- Excellent for X-ray quality welds.

- Requires less preheat than other electrodes.

- Can produce excellent multiple pass, vertical and overhead welds in carbon steel plate.

- Best choice for galvanized metal.

- Reduces the likelihood of underbead and micro-cracking of high-carbon and low-alloy steels on thick weldments.

SMAW Electrode Dimensions

SMAW electrodes are 18 or 36" in length and come in the following core wire diameters: $^{1}/_{16}$, $^{3}/_{32}$, $^{1}/_{8}$, $^{5}/_{32}$, $^{3}/_{16}$, $^{7}/_{32}$, $^{1}/_{4}$ and $^{5}/_{16}$ inches. Welding electrodes are usually supplied in 50 lb. cardboard containers or in sealed metal cans to keep out moisture.

Electrode Moisture Problems

Water absorbed out of the atmosphere by the flux on the electrode will introduce hydrogen into the weld. If not baked out, this moisture will cause cracking and brittleness. Dry electrodes need only from 30 minutes to four hours to pick up enough water—and the water's hydrogen—to affect weld quality. For this reason, low-hydrogen electrodes must be kept in drying ovens after they are removed from sealed electrode dispensers and kept there until immediately before use.

Be sure to determine which electrodes are to be heated and dried before use, and which are not. The minimum drying time after exposure to the atmosphere and the maximum time out of the original container before use is specified in the manufacturer's instructions for the specific electrode.

See the low-hydrogen electrode usability times in Table 5-4.

Tensile Strength EXX Series	Hours Usable after Oven Drying Cycle
E70XY	4
E80XY	2
E90XY	1
E100XY	$^{1}/_{2}$

Table 5-4. Low-hydrogen electrode usability after oven drying cycle.
All low-hydrogen electrodes have a last digit, Y, equal to 5, 6 or 8.

To remove moisture from low-hydrogen electrode coverings that conform to AWS 5.1, bake them for at least *two hours* at temperatures of 500–800ºF. For those low-hydrogen electrodes conforming to AWS 5.5, bake them for at least *one hour* from 500–800ºF.

Including carbon steel, there are eight specifications for ANSI/AWS electrodes. Table 5-5 shows the electrode applications and the ANSI/AWS specification numbers.

Electrode Application	ANSI/AWS Specification
Carbon steel	A5.1
Low-alloy steel	A5.5
Corrosion-resistant steel	A5.4
Cast iron	A5.15
Aluminum and its alloys	A5.3
Copper & its alloys	A5.6
Nickel & its alloys	A5.11
Surfacing	A5.13 & A5.21

Table 5-5. ANSI/AWS specification numbers for SMAW electrodes.

Electrode Selection

Because there are trade-offs between speed, total welding cost and weld strength, electrode selection is not a simple decision. Here are the major factors that determine electrode selection:

- Electrode wire steel should have the same or higher tensile strength as the base metal and have similar chemical properties.
- Welder skill.
- Properties of the base metal.
- Position of the weld joint and type of joint.
- Type of power supply.
- Tightness of the joint fit-up.
- Total amount of welding needed.
- Need for low-hydrogen electrodes.

Selecting Electrodes for Carbon Steel

Using Figures 5-7 through 5-11 as a guide, determine the joint, position and metal thickness which best illustrates your welding task and read the electrode recommendation for the joint.

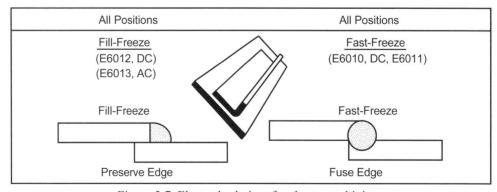

Figure 5-7. Electrode choices for sheet metal joints.

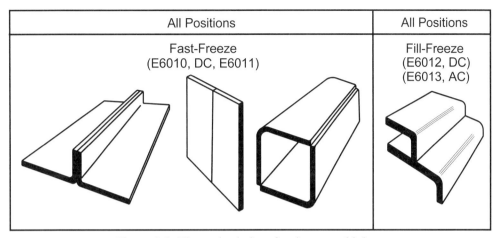

All Positions	All Positions
Fast-Freeze (E6010, DC, E6011)	Fill-Freeze (E6012, DC) (E6013, AC)

Figure 5-8. Electrode choices for sheet metal joints.

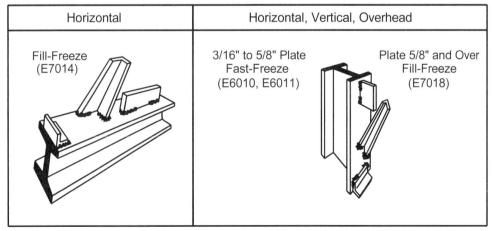

Flat	Horizontal	Inclined	Flat	Inclined	Vertical
Fast-Fill/Low Hydrogen (E7024, E7028)	Fast-Fill/Low Hyrdogen (E7024, E7028)	Fast-Freeze (E7014, E7018)	Fast-Fill/Low Hydrogen (E7024, E7028)	Fill-Freeze (E7014, E7018)	3/8" - 5/8" Plate Fast-Freeze (E6010, E6011) Plate 5/8" and Over Fill-Freeze (E7018)
		20°		15°	

Figure 5-9. Electrode choices for light plate joints.

Horizontal	Horizontal, Vertical, Overhead	
Fill-Freeze (E7014)	3/16" to 5/8" Plate Fast-Freeze (E6010, E6011)	Plate 5/8" and Over Fill-Freeze (E7018)

Figure 5-10. Electrode choices for short fillets on $^3/_{16}$–$^5/_8$" plate.

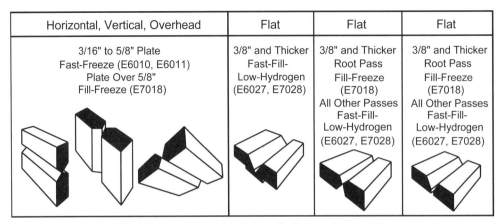

Horizontal, Vertical, Overhead	Flat	Flat	Flat
3/16" to 5/8" Plate Fast-Freeze (E6010, E6011) Plate Over 5/8" Fill-Freeze (E7018)	3/8" and Thicker Fast-Fill- Low-Hydrogen (E6027, E7028)	3/8" and Thicker Root Pass Fill-Freeze (E7018) All Other Passes Fast-Fill- Low-Hydrogen (E6027, E7028)	3/8" and Thicker Root Pass Fill-Freeze (E7018) All Other Passes Fast-Fill- Low-Hydrogen (E6027, E7028)

Figure 5-11. Electrode choices for heavy plate welds.

Electrode Diameter

The best choice of electrode is the one that will produce the required weld in the least time. Usually larger diameter electrodes are used for thicker materials and flat welds where their high deposition rates can be an advantage. Because gravity works against the welder working in non-horizontal positions, smaller electrodes are used to reduce the weld pool size. Here are the main things to consider when selecting electrode diameter:

• Joint thickness.

• Welding position.

• Type of joint.

• Welder skill.

How to Set up an SMAW Outfit

1. Put on safety glasses, and, when welding, wear them under your welding helmet.

2. Set out the electrodes and welding safety equipment—helmet, cap, gloves and leathers.

3. Position the welding power supply near the work and note the location of the AC power shut-off switch in case of emergency. Make sure the welding power supply is grounded. If an engine-generator is the welding power source, locate the engine shut-off switch.

4. Make sure the areas around the power supply and the work are dry.

5. Remove flammable materials near the spark stream area and insure that fire fighting equipment is close at hand.

6. Based on the job requirements or drawings, select the electrode material and diameter.

7. Set welding polarity and current on the welding machine.

8. Stretch out the welding cables and securely attach the work lead to the work. Clean the grounding area of the work, if necessary, then attach the ground clamp.

9. Insert the electrode into the holder, turn on the welding machine, drop your welding helmet, and strike the arc.

10. Now you can begin welding.

Striking the SMAW Arc

*   *Scratch-start*, usually used for AC, is performed by tilting the electrode about 15° in the direction of travel, and while drawing the electrode above the work as if striking a match, allow it to momentarily touch the work. This strikes the arc. The electrode is then raised above the work to a height equal to its own diameter.

*   *Tap-start*, usually used for DC, is performed by lowering the electrode quickly until an arc forms, and then raising the electrode its own diameter above the work.

*   To start the arc for an existing weld bead, strike an arc about an inch farther along the weld path than the interrupted weld bead, then carry the arc back to the previous stopping point and begin welding again. The new weld bead will melt into the old weld bead and cover the marks of the strike.

Determining Welding Technique

The joint type and welding position determine which welding technique and orientation will work best.

See Table 5-6.

Type of Joint	Welding Position	Work Angle (degrees)	Travel Angle (degrees)	Technique of Welding
Groove	Flat	90	5–10*	Backhand
Groove	Horizontal	80–100	5–10	Backhand
Groove	Vertical Up	90	5–10	Forehand
Groove	Overhead	90	5–10	Backhand
Fillet	Horizontal	45	5–10*	Backhand
Fillet	Vertical Up	35–45	5–10	Forehand
Fillet	Overhead	30–45	5–10	Backhand

*Travel angle may be 10–30° for electrodes with heavy iron coatings.

Table 5-6. SMAW orientation and welding technique for carbon steel electrodes.

Using SMAW to Repair a Waddled Out Bearing

Figure 5-12 shows a worn bearing on an earth excavator bucket. Dirt and friction made its bore oversized. Although this bearing could be repaired with a bore welding machine, there is a much simpler way:

1. Position the bucket so the bearing bore is vertical. There are two reasons for this: the welding can be done in the flat position and the welding smoke will flow out of the bore.

2. Clamp a $1/2$" thick copper plate over the bottom of the bore. This supports the flux of the first two SMAW welded-ring passes.

3. Using 7018 welding rod, weld the first two rings, or passes, inside the bore. Other rods will not work as well as 7018.

4. Remove the copper plate to let the smoke out from the rest of the welding passes. Do not chip any flux until all the welded rings are complete.

5. Maintain the same angle of the welding rod with respect to the bore for all welding passes. This angle is needed to get penetration into the side wall of the bore.

6. Chip out the flux and you are ready to re-machine the bore to size.

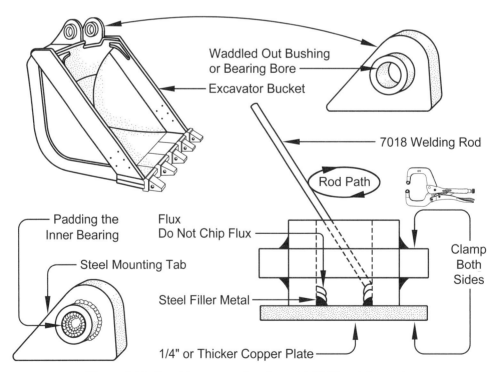

Figure 5-12. Repairing a worn bearing with 7018 welding rod.

Chapter 6

Wire Feed Welding – Gas Metal, Flux Cored & Metal Cored Arc Welding

Genius is the ability to reduce the complicated to the simple.

—C.W. Cram

Introduction

All wire feed processes use a continuous electrode fed into the welding pool. The weld pool is protected from the atmosphere by shielding gas which is either supplied from a cylinder or produced by the welding electrode itself.

Today these processes consume over 70% of the total filler materials used and this percentage continues to increase. These wire-feed welding processes use the same power supplies and electrode wire handling equipment, but they all have different weld bead properties. Although they apply the same type of welds as the older SMAW process, the higher productivity of wire feed equipment easily makes up for the higher cost. Wire feed processes are popular because they are easy to learn and readily adapted to robotic welding.

Section I – Process Basics

Equipment

- *Constant-voltage DC welding power supply* with a current capacity from 90–850 A and from 13–45 V. The smallest wire feed welders run on 20 A 110 VAC house outlets, but the larger units require three-phase power.

- *Wire feed mechanism,* which contains an electrode wire spool support, feed motor, wire-feed drive rolls and the associated electronics. This mechanism may be housed in the same cabinet as the welding power supply or in a separate unit. In general, the higher the current capacity of the power supply—the heavier wire it can run and the greater the weight of the unit—the more likely it will require two units: a power supply and a wire feeder. The welding power supply and the wire feeder are interconnected electrically.

- *Welding cable,* which runs from the wire feeder to the welding gun, contains:

  - Heavy copper conductor that brings the welding current to the torch.

  - Control circuit wires for the gun's trigger switch.

  - Hose for shielding gas, if used.

  - High-current guns have two hoses for cooling water in and out.

  Hoses and conductors inside the welding cable make the cable stiff and relatively inflexible. Cables are about $^3/_4$" diameter for the smallest torches and upwards of one inch on large torches. Cables are offered in 8, 10, 12, 15, 20 and 25 foot lengths. The longer the cable and the thinner the electrode wire, the more difficult it is to push the electrode wire through the cable. This limits the maximum practical length of a cable to 25 feet.

- *Welding gun* – Figure 6-1 shows an air-cooled GMAW gun with provisions for shielding gas. This gun can also be used without shielding gas for self-shielded flux core arc welding. Removing the shielding gas nozzle provides better weld pool visibility and the ability to easily enter smaller joints than with the nozzle attached. Although this gun can be used without the shielding gas nozzle, any contact with the workpiece will weld the contact tube to the work. For this reason a small insulated extension guide is usually placed over the contact tube.

  Because very high welding currents are used—they can exceed 250 amperes—many FCAW guns have a sheet metal heat shield to protect the operator's hands from the intense arc heat. See the gun in Figure 6-2 with its heat shield installed. Most welding guns are air-cooled, but some FCAW water-cooled guns operate on the 100% duty cycle needed for robotic welders.

- Grounding clamp, work lead cable and terminals.

- The gas-shielded processes—GMAW, FCAW-GS and MCAW—also require hoses, a pressure regulator, pressure gauges or a flowmeter, a compressed gas cylinder, and shielding gas.

Figure 6-3 shows how components of a wire-feed outfit hook together.

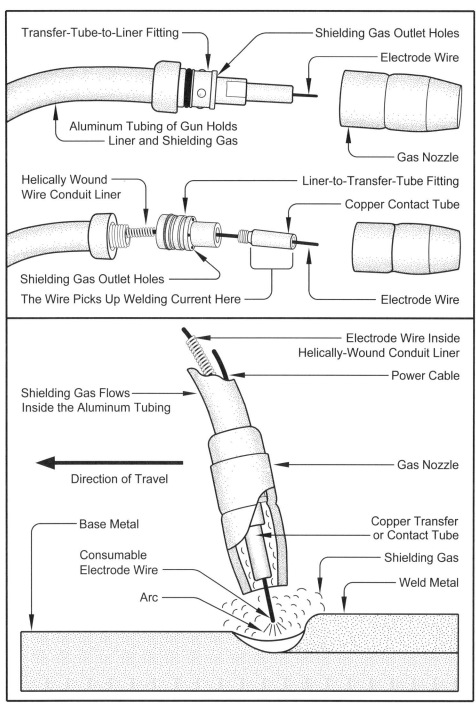

Figure 6-1. Air-cooled GMAW gun. Because this gun can provide shielding gas, it also supports FCAW-GS and MCAW. It is easily converted to FCAW by changing the electrode wire, turning off the shielding gas, and usually, changing the power supply polarity.

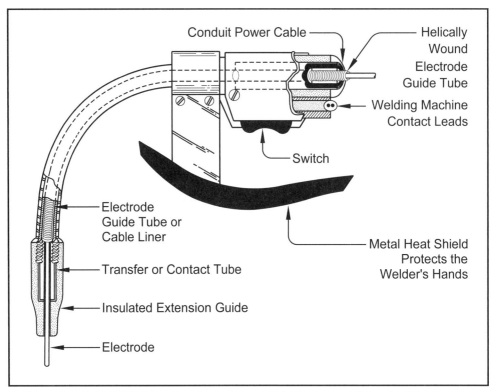

Figure 6-2. An FCAW-SS gun with metal heat shield has no provision for shielding gas.

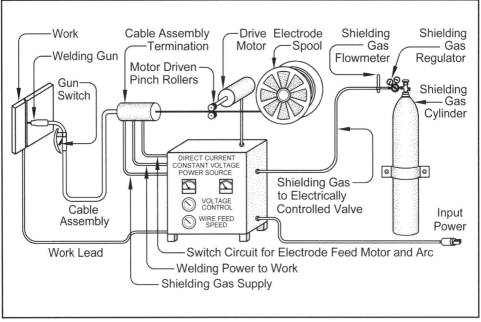

Figure 6-3. Wire feed welding outfit for GMAW, FCAW-GS and MCAW.
FCAW-SS uses the same setup except it requires no provisions for shielding gas.

Additional equipment is sometimes attached to GMAW equipment. These additions include:

- *Water cooler* – Welding guns operated continuously at high amperage levels get so hot that the gun literally burns up from both the heat of the weld and the heat from the contact tip. Feeding cooling water into the gun keeps its temperature down. The water, after it is heated by the tip, is then recirculated back to the water cooler. The water cooler consists of a pump, a fan, and an internal spray, much like an evaporative cooler.

- *Smoke evacuator* – Some guns have built-in systems at the nozzle of the welding gun for capturing and removing welding smoke. There are also free-standing smoke evacuators. Reducing the level of smoke increases welder safety, comfort and visibility, but on the down side, the incorporation of smoke evacuators in the welding gun increases the gun's weight and contributes to welder fatigue.

Transfer Tube

All torch designs supply current to the gun through a braided *copper conductor* located inside the welding cable. At the end of this braided cable, welding current transfers to the electrode wire through the copper *transfer tube*. The transfer tube is subject to wear and is a consumable. Refer to the transfer tubes in Figures 6-1 and 6-2.

Both the gas nozzle of the GMAW gun and the *extension guide* on the FCAW gun are electrically insulated from the transfer tube to prevent them from becoming welded to the workpiece.

Welding Process

The welder starts by positioning the electrode wire where the weld bead is to begin, actually touching the welding wire to the work metal. When the welder drops his hood and squeezes the welding gun trigger, six events happen simultaneously:

- The DC constant-voltage welding power supply turns on, supplying power to the welding gun.

- The wire feed mechanism pulls electrode wire from the spool and pushes it through the electrode cable liner and out the transfer tube.

- For GMAW, a solenoid—an electrically operated valve—opens and releases shielding gas from the regulator and flowmeter. This gas surrounds the electrode and the weld pool, shielding them from the atmosphere.

- Then, the electrode wire between the contact and the base metal is heated and deposited into the weld. As the wire is consumed, the feed mechanism supplies more electrode wire at the proper rate to maintain a stable arc.

- The welder manipulates the gun to deposit the weld metal in the desired pattern. When the weld is completed, the welder releases the trigger shutting off the welding current, wire feed and shielding gas.

- Control electronics continues the shielding-gas flow for a second or two after the arc is extinguished to protect the weld metal by keeping air away—particularly oxygen and nitrogen—until the weld metal cools.

Wire Feed Welding Setup Procedure

1. Make sure the welder and wire feeder power is turned OFF.

2. Mount the electrode wire spool on the wire feeder.

3. Without letting go of the wire—it will uncoil and make a snarl if you do—use a file to remove burrs from the end of the electrode wire to prevent damage to the cable liner and transfer tube. Then, open the *pinch,* or *feed roller gate,* and insert the electrode wire into the feed-roller mechanism and the liner tube. Close the gate, securing the wire. Make sure the wire drive wheels match the wire diameter and wire type. Smooth-groove rollers are used for solid wire and serrated rollers are used for flux-cored or metal-cored wire. See Figure 6-4.

4. Turn on the power for the wire-feed motor, then use the JOG or INCH button to load the wire into the welding cable liner and up to and through the welding gun.

5. Use the JOG or INCH button on the wire feeder or power supply to actuate the electrode-wire drive motor, then adjust the feed roller pressure until the wire feeding into the rollers can no longer be stopped by pinching the electrode wire between your thumb and index finger. Erratic wire feeding usually results from too much roller pressure, which causes the electrode wire to flatten—and loose feed—as it passes through the rollers.

6. Properly secure the compressed shielding gas cylinder and crack the valve to remove any dirt. Then, put the regulator—usually containing a flowmeter as well—on the cylinder valve and secure the other end of the gas line into the welding machine.

7. Turn the welding power supply to ON and hold the PURGE button down for 5 seconds to flush air from the gas lines and fill them with shielding gas. If there is no PURGE button on the welding machine, then, making sure the gun is not touching anything or anybody, open the pinch roller gate and squeeze the welding gun trigger for 5 seconds. While performing this purge, set the flowmeter or pressure regulator for the recommended purge gas-flow rate: 20 ft^3/hour for 0.032" wire would be a good starting point. On larger diameter electrode wire, begin with 20 ft^3/hour on horizontal and 30–35 ft^3/hour on out-of-position welds.

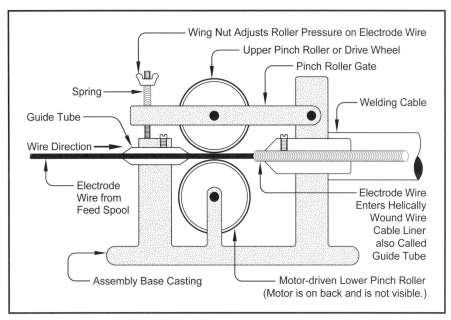

Figure 6-4. Typical wire-feed mechanism using two drive wheels.

8. Set the polarity to DCEN for GMAW and DCRP for most FCAW processes. Set the voltage and wire-feed speed. Get this information from the manufacturer's data sheets for the electrode wire or from tables attached to the welding machine. Always make a test weld on scrap first to check your settings.

9. Attach the work lead to a clean area on the work.

10. Use wire cutters to trim the electrode stickout to the proper length—about $^1/_2$ inch.

11. Make sure the welding area is dry and free of flammable materials as well as volatile fumes, and that other personnel are protected from arc radiation and sparks.

12. Put on your leather gloves and helmet, position the electrode against the work, squeeze the trigger, and begin welding.

Tip: Keep a wire cutter handy to remove the melted metal ball from the end of the electrode after completing one bead and before starting another.

Slope & Its Adjustment

Many larger welding power supplies have a slope adjustment which optimizes the short-circuit metal transfer in the GMAW process to minimize spatter. Slope controls the amount of the short-circuit current—the amperage flowing when the electrode is shorted to the work. Increasing slope on the power supply adds inductance in series with the arc. This retards rapid arc current changes and limits maximum short-circuit current, which reduces spatter.

Slope adjustment is not needed for the other metal transfer modes as little slope is used on them. Many newer welding machines do not have slope adjustments. See page 498 of *Chapter 18 – Power Supplies & Electrical Safety* for more information on slope.

Setup for the Small 20 A 110 VAC Welders

If you have no additional setup information, start by adjusting the voltage to 18 volts and the speed control knob to the 10 o'clock position. Try a weld on a scrap of the same type and thickness as the work to check the power supply settings. If the wire stubs, turn the voltage up until it does not. Conversely, if the wire globs, turn the voltage down. This approach works on a wide range of material thicknesses—22 gauge to $^1/_4$" thick. Remember to set the voltage and feed rate so the welding sounds like frying bacon and eggs. After learning the crackling sound of a good GMAW weld, setting parameters is easy.

Section II – The Four Wire Feed Welding Processes

Gas Metal Arc Welding (GMAW)

This process is also called *MIG*, from *Metal Inert Gas Welding*. In Europe it is sometimes called *MAG* from *Metal Active Gas Welding*. GMAW uses a solid electrode wire. Sometimes the wire has a very thin copper coating to prevent rust and improve wire feeding, but this coating plays no major role in the welding process. Shielding gas from the welding gun protects the weld bead from atmospheric oxygen and nitrogen while it cools, so this process cannot be performed in windy conditions. GMAW welds all commercial metals, both ferrous and nonferrous. There are dozens of different alloy welding wires.

Self-shielded Wire Welding (FCAW-SS)

Self-shielded Wire Welding (FCAW-SS) sometimes called *Gasless Welding* or *Innershield Welding* after Lincoln Electric's tradename, uses a thin tubular electrode filled with powdered materials which generate both a shielding gas and a protective slag when they enter the welding arc. This powder also contains scavenger elements like silicon which are used to capture oxygen and nitrogen compounds. In addition, this powder may contain a small percentage of powdered metal and alloying elements that improves bead metallurgy. The main purpose of the powder, though, is to generate shielding gas and slag. No additional shielding gas is required. Although the wire-feed speed for FCAW is higher than GMAW, the deposition rate can be about the same for the same diameter wire. This is because the core of the FCAW wire is slag, flux and arc enhancers, and they cannot contribute to the metal of the weld bead.

Gas Shielded FCAW (FCAW-GS)

Sometimes called *Dual-shielded Wire Welding*, this process also uses a tubular electrode with gas and slag producing ingredients. FCAW-GS is frequently used in structural steel welding, particularly indoors, as it produces much less smoke than FCAW-SS and its slag is more easily removed. This dual-shielded process is not popular or necessary outside of heavy industry.

FCAW-SS is much more popular than FCAW-GS because the FCAW-SS process does not use shielding gas, is not sensitive to wind, and can be used outside. GMAW cannot be used in winds higher than 5 mph.

Metal Core Arc Welding (MCAW)

This is a relatively new process that uses a tubular mild steel electrode much like FCAW, but instead of containing gas and slag-producing powder, the tubular electrode contains powdered metal. The powdered metal contains iron and other alloying metals to improve and modify the mild steel of the outer sheath. This electrode construction makes it possible to produce alloys that could not be made using the conventional wire-drawing processes. Additionally, because the powder is added to a mild steel casing, it is economically practical to make small, special-purpose alloy production runs.

External shielding gas from the welding gun protects the weld, so the electrode core does not have to produce shielding gas. With MCAW, it is critically important to read the manufacturer's recommendations on voltage and wire speed settings.

Tip: While it is possible to make welds with the wire feed set too fast and welding current too high, the consequence is that the weld bead metallurgy will be modified and be weaker than a properly applied bead. Also, this high heat may create too large a weld pool which leads to bead cracking.

Section III – Comparison of the Four Processes

Advantages Common to All Wire Feed Welding Processes

- With no need to stop welding to change consumed electrodes, the continuous-wire electrode avoids the start-and-stop cycle of SMAW and results in fewer discontinuities and higher deposition rates.

- Higher utilization of filler metal than with SMAW because there is no end loss, or stub, as with the upper, unconsumed end of an SMAW electrode.

- All four processes can easily be adapted to fully automated welding.

- Easier to learn than most other welding processes.

- No practical thickness limitations.

- Because the GMAW electrode has a smaller diameter than the SMAW electrode, it can get to the bottom of a narrower V-groove. Therefore, V-grooves for GMAW can have a smaller angle. This saves welding time and as much as 50% on welding filler metal. There is no problem using an

SMAW V-groove design for GMAW; it will just take longer to complete
and consume more filler metal. See the comparison in Figure 6-5.

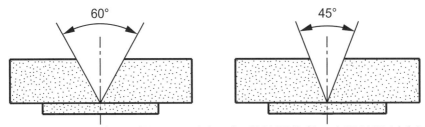

Figure 6-5. Comparison of V-groove joints for SMAW (left) and GMAW (right).

Disadvantages Common to All Wire Feed Welding Processes

- The cost of a wire feed welding outfit is always higher than that of an
  SMAW unit of the same capacity. This is due to the wire-feed mechanism
  and the need for a DC constant-voltage power supply. In production
  situations, this cost disadvantage is easily overcome by the increased
  productivity of wire feed welding over SMAW.

- The welding gun cable, the cable from the wire feeder to the welding gun
  itself, is relatively stiff and much harder to work with in tight quarters than
  the thinner SMAW cables.

- Many applications, particularly those which are performed high off the
  ground, do not permit the use of a wire feed process because the
  maximum distance of the wire feed welding gun from the wire feeding
  unit is limited by the ability of the electrode to be pushed through the gun
  cable liner. These cables are typically 12–15 feet and have a practical
  upper limit of 25 feet.

- Wire feed welding lacks the wide selection of high-performance repair
  electrodes that SMAW offers. These high-performance electrodes are
  critical in many repair situations.

Wire Feed Processes for the Casual Welder

If you are a shade-tree welder, here is all you need to know about the
differences between the wire feed welding processes:

- GMAW requires shielding gas, cannot be performed in more than a light
  breeze, produces no slag and little spatter. The bead usually requires little
  grinding to improve its appearance.

- FCAW-SS does not require shielding gas, can be done outdoors in windy
  conditions, but does produce slag and spatter. It has better penetration than
  GMAW, but produces a lot of smoke and should not be done indoors.

- FCAS-GS and MCAW are not needed outside of heavy industry.

Gas Metal Arc Welding (GMAW)

The advantages are:

- GMAW welds most commercial metals, both ferrous and non-ferrous, including mild steel, low-alloy steel, stainless steel, aluminum, copper, magnesium, titanium, and nickel alloys.

- Generally, lower cost per length of weld metal deposited when compared to other arc welding processes.

- Welds are slag-free, smooth, and produce little spatter. Many welded products can be painted or plated without first grinding and chipping.

- Metals as thin as 24 gauge (0.023") can be welded.

- Spray transfer provides deeper penetration than SMAW. This permits GMAW to make smaller fillets of the same strength and at higher deposition rates.

See the GMAW process in Figure 6-6.

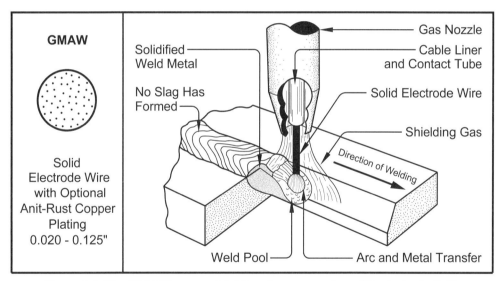

Figure 6-6. The GMAW process (right) and a cross section of its electrode (left).

The major disadvantage is:

- A breeze faster than 5 mph blows away the GMAW shielding gas and allows air to reach the molten weld bead, damaging it. This limits its use to indoors and non-windy days.

Self-Shielded Wire Welding (FCAW-SS)

The advantages are:

- Better penetration than GMAW.

- Excellent weld pool control.

- Because of its excellent penetration, FCAW can use groove angles as narrow as 30°. This saves as much as 50% of the filler metal needed for SMAW, which requires larger groove angles.

- Since FCAW welding guns do not use external shielding gas, they do not need a gas nozzle on the torch end, just a much smaller insulated cover for the transfer tube. This allows excellent access and provides better weld pool visibility for the welder than with GMAW.

- Because the ingredients in the welding wire create their own stream of protective shielding gas, FCAW-SS is not affected by wind, making it suitable for outside structural work.

- Different thicknesses of material can be welded using the same electrode with only a power supply adjustment.

- FCAW is often permitted by codes for critical welds on boilers, pressure vessels, and structural steel.

- FCAW oxidizers and fluxing agents permit excellent quality welds to be made on metals having some surface oxides and mill scale. Often flame cut metal can be welded without further preparation, a major cost savings.

- High deposition rates of more than 25 lb/hour are possible with $^1/_4$" diameter electrodes, compared with 10 lb/hour for SMAW. This saves time and money.

- Welds in all positions are possible.

- No need for shielding gas, regulators, and cylinders.

- Relatively easy for new welders to become proficient.

- Easy to adapt to robots.

The disadvantages are:
- Welds only ferrous metals.

- Slag is hard to remove and, unfortunately, it must be removed between passes.

- FCAW-SS produces a lot of spatter and leaves a rough weld bead surface which may require grinding in some applications.

- Self-shielded wire welding is the most smoky of any of the wire feed process, so it must be done outdoors or indoors with breathing equipment that supplies the welder with clean air.

See the FCAW self-shielded process in Figure 6-7.

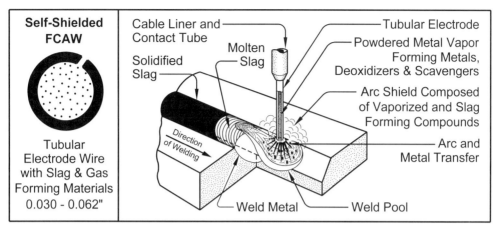

Figure 6-7. The FCAW self-shielded process (right) and a cross section of its electrode (left). Notice that the outer sheath is formed into a roll and closed up around its core.

Gas Shielded FCAW (FCAW-GS)

The advantages are:

- Less smoke than FCAS-SS and is used in structural steel, shipbuilding and other heavy industry where the welding is done indoors.

- Less slag than with FCAW-SS and the slag is easily removed.

The disadvantages are:

- Welds only ferrous metals.

- Cost-effective only when using spray transfer.

See the FCAW gas-shielded process in Figure 6-8.

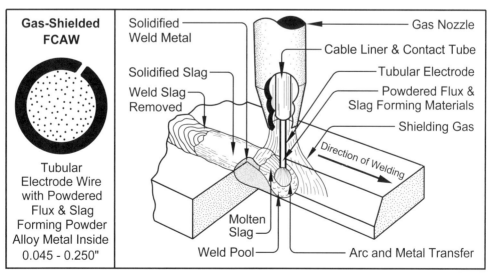

Figure 6-8. The FCAW gas-shielded process (right) and a cross section of its electrode (left).

Metal Core Arc Welding (MCAW)

The advantages are:

- Welds have high deposition rates and travel speeds with high deposition efficiency, so most of the welding wire ends up in the weld bead, not as spatter or metal vapor.

- Unlike many other processes, MCAW can bridge uneven fit-ups and weld thinner metals without burning through them.

- MCAW can incorporate many specialized alloys, including those not otherwise available. High-chromium stainless steel alloy electrodes are often made for MCAW. Many times this process is chosen in a production setting because its low spatter reduces damage to production fixtures. Low-hydrogen electrodes are also available for this process.

- The magic of MCAW electrodes is the formation of the point-of-melt alloys in the arc between the mild steel sheath and the metal core powder.

- Because most of the welding current travels down the outer mild steel sheath of the electrode and not through the powder inside the sheath, MCAW provides a more uniformly shaped weld nugget. This results in a more deeply penetrating weld than that of solid wire at the same welding speed and current setting. See the comparison in Figure 6-9.

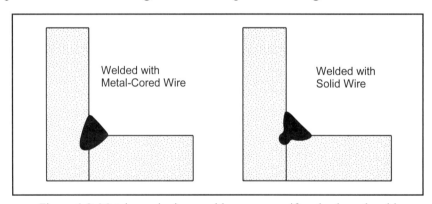

Figure 6-9. Metal-cored wire provides a more uniformly shaped weld nugget and better penetration than that of solid wire.

The disadvantages are:

- Welds only ferrous metals.

- MCAW wire only becomes cost effective when spray transfer is used. It is not a substitute for solid wire at currents below 200 A, which is about where spray transfer begins for most welds.

See the MCAW process in Figure 6-10.

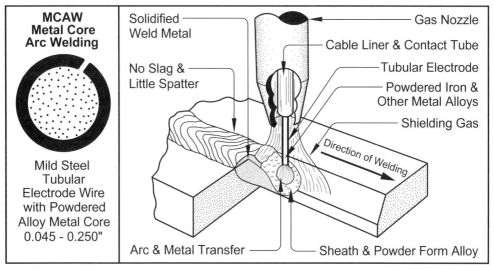

Figure 6-10. The metal core arc welding process and a cross section of its electrode.

Section IV – Welding Variables

Introduction

Welding variables affect penetration, bead shape, and weld quality. They fall into three categories:

- *Task variables* – Workpiece metal and thickness, the joint type, and the welding position are the task variables defined by the job itself.

- *Electrode choice* – The task variables determine the electrode choice including its diameter, welding polarity, and use of shielding gas.

- *Operating variables* – While the task variables and electrode choice are strongly influenced by the job, the welder himself controls the operating variables and must choose them to produce the desired weld. These variables include:

  - Arc voltage.
  - Electrode extension or stickout.
  - Electrode orientation with respect to the weld bead.
  - Travel speed.
  - Wire feed rate, which controls welding current.

Arc Voltage

We really want to control arc length, yet it is hard to measure. But since arc length is closely related to arc voltage, we choose instead to control arc voltage. Most welding specifications indicate arc voltage setting, and not arc length.

This is because, with all other variables held constant, arc length is proportional to arc voltage. Arc voltage depends on the materials welded, the choice of shielding gas, and the metal transfer mode.

Controlling arc voltage is important because:

- Too short an arc can produce *stubbing*. This is when cold wire pushes into the workpiece upsetting the smooth flow of shielding gas and pumping air into the arc stream. Stubbing causes porosity and cracking from atmospheric nitrogen.

- Too long an arc can cause *arc wander*, which reduces both penetration and weld bead quality. In general, higher arc voltages tend to flatten the weld bead and increase the width of the fusion zone, while very high arc voltages cause porosity, undercut, and spatter.

The best way to set arc voltage is to begin at the recommended voltage based on AWS welding tables or on the electrode manufacturer's data sheets. The base metal, type of metal transfer, and the type of shielding gas all determine the starting point, but the exact refinement comes after several trial runs. Manufacturers' Internet sites are also sources of starting settings for wire-feed speed and voltage.

The welding current on a CV power supply cannot be adjusted directly. Figure 6-11 shows that higher wire feed speeds require higher currents and that more current is required for larger electrodes at the same wire feed speed.

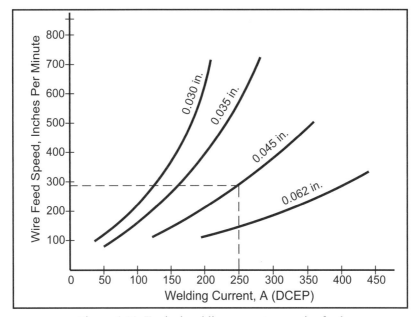

Figure 6-11. Typical welding currents vs. wire feed
speeds for carbon steel electrode wire.

With all other welding variables held constant, an increase in wire feed speed, and thus welding current will:

- Increase the depth and width of weld penetration.

- Increase deposition rate.

- Increase the size of the weld bead.

Polarity

- GMAW always uses DCEP to move the positively charged metal ions to the weld. These positive ions must travel through a positive-to-negative voltage field—just what DCEP provides.

- Most FCAW processes and all MCAW processes require DCEN, but a few FCAW processes require DCEP. If unsure which polarity to use, check the data sheet of the electrode manufacturer.

Electrode Extension or Stickout

Electrode extension, also called *stickout,* is the distance between the end of the contact tube and the end of the electrode wire as shown in Figure 6-12.

- If the stickout is too long, the electrode wire overheats because of the amount of current flowing through it on the way to the weld.

- If the stickout is too short, the electrode wire will not get hot enough to make a properly fused weld bead.

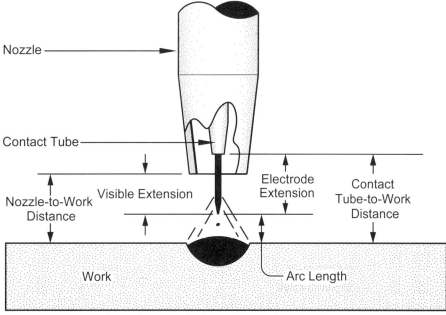

Figure 6-12. GMAW electrode-to-work dimensions. With the FCAW-SS process the nozzle is eliminated from the gun for better welder visibility, so use the contact-tube-to-work distance, sometimes abbreviated as CTW, for measuring stickout.

Effect of Travel Speed

Travel speed measures the arc's rate of progress along the weld line in inches/minute. If all other variables are held constant, the greatest weld penetration will be at an intermediate speed. Too low a travel speed, the electrode melts on the top of the weld pool and penetration is poor. At slightly higher travel speeds, the welding wire melts on touching the base metal, increasing penetration. At still higher travel speeds, the heat input becomes too low for good penetration so travel speed must be reduced.

Joint Position

When the work is fixed in place, there is no choice of welding position, but when it can be moved, repositioning the work can offer several advantages:

- It can allow the use of spray metal transfer which is usually done in the flat position because higher deposition rates are possible and it is easier to control a large weld pool in the flat position. Flat welds are more uniform than the same type of welds applied in the horizontal position.

- Welds can be made with electrode wire of 0.045" or less in either the overhead or the vertical position, which makes weld pool control easier by making the pool smaller.

- Sometimes welding in a downhill position of about 15° can increase welding speed, decrease penetration, and reduce weld thickness. This tactic is helpful in welding thinner sheet metals. Many times using a larger electrode wire is also helpful because larger wire requires more heat so there is less heat available to burn through or melt the workpiece.

- Pulsed and short-circuit metal transfer may be done in any position, so the work can be positioned for the most comfortable arrangement for the welder.

Electrode Diameter

In general, the larger the electrode diameter, the higher the *minimum* welding current needed to perform a given metal transfer process.

Here are some typical factors in determining electrode diameter selection:

- On thick workpieces the highest available welding current determines the maximum electrode diameter and results in the maximum deposition rate.

- When the power supply limits the welding current, using a small diameter electrode wire provides better penetration because there is more heat energy available to put into a given volume of wire.

- Sometimes using larger diameter wire at a lower amperage can provide better weld pool control and reduce burn-through on thin stock.

Electrode Orientation

How the welding gun is positioned with respect to the weld axis and travel direction controls electrode orientation which, in turn, influences penetration, bead height, and bead width.

- In the *forehand position* with a lead angle, the gun is tipped *toward the direction of welding*. Going from perpendicular to a lead angle gives less penetration and a wider, thinner weld. On some materials, particularly aluminum, using a lead angle produces a cleaning action just ahead of the weld pool. This cleaning action promotes wetting, which is the visible intermelting and fusion of the wire-feed electrode with the base metal, and reduces base metal oxidation.

- In the *perpendicular position*, the gun is held perpendicular to the direction of the welding. It has neither a lead nor a drag angle, and produces a weld bead with characteristics midway between forehand and backhand welding.

- In the *backhand position* with a drag angle, the gun is tipped *away from the direction of welding*. Maximum penetration occurs in the flat welding position with a drag angle of 25° from perpendicular. For all other positions, the backhand position is used with a 5–15° drag angle.

See Figure 6-13.

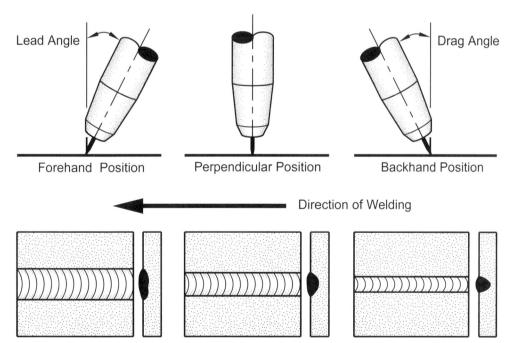

Figure 6-13. Weld beads made using the forehand position (left), the torch perpendicular position (center) and the backhand position (right).

The Effects of Changing Welding Variables

Table 6-1 summarizes the impact of changing weld parameters.

Welding Variable ↓	Result Wanted							
	Penetration		Deposition Rate		Bead Size		Bead Width	
	▲	▼	▲	▼	▲	▼	▲	▼
Wire Feed Rate (Current)	▲	▼	▲	▼	▲	▼	⇔	⇔
Voltage*	Little Effect	Little Effect	⇔	⇔	⇔	⇔	▲	▼
Travel Speed	Little Effect	Little Effect	⇔	⇔	▼	▲	▲	▼
Stickout	▼	▲	▲	▼	▲	▼	▼	▲
Wire Diameter	▼	▲	▼	▲	⇔	⇔	⇔	⇔
Electrode Orientation	Back Hand	Fore Hand	⇔	⇔	⇔	⇔	Back Hand	Fore Hand
Shield Gas %CO_2	▲	▼	⇔	⇔	⇔	⇔	▲	▼

▲ = Increasing   ▼ = Decreasing   ⇔ = No Effect
* Voltage settings can be important for sheet metal.

Table 6-1. Effects of changing weld parameters.

Welding Machines & Workpiece Thickness

There are several important things to keep in mind when considering what size power supply is required:

- The minimum and maximum thickness of workpiece metal and the type of metal. Table 6-2 shows how much more amperage is required to weld aluminum than to weld the same thickness of steel.

- For a ferrous workpiece, both GMAW and FCAW are options, but welding smoke and penetration become important factors. For non-ferrous workpieces, only GMAW works.

- Electrode diameter and alloy are also important considerations for penetration and deposition rate.

- The available utility power: single-phase 110/220 V or three-phase 208/480/525 V. Some medium-size power supplies can run on both single- and three-phase power, but they usually have a lower maximum output current rating on single-phase input power.

- All welding machines above 300 A require three-phase power.

Rating (A/V/% Duty Cycle)	Mild Steel Thickness (inches)		Aluminum Thickness (inches)	
	Minimum	Maximum	Minimum	Maximum
90/20/20	0.024	$^3/_{16}$	0.040	0.064
135/22.5/30	0.024	$^5/_{16}$	0.040	$^1/_4$
160/24.5/60	0.024	$^3/_8$	0.064	$^3/_8$
170/25/60	0.030	$^3/_8$	0.070	$^3/_8$
200/28/60	0.030	$^1/_2$	0.064	$^1/_2$
300/32/60%	0.024	$^1/_2$	0.040	$^1/_2$
450/38/100	0.020	1	0.050	1

Table 6-2. Typical welding power supply ratings with their minimum and maximum metal thickness welding capacity. To weld aluminum all welding machines require a spool gun to pull the aluminum filler wire through the cable to the torch. Pushing it from the power supply pinch rollers alone will cause the wire to kink.

- Manufacturers often incorporate the *maximum* amperage a machine is capable of into their model name. This can be misleading because for most machines this current can only be sustained for a short time before the machine overheats and shuts down. What you need to look at is the rating at a duty cycle *typical* for your application. See *Chapter18 – Power Supplies & Electrical Safety* for more information on duty cycles.

- Short-circuit transfer may be satisfactory for thinner materials, but when penetration and speed are important, a higher current machine for spray or spray-arc transfer is needed.

- As a rule, power supplies of 350 A and higher have a separate wire feeder.

Section V – Transfer Mechanisms

Introduction

There are four metal deposition processes: *short-circuit transfer*, *globular transfer*, *spray transfer* and *pulsed-arc spray transfer*. See Figure 6-14. All four types of wire feed welding processes can be adjusted to perform all four transfer mechanisms. Arc voltage—and thus arc current—determines which transfer type occurs. Smaller machines have limited current capacities, so they can never reach the 200 A threshold for spray transfer, the most efficient and best penetrating process. Only larger and more sophisticated welding power supplies have the electronics to create pulsed-spray transfer, so it does not occur with small machines.

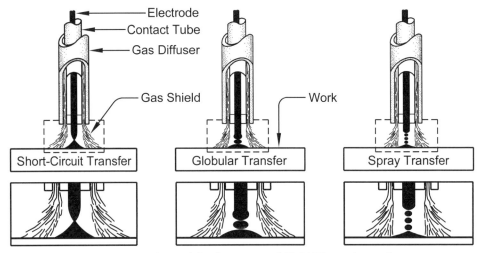

Figure 6-14. Three of the four types of GMAW metal transfer:
short-circuit (left), globular (middle) and spray (right).

The choice of metal transfer process is determined by:

- Maximum welding current available from the welding power supply.

- The type of metal and the thickness of the workpiece.

- Electrode parameters: diameter, composition, stickout, and shielding gas.

Short-Circuit Transfer

This transfer occurs at the lowest current ranges and electrode diameters. It produces a small, fast-freezing weld pool suitable for joining thin sections, making open root passes and for performing out-of-position welds. Short-circuit transfer has relatively poor penetration. Metal transfers only when the electrode is in contact with the weld pool at 20–200 times/second. There is no transfer of metal ions through the arc plasma. To understand the short-circuit metal transfer process in detail, follow the explanation for Figure 6-15 (A–I).

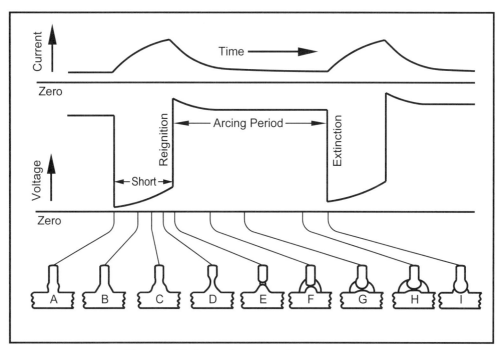

Figure 6-15. Short-circuit metal transfer process.

A. Start by assuming that we are looking at the process after it has been established. While the arc operates, both the base metal and the electrode wire are at a high temperature and the wire feed mechanism steadily advances wire. When the wire touches the weld puddle, three events happen simultaneously:

- Heavy current flows through the electrode into the weld and the base metal, causing the end of the electrode to begin melting.

- As a result of the short-circuit between the electrode and the work, the current rises rapidly.

- The voltage drops from the arc voltage to a much lower value with the beginning of the shorted electrode. This causes the arc to go out.

B. Current continues to rise as the constant-voltage welding power supply attempts to maintain its voltage setting and raise the voltage. The arc stays out, while the melting electrode continues to deposit metal into the weld pool.

C. As the voltage and current continue to rise, the electrode begins to form an inverted cone on the weld. More electrode wire is pushed onto the inverted cone by the continuous wire feed action. Voltage and current continue to rise, and the cone gets bigger as additional electrode wire is fed into it.

D. The electrode wire on top of the inverted cone begins to neck down to prepare for the pinch-off of the next step. This electromagnetic pinch-force results from the welding current flowing through the short circuit between the electrode and the deposited metal on the weld and acts radially inward around the electrode. This pinch force disconnects the drop of molten weld metal from the electrode.

E. Just after point D, the electrode separates from the cone formed over the weld, the arc reignites, the current begins to fall off, and the voltage rises to arc-voltage from short-circuit voltage. The metal transfer ceases.

F. The arc heats both the electrode and the weld.

G. During the arcing period the arc heat smoothes out the cone, flattening it into the weld and heats up both the weld and the electrode preparatory to the next cycle.

H. The cycle is complete when the voltage drops below arc voltage and the electrode wire touches the weld.

I. The arc extinguishes.

Electrode metal is transferred to the weld *only* under short-circuit conditions; no metal ions travel through the arc.

- The short-circuit metal transfer cycle repeats 20–250 times per second.

- The magnetic field from the welding current is the major force in the short-circuit metal transfer process. Gravity is not a major factor, so all welding positions may be used.

- The electromagnetic field around the welding electrode causes the pinch-off effect. The drop of molten metal on the tip of the electrode transitions to a molten spherical drop of metal attached to the tip. This drop of metal, which is pinched off by the electromagnetic forces to become a free drop of metal, is driven into the weld pool. The spherical drop can be seen on the electrode when the tip is withdrawn at the end of a weld.

- Short-circuit metal transfer is used with electrodes under 0.045" diameter.

- Larger diameter electrodes are used on thicker stock and utilize the spray transfer method for deposition efficiency. Whether or not they operate under spray transfer, thicker workpieces require higher currents.

- Short-circuit metal transfer has a low heat input to the base metal making it ideal for welding thinner sheet metals—typically less than $^3/_{16}$" thick—without the risk of burn-through. This process works well in small, low-amperage welding machines used on light metal. Short-circuit metal transfer, though, has relatively poor penetration, making it unsuitable for thick sections.

Globular Transfer

Globular transfer occurs as the short-circuit mode transitions to the spray transfer or pulsed-arc spray transfer mode. Globular transfer has poor penetration and a tendency to produce spatter. If the current capacity of the welding power supply is a limiting factor, the best choice is short-circuit transfer. But if the welding power supply can provide adequate current, then spray transfer is the right choice. Globular transfer, because it is a transitional phenomena, occurs over a narrow current range that makes it difficult to control and maintain. Other than the metal transfer during the background period of pulsed-arc metal transfer, globular transfer is not commonly used.

Spray Transfer

There are three requirements for spray transfer:

- Argon-rich shielding gas.

- DCEP polarity.

- Welding current is above a critical value, called the *transition current.* Below the transition current, the transfer is globular, above it, the transfer is by spray mechanism.

See Figure 6-16.

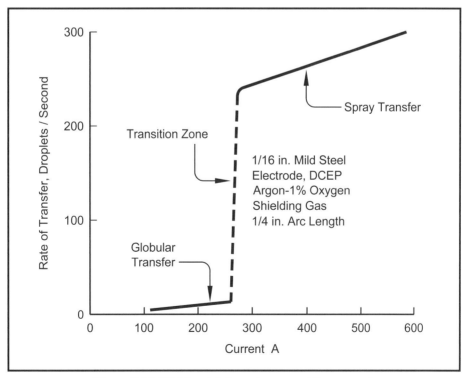

Figure 6-16. Weld metal drop size vs. welding current.

Spray transfer produces a stream of individual metal droplets that are accelerated by electrical forces to overcome the effects of gravity. The result is no short-circuiting, which means no spatter, excellent penetration, and the ability to weld out of position. High deposition rates are possible and very desirable in the production welding of thick workpieces where high-amperage power supplies are available. In heavy industry, spray transfer is the most commonly used metal transfer process. When welding thin sheet metal, use of the spray transfer mode is limited because the higher voltages needed to initiate spray transfer cuts the sheet metal instead of welding it. However, spray transfer can produce high deposition rates in the flat position on metal thicker than $^1/_8$ inch.

Pulsed-Arc Spray Metal Transfer

Pulsed-arc spray metal transfer uses a special welding power supply. This supply produces a constant low-level background current output and periodically adds a much higher current pulse on top of the background current. See this waveform in Figure 6-17. The idea is that the background current sustains the arc and keeps the electrode and base metal hot, but does not transfer any metal to the weld. This is because the background current is below that required for spray metal transfer and not long enough in duration, meaning it is not more than one-tenth of a second, for globular transfer to begin. During the peak portion of the higher current pulse, spray metal transfer occurs, directing a stream of small metal droplets into the weld pool. For pulsed-arc spray transfer mode, the voltage ranges from 25–45 volts. For more on pulsed waveforms see *Chapter 18 – Power Supplies & Electrical Safety.*

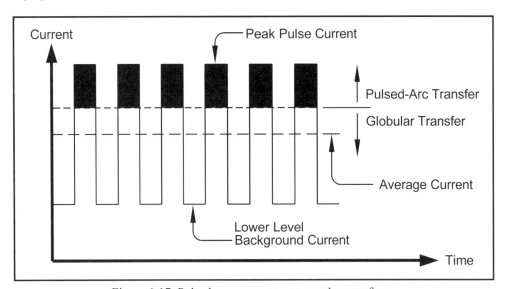

Figure 6-17. Pulsed-arc spray power-supply waveform.

Pulsed-arc metal transfer allows spray metal transfer at substantially lower average currents—and therefore lower heat input—than would be possible with constant DCEP spray metal transfer. The high currents necessary to produce DCEP spray metal transfer tend to burn through or cut thinner metals. Because of this, there are distinct advantages to pulsed-arc metal transfer: the ability to weld thinner gauge sheet metal with more control of the weld pool, the use of spray transfer mode in not only flat, but vertical position welding, and freedom from spatter when joining thick weldments.

See Table 6-3 for a comparison of the four transfer modes.

	Transfer Mode			
	Short-Circuit	Globular	Spray	Pulsed-Arc
Conditions for This Mode	• Low current levels • Small diameter electrodes	• Current levels just above short-circuit transfer • Occurs between short-circuit and spray transfer	• Occurs at above transition current • DCEP • Argon-rich shielding gas	• Same as spray but using pulsed power source
Characteristics	• Low deposition rates	• Spatter • Poor penetration	• High deposition rates • Spatter-free • High penetration	• Same as Spray, but in all positions
Applications	• < 12 gauge • Root pass • Vertical up • Vertical down • Overhead • Flat & horizontal	• > 12 gauge • Vertical down	• > $\frac{1}{8}$" • Flat horizontal	• > $\frac{1}{8}$" • All positions

Table 6-3. Conditions for GMAW metal transfer and applications.

Section VI – Shielding Gases

Shielding Gas Functions

Most metals in the molten state combine with atmospheric oxygen and nitrogen to form oxides and nitrides. These two classes of compounds can leave the weld with porosity, embrittlement or trapped slag which greatly reduce the weld's mechanical properties. Shielding gas prevents atmospheric oxygen and nitrogen from reaching the molten metal of the weld and altering its metallurgy. Shielding gas also:

• Stabilizes the arc.

- Controls the mode of metal transfer.
- Establishes the penetration level and weld bead shape.
- Enhances welding speed.
- Minimizes undercutting.
- Cleans off oil or mill scale just prior to welding.
- Controls weld tensile strength and brittleness.

Shielding Gases

The most common are argon-carbon dioxide mixtures in 75–25%, 80–20% and 85–15% ratios. Some of the other common gases and gas mixes are:

- Ar
- $Ar + He$
- $Ar + O_2$
- CO_2
- He
- $He + Ar + CO_2$

Carbon dioxide is a low-cost gas commonly used when welding mild steel. A 75% carbon dioxide + 25% argon gas mixture is used for general welding of carbon steel and low-alloy steel and produces excellent results. In selecting a shielding gas, consider cost, weld appearance, and weld penetration. In some cases, mixes of different gases are best for the job because the benefits of inert gases and active gases can be combined.

Inert GMAW Shielding Gases

- *Argon (Ar)* – Often used for out-of-position welding because of its lower heat conductivity. Argon is also ten times heavier than helium so it blankets the weld better than helium.
- *Helium (He)* – This gas is an excellent heat conductor, bringing heat from the arc into the weld area. It is used for high heat input, as when joining thick sections and when welding copper and aluminum, two metals which rapidly conduct the needed heat away from the welding zone.

Reactive GMAW Shielding Gases

- *Carbon dioxide (CO_2)* – Creates better metal transfer, lower spatter, a more stable arc, and improved flow of metal to reduce undercutting.
- *Oxygen (O_2)* – Same characteristics as carbon dioxide.
- *Hydrogen (H_2)* – In small percentage concentrations, hydrogen removes light rust and eliminates the need for surface cleaning.
- *Nitrogen (N_2)* – Used on copper.

Reactive gases, when added to shielding gases, form compounds with other chemical elements. In GMAW they are used to achieve specific objectives.

For example, oxygen and carbon dioxide added to argon reduce the chance of undercutting, smooth the arc, and increase penetration.

Gas mixtures produce better arc stability, lower spatter, and better bead structure than any one gas alone. By mixing gases we get the best performance properties that each component gas can produce. Figure 6-18 shows the effect of different shielding gas mixtures on weld beads.

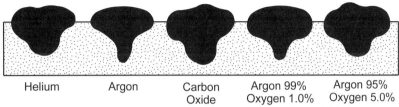

| Helium | Argon | Carbon Oxide | Argon 99% Oxygen 1.0% | Argon 95% Oxygen 5.0% |

Figure 6-18. Weld bead shape and penetration with various shielding gases.

Shielding & Polarity for Mild Steel FCAW Electrodes
See Table 6-4.

AWS Electrode Classification	External Shielding Medium	Current & Polarity
EXXT-1 (Multiple-Pass)	CO2	DCEP
EXXT-2 (Single-Pass)	CO2	DCEP
EXXT-3 (Single-Pass)	None	DCEP
EXXT-4 (Multiple-Pass)	None	DCEP
EXXT-5 (Multiple-Pass)	CO_2	DCEP
EXXT-6 (Multiple-Pass)	None	DCEP
EXXT-7 (Multiple-Pass)	None	DCEN
EXXT-8 (Multiple-Pass)	None	DCEN
EXXT-9 (Multiple-Pass)	None	DCEN
EXXT-10 (Single-Pass)	None	DCEN
EXXT-11 (Multiple-Pass)	None	DCEN
EXXT-G (Multiple-Pass)	As agreed upon between supplier and user.	
EXXT-GS (Single-Pass)	As agreed upon between supplier and user.	

Table 6-4. Shielding and polarity requirements for mild steel FCAW electrodes.

Shielding Gas Metering Systems
Although all gas metering systems use a pressure regulator similar to an oxygen cylinder pressure regulator, there are two ways, as shown in Figure 6-19, to set the shielding gas flow rate on the low-pressure side of the regulator.

- Using a *pressure gauge* on the low-pressure side of the regulator indirectly measures gas flow. While acceptable, pressure gauges are not as accurate as the slightly more expensive ball-in-tube flowmeter.

- A *ball-in-tube flowmeter* on the low-pressure side of the regulator measures gas flow directly and accurately. With argon and argon mixes, because these gases are expensive, use the minimum gas flow needed to shield the work.

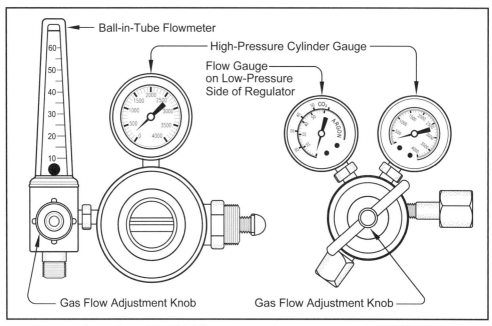

Figure 6-19. Two shielding-gas metering systems: regulator with ball-in-tube flowmeter (left) and regulator with gauges (right).

Section VII – Electrode Wire Handling

Introduction

In *Section I – Process Basics*, the wire feed mechanism was introduced. Here is a more in-depth look at electrode wire handling.

The wire-feed mechanism, or feed-roller mechanism, pushes the electrode through the *cable liner* which runs through the welding gun cable to the torch. The cable liner consists of a *helically wound wire tube* with a bore large enough to admit the electrode wire.

One or more pairs of *drive wheels,* also called *feed rollers,* in the wire-feed machine pinch the electrode wire and push it through the cable liner to the welding gun. This is by far the most common arrangement and it works well except with very soft electrodes such as aluminum.

Wire feeders for larger diameter electrode wires have four feed rollers instead of two. This reduces the feed-roller pressure on the wire to avoid damage to the wire. Larger welding machines and wire feeders not only have two pairs of pinch rollers, the rollers themselves are geared together to increase the push power. The principal problems confronting wire feeding are:

- Gripping the electrode wire firmly enough to apply adequate pushing force without crushing or damaging the wire. Having two pairs of pinch rollers and gearing the rollers so they turn in unison are solutions for this problem. Also, adding serrations or teeth around the periphery of the feed rollers for solid wire helps improve feeding. Toothed feed rollers cannot be used with FCAW and MCAW wire because their powdered metal core makes the electrode wire soft and easily crushed.

- Having a motor and gearing strong enough to force the electrode wire through the gun liner. This need is particularly true for ferrous wires over $^1/_8$ inch because they are quite rigid and create a lot of friction with the cable liner.

- Collapsing and kinking of aluminum electrode wires can only be avoided with *pull guns* or *spool guns,* discussed later in the chapter. Because of its softness, aluminum just cannot be fed from only one end of the welding cable. It needs to be both pushed and pulled.

- On large-diameter electrodes, the *cast* of the wire is a major problem. A cast is the inherent memory of the wire of its previous coiling and its tendency to try to return to that shape. This condition can cause feeding jams. Larger wire feeders have a *wire straightener*, which consists of several more rollers in addition to the feed rollers.

Equipment Configuration

There are two common configurations of wire feed welding equipment:

- *Single-Unit Designs* – In this configuration the welding power supply and the wire feeding equipment are contained inside a single cabinet. This design is compact, convenient, and economical for welding machines under 200 A. Figure 6-20 shows a small, portable Miller welding machine that runs on a 20 A/110 VAC outlet. This is a popular and established single-unit design. Similar competitive machines are offered by many other suppliers. Larger single-unit machines under 200 A—basically scaled up versions of this machine—require 220 VAC single-phase or three-phase power. Both of these units are used for home, farm, and factory maintenance.

- *Two-Unit Designs* – This configuration is used for larger welding machines, typically those over 200 A. These machines require three-phase power and have two separate units: a welding power supply and a wire feeder. These units are used for heavy fabrication. See the two-unit design in Figure 6-21.

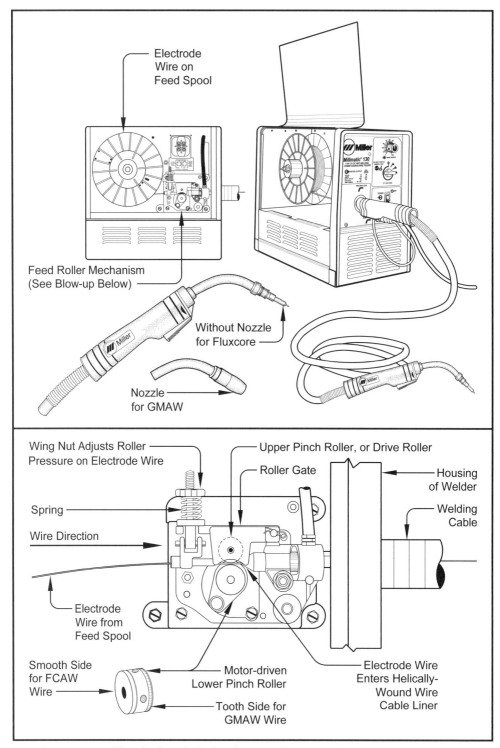

Figure 6-20. Miller single-unit design for a small GMAW/FCAW wire feed welding machine that runs on 20 A/110 VAC outlets and a detail of its wire feed mechanism.

Advantages of a Separate Wire Feeder

Figure 6-21 shows a typical setup of a high-current welding machine that has a separate wire feeder.

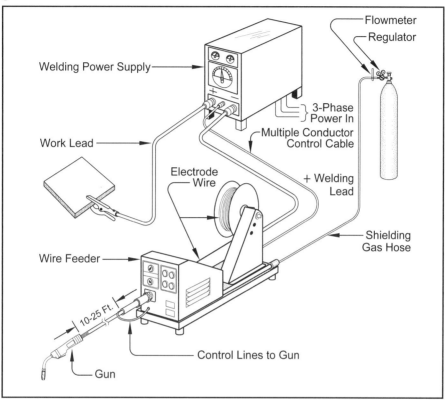

Figure 6-21. A welding machine with a separate free-standing wire feeder.

- The wire feed unit can be placed in a convenient location within 10–25' of the welding gun and, because the two units are connected by welding power and control cables, the welding power supply can be 50–500' away. This is important when the welder must be up in the air on a platform or inside a vessel where bringing along a 400–600 pound power supply would be a problem. This setup also eliminates having to continuously relocate heavy, high voltage and potentially dangerous electrical lines.

- When a welder can switch between two or more wire feeders, he can quickly change electrode wire alloys without rethreading the wire feeder, yet use just a single power supply. In many fabrication shops the power supply is on the floor, but the wire feeder is at the end of a moveable boom to make maneuvering around the work easy for the welder. Using two different electrode wires on the same weld is necessary when expensive filler wire is used against the workpiece for the root pass and another, less expensive electrode wire is used on the rest of the weld.

- The failure of one wire feeder does not stop welding operations because another feeder can be swapped out on the same power supply.

Aluminum Electrode Feed Problems

Because aluminum electrode wire is soft, a wire feeder alone cannot push it through the gun cable and its liner. Aluminum electrode wire collapses, kinks and *birdnests* just beyond the pinch rollers. There are two welding accessories that make welding with aluminum electrode wire possible:

- *Push-pull guns*, as shown in Figure 6-22, consist of a torch assembly containing a small DC motor and drive wheels, which *pull* the soft aluminum wire through the cable liner and pushes it out the torch tip. Modern push-pull guns are electrically synchronized with the motor of the wire feeder so both motors work together to minimize compressive force on the welding wire. Since only GMAW welds aluminum, push-pull guns are usually used with aluminum wire for spray transfer. Push-pull guns have a big advantage in industrial production, they can draw their electrode wire from spools too big to fit into a wire feeder or directly from a 275-pound coil in a cardboard container on a wooden skid. With this setup, wire rethreading does not need to be done very often.

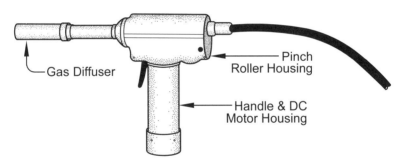

Figure 6-22. A push-pull gun solves the problem of handling aluminum electrode wire.

- *Spool guns,* as shown in Figure 6-23, are a torch assembly containing both a small spool of electrode wire, such as aluminum, and a DC motor. Because this motor only needs to push the electrode wire through a few inches to the contact tube, even soft aluminum wire feeds easily. Spool guns not only solve the aluminum electrode feeding problem, they offer several other advantages:

  - Because the spool gun holds the electrode wire spool itself and only requires power and control cables to the welding power supply, the gun can be used up to 200 feet from the welding power supply. This is particularly helpful when the power supply is large and heavy or when the welding is high off the ground.

- Spool guns make it easy to quickly change the electrode wire.

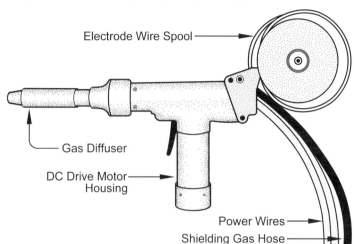

Figure 6-23. A spool gun is another solution for feeding
soft electrode wires, such as aluminum.

- Changing small spools of electrode wire is much faster and simpler than rethreading a wire feeder and running the wire through the welding cable liner to the gun.

- A welder can afford to stock a variety of electrode alloys since he can purchase as little as a one-pound spool. This provides more problem-solving options to the welder.

Section VIII – Electrode Wire and Joint Preparation

GMAW Joint Preparation

- Metals from $^5/_{1000} - ^3/_{16}$" can be welded without edge preparation.
- Metals from $^1/_{16} - ^3/_8$" can be welded in a single pass *with* joint edge preparation.
- Multi-pass welding is required with thicknesses above $^3/_8$" and edge preparation is needed. There is no limit to the thickness of metal that can be welded.

Electrode Diameters & Packaging

In inches, the following are common GMAW electrode diameters: 0.020, 0.023, 0.030, 0.045, 0.052, $^1/_{16}$, $^5/_{64}$, and $^3/_{32}$. FCAW electrodes follow the same increments, but begin at 0.030 inches diameter. Small welding machines use electrode wire on one or ten pound spools. Large machines use 30, 50 or 60 pound spools. They can also feed electrode wire from cardboard drums or coils on 48" × 48" pallets.

GMAW Electrode Specification

Table 6-5 details the characteristics of some common mild steel GMAW electrode wires corresponding to AWS specification A 5.18.

AWS Designation	Characteristics	Shielding Gas(es)
ER70S-2	Contains deoxidizers that permit welding on thin rust coatings. Can weld in any position. Excellent for out-of-position short-circuit welding. Makes excellent welds in all mild steels.	$Ar-O_2$ $Ar-CO_2$ CO_2
ER70S-3	Single or multi-pass beads. Base metal must be clean. Preferred for galvanized metals. Used on autos, farm equipment and home appliances. Has better wetting action and flatter beads than ER70S-2.	$Ar-CO_2$ CO_2
ER70S-4	Good for structural steels like A7 and A36, for both short-circuit and spray transfer. Used in shipbuilding, pipe welding and pressure vessels. Produces flatter and wider beads than ER70S-3.	$Ar-O_2$ $Ar-CO_2$ CO_2
ER70S-5	Used on rusty steel. Not recommended for short-circuit transfer mode. Flat position only.	$Ar-O_2$ $Ar-CO_2$ CO_2
ER70S-6	General purpose wire used on sheet metal. Will weld through thin rust. Welds all positions. Used with high welding currents.	$Ar-O_2$ $Ar-CO_2$ CO_2
ER70S-7	Used on heavy equipment and farm implements. Welds in all positions.	$Ar-CO_2$ CO_2

Table 6-5. Common GMAW electrode wires for mild steel.

Figure 6-24 explains the electrode identification system for AWS A 5.18 mild steel electrodes and metal-cored electrodes for mild steel.

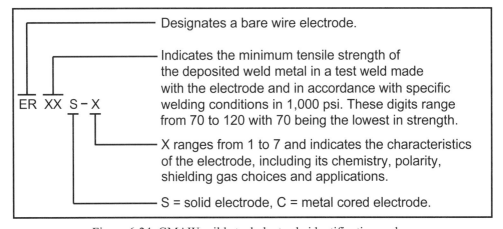

Figure 6-24. GMAW mild steel electrode identification codes.

FCAW Electrode Wire Classification

Figures 6-25 and 6-26 detail the American Welding Society FCAW electrode classification for mild steel, low-alloy steel, and for stainless steel.

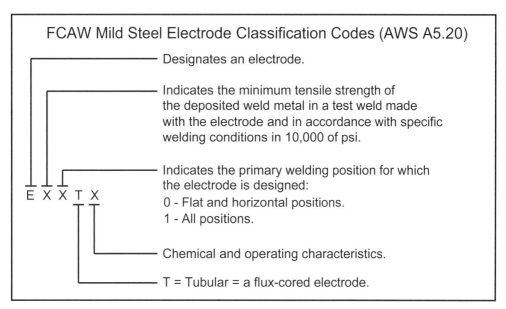

Figure 6-25. FCAW mild steel electrode classification codes.

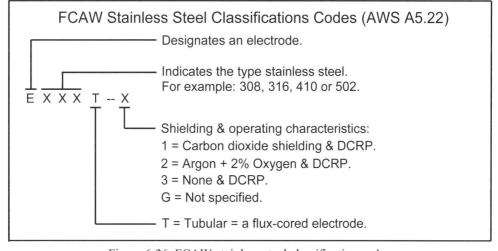

Figure 6-26. FCAW stainless steel classification codes.

Section IX – Troubleshooting

FCAW Troubleshooting

Table 6-6 lists some typical FCAW problems, their possible causes, and their solutions.

Problem	Possible Cause	Solution
Porosity	1. Low gas flow. 2. High gas flow. 3. Excessive wind drafts. 4. Contaminated gas. 5. Contaminated base metal. 6. Contaminated filler wire. 7. Insufficient flux in core. 8. Excessive voltage. 9. Excess electrode stickout. 10. Insufficient electrode stickout. 11. Excessive travel speed. 12. Excessive voltage. 13. Insufficient electrode stickout (FCAW-SS electrodes only). 14. Excessive travel speed.	1. Increase gas flow setting. Clean spatter-clogged nozzle. 2. Decrease to eliminate turbulence. 3. Shield weld zone from wind. 4. Check gas source. Check for leak in hoses & fittings. 5. Clean weld joint faces. 6. Remove wire drawing compound. Clean oil from feed rollers. Avoid shop dirt. Rebake filler wire. 7. Change electrode. 8. Reset voltage. 9. Reset stickout & current. 10. Reset stickout & current. 11. Adjust speed. 12. Reset voltage. 13. Reset stickout and balance current. 14. Reset stickout and balance current.
Incomplete Fusion or Penetration	1. Improper manipulation. 2. Improper parameters. 3. Improper joint design.	1. Direct electrode to joint root. 2. Increase current. Reduce travel speed. Decrease stickout. Reduce wire size. Increase travel speed on FCAW-SS only. 3. Increase root opening. Reduce root face.
Weld Cracking	1. Excessive joint restraint. 2. Improper electrode, insufficient deoxidizers, or inconsistent flux fill in core.	1. Reduce restraint. Use preheat. Use more ductile metal. Employ peening. 2. Check formulation of flux.

Table 6-6. FCAW problems and solutions.

GMAW Troubleshooting

Table 6-7 lists some typical GMAW problems, their possible causes and their solutions.

Problem	Possible Cause	Solution
Electrode Feeding Improperly	1. Excessive contact tip wear. 2. Melted or stuck contact tip. 3. Dirty wire conduit in cable.	1. Reduce drive-roll pressure. 2. Reduce voltage, replace liner. 3. Change conduit liner. Clean out with compressed air.
Undercutting	1. Travel speed too high. 2. Welding voltage set too high. 3. Excessive current. 4. Insufficient dwell. 5. Wrong gun angle.	1. Use slower travel speed. 2. Reduce voltage. 3. Reduce wire feed speed. 4. Increase dwell at puddle edge. 5. Change gun angle so arc force helps in placing metal.
Porosity	1. Inadequate shielding gas coverage. 2. Gas contamination. 3. Electrode contamination. 4. Workpiece contamination. 5. Arc voltage too high. 6. Excess contact tube-to-work distance.	1. Gas flow too high or too low. Shield work from drafts. Decrease torch-to-work distance. Hold gun at end of weld until metal solidifies. 2. Use welding grade shielding gas. 3. Use clean and dry electrodes. 4. Remove all dirt, rust, paint, and moisture from the work surface. 5. Reduce voltage. 6. Reduce stickout.
Incomplete Fusion	1. Weld zone surfaces unclean. 2. Insufficient heat input. 3. Too large a weld puddle. 4. Improper weld technique. 5. Improper joint design. 6. Excessive travel speed.	1. Clean weld surfaces carefully. 2. Increase wire feed speed, & voltage. Reduce electrode extension. 3. Reduce weaving and increase travel speed. 4. When weaving, dwell momentarily at edge of groove. 5. Use joint design angle wide enough to access complete groove bottom. 6. Reduce travel speed.
Incomplete Joint Penetration	1. Improper joint design. 2. Improper weld technique. 3. Inadequate welding current.	1. Joint design must provide access to bottom of groove. 2. Reduce root face. Keep electrode normal to work. Keep arc on leading edge of puddle. 3. Increase wire feed speed.
Excessive Burn-Through	1. Excessive heat input. 2. Improper joint penetration.	1. Reduce wire feed speed. 2. Reduce root opening. Reduce root face dimension.

Table 6-7. GMAW problems and solutions.

Problem	Possible Cause	Solution
Weld Cracking	1. Improper joint design. 2. Too high a weld depth-to-width ratio. 3. Too small a weld bead (particularly in fillet and root beads). 4. Hot shortness, the tendency of the workpiece to bend before there are any visible signs that it is about to melt. 5. High restraint of joint members.	1. Modify joint design. 2. Decrease arc voltage, decrease wire feed speed or both. 3. Decrease travel speed. 4. Use electrodes with higher manganese content. Increase groove angle to increase filler metal in weld. Change filler metal. 5. Use preheat. Adjust welding sequence.
Heat-Affected Zone (HAZ) Cracks	1. Hardening in the HAZ. 2. Residual stresses too high. 3. Hydrogen embrittlement.	1. Preheat to retard cooling rate. 2. Use stress relief heat treatment. 3. Use clean electrode. Use dry shielding gas. Hold weld at elevated temperature for several hours to permit diffusion of hydrogen out of the weld.

Table 6-7. (continued) GMAW problems and solutions.

Chapter 7

Gas Tungsten Arc Welding

Have no fear of perfection.
You will never achieve it.
—Salvador Dali

Section I – Process Overview

Introduction

Russell Meredith at Northrop Corporation in California refined tungsten arc welding (GTAW) into a workable process early in WWII. It replaced oxyacetylene welding of aircraft aluminum and magnesium, but it wasn't until the 1950s that commercially available equipment reached the market.

Although gas tungsten arc welding accounts for just a few percent of filler metal consumed, it is an important, and in many applications, an irreplaceable process. Most welds made by GTAW are on steel, stainless steel, aluminum and magnesium under $1/8$" thick, but it can weld all pure metals and most alloys. A few alloys, such as brass, cannot be welded because one alloy component is vaporized before another melts.

GTAW differs from other welding processes because:

- Its very high temperature arc is concentrated in a small area, so the heat-affected zone is smaller when compared with other welding processes.

- Because the welder positions both the filler metal and the torch independently, *and* can adjust the torch heat during the welding process, GTAW provides more control over the weld pool than any other process.

- The welder can adjust torch heat with his foot pedal or torch-mounted control. This ability to add heat when starting a weld and reduce it as the bead progresses gives GTAW unique capabilities. In some ways the GTAW process can be thought of as a high-temperature oxyacetylene torch with a heat-volume control.

- A sustained electrical discharge through a plasma arc between the work and a non-consumable tungsten electrode provides the welding heat. No filler metal is transferred across this arc.

- In addition to providing heat, the arc removes oxides from the workpiece through ionic bombardment and electron flow out of the work. This oxide removal is essential to the welding of aluminum and magnesium.

Although the majority of GTAW welding is performed manually, it has been automated too. Some processes use filler metal and some are *autogenous*—the parts to be joined are fused together without adding filler metal. Thin-walled stainless steel tubing for food processing and semiconductor manufacturing is usually joined this way under automation.

GTAW is commonly called *TIG* welding from *Tungsten Inert Gas* welding. Early in its development, it was called *Heliarc* from its use of helium shielding gas. In Europe it is called *WIG* for *Wolfram Inert Gas* after the German name for the element tungsten, which is used for electrodes.

How GTAW Works

Figure 7-1 shows an air-cooled torch performing the GTAW process:

- A low-voltage, high-current continuous arc between a tungsten electrode and the workpiece flowing through an inert shielding gas produces the welding heat. Temperatures in the arc can exceed 35,000°F. Although the electrode is called *non-consumable,* it does gradually wear away over time in a process called *burn-off,* but it does this very slowly so the tungsten in the electrode is not a factor in the weld metallurgy.

- The welding arc has a point-to-plane geometry between the arcing end of the electrode and the weld pool. Regardless of electrode polarity, the arc is restricted at the electrode end and widened out at the weld pool. When the arc length becomes too long, the arc is extinguished. The temperature and diameter of the arc depend on the arc-current level, the shielding gas, the electrode tip shape, and the alloy.

- An inert gas, usually argon or helium from a high-pressure cylinder, flows out and surrounds the tungsten electrode forming a gaseous shield over the work. This shielding gas:

  - Prevents atmospheric contamination of the molten weld metal, but does not react *with* the weld metal.

  - Provides an easily ionized and stable arc path between the electrode and the workpiece.

  - Cools the electrode, the torch, and the collet body so they do not melt.

- On thicker materials, the welder adds filler metal to the weld pool as the weld progresses. The filler metal can be in the form of a rod, a wire or a strip of metal. To add very small quantities of filler metal to parts being repaired without disturbing the surrounding structures, electrode wire as small as 0.010" can be used. For the repair and refurbishment of injection plastic molds, jet engine components, and tool steel parts, GTAW is the only choice.

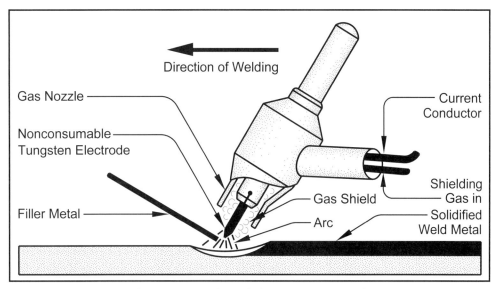

Figure 7-1. An air-cooled GTAW (TIG) torch.

Metals Welded

GTAW welds nearly all metals: ferrous, non-ferrous and precious. The notable exceptions are brass, pot metals, and the leaded steels. Brass and pot metals contain zinc, which comes out of the alloy and vaporizes before the alloy's other constituents melt. Leaded steels, like 12L14, are chosen for their excellent machining properties, but because they contain a mere fraction of one percent of lead, these steels have a similar problem—the lead vaporizes before the steel melts. For this reason leaded steels cannot be TIG welded.

Although there are a few exceptions, most members of the Series 2000 and Series 7000 aluminum alloys cannot be TIG welded because the zinc content creates pinholes in the weld, but most other aluminum alloys weld without problems.

Many aluminum alloys develop their strength from heat treatments and complex alloys. Welding heat usually removes the positive effects of this heat treatment by annealing the aluminum. Even if the aluminum welds well, remember that welding heat can severely weaken the base metal.

Advantages of GTAW (TIG)

* Because the heat source and filler metal arc controlled independently as the weld progresses, welds which require different heat inputs at different points can be made without burn-through or inadequate penetration—a common problem in repair work and on complex parts.

* GTAW welds are of high quality, free of spatter, and usually are free of inclusions and defects.

* GTAW can weld nearly all metals and most alloys and is especially effective in joining refractive metals such as aluminum, magnesium and titanium.

- All weld positions are possible.

- GTAW allows precise control of the welding variables.

- Excellent welder visibility of the arc and the weld pool because there is no smoke.

- On thinner work, *autogenous* welds—those without additional filler metal—can be used.

- GTAW provides excellent welder control of root-pass weld penetration, particularly on critical pipeline and structural welds.

- Joins dissimilar metals.

- TIG welds on autobody steel are softer and more malleable than GMAW welds, making them more suited to forming and shaping without cracking.

Disadvantages of GTAW

- Higher skill—hand dexterity and coordination—are required than for other welding processes. The welder must control both the torch and the filler metal position. With complex and demanding work, the welder must also control the arc current with a foot pedal or a fingertip control as the weld bead progresses.

- GTAW has lower deposition rates and productivity compared with other processes.

- Equipment is more complex and more expensive than other processes.

- Workpiece metal must be clean because GTAW has a low tolerance for contaminants in filler or base metals. Unlike SMAW and FCAW processes, GTAW will *not* burn through paint, dirt and rust. Even very small amounts of surface contaminants can cause weld defects.

- Shielding gas can be blown away in drafty environments.

- Less economical than consumable-electrode arc processes for workpieces greater than $^3/_8$" thick.

- Tungsten inclusions can occur if the electrode touches the workpiece, which is common with less experienced welders.

- Water-cooled torches can leak and contaminate the welds, and the water leakage can create dangerous shock hazards.

GTAW Equipment

Figure 7-2 shows a typical water-cooled GTAW outfit.

- The *torch* is designed solely for GTAW and contains cooling water going in and out, a welding power supply, and shielding gas. Torches usually have a 12–25 foot cable which runs back to the power supply, gas cylinder, and water supply.

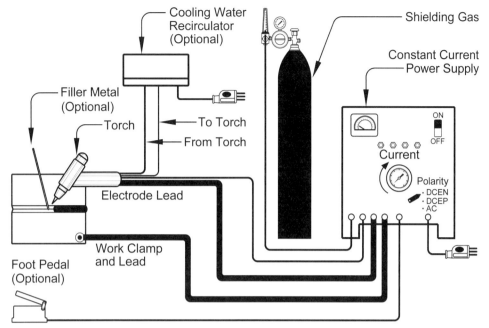

Figure 7-2. A water-cooled GTAW outfit.

- A *foot pedal* or a *fingertip amperage control* on the torch body gives the welder the ability to change the amperage while welding. This is critically important when performing difficult welds. Not all torches and all welding power supplies have these controls. Less expensive GTAW power supplies lack this key feature.

- The *constant-current power supply* may be as simple as a transformer and an inductor, or as complex as a microprocessor-controlled inverter.

- *Shielding gas* requires a gas cylinder, regulator, flowmeter, and hoses.

Cost Comparison

GTAW is more expensive than SMAW due to the additional cost of the inert shielding gas and because it has just 10–20 percent the deposition rate of GMAW. Often the cost of GTAW is justified by its high quality welds. With many aluminum and magnesium welds, GTAW is the better choice.

Section II – The Welding Arc

GTAW Arc

Unlike the other electrically-based welding processes—SMAW, GMAW and FCAW—the GTAW welding arc provides only welding heat and plays no part in the transfer of filler metal ions across the arc. The GTAW arc is:

- Shaped much like an inverted funnel; the arc is nearly a point at the electrode tip and flares out to a circle on the workpiece metal.

- In general, the length of the arc is proportional to arc voltage and can be up to four times the electrode diameter.

GTAW Polarity

- *DCEN* – When a torch is connected to DCEN, as the arc begins the electrode metal heats, giving it enough energy to release electrons from its surface. This process is called *thermionic emission*. The voltage, or electric field, between the electrode and the work exerts a strong pull, drawing the cloud of electrons around the surface of the electrode toward the positively charged work surface. This accelerates the electrons to high speed. Both the heat generated inside the arc and the impact of these electrons onto the work, heat the workpiece and the weld pool. Although the melting point of the tungsten electrode is considerably lower than that of the arc, the electrode does not melt because:

  - The torch collet conducts heat away from the electrode and transfers it to the shielding gas for gas-cooled torches or to the cooling water for water-cooled torches.

  - Electrons leaving the electrode absorb additional heat, and the result is that the tip of the electrode is the coolest part of the torch.

- *DCEP* – In this polarity, electrons leave the work and accelerate under the influence of the voltage across the arc as they make their way through the ionized gas to the electrode. Their impact on the electrode generates intense heat that will melt the electrode if this heat is not removed by the collet. Because this electron bombardment produces more heat at the electrode with DCEP than with DCEN, a larger electrode, running at the same current level, must be used to absorb this additional heat. In fact, DCEP can handle only 10% of the current that the same sized electrode can handle with DCEN. While DCEP produces less penetration than DCEN, it provides a wider area of heating than DCEN.

  More importantly, direct-current electrode positive (DCEP) provides a cleaning effect on the workpiece. Positive ion bombardment onto the work and the pull of the electric field on suboxide electrons produces *cathodic etching*. This cleaning effect is critical when welding metals such as aluminum and magnesium because these metals instantly form surface oxides when in contact with the atmosphere and prevent welding. Cathodic etching disrupts and removes these oxides, and GTAW's inert-gas blanket prevents them from reforming. DCEP is infrequently used on thin ferrous metals; its real importance is the *DCEP portion of the AC cycle* which removes oxides.

- *AC* – Because the arc voltage reverses once during each cycle, AC provides equal heat distribution between the electrode and the work since each receives electron bombardment half of the time. The balanced wave of AC provides penetration midway between DCEN and DCEP and is essential for welding aluminum and magnesium because of its oxide cleaning action.

See Table 7-1.

	Polarity		
	DCEN	**DCEP**	**AC Sine Wave or Balanced Wave**
Electron & Ion Flow Penetration Characteristics			
Oxide Cleaning Action	No	Yes, but does not apply enough heat to the work to weld aluminum.	Yes, once every half cycle, so both cleans and welds on alternate cycles.
Heat Balance in the Arc	70% ➜ Work 30% ➜ Electrode	30% ➜ Work 70% ➜ Electrode	50% ➜ Work 50% ➜ Electrode
Penetration	Deep & Narrow	Shallow & Wide	Medium
Electrode Capacity	Excellent $^1/_8$" @ 400 A	Poor $^1/_4$" @ 120 A	Medium $^1/_8$" @ 225 A
Electrodes	All compositions except pure tungsten.		Pure Tungsten
Metals Welded	Steels, stainless steels & all other metals, except aluminum & magnesium.	Sometimes used for thin sections on steels & all other metals, except aluminum & magnesium.	Essential for aluminum & magnesium because of its oxide cleaning
Electrode Shape	Usually 60° point.		Blunt or Ball Tip.
Shielding Gas	Usually Argon, but Argon + Helium mixes for special applications.		

Table 7-1. Summary of GTAW polarity and waveforms for conventional
non-pulsed DC & AC sine wave or balanced wave constant-current power supplies.

Section III – Power Supplies & Wave Forms

Power Supply Electrical Characteristics

Arc currents can range from 1–3000 A, but most TIG power supplies range from 5–200 A. Arc voltages run from 10–35 volts. GTAW constant-current power supplies usually have a slightly drooping static output characteristic of several volts per 100 Amperes and are quite similar to SMAW power supplies. Static output characteristics are discussed in *Chapter 18 – Power Supplies & Electrical Safety.*

Modern Power Supply Enhancements

Although SMAW AC/DC power supplies—both rotary and transformer-based—are the basis of traditional TIG welding power supplies, modern TIG power supplies have enhancements that can do the following:

- Provide easier arc starting without the risk of electrode contamination.

- Stabilize the arc, particularly on AC.

- Allow adjustment of the heat balance between the electrode and the work when running AC polarity.

- Increase weld penetration and reduce the heat-affected zone by focusing the arc with short pulses.

- Improve weld quality by adding a *crater-fill* function at the end of a bead.

- Agitate the weld pool with a low-frequency pulse to bring impurities to the surface and prevent discontinuities.

In general, these enhancements will be found on newer, more expensive power supplies with foot pedal or fingertip arc control, transistors, and microprocessor control. Often they will be inverter-based designs. Although the simpler traditional 60 Hz transformer-based designs, usually modeled after older SMAW designs, can get the job done, these newer welding machines are easier and more forgiving to use.

Arc Initiation

- *Scratch-Start* – While the TIG arc can be started using the scratch-start technique sometimes used for initiating the SMAW arc, this method is undesirable because it contaminates the workpiece metal with tungsten and the tungsten electrode with workpiece metal. This cross contamination reduces the electrode's ability to emit electrons and inhibits the arc.

- *Lift-Start* – Power supply electronics provides this function. When the electrode touches the work and is then lifted away from it, a momentary high-voltage pulse ionizes the arc path until the regular arc voltage sustains it. The lift-start produces less contamination than the scratch-start method, but can still be improved upon by the snap-start.

- *Snap-Start* – To initiate a snap-start the welder holds the electrode about $1/16$" above the workpiece and starts the welding cycle. The gas solenoid opens, releasing gas over the welding area and providing an ionized (conducting) path for the arc. Next, the power supply provides the high-voltage snap-start pulse to initiate an arc through the gap. Once started, the arc continues with the regular welding voltage. The electrode tungsten never touches the work. Besides being a great convenience for the welder, the snap-start reduces cross contamination and works for both AC and DC welding machines. Snap-start electronics are often included in SMAW power supplies.

Although welders with a steady hand can hold the electrode tip $^1/_{16}$" above the work without touching it, not everyone can. Figure 7-3 shows the *rollover technique* that guarantees a perfect snap-start without risking electrode contact with the work.

Here's how it's done:

1. The welder tilts the torch and lowers it to the work so only the side of the cup touches the work.

2. He turns on the welding torch and slowly rolls the torch upright.

3. When the electrode distance to the work becomes short enough, the snap-start ignites the arc. Snap-start electronics are often included in SMAW power supplies.

4. Bring the torch to the vertical position and begin welding.

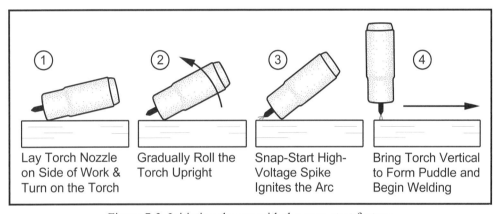

Figure 7-3. Initiating the arc with the snap-start feature.

Improving AC Arc Stability with High Frequency

AC is essential for welding aluminum and magnesium because of its oxide cleaning action. Without further refinements, though, the AC arc is unstable and unusable because it is interrupted during the low-voltage portion of the wave following the zero-crossover portions of each cycle. This interruption causes arc instability. See the arc in Figure 7-4.

One solution to arc instability is to add a high-frequency high-voltage source, similar to a Tesla coil, in series with the welding-current supply. These pulses maintain the arc by keeping the plasma alive during the low-voltage portions of the AC cycle. This stabilizing voltage, often called *HF* or *high frequency*, can be several thousand volts at a very low current and at frequencies as high as several megahertz.

The less sophisticated supplies have *free-running* HF. That is, the high-voltage spikes are not synchronized with the AC crossover points. There are just so many spikes that there are enough at or near the critical times to keep the arc alive. Many modern power supplies apply the HF only at the low-voltage crossover points. While HF is always needed for AC, it is often used just to initiate the DC TIG arc and then shuts off automatically.

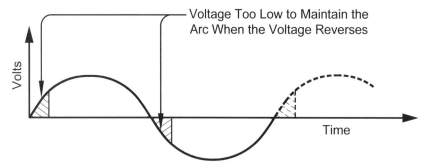

Figure 7-4. The low-voltage sections of each AC cycle creates an unstable arc.

The HF voltage spikes themselves only stabilize the arc. They play no role in actually heating the weld puddle. Welders often wear cotton gloves to avoid getting a nasty shock from these high-voltage spikes. In Figure 7-5, the height of the welding voltage waveform and the HF waveform are not to the same scale. The AC waveform is typically 20–30 volts in the hundreds of amperes, while the HF waveform is in the *thousands* of volts at tens of microamperes.

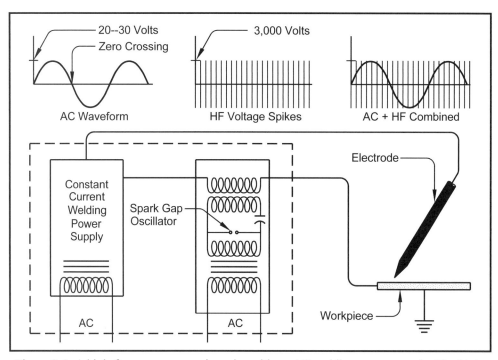

Figure 7-5. A high-frequency source in series with an AC welding power supply. The high-frequency supply can be integrated with the GTAW power supply or in a separate accessory box to convert an SMAW power supply for AC TIG welding of aluminum.

Accessory HF power supply boxes are available that can be placed in series with SMAW AC power supplies to provide a stable arc so that these machines can weld aluminum and magnesium.

Tip: Vehicle batteries must be disconnected when TIG welding is performed so the HF voltage spikes do not pass through the battery and damage the vehicle's electronics.

AC Heat Balance

The sine-wave, or *balanced,* AC waveform has equal durations of positive and negative. See Figure 7-6 (top). These sine-wave supplies have been used for decades and are adequate for TIG welding. Older SMAW and TIG welding power supplies that have these balanced AC waveforms must use a pure tungsten electrode with a ball tip. A pointed tip would melt in the intense heat produced in the DCEP portion of the AC cycle. The drawback is that the ball tip does not produce as tightly focused an arc as a pointed-tip electrode.

Because balanced waveforms divide the welding heat equally between the work and the electrode, the following occurs:

• The electrode remains positive for a much longer period than is needed to remove oxide from the work and heat is wasted on the electrode that could be better used to heat the weld pool.

• As mentioned above, the excessive heat on the electrode prevents the use of pointed-tip electrodes that better focus the arc onto the work than the ball-tip electrodes which must be used on balanced AC sources. A pointed or sharpened electrode tip on a balanced AC source quickly melts into a rounded tip, so ball tips are formed and used by necessity.

Adding a DC component to the balanced AC waveform shifts the waveform upwards and reduces the time when the electrode is positive, producing an *unbalanced* AC waveform. See Figure 7-6 (bottom). This puts more heat into the weld, keeps the electrode cooler, and allows the use of a sharpened electrode to better focus the arc. When using an unbalanced AC waveform there is still enough electrode-positive time to perform oxide cleaning.

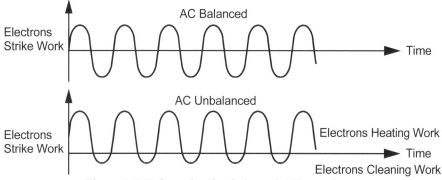

Figure 7-6. Balanced and unbalanced AC waveforms.

Another approach to shifting heat from the electrode to the workpiece uses an unbalanced square wave as shown in Figure 7-7. Changing the shape of this square wave shifts the heat balance between the electrode and the work which changes the oxide cleaning time and increases weld penetration. Another benefit of this approach is that the square wave has very little no-voltage time and the arc does not completely extinguish as the waveform goes through zero, so it produces a stable arc. HF is usually not needed for a stable arc after ignition, which means there is no shock hazard.

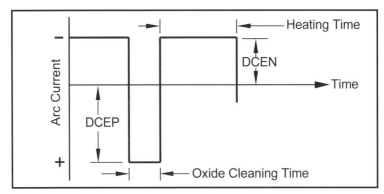

Figure 7-7. Unbalanced pulses of unequal positive and negative duration alter the heat distribution between the electrode and the workpiece, but still provide enough DCEP time for complete oxide removal.

Weld Penetration

While greater penetration can be achieved by increasing arc current and welding heat, too much arc heat causes too large a weld pool, larger heat-affected zones, and excessive workpiece melting. A pulsed DC waveform of 2–20 pulses/second permits metal transfer at a high enough current—during the peak pulses—to achieve a forceful, penetrating arc without overheating the work. The background current provides enough energy to maintain a stable arc, yet prevents the transfer of metal. This reduced background current allows the weld pool to cool between cycles. The low-frequency arc pulses agitate the weld pool, bringing the contaminants to the surface where they do not cause discontinuities. See the pulsed DC waveform in Figure 7-8.

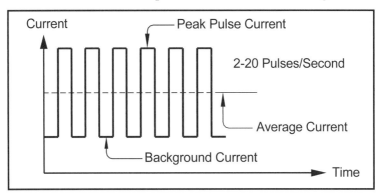

Figure 7-8. Pulsed DC waveform.

Arc Concentration or Focus

High-frequency DC pulses of 20 kHz increase the force of the arc by as much as four times, which reduces arc blow and the effect of wind on shielding gas. Because the pulses are so close together, there is little zero-voltage time across the arc plasma so it does not have time to cool and extinguish. This provides a more stable arc. Note that this high-frequency pulse is not a high-voltage pulse like those used for arc stability on AC welding machines. Inverter-based welding machines readily provide this pulsed-output waveform. See Figure 7-9.

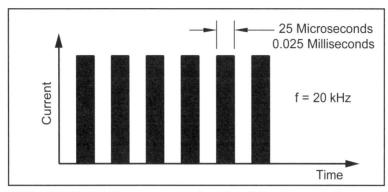

Figure 7-9. In GTAW, 20 kHz pulses maintain a forceful, stable arc without overheating.

Crater-Fill Function

When most electrical welding processes stop, a crater is formed at the end of the bead. Craters are discontinuities and a source of stress concentration and cracking. Here is how a crater forms:

- As the weld bead nears its end, the volume of metal surrounding the weld decreases. This is because there is less metal ahead of the weld as the bead approaches the edge of the work, while the arc heat typically remains the same. This combination of events increases the size of the weld pool and makes the molten metal more fluid.

- Normally the arc force pushes molten metal ahead of itself when the arc is pointed in the direction of the weld and filler metal is added to replace the metal pushed out of the way. But at the end of the weld, because no additional filler is added, the plasma force pushes some of the weld puddle out of the way, forming a crater.

Although a skilled welder can manipulate his foot pedal or fingertip arc control to taper off the arc current at the end of the bead and add additional filler metal to fill in the crater, more modern welding machines do this automatically using *DC pulse waveforms with ramps up and ramps down*. These ramps provide a gradual starting current (the *upslope*), a stable welding current, and a gradual tapering off of the current when stopping (the *downslope*). The downslope allows the final weld pool to be completely filled without leaving a crater. This is called the *crater-fill function*.

The ramp up at the start of the welding cycle, sometimes called a *soft-start* or *slope-up*, gives the arc time to gradually stabilize. This prevents workpiece burn-through and also prevents back-splash of the initial weld pool that can contaminate the electrode. Welding machines with this slope-up feature usually provide adjustment from 0–10 seconds.

Note that the term *slope,* as used here, has nothing to do with the static-output characteristic slope of a constant-current power supply, but refers to the shape of the current waveform when starting and stopping the arc. Welding machines with this output waveform are programmable to tailor the pulse to the work. Although the welding voltage fluctuates up and down, it does not become negative during its cycle, so this waveform is not considered AC, does not perform oxide removal, and cannot weld aluminum or magnesium. See Figure 7-10.

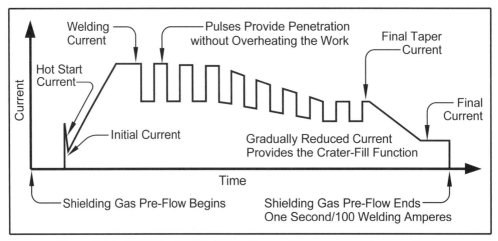

Figure 7-10. GTAW pulsed DC waveform with ramps up and ramps down.

Offset Square Waves

Figure 7-11 shows another approach for an AC welding power supply. This power supply arrangement provides:

- A stable arc with a square wave due to the absence of a zero-voltage time at crossover points.

- Stirs the weld pool with the arc force to bring dirt to the weld-pool surface and keep it out of the weld. This prevents discontinuities.

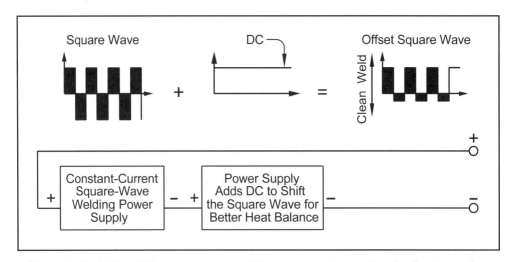

Figure 7-11. Adding DC to a square-wave CC power supply provides the cleaning action essential for GTAW welding of aluminum and puts more welding heat into the work.

- A better balance of heat onto the work and oxide cleaning are obtained with the DC bias. Without the additional DC supply, the heat balance would be like that of the balanced AC supply—not optimum.

Combination SMAW/GTAW Power Supplies

A DC SMAW power supply can be adapted to perform TIG welding—just exchange the electrode holder for a TIG torch with a fingertip gas-control valve and add an argon regulator and cylinder. Set up the polarity for DCEN and you're ready to weld ferrous metals.

To weld aluminum and magnesium, place an accessory HF supply in series with the TIG torch. Then, using AC polarity to provide oxide cleaning and arc stability, aluminum and magnesium can be welded. The drawback is that most SMAW power supplies do not have foot pedal or fingertip arc controls and the best capability of GTAW—control—is lost.

Many manufacturers offer welding power supplies that perform both SMAW and GTAW since the basic power supplies are so similar. These combined units provide an additional capability: they can use the foot pedal arc-amperage adjustment when doing SMAW. This arc control is useful when welding material of varying thickness. See Figure 7-12.

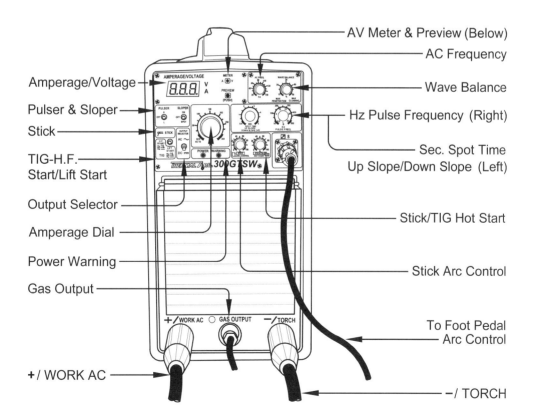

Figure 7-12. Front view of a Thermal Arc SMAW/TIG inverter welding machine.

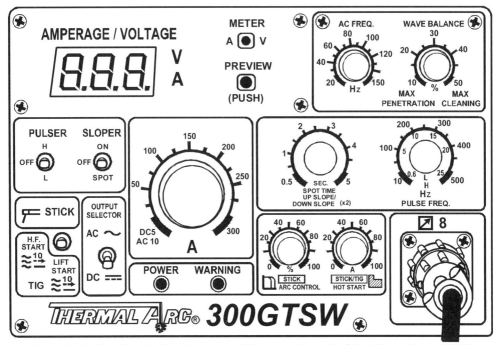

Figure 7-12. (Continued) Detailed view of the control panel of the Thermal Arc 300TS welding machine. This is a deluxe machine with controls many other machines lack. In fact, many later model machines have been dummied down and have fewer adjustments.

Section IV – GTAW Torches

Torch Designs

Torches are rated in accordance with the maximum current capacity they can use without overheating. Usually, manual torches have the electrode mounted at an angle to the cables to relieve the welder of having to support the twisting force of cables coming out of the back of the torch. However, some jobs are more easily done with pencil-style or straight-line torches where the cables come directly out of the back of the torch like those designed for automatic applications. These smaller, pencil-style manual designs, as in Figure 7-16, are available in both air-cooled and water-cooled models.

All torches have precision copper collets that grip and center the tungsten electrode in the torch. Collets have several other functions:

• Collets transfer welding current from the welding power cable to the tungsten electrode.

• Collets fit snugly around the electrode to conduct heat away from the electrode to keep the torch from overheating. *Gas-cooled torches,* sometimes called *air-cooled torches,* transfer this electrode heat to the incoming shielding gas. *Water-cooled torches* transfer this heat to the circulating cooling water. Air-cooled torches usually are limited to 200 A because of their inability to remove enough heat from the tungsten electrode to prevent them from burning up.

- Distribute inert shielding gas through holes or ports surrounding the collet holder to flow it evenly over the weld pool.

Torch Sizes

- Small *gas-cooled*, also called *air-cooled*, manual welding torches are rated up to 200 A. In this design, the relatively cool inert shielding gas running through the torch on its way to the arc also cools the torch. No cooling water is used. See Figures 7-13 and 7-14.

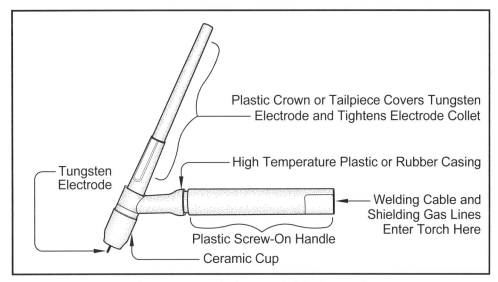

Figure 7-13. Typical gas-cooled GTAW torch.

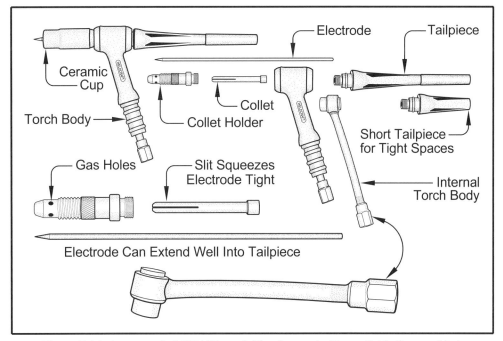

Figure 7-14. A gas-cooled GTAW torch like the one in Figure 7-13 disassembled.

• *Medium-sized water-cooled torches,* as in Figure 7-15, are good for welding tasks that operate continuously. Using tap water or a recirculating cooler prevents the heat from the tungsten electrode from burning up the torch. The torch in Figure 7-15 has a clear Pyrex cup for better visibility.

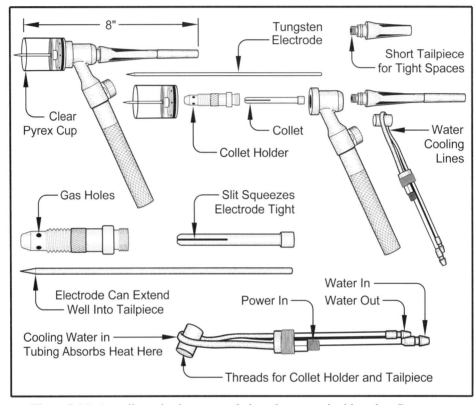

Figure 7-15. A medium-sized water-cooled torch mounted with a clear Pyrex cup.

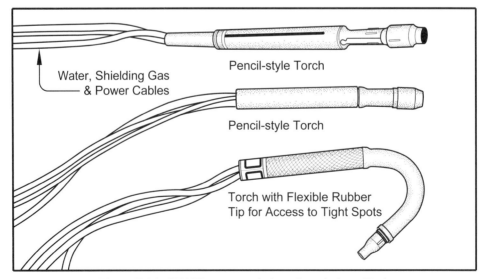

Figure 7-16. GTAW water-cooled torch variations. Both
water-cooled and air-cooled pencil torches are available.

- *Large water-cooled manual welding torches,* as in Figures 7-17 and 7-18, are rated over 200 amperes. The torch body is made entirely of copper. Here are the components it contains and how they work:

    - The threaded copper junction block secures the insulating torch handle and holds the copper and stainless steel tubing lines in alignment.

    - Cooling water enters the torch through a threaded fitting on the junction block. The power conductor, which runs *inside* the cooling-water line, connects to the junction block through this fitting, making the entire copper body at electrode potential. The cooling water absorbs heat from the power conductor to prevent the conductor from burning up.

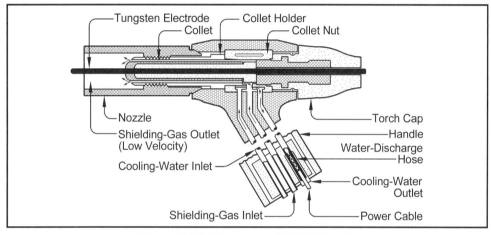

Figure 7-17. Water-cooled GTAW torch.

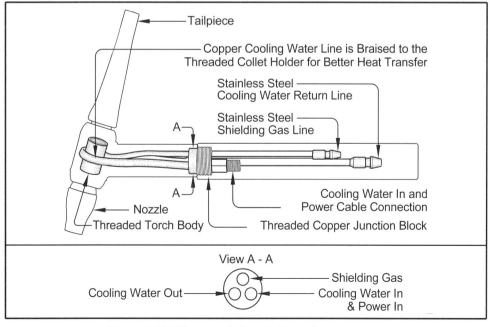

Figure 7-18. Water-cooled torch internal components.

Gas-Cooled vs. Water-Cooled Torches

Here is a comparison of these two torch designs.

Gas-cooled torches:

- Weigh less than water-cooled torches of the same amperage rating.

- Do not require a source of cooling water.

- Are excellent for low-amperage work or for short welds at medium amperage, but with extended use they can be uncomfortably hot to hold and their components can be damaged by the heat.

- As a gas-cooled torch heats up during use, the interior torch components transfer more heat to the shielding gas. This heating causes changes in both the shielding gas volume and temperature. To compensate for these changes, the welder must continuously readjust the gas flow.

Water-cooled torches:

- Require either a recirculating water cooler, much like a car radiator, or a source of tap water which is run through the torch once and sent to a drain.

- Using a water-cooled torch in the field is cumbersome because the cooling-water lines increase the weight of the torch and add rigidity to the torch. Water-cooled torches are usually avoided for fieldwork.

- Can be run at high-amperage levels for long periods while remaining comfortable to hold.

- Collets and collet holders last longer in water-cooled torches because the collet temperatures are kept lower.

Insulating Nozzles

Insulating nozzles, also called *cups,* are made from ceramic, Pyrex, alumina, or fused quartz. See Figure 7-19 for a sampling of the variety of insulating nozzles available.

The function of an insulating nozzle, or cup, is to flow gas around the electrode and into a stream at the weld pool. Their inside diameter is measured in sixteenths of an inch. If a nozzle is described as a number 5, its inside diameter is $5/16$", and a number 10 is $10/16$" or $5/8$" inside diameter. Nozzle diameters should be at least three times the electrode diameter. Insulating nozzles are available in many sizes, shapes and materials and are selected based on several criteria:

- How evenly they distribute shielding gas and protect the work.

- Weld puddle visibility.

- Their size and ability to get into tight locations.

- Cost is often a consideration as cups are expensive, fragile and do break.

There are two distinct nozzle designs: ceramic cups, the more common and less expensive design, and transparent cups, which are more expensive and offer better work visibility. The Pyrex nozzles, which can withstand both shock and intense heat, are more expensive than the other nozzle materials, but provide see-through visibility. Eventually, though, contamination from metal vapors condensing on the clear Pyrex nozzles causes them to become opaque and useless. See the Pyrex nozzles in Figure 7-21.

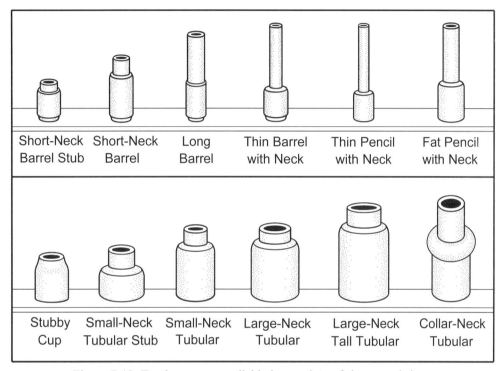

| Short-Neck Barrel Stub | Short-Neck Barrel | Long Barrel | Thin Barrel with Neck | Thin Pencil with Neck | Fat Pencil with Neck |

| Stubby Cup | Small-Neck Tubular Stub | Small-Neck Tubular | Large-Neck Tubular | Large-Neck Tall Tubular | Collar-Neck Tubular |

Figure 7-19. Torch cups are available in a variety of shapes and sizes.

Gas Lenses

A *gas lens* increases the area protected by the shielding gas by reducing turbulence and increasing *laminar flow*. Turbulence has the effect of drawing air into the shielding gas cover and reducing the size of the effective shielding area. See the gas lenses in Figures 7-20 through 7-22.

Gas lenses have the following advantages:

• Additional area of shielding gas coverage, which can be critical in tight joints such as inside corners where access is limited.

• Nozzle can be farther from the work and the electrode can extend as much as one inch for greater visibility of the arc, weld puddle, and joint. Extended electrode stickout provides access to hard-to-reach portions of the weld.

• Atmospheric contamination from air drawn into the shielding gas is reduced and this lessens the chances of weld discontinuities. This is particularly important on stainless, aluminum, magnesium, and titanium.

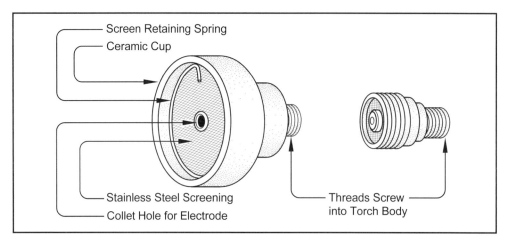

Figure 7-20. Large diameter diffuser and gas lens (left) and
a small gas lens without its cup or nozzle (right).

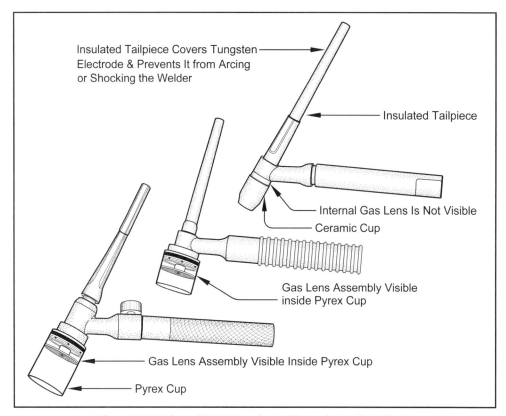

Figure 7-21. Three GTAW torches with gas lenses installed.

- In some applications gas lenses can reduce shielding gas consumption, but this is not the primary reason for choosing to use a gas lens.

- Gas lenses replace the collet holder and use several layers of stainless steel screens to produce laminar-shielding gas flow. They are available for use on ceramic or Pyrex cups.

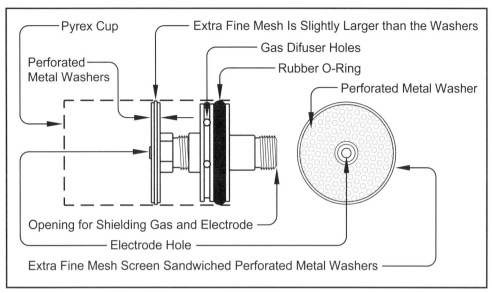

Figure 7-22. Detail of gas lens construction.

Section V – Tungsten Electrodes

Electrode Behavior

While the electrodes in other electrically-based welding processes supply filler metal and are consumed in the welding process, GTAW tungsten electrodes do not supply filler metal and are not consumed. Their function is to provide a source of heat from the arc they form with the work and to direct the arc. Though a very small amount of the electrode does melt and ends up in the weld, tungsten electrodes resist melting because:

- Tungsten has the highest melting point of all metals—6170°F.

- Tungsten has high thermal conductivity so heat can readily flow away from the electrode to the collet.

- Heated tungsten readily releases electrons from its surface to form the welding arc. Not all metals have this property.

- Torch collets are designed to remove heat from the electrode, and the torches themselves are gas or water-cooled.

- With DCEN polarity, which is most often used on ferrous metals, the electrons leaving the tungsten remove a great deal of heat and serve to cool the electrode.

Electrode Metallurgy

Table 7-2 shows the AWS classification and color coding of GTAW electrodes. Pure tungsten, *EWP*, is the least expensive electrode material and is only suitable for aluminum and magnesium on older balanced sine-wave welding machines. The other electrodes are tungsten alloys, and during AC operation on balanced-wave power supplies they are likely to transfer some of their alloy components to the work, contaminating it during the DCEP portion of the AC cycle. This is called *electrode spitting* and it occurs because the electrode gets too hot and positive ions are pulled away from it.

Alloyed electrodes are suitable for welding carbon steel, stainless steel, titanium, nickel alloys, and copper. Because they are usually operated with DCEN polarity, there is little risk of contaminating the work with the non-tungsten alloy components. Only electrons are pulled off the electrode, not metal ions. These alloyed electrodes provide easier starting, more current-carrying capacity, and a more stable arc than pure tungsten.

AWS Class	Composition	Properties	Color Code
EWP	Pure Tungsten. No intentional alloying elements.	Least expensive electrode. Maintains clean, balled end suitable for AC welding of aluminum and magnesium only. Has the lowest melting point and current-carrying capacity of all electrodes.	Green
EWCe-2	2% Cerium Oxide.	Developed as possible replacement for thoriated electrodes. Less burn-off than tungsten electrodes.	Orange
EWLa-1	1% Lanthanum Oxide.	Properties similar to 2% cerium oxide.	Black
EWTh-1	1% Thorium Oxide.	20% greater current-carrying capacity, easier to start, better resists sagging when red hot and carries a more stable arc than pure tungsten. Capable of holding a fine point for small welds at low currents. Much better lot-to-lot performance uniformity than other rare earth electrodes.	Yellow
EWTh-2	2% Thorium Oxide.		Red
EWZr-1	0.25% Zirconium Oxide.	Welding characteristics fall between pure tungsten and thoriated electrodes.	Brown
EWG	94.5% Tungsten, remainder not specified.	Depends on alloying elements. Used for welding special alloys.	Gray

Table 7-2. AWS tungsten GTAW electrode classification.
Except for pure tungsten, all electrodes are for DC operation.

In general, the best choice for ferrous metals is 2% thoriated tungsten electrodes. Adding thorium increases the electrode melting temperature and its ability to release surface electrons when heated. This provides higher current capacity and easy starting. The thorium 232 added is naturally mildly radioactive and emits alpha particles—high speed electrons. Thorium's radioactivity has a half-life of over 14 billion years so there is no point in waiting for the radioactivity to subside. Good practice is to capture and vent the thorium grinding dust so the dust and its alpha particles are not inhaled.

Table 7-3 shows recommended electrode choices for GTAW.

Welding Power Supply Output Waveform	GTAW Electrodes	
	Ferrous Metals	Aluminum & Magnesium
Sine or balanced wave, usually 60 Hz output.	Tungsten alloys with 2% thorium preferred, other tungsten alloys, pure tungsten will also work. All of these electrodes use pointed tips.	Pure tungsten with ball tip.
Modern inverter-based machines with variable frequency, variable positive-negative cycles, pulse output.		Tungsten alloys with pointed tip, 2% thorium preferred, but pure tungsten with pointed tip or ball tip will also work.

Table 7-3. GTAW electrode recommendations.

Electrode Sizes

Tungsten electrodes are available from 0.020–0.250" diameter and from 3–24" in length. The most common electrode length is 7 inches.

Surface Finishes

Electrodes are available *chemically cleaned*, the less expensive and usually adequate choice, but *polished*, or *centerless ground*, are also available. The advantage of the more expensive centerless-ground electrodes is that their smoother, more cylindrical surface transfers slightly more heat and current with the collet than the chemically-cleaned electrodes. Centerless-ground electrodes are used for very critical welds.

Chamfering

All electrodes should have a small 45º chamfer ground onto their unsharpened end. This chamfer allows the electrode to easily slip into the torch collet even though the two are a snug fit.

Shortening Electrodes

There are two reasons for adjusting the length of an electrode:

- The tip has become contaminated and a clean, new section of the electrode must be ground to a point.

- When a short tailpiece is used to gain access to a tight spot, the electrode must be shortened. There are two ways to do this:

  - Nick the electrode at the proposed break point with a grinding wheel or belt, and using two pliers, snap the electrode at the nicked point.

  - Electrodes are brittle and can be laid across the edge of an anvil or steel workbench and then struck with a hammer to break off a short length.

Forming Ball-Tip Electrodes

On pure tungsten electrodes running DCEP for welding aluminum and magnesium, a ball-shaped tip is required by the older sine-wave or balanced-wave AC welding machines because the high heat on the tungsten will melt a sharpened tip. A ball-tip is essentially a pre-melted pointed tip.

To form the ball tips in Figure 7-23, follow these steps:

1. Place an electrode in the torch.

2. Set the polarity to DCEP to put maximum arc heat on the electrode.

3. Strike an arc and allow the tip to become white hot.

4. When the heated tip melts and capillary attraction pulls the tungsten into a ball, shut off the torch and allow the tip to cool. For a rounded blunt tip, remove the electrode before the surface tension forms a ball.

5. Remember to change the polarity to AC if you are welding aluminum next.

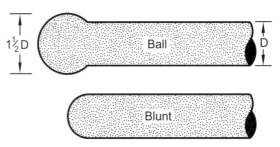

Figure 7-23. Ball and blunt tips are required on pure tungsten electrodes for AC welding on older balanced-wave AC welding machines.

Grinding or Forming Pointed-Tip Electrodes

Other electrodes that are not running AC require a pointed tip. The sharper the point, the more focused the arc. See the electrode tips in Figure 7-24.

Here are some sharpening suggestions:

• Reserve a grinding wheel for grinding electrodes only so that no other metals will contaminate the tip and the weld. Contaminated electrodes do not emit electrons as well as clean ones.

• For less demanding work, electrodes can be sharpened on a belt sander or an aluminum oxide grinding wheel. For quality work, a very smooth pointed electrode surface is desirable and can be applied starting with a green, or silicon dioxide, wheel and then the final smoothing applied with a diamond wheel. Grind with the axis of the electrode held perpendicular to the face of the wheel. The smoother the sides of the electrode point, the more stable the arc. Do not grind on the side of the grinding wheel. They are not made for this.

When grinding short electrodes for use in tight quarters, holding the electrodes in a pin vise will save injury to your fingers. Alternatively, for a perfect point, short electrodes may be run against a belt or grinding disc or wheel while held in a battery-powered electric drill.

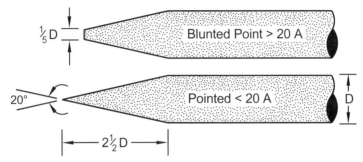

Figure 7-24. Modern pulse waveform machines can use pointed electrodes, which better focus the arc. The included point angle is about that of a lead pencil. All alloy electrodes may be used on all metals for both AC and DC welding on pulse waveform machines.

• Electrodes can also be chemically sharpened, a good alternative in the field or when working off the ground with poor access to grinders. When chemically sharpening the tip, heat it red hot by arcing it against a steel or copper plate and then swirl it in a sodium nitrate sharpening compound. Each time this heating-swirling cycle is done, the point becomes sharper.

Bending Electrodes

Figure 7-25 shows a pure tungsten electrode that has been bent to complete a weld in a tight space. To bend a tungsten electrode, heat it with an oxyacetylene torch to a dull red heat and bend it to shape with two pairs of pliers. Be sure to grind the point *before* bending the electrode.

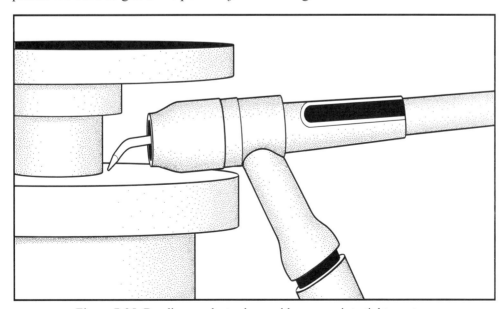

Figure 7-25. Bending an electrode provides access into tight quarters.

Joining Electrodes Together

When a job calls for an electrode with a sharp bend, electrodes can be welded together into the desired shape. Since a pure tungsten electrode will be used for the filler metal, the electrodes to be welded must have a higher melting temperature so they do not melt. Two percent thoriated tungsten is the first choice, but other tungsten alloys can be welded, and remember, the lower-melting pure tungsten must be the filler metal. Following the technique in Figure 7-26, here are the steps to join two electrodes:

1. Sharpen the thoriated electrode to the desired point *now*. It will be much harder to point the electrode after it is welded.

2. Using an abrasive wheel, add a snap groove so the pointed electrode can be snapped to its finished length without stressing the weld joint.

3. Place the electrodes to be joined into the grooves cut into the carbon or graphite block shown in Figure 7-26. The block will not melt or wet with weld metal and the electrodes are easily removed after they are joined.

4. Set the welding power supply to DCEP. This makes the alloy electrodes, the ones to be joined, negative so they will receive the most heat.

5. Using a clean pure tungsten electrode, set the welding polarity to DCEN and weld the electrodes together using the pure tungsten electrode as filler metal. The tungsten will wet the electrodes to be joined. Let them cool.

6. Snap off the long end of the electrode using the snap groove.

7. Smooth the edges of the weld joint as in Figure 7-27, and you are ready to weld. This figure shows the completed welded electrode in a torch.

8. Because these welded electrodes must sometimes be used with considerable stickout to reach into awkward spots, there is a chance that some part of it will contact the workpiece as it goes into welding position. To prevent this, wrap Pyrex onto the electrode to insulate it. Simply heat both the electrode and a Pyrex square rod in an oxyacetylene torch. Then, wind the Pyrex, like spaghetti on a fork, onto those parts of the electrode you want to insulate.

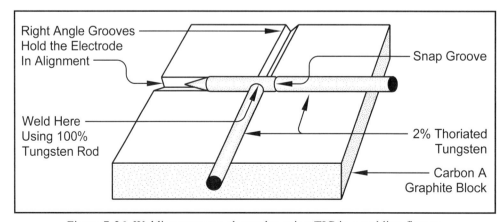

Figure 7-26. Welding tungsten electrodes using TIG in a welding fixture.

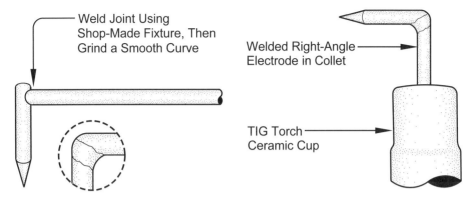

Figure 7-27. Welded tungsten electrode installed in a TIG torch. Be sure to smooth the joint edges to prevent them from emitting an arc from their points.

Section VI – Shielding Gases

Shielding Gas Control

Some SMAW power supplies used for TIG welding have a fingertip gas valve attached to the torch, but modern TIG power supplies have an electrically operated gas valve called a *solenoid* integrated into the power supply electronics. These valves open before the arc starts so the shielding gas protects the electrode from oxidation, provides an ionized path for the arc, and keeps the atmosphere away from the weld pool. This shielding gas function is called *pre-flow*.

The solenoid also remains open after welding stops. This is called *post-flow*, and it protects the red-hot electrode and the molten weld pool until they cool. Without adequate post-flow, the electrode will oxidize and then function poorly on the next weld. The welder must continue to hold the TIG torch in place at the end of the weld for the duration of the post-flow period. In general, one second of post-flow gas is needed for every 10 A of welding current, but with long electrode stickout, considerably more post-flow time is needed. Both pre-flow and post-flow duration are operator adjustable on modern full-featured welding machines.

Gases

- *Argon*, the most commonly used and least expensive shielding gas, is a monoatomic inert gas extracted from the atmosphere by the distillation of liquid air. It can be used for welding both ferrous and non-ferrous metals. Welding grade argon has a minimum purity of 99.95% which is fine for most metals except reactive and refractory metals that need 99.997% purity. Unless there are compelling technical reasons for other shielding gases, use argon.

  Here are the major advantages of argon gas:

  - Smoother and more stable arc action than helium.
  - Reduced penetration and less burn-through than helium.

- Oxide cleaning action on aluminum and magnesium.

- Lower cost and greater availability than helium.

- Because argon is both heavier than air and ten times heavier than helium, which is lighter than air, it can flow at lower rates than helium and still provide adequate shielding.

- Better resistance to cross-drafts because it is heavier than air.

- Easier arc starting than with helium.

• *Helium* provides much better penetration than argon and is sometimes used to join metals with high thermal conductivity or to make joints on thick aluminum sections. Mixtures of both helium and argon can be used to get some of the best characteristics of both gases. Helium works better when welding aluminum and magnesium, but it is much lighter than air and has a tendency to float up and away from the weld pool instead of blanketing it. However, this property does make helium better than argon for overhead welds.

• *Helium-argon mixtures* produce a higher arc temperature than pure argon and promote higher welding speeds and deeper weld penetration. The disadvantages of using helium or a helium/argon mixture is the high cost of the gas and the difficulty of starting the arc.

• *Argon plus 2–5% hydrogen* makes a gas that is slightly reducing and produces cleaner-looking welds without surface oxidation. The arc is hotter and more constricted, which permits higher welding speeds. The disadvantages include the risk of hydrogen cracking in carbon steels and weld metal porosity in aluminum alloys.

Figure 7-28 shows the effect of these gases on the shape of the weld bead.

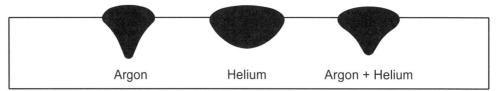

| Argon | Helium | Argon + Helium |

Figure 7-28. Shielding gases vs. weld profiles for DCEN on $^1/_2$" steel plate at 230 A.

Gas Metering Equipment

Shielding gas cylinders, pressure regulators, and flowmeters for GTAW are similar to those used for GMAW, which uses argon plus carbon dioxide shielding. Because argon, helium and their mixes have different densities, ball-in-tube flowmeters are accurate for only one particular gas.

Table 7-4 shows correction factors for other gases measured by ball-in-tube flowmeters calibrated for argon.

Shielding Gas	Correction Factors for Argon Flowmeters
100% Argon	1.00
75% Argon + 25% Helium	0.95
50% Argon + 50% Helium	0.75
25% Argon + 75% Helium	0.57
100% Helium	0.32

Table 7-4. Correction factors for measuring gas
flow in ball-in-tube flowmeters calibrated for argon.

Gas Adjustment

Adjust shielding gas flow according to either the AWS specification or to the manufacturer's data sheet. If neither is available, begin at about 20 ft^3/hour and increase the gas flow until visible signs of weld porosity cease.

Too high a shielding gas flow-rate results in turbulence. Turbulence brings air into the area we want to shield, ruining the weld. Getting an effective inert gas shield depends on both having enough gas flow and on maintaining a laminar flow.

Methods to Contain Shielding Gases

By using the barriers shown in Figure 7-29, shielding gases are better contained than when using the gas from a torch alone.

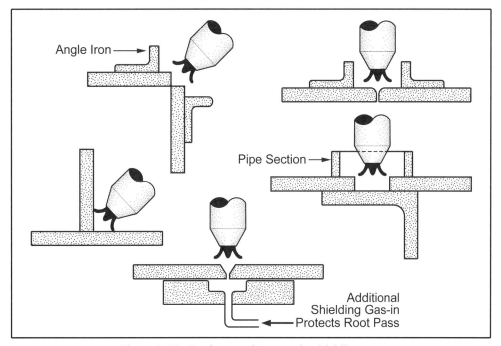

Figure 7-29. Barriers used to contain shielding gas.

Trailing Shields

For metals like titanium, a trailing shield is necessary to keep air away from the molten metal until it has cooled. These shop-made stainless steel shields, which can be shaped to fit the job, are often used when welding in a gas-purged chamber is not possible. See Figure 7-30.

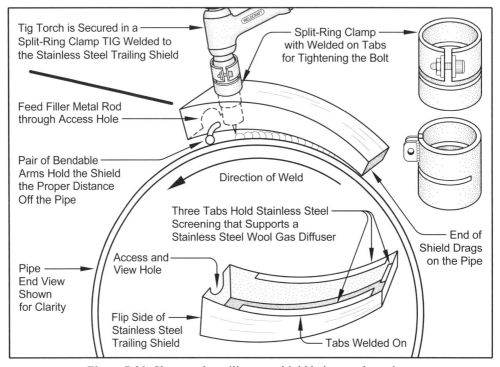

Figure 7-30. Shop-made trailing gas shield being used on pipe.

Welding inside Pipes & Cavities

Getting adequate shielding gas coverage at the bottom of a deep cavity can be a problem. Argon gas will want to flow out of the cavity if there is a hole in the bottom, and helium will want to float up and away from the weld. Also, gas flowing from the torch will tend to form turbulence when the torch is used in an inside bottom corner.

The solution is to add additional shielding gas from either the top or the bottom of the cavity. See Figure 7-31. Flooding a cavity with shielding gas can allow increased electrode stickout, often more than an one inch, and this can provide the visibility needed to apply the filler metal in the correct spot despite the torch being in the way. But even though the shielding gas coverage prevents electrode oxidation, as the stickout increases, it eventually becomes too long for adequate cooling through the collet, and the electrode will melt.

The filler metal rod may be bent at a 45° angle to reach the electrode tip, or a pre-form can be put in place before the torch is inserted.

The welded right-angle electrode in Figure 7-27 would be excellent for welding on the inside walls of a cavity, as shown in Figure 7-31 (B).

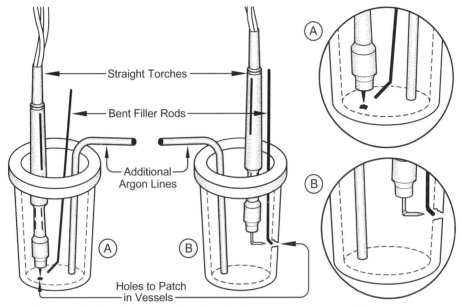

Figure 7-31. Flooding a cavity with shielding gas to insure shielding coverage.

Section VII – Filler Metals

GTAW Filler Metal Classifications

See Table 7-5.

Material	AWS Specification
Aluminum	A5.10
Chromium & Chromium Nickel	A5.9
Copper & Copper Alloys	A5.7
Nickel Alloys	A5.14
Magnesium	A5.19
Surfacing Materials	A5.13
Titanium	A5.16
Zirconium & Zirconium Alloys	A5.24

Table 7-5. AWS filler metal comparison chart for GTAW.

Brazing Filler Metals for TIG

A TIG torch can perform brazing using *silicon bronze, aluminum bronze* or *Silfos 5* filler metal. The torch is operated at a low current so only the filler metal melts, not the work. Brazing is performed at a much lower temperature than welding, so there is much less heat-induced distortion. Additionally, all three filler metals have about a 10% lower coefficient of thermal expansion than steel, and this helps reduce distortion. Another advantage of brazing with these three filler metals is that no flux is required, but careful workpiece cleaning is. Because these filler metals have roughly half the strength of a steel weld, they should not be used for critical welds requiring strength. Table 7-6 lists some of the important characteristics of these filler metals.

	Silicon Bronze	Aluminum Bronze	Sil-Fos 5
Alloying Elements	Cu 97%/Si 3%	Cu 83%/Fe 5%/Al 12%	Cu 89%/Ag 5%/P 6%
Melt/Flow (F°)	1866/1904	1880/1913	1190/1495
Yield Strength (psi)	50,000	40,000	35,000–40,000
Elongation in 2" (%)	30	23	20
Coefficient of Thermal Expansion* (μinches/inch-°F)	9.0	9.9–10.0	9.0–10.0
Electrical Conductivity (% IASC annealed)	7.0	12–13	11.0
Brinell Hardness	80–100	130–150	110
Metals Brazed (to same metal or to each other)	Steel, stainless steel, silicon bronze, bronze, cast iron and copper.	Bronze, manganese bronze, aluminum bronze, cast iron, copper-nickel alloys and steel.	Compatible with all metals except aluminum.
Supplied	$^3/_{32}$" or $^1/_8$" × 36" Rod	$^3/_{32}$" or $^1/_8$" × 36" Rod	0.125" × 0.050" × 20" Flat Bars

* Coefficient of Thermal Expansion for Steel = 11.0–13.0 μinches/inch-°F.

Table 7-6. Characteristics of three filler metals that TIG can braze.

Each of these filler metals has different applications and advantages:

- Silicon bronze:

  - There is a greatly reduced chance of burn-through on thin panels versus welding and this makes silicon bronze excellent for brazing together vehicle body panels.

  - Unlike brass brazing alloys, paint and auto body filler readily adheres to silicon bronze, which easily blends with surrounding surfaces.

  - Resists many types of chemical attack, particularly seawater.

  - Small parts can be brazed to larger ones without the risk of melting the smaller part and losing its detail.

  - When brazing steel or stainless steel with silicon bronze, the brazing temperature is at least 500°F below welding temperature and the result is a lot less heat-induced distortion of the work.

- Aluminum bronze:

  - Excellent for building up surfaces for wear and corrosion resistance or to form a bearing surface. For example, aluminum bronze is often used for the maintenance and repair brazing of ship propellers, pump housings, piston heads, and bearings.

- Often used for joining parts of silicon bronze castings, particularly statuary, and can have excellent color match.

- Requires more skill and experience—especially puddle-size control—than Sil-Fos.

• Sil-Fos 5:

- Easy to work with, very forgiving, excellent for beginners, and it brazes most metals including cast iron, but not aluminum.

- Excellent for joining electrical conductors for commutator bars or in the form of square or round copper tubing induction coils.

- Because Sil-Fos can be brazed 300–400ºF farther below the brazing temperatures for silicon bronze and aluminum bronze brazing, it can be used in tight quarters where the surrounding items are temperature sensitive.

Section VIII – Setting Up a GTAW Outfit

Process Setup

1. Place the welding power supply in a dry area, set the power switch to OFF, and attach the unit to the power source.

2. Secure the inert gas cylinder with a safety chain or a metal strap so it will not tip over, remove the cylinder cap, crack the cylinder valve to remove any dirt and, using a wrench, attach the regulator to the cylinder. If there is a flowmeter tube, make sure it is vertical.

3. Connect the gas hoses:

- From the flowmeter or flow regulator to the welding machine.

- Between the welding machine and the torch hose.

4. If water-cooled, connect the water lines:

- From the water source to the water IN connection.

- From the water OUT connection on the torch cable to the water drain.

5. In the case of a recirculating water cooler, the IN and OUT water lines from the cooler are connected to the torch cable.

6. Complete the electrical power and control connections between the torch and the welding power supply.

7. Insert a clean and sharpened electrode in the torch collet and tighten. Install the cup, if used.

8. With the electrode and torch positioned so as not to strike an arc, turn on the power supply and apply power to the torch. Check for inert gas and water leaks and tighten fittings if needed, then adjust the gas for proper flow rate, usually about 20 ft^3/min.

9. Set the arc current level and polarity, and secure the work lead to the work.

10. Set any other parameters on the welding power supply. These could include:

    -   Mode switch, if using a combination GTAW/SMAW power supply.

    -   High frequency switch: Set to START on DC, CONTINUOUS for AC and OFF if pulse waveforms are used.

    -   Set pre-flow and post-flow gas times.

11. If using a pulse waveform machine, set the following:

    -   Ramp-up time (shielding gas pre-flow time).

    -   Ramp-down time (shielding gas post-flow time, usually one second/ 10 A of welding current).

    -   Pulse rate.

    -   Background current.

    -   Percent power-on time.

12. Select the weld filler metal, if used.

13. Put on your helmet over your safety glasses and then put on gloves. Now you are ready to weld.

Section IX – Welding Techniques

Good to Know Tips

-   Use a dedicated stainless steel wire brush for steel, aluminum and stainless steel. TIG is very sensitive to cross-contamination between metals. This is particularly true for the iron contamination of aluminum welds. Mark the handle of each brush with the metal it is to be used with as shown in Figure 7-32. Before beginning each bead, run this brush over the joint area.

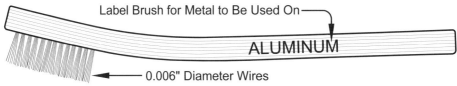

Figure 7-32. Small stainless steel welder's brush.

-   When welding copper, use *deoxidized copper* welding rod, not electrical wire, because electrical wire will cause bubbles and pinholes. Electrical wire can be used only if welding current, penetration, and weld pool agitation are minimized.

-   TIG does not burn through paint, dirt, grease, oil, plating, anodizing, or the gray oxide on hot-rolled steel. The weld area must be shiny clean. The zinc in galvanized steel will contaminate the electrode as well as the weld itself and must also be removed. Remove these contaminants with a clean-and-strip disc or an 80-grit abrasive disc. Do not cross-contaminate abrasive grinding discs between metals. Critical welds should be wiped down with acetone or alcohol before welding. If black soot appears around a finished weld, this is a sign of organic compound contamination.

- When repair-welding aluminum, look for possible *clear* anodizing which can be difficult to spot. This anodizing will prevent welding and must be ground off to bare metal.

- GMAW filler wire may be used for GTAW welding.

- Auto-darkening welding helmets make learning to weld easier by providing continuous visibility on the torch and work position whether the arc is off or on.

- Because many TIG welds are small, precision control is needed. Here are progressively better ways to stabilize yourself for better control:

  - Lean with your hip or shoulder pressed against the workpiece or wall.

  - Sit while you are welding and then lean against the workbench with your elbows.

  - Sit while resting your forearms on the work or on the workbench.

- Rough arc starts and crater finishes can be avoided by using a run-on and run-off plate for critical welds.

- While most titanium is welded in a helium/argon-filled *glove box*, it is possible to weld with shielding gas from the torch alone using these precautions:

  - Turn off the heating and air conditioning in the welding area to minimize air currents and before welding allow time for the air currents to die down.

  - Prevent others from walking around the welding area before and during welding. Air they stir up will disturbs shielding gas coverage.

  - Use a gas lens to increase the shielding area and to reduce the amount of air drawn into the shielding gas.

  - A trailing gas shield permits faster welding speeds because the shield provides additional time that the weld pool is protected by the gas shield.

- The newer inverter machines are more sensitive to poor grounds than sine-wave machines. If the electrode gets red-hot along its entire length, but still does not weld properly, check for a solid ground.

- Many different filler metal alloys look alike and once mixed up, cannot be identified. Store filler rods in labeled and capped PVC tubes. Do not allow bits of used filler rod to accumulate on your bench because they are likely to be mistaken for the proper alloy. Using the wrong rod can cause weld failure.

- It is very important to keep the torch with post-flow shielding gas held over the weld until the metal is completely cooled.

- Place a copper or aluminum plate under steel workpieces when they are being welded on top of a steel welding table to prevent the part from being welded to the table.

- Make a torch holder, such as the one shown in Figure 7-33. This holder will keep the torch from being knocked or pulled off the bench by the weight of its cables and will also save the gas nozzle from shattering when it hits the floor.

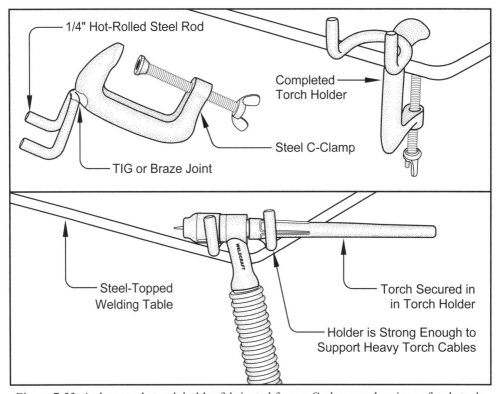

Figure 7-33. A shop-made torch holder fabricated from a C-clamp and a piece of rod stock.

Starting a Puddle & Adding Filler Metal

Figure 7-34 shows how to start a puddle and the typical torch and filler metal angles. The torch is held perpendicular to the work and moved in a circular motion, then the torch is tilted and filler metal is added.

It is important to keep the hot tip of the filler-metal rod inside the shielding gas or the tip will oxidize. However, the tip of the rod must be far enough from the torch heat so it does not melt before it is dipped into the puddle. This balancing act is learned with experience.

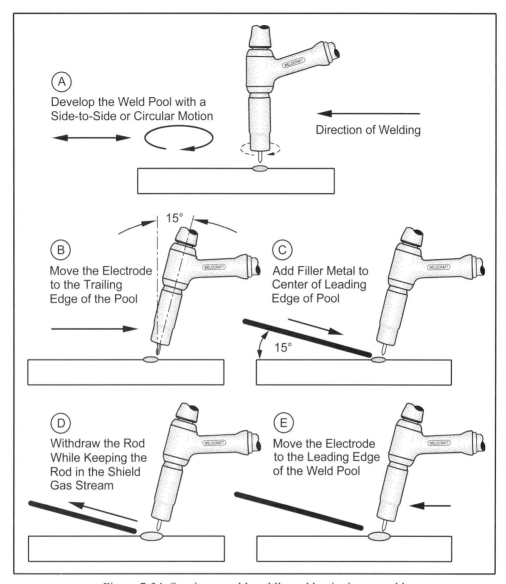

Figure 7-34. Starting a weld puddle and beginning to weld.

Thickness Range of GTAW

- Single-pass welds can be made with no preparation on material with a thickness of 0.005–0.125 inches.

- Single-pass welds can be made with preparation on material with a thickness of $^1/_{16}$–$^3/_{16}$ inches.

- Multi-pass welds can be made with preparations on material with a thickness of $^1/_8$–2 inches and greater. There is no real upper limit to the thickness of welds that can be made with GTAW, but for economic reasons, other welding processes with much higher deposition rates make more sense.

Section X – GTAW Troubleshooting

Table 7-7 lists some typical GTAW problems, causes and solutions.

Problem	Possible Cause	Solution
Excessive Electrode Consumption	1. Inadequate gas flow. 2. Operating on reverse polarity. 3. Improper size electrode for current needed. 4. Excessive heating in holder. 5. Contaminated electrode. 6. Electrode oxidation during cooling. 7. Using gas containing carbon dioxide or oxygen.	1. Increase gas flow. 2. Use larger electrode or change to DCEN. 3. Use larger electrode. 4. Check for proper collet contact. 5. Remove contaminated portion. 6. Keep gas flowing after arc stops for at least 10 to 15 seconds. 7. Change to proper gas.
Erratic Arc	1. Base metal is dirty or greasy. 2. Joint is too narrow. 3. Electrode is contaminated. 4. Arc too long. 5. Voltage too low.	1. Use chemical cleaners, wire brush or abrasive wheels. 2. Open joint groove, bring electrode closer to work, decrease voltage. 3. Remove contaminated portion of the electrode. 4. Bring holder closer to work. 5. Increase voltage.
Porosity	1. Entrapped gas impurities (hydrogen, nitrogen, air and water vapor). 2. Defective gas hose or loose connections. 3. Oil film on base metal. 4. Too windy.	1. Blow out air by purging gas line before striking an arc. 2. Check hoses and connections for leaks. 3. Clean with chemical cleaner not prone to break up arc. 4. Shield work from wind.
Tungsten Contamination of Workpiece	1. Poor scratch starting technique. 2. Electrode melting and alloying with base metal. 3. Touching tungsten to molten pool. 4. Using excessive electrode extension. 5. Inadequate gas shielding or excessive drafts. 6. Wrong gas.	1. Use high-frequency starter, use copper striker plate. 2. Use less current, or larger electrode; use thoriated or zirconium-tungsten electrode. 3. Keep tungsten out of molten pool & maintain proper arc length. 4. Reduce electrode extension. 5. Increase gas flow, protect the arc from wind or use a gas lens. 6. Use correct gas; do not use $ArCo_2$ for GMAW.

Table 7-7. GTAW troubleshooting.

Problem	Possible Cause	Solution
Short Parts Life	1. Short water cooling lead life. 2. Nozzle or cups shattering or cracking. 3. Short collet life. 4. Excessive heating in holder. 5. Short torch head life.	1. Check flow direction, look for blockage or leak. 2. Change cup size or tungsten stickout. 3. Change to wedge-style collet. 4. Check for proper collet contact. 5. Operate the torch within its rated capacity.
Arc Blow	1. Induced magnetic field from DC welding current. 2. Arc is unstable from magnetic fields.	1. Change to AC with HF and relocate the ground connection. 2. Reduce welding current and minimize arc length.

Table 7-7. (Continued.) GTAW troubleshooting.

Section XI – Safety

GTAW Safety

In addition to the safety measures outlined in *Chapter 2 – Safety*, there are several additional safety issues.

- Because the GTAW process is smokeless and there are no visible fumes to block or absorb radiation, heat and light from its arc are intense. Proper lens shade selection is important. See Table 2-1 for suggested lens shades. Also, cover all exposed skin to prevent radiation burns. Wear a shirt of non-synthetic material, preferably heavy cotton. Protect your forearms by rolling down your shirtsleeves and making sure that the shirt material has a tight enough weave to prevent arc-burn through the fabric.

- When welding in confined spaces such as inside tanks, provisions must be made for fresh air to replace the inert gas used in the process.

- Good ventilation is vital since the arc generates dangerous ozone levels. Good ventilation will also prevent argon asphyxiation from slow leaks since argon is heavier than air and will tend to collect in low spots.

- Always be sure to turn off the power supply when changing electrodes because some power supplies have open-circuit voltages as high as 85 volts, enough to be a lethal shock hazard.

- Wear dry gloves without holes and never weld barehanded. Gloves protect against radiation burns and electric shock. Although some welders wear calfskin gloves, tanning chemicals in the leather can stain steels, particularly tool steels, with the sulfur content of their chemicals. Many welders wear cotton gloves to avoid this staining. Should you touch the filler wire or rod to the electrode, the full voltage of the power supply will be on the filler and you could become part of a lethal circuit.

- Though TIG torch cables are usually sold without protective covers, these covers, which can be made from nylon, rubber tubing, or leather are a valuable safety aid. Nylon covers have a non-conductive zipper to hold the sheath closed, rubber covers slide over the cables, and leather covers are held shut by steel snaps.

Cable covers are an essential safety device on water-cooled torches. They not only protect the cables from abrasion and shop wear, they reduce the chances of an electrical shock which can occur if the cooling water line bursts and puts the welder in a pool of water that sits between the power supply open-circuit voltage and ground. In this situation, the welder completes the circuit. Although TIG welding power supplies typically deliver 10–35 volts under load, their open-circuit voltage can be as much as 85 volts. This voltage is high enough to be lethal.

The leather covers are the most expensive and also the most resistant to burn-through when touched with a red-hot electrode. Do not operate a water-cooled torch without a cable cover.

Chapter 8

Oxyacetylene

Facts do not cease to exist because they are ignored.

—Aldus Huxley

Introduction

One of the earliest welding processes, oxyacetylene welding was first used industrially in the early years of the twentieth century. Although this process makes excellent welds in steel, today it is not a major industrial welding process except with makers of light aircraft and race car frames, since now there are other more efficient welding processes available. However—and this is a big however—oxyacetylene has many other important uses: cutting, hardening, tempering, bending, forming, preheating, post-heating, brazing, and braze welding. Because of the precise control the welder has over its heat input and its high-temperature flame—together with its low equipment cost, portability and versatility—oxyacetylene torches remain an essential tool. No welding shop or even industrial shop is complete without one.

This chapter is devoted to oxyacetylene equipment because of its key importance to welders and machinists. It pays special attention to safety because, as with all effective tools, oxyacetylene is inherently hazardous. With this equipment, accidents happen amazingly fast, and once they begin—they cannot be stopped.

We will cover the theory and use of oxyacetylene in depth so you can use the equipment with confidence and safety. This chapter will prepare you for the later chapters on cutting, brazing, and bending because many components and techniques are common to all of these processes. There are also several commercial issues on cylinder ownership which this chapter will explain.

Oxyacetylene offers several advantages over other torch fuels:

- Heats metal quickly. Only welding arc plasma, nuclear explosions, and the sun produce higher temperatures than a 5600°F oxyacetylene flame.

- Provides excellent control of heat input and puddle viscosity as well as good control of bead size and shape.

- The single, low-cost outfit is multifunctional. It not only welds, it cuts, heats, bends, anneals, and brazes.

Section I – Equipment

Welding Outfit

Figure 8-1 shows the components of a complete oxyacetylene welding outfit: an oxygen cylinder, an acetylene cylinder, pressure regulators, hoses and a torch. Later in the chapter each part will be discussed in depth. Oxyacetylene equipment is light enough to be readily portable and it requires no external electrical power source.

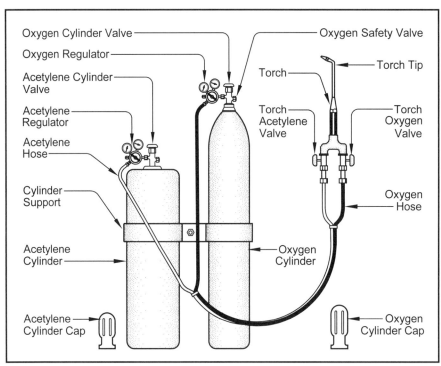

Figure 8-1. Oxyacetylene welding outfit.

Section II – Gases

Acetylene

Acetylene is a clear, lighter than air gas with a chemical formula of C_2H_2. It is man-made and does not occur in nature. Each molecule of this hydrocarbon compound contains two carbon atoms and two hydrogen atoms. Placing calcium carbide in water releases acetylene gas. One pound of calcium carbide generates about 10 ft^3 of acetylene gas. Pure acetylene has an ether-like odor, but commercial quality acetylene, the type used by welders, has a garlic-like odor from the impurities found in the calcium carbide.

The chemical equation of combustion of acetylene in a neutral flame is:

$$C_2H_2 + 2.5\,O_2 \rightarrow 2\,CO_2 + H_2O$$

One part acetylene and two and a half parts oxygen combine to produce a neutral flame. Equal volumes of acetylene and oxygen from the compressed gas cylinders combine with an additional one and a half parts of oxygen, which comes from the surrounding atmosphere. This type of flame has just the right amount of fuel and oxygen so that after combustion there is neither an excess of oxygen nor of fuel.

Acetylene is potentially dangerous for two reasons:

- Acetylene forms explosive mixtures with air at concentrations from 2.5–80 percent. This is the widest explosive range of any common gas and almost insures an explosion when leaking acetylene ignites.

- Acetylene gas must never be drawn from its cylinder at pressures above 15 psi because it can spontaneously and explosively disassociate into its components. This is why acetylene regulator gauges display a red warning arc above 15 psi.

Oxygen

Atmospheric air is repeatedly cooled and compressed until it becomes a very cold liquid. As this liquid air is gradually warmed, each of its component gases reaches its vaporization temperature, comes out of the liquid air, and separates into its individual gases, one of which is oxygen. This process is called the *fractional distillation of liquid air*. Other gases important in welding—nitrogen, carbon dioxide and argon—are also made using this process. Oxygen can also be made by electrolysis of water, but for industrial quantities this is not cost-effective due to the expense of the electricity needed.

Other Welding Fuels

Though not strictly used for oxyacetylene, this is a good time to discuss other welding fuels. For economy and safety reasons, other gases, such as natural gas, propane, hydrogen and proprietary gases based on mixtures of these, are frequently used for non-welding processes. Table 8-1 shows the maximum temperature achievable with these alternative fuel gases as compared with the temperature of acetylene.

These other fuels work well for soldering, brazing, preheating and oxygen cutting, but are seldom used for welding. Slightly different torch tips may be needed if alternative fuel gases are used with an oxyacetylene outfit. Where even lower temperatures are acceptable, such as when sweating copper tubing or performing small soldering tasks, a single cylinder of fuel gas using only atmospheric oxygen is effective and economical. In some foreign countries where acetylene is not readily available, gasoline is used, but only for cutting.

Fuel Gas	Oxygen-to-Fuel Gas Combustion Ratio	Neutral Flame Temperature with Oxygen °F	°C	Total Heat (Btu/ft³)	Specific Gravity (Air = 1.0)
Acetylene	2.5	5589	3087	1470	0.906
Propane	5.0	4579	2526	2498	1.52
Propylene	4.5	5250	2900	2400	1.48
Natural Gas	2.0	4600	2538	1000	0.60
Hydrogen	0.5	4820	2660	325	0.07

Table 8-1. Combustion properties of fuel gases.

MAPP Gas

MAPP gas is a trademarked name owned by Pétromont & Co. of Varennes, Quebec, Canada, for a fuel gas based on a mixture of methylacetylene-propadiene propane. Although this gas has not been made in North America since 2008, much of it is still around. Its many advantages make it likely to eventually reappear on the market. The Chinese manufacture an identical product, but it is not yet available in the U.S.

MAPP gas was developed as a lower-cost substitute for acetylene in air-MAPP torches that are used for plumbing and refrigeration soldering and in oxygen-MAPP torches used for cutting, brazing, and bending. MAPP gas is not suitable for welding because its high hydrogen content causes embrittlement in steel welds.

Here are some of its advantages:

- MAPP gas is safer to handle than acetylene because it does not decompose explosively at pressures above 15 psi.

- MAPP can be stored and transported in cylinders *without* the inert filler and acetone that acetylene requires, so more gas can be delivered in a given size cylinder. Also, unlike acetylene, MAPP cylinders can be filled and drained rapidly, rather than the seven hours required to fill and empty an acetylene cylinder.

- When MAPP gas is used with oxygen its temperature is slightly lower than acetylene-oxygen, but the heat is more evenly distributed throughout the flame envelope, making it excellent for brazing, heating, and bending.

Today, propylene is offered as a substitute for MAPP gas. It works acceptably well in air-propylene torches, but not very well in oxygen-propylene torches. MAP/Pro, one of the commercial names for the MAPP substitute, propylene, is confusingly similar to MAPP. Although the 14.1 ounce cylinders are the same yellow color and carry the same UPC code as the discontinued MAPP gas cylinders, the two are actually different products sold in deceptively similar packaging.

Section III – Compressed Gas Cylinders

Oxygen Cylinders

High-pressure cylinders are used for oxygen and for shielding gases. These cylinders are seamless, high-strength alloy-steel pressure vessels made from a single billet by a rotary draw-forging process. U.S. Department of Transportation (DOT) regulations require that high-pressure cylinders be hydrostatically tested at either 5 or 10 year intervals depending on their steel alloy to insure they will not rupture in use. Cylinders have an unlimited life provided they pass hydrostatic testing.

To conduct a hydrostatic test, the cylinder is vented, its valve is removed, and the cylinder is filled with water. Next, the cylinder is placed in a container filled with water and the cylinder is pressurized to $^5/_3$ of its working pressure for a minimum of 30 seconds. Water is used instead of air to pressurize the cylinder so there will be no flying steel if the cylinder ruptures. Under testing, the pressurized cylinder expands much like an inflated balloon, but on a much smaller scale. As shown in Figure 8-2, the displacement of water from the surrounding cylinder measures the expansion of the cylinder walls under test pressure.

The cylinder passes hydrostatic testing only if:

- It expands less than 10% of its internal volume at test pressure as measured by the sight gauge.

- The cylinder shrinks back to within one percent of its original size when the test pressure is removed.

If either one of these conditions is not met, the cylinder will be condemned because it has lost its elasticity and is no longer safe to use.

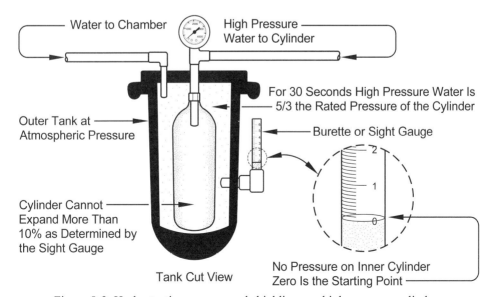

Figure 8-2. Hydro testing oxygen and shielding gas high-pressure cylinders.

Acetylene Cylinders

Most acetylene cylinders are fabricated—welded from several pieces of steel—and since they operate at 225 psi, a relatively low pressure, no hydrostatic testing is needed, just a periodic visual inspection. See both the oxygen and acetylene cylinders in Figure 8-3.

Outside of the U.S., many countries are now switching to one-piece forged cylinders and eliminating the fabricated acetylene cylinders for increased safety.

In the U.S. today, acetylene cylinders are packed with inert, porous silica lime filler. Previously, asbestos, cement, and charcoal were used. The silica lime filler is then saturated with acetone. Together, the porous filler and the acetone provide a safe way to store and transport acetylene.

As mentioned before, acetylene can spontaneously and violently disassociate into its components at pressures above 15 psi. For this reason it cannot be stored as a free gas, but it can be safely *dissolved* in acetone at 225 psi in the same way carbon dioxide is dissolved in water to make club soda. At 225 psi, up to 25 ft^3 of acetylene can be dissolved in each cubic foot of acetone. Should disassociation begin, the porous filler prevents it from spreading throughout the cylinder, which prevents an explosion.

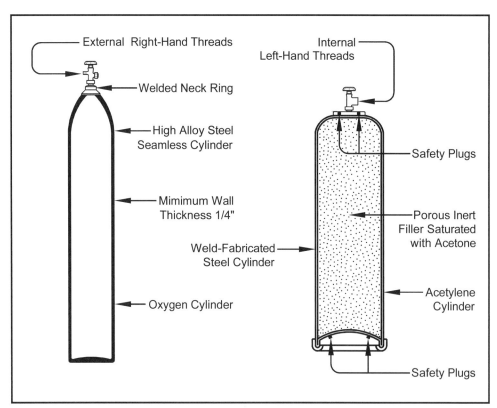

Figure 8-3. Oxygen and acetylene cylinder cross sections.

Because the acetylene is *dissolved* in acetone, not just pumped into a cylinder, filling takes seven hours as the acetylene gradually goes into solution in the acetone. Similarly, an acetylene cylinder can only deliver one-seventh of its capacity per hour as the acetylene will not come out of solution in the acetone any faster than it went in.

If more acetylene is drawn from a cylinder than can be released from the acetone solution, both acetylene and acetone will exit the cylinder in the same way beer foams out of a warm bottle when suddenly opened. This simultaneous release of both acetylene and acetone damages hoses and O-rings. A sign of simultaneous release is, when welding, the torch emits a green flame. This green flame indicates that acetone has become mixed with acetylene.

If an acetylene cylinder is tipped over onto its side, as sometimes happens during transport, this causes the acetone and acetylene to become mixed at the top of the cylinder, and this mixture enters the regulator and acetylene hose together. Though mentioned above, this is worth repeating, the acetone in the regulator and torch will damage any hoses and O-rings in its path. To prevent this dangerous and costly situation, wait at least one-half hour before connecting and using a cylinder which has been tipped. This allows the liquid phase of the acetone to separate from the acetylene gas in the upper portion of the cylinder.

Acetylene Gauge Pressure

Pressure gauges on acetylene cylinders are poor indicators of the remaining gas quantity. This is because as acetylene gas is withdrawn from solution in acetone, gas pressure remains nearly constant at a given temperature until very little gas remains. The best way to determine the remaining contents of a cylinder is to compare its current weight with its empty, or *tare*, weight. The empty cylinder weight—including its porous silica lime filler and acetone—is stamped on top of the cylinder.

Look ahead to Figure 8-9 to see the marking on an acetylene cylinder. The weight figures, in pounds and ounces, are separated by a dash. There are 14.6 ft^3 of acetylene measured at 20°C at atmospheric pressure for every pound of cylinder weight over its empty weight.

Cylinder Safety Devices

Fire is always a safety hazard when dealing with oxygen and other high-pressure cylinders. To prevent gas cylinders from exploding should they be exposed to fire, they are equipped with two types of pressure relief safety devices:

- Oxygen and other high-pressure cylinders have a *metal burst diaphragm*, also called a *rupture disc* or a *safety disc*, in a section of the cylinder valve as shown in Figure 8-4. This safety disc ruptures at 3360 psi, relieving the cylinder pressure to the atmosphere.

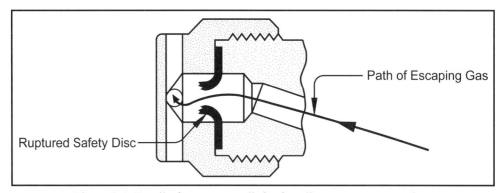

Figure 8-4. Detail of a pressure relief safety disc on an oxygen valve.

- Most acetylene cylinders have one or more *safety plugs*. These plugs are bolts that have an inner core made of a fusible metal alloy which melts at 212°F. When this metal melts, acetylene gas escapes from the cylinder and prevents the cylinder from exploding. Refer back to the bottom right of Figure 8-3 to see their location and to Figure 8-5 for a detailed view of a safety plug. Depending on the size of the cylinder, there are one to four safety plugs. The 10 ft^3 MC-size cylinders and the 40 ft^3 B-size cylinders have fusible channels incorporated into their valves instead of separate plugs.

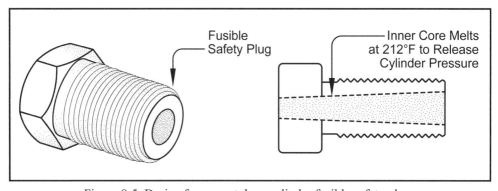

Figure 8-5. Design for an acetylene cylinder fusible safety plug.

Oxygen Cylinder Valves

Because oxygen cylinders are filled to such a high pressure, in order to prevent leakage around the valve stem when the valve is open, oxygen and all other high-pressure cylinders have a second valve seat, called the *back-seating O-ring seal*, to make a solid seal around the valve stem.

See the oxygen cylinder valve cross section in Figure 8-6.

By fully opening the oxygen cylinder valve, this second valve seat engages and prevents gas loss from around the valve stem. Oxygen cylinder valves have *metal-to-metal seals* and for this reason, if the valve is securely closed, they can store gas for decades without loss.

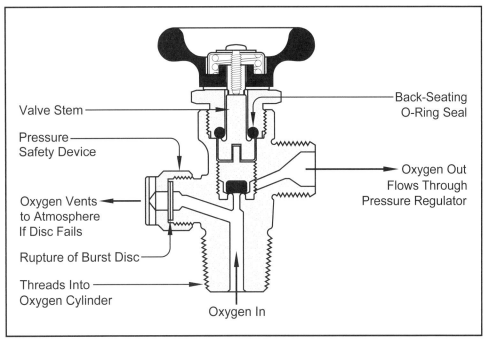

Figure 8-6. Cross section of an oxygen cylinder valve showing the back-seating
O-ring seal on the stem, which engages when the valve is fully open to
prevent leaks around the valve stem.

Acetylene Cylinder Valves & Wrenches

Because an acetylene cylinder valve sees a relatively low pressure, leakage around the valve stem when the valve is open is small, so only a single bottom-valve seat is needed. Since the acetylene valve can deliver adequate volume with one turn open, opening the valve more just increases its closing time in an emergency. Do not open the valve more than one turn.

Although most acetylene cylinders have round, permanent valve handwheels, some older MC- and B-size cylinders do not. They require removable valve wrenches which should be kept on the cylinder so the valves can be closed quickly in an emergency. The MC-size cylinders are the smallest in service and are popular with refrigeration repairmen, while the B-size cylinders are slightly larger and mostly used by plumbers. Refer to the cylinder size chart in Figure 8-12.

Figure 8-7 (top) shows the standard wrenches for MC- and B-size cylinders. Many welders cut these double-ended stamped steel wrenches in half and then weld longer handles onto each half end, as in Figure 8-7 (second from top). Often a lanyard is attached to these modified wrenches to keep them on the cylinders so they are handy when needed. Some welders cut a square opening in a Crescent-style adjustable open-end wrench to make a cylinder valve/Crescent wrench combo as in Figure 8-7 (bottom). Some old-style acetylene cylinders have valves with large square or triangular valve stems and require the wrench shown in Figure 8-7 (second from bottom).

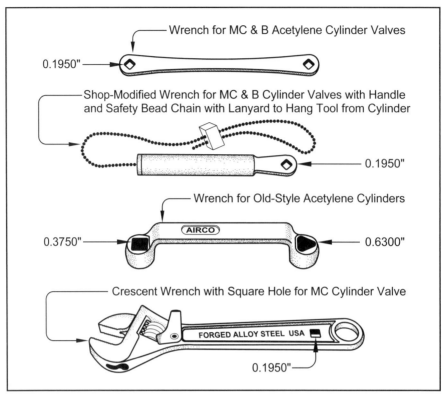

Figure 8-7. Acetylene cylinder-valve wrenches.

Hose Fitting Identification

Like most other fuel gas handling equipment, acetylene fittings have a notch or groove cut in the middle of their outside hexagonal faces. This is a flag indicating that the nut has left-handed threads. See Figure 8-8. Oxygen fittings have right-handed threads, so the chances of mixups are reduced.

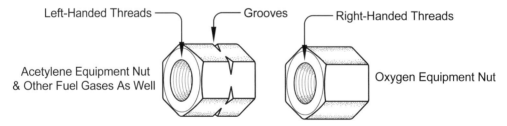

Figure 8-8. Nuts used on acetylene and oxygen equipment. The distinctive groove on the acetylene nut indicates left-handed threads. Most other fuel gas fittings are also grooved.

Stamped Cylinder Markings

The stampings on cylinders indicate which U.S. Department of Transportation specifications the cylinder meets, what type of steel was used in its manufacture, who fabricated the cylinder, and when. The stampings also indicate serial numbers, purchaser, inspector marks, test dates, and empty cylinder weight. See these markings in Figures 8-9 and 8-10.

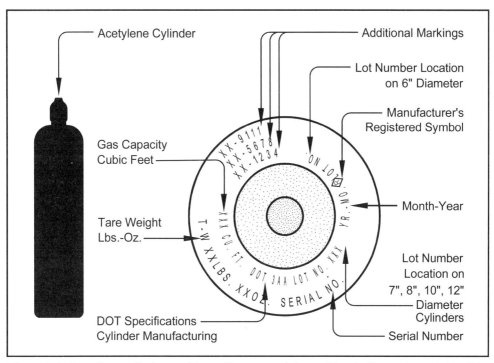

Figure 8-9. Acetylene cylinder markings. The tare weight marking indicates the weight of the cylinder—including its porous filler, acetone, and valve—when empty of gas.

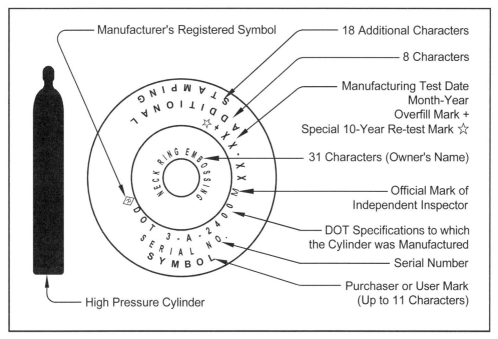

Figure 8-10. High-pressure cylinder markings for oxygen or shielding gases. The type of gas the cylinder contains is found on the adhesive label on the cylinder.

- The oldest date stamped on the cylinder indicates the month and year of manufacture. Subsequent dates, usually at five year intervals, indicate when mandatory hydrostatic pressure testing was performed and by whom.

- The steel stamp marking "DOT-3A-2400" indicates that the cylinder was made to meet DOT specifications, the "3A" denotes chrome manganese steel (or "AA" for molybdenum steel) and the "2400" is the maximum filling pressure of the cylinder in psi.

- The neck ring embossing has the owner's name. Cylinder ownership can be controversial. See the in-depth discussion on ownership on pages 182–184 of this chapter.

Cylinder Colors

Although some cylinders, such as medical oxygen cylinders, are painted green or have a green band, the only sure way to determine the contents of a compressed gas cylinder is to *read* the adhesive label on it. This label is required by law and should not be removed. Do not go by cylinder color as there is no real color code. Unlike civilian industry, the U.S. Armed Forces *do* color code their cylinders.

Cylinder Sizes

Figure 8-11 shows high-pressure cylinder sizes spanning from 23–190 pounds in weight. In addition to oxygen, other gases such as helium, hydrogen, nitrogen, carbon dioxide and argon are supplied in the same type of high-pressure cylinders. These cylinders are rotary forged, meaning that they are formed in a red-hot plastic state from a single steel billet, unlike acetylene cylinders which are usually fabricated from several pieces of steel.

Figure 8-12 shows common acetylene cylinder sizes. Small cylinders are suitable for refrigeration repairman who must climb ladders with OAW equipment, but the limited capacity of these cylinders makes them impractical for most work. For example, a 75 ft^3 oxygen cylinder, which weights 44 pounds empty, would last slightly more than an hour while cutting $^1/_8$" steel plate. In general, the mid-sized cylinders offer the best compromise of economy and convenience.

High-pressure gas cylinders are sometimes called *bottles*. The term oxygen bottle is used in the medical industry to refer to the small oxygen cylinders used with portable oxygen units.

In addition to *Compressed Gas Association (CGA)* standards, independent testing labs, such as *Underwriters Laboratories*, may place additional requirements on the design and performance of cylinders.

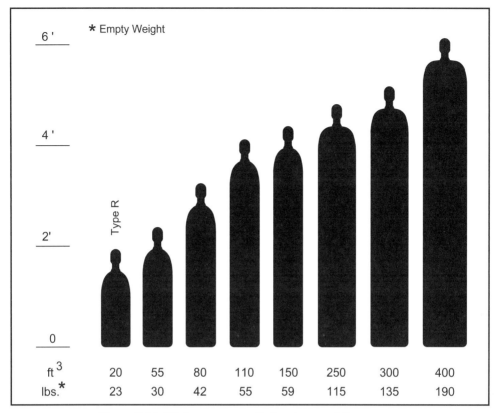

Figure 8-11. High-pressure cylinder sizes used for oxygen,
helium, argon, hydrogen, and carbon dioxide.

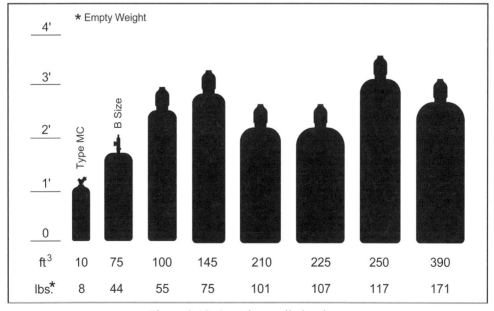

Figure 8-12. Acetylene cylinder sizes.

Cylinder Valves

Table 8-2 shows the valve style required by the Compressed Gas Association on each type of gas cylinder.

Cylinder Contents	Valve Style	Notes
Oxygen	CGA-540	This valve is available in ½-, ¾- and 1-inch models, but the ¾-inch version is the most common.
Inert Shielding Gases	CGA-580	—
Acetylene – MC Size	CGA-200	Threads to the regulator are right-handed on this valve. All other acetylene valves have left-handed threads to regulators. Uses separate valve wrench.
Acetylene – B Size	CGA-520	Uses a separate valve wrench.
Acetylene ≥ 75 ft^3	CGA-300 or CGA-510	—

Table 8-2. CGA valve style requirements for compressed gas cylinders.

Cylinder Ownership & Gas Distributor Practices

Compressed gas cylinders are available three ways:

- *Outright sale of the cylinder* with the right to exchange it for a filled one of equal size after paying for a refill. This is the most economical choice in the long run and is the most common type of ownership today. These cylinders do not have neck rings embossed with the distributor's or the seller's name.

- *Cylinders can be rented by the day, week, month or year.* This arrangement is excellent when the cylinders are not needed for long-term use. These rentals carry neck rings embossed with the distributor's name.

- *Cylinders can be leased for 99 years for a one-time fee.* In this situation, the customer never actually owns the cylinders. Although at one time all size cylinders were leased, today usually only large cylinders—those over 80 ft^3—are leased. These leased cylinders have neck rings embossed with the distributor's name.

Many factors underlie the current issues of cylinder ownership:

- As old welders like to say, "Compressed gas cylinders are the opposite of jewelry boxes." This is because, unlike jewelry boxes, cylinders are worth much more than their contents. Cylinders are valuable assets, usually *corporate* assets, and, depending on the gas, may be worth 5–8 times more than the cost of their contents. Cylinders also have very long lives; many have been in use for over fifty years.

- The welding supply and compressed gas distribution business has been undergoing a series of consolidations over the last 15 years as larger companies purchase smaller independent businesses. This consolidation continues as billion-dollar international corporations purchase mom-and-pop local and regional distributorships, replacing the small business owners who personally knew their customers and their needs with hourly clerks who do not know the business.

- Not only are large corporations buying small independent distributors, large corporations are also buying smaller, older corporations. In several instances, four or five levels of ownership have collapsed into one when a corporation buys a corporation that buys another corporation until the head office is nearly impossible to locate.

- Many of these merged businesses have leased or rented cylinders over many years so there are hundreds of thousands of cylinders in customers' hands. These cylinders usually have the names of the old merged and now defunct distributors in raised letters on their neck rings. A large number of these cylinders have been refilled or exchanged dozens of times over the years and passed on to heirs as their original owners died. Now here's the important part: Cylinders that carry embossed neck rings legally belong to the successor corporations despite the long time—possibly decades—they have been in the customer's possession.

- Today, only half of the compressed gas cylinders in existence have been bar coded, and it will take another 25 years to mark the remainder. Bar coding not only makes it easier to track ownership, hydro testing, rental and leasing fees, it can also track ownership and identify a cylinder as a valuable corporate asset. Despite each cylinder having a stamped serial number, ownership is still hard to prove because most records have been lost in the process of consolidation.

Although U.S. Department of Transport regulations, namely Title 49 §CFR 173.301–309, governs the use, transport, cylinder design, and testing, (along with some state laws); corporate, regional and industry practices vary widely. In fact, one of the largest gas distribution corporations has different practices in different regions of the U.S.

For decades, virtually any compressed gas cylinder could be exchanged for a filled one of the same size without question or paperwork. As the number of welding gas supply companies shrinks, the surviving giants often enforce the DOT requirement that "A cylinder filled with a hazardous material may not be offered for transportation unless it was filled by the owner of the cylinder or with the owner's consent." Here is the consequence of this:

- If you do not have proof of cylinder ownership or your 99-year lease paperwork, some welding supply stores will refuse to fill your cylinders. Thus, it is important to keep receipts which show ownership for when you exchange empty cylinders for filled ones.

- If the neck ring of your cylinder has an embossed distributor's name on it—even a long-defunct name—the successor corporation's store may decline to fill it, hydro test it, or swap it for a filled cylinder. Sometimes they actually claim the cylinder as their own. Usually these stores do not have access to the records to determine if the cylinder is still on a 99-year lease, but because the neck ring has their name on it, they confiscate the cylinder claiming it as their corporate property. You may still be on a valid lease, but if you cannot prove it, your cylinder may be essentially useless despite the fact that very few 99-year leases have expired.

However, there are still many dealers who *will* swap neck-ring-embossed cylinders, especially if you are a large or long-time customer.

Some customers with access to large lathes, chuck up their cylinders and turn off the embossing. Others put their cylinders on rotary tables and remove the embossing during several revolutions with an abrasive flap wheel. With a quick coat of paint—the ownership problem is solved!

Old & New Cylinders

A very annoying practice that is worth mentioning almost ranks as a bait-and-switch. Some gas distributors try to sell you a brand-new cylinder for more money than a cylinder with previous use—an "old" one. But since most cylinders cannot be refilled immediately on site, chances are that you will exchange your "brand new" cylinder for an "old" one when you get your first refill. Also, if you exchange an empty but nearly new cylinder for a filled cylinder, make sure that the hydro test date is as far off as the date of the cylinder you turned in because hydro testing is usually done at the customer's expense.

Section IV – Cylinder Pressure Regulators

Regulator Function

Regulators reduce the pressures of welding gases from the very high pressures inside cylinders to the low pressures needed by torches. In addition, as the cylinder supply pressure falls with gas consumption, the regulator maintains the constant pressure needed at the torch. For example, an oxygen cylinder may contain oxygen at 2250 psi and the torch requires only about 4–6 psi to operate. Similarly, a full acetylene tank may contain gas at 225 psi and the torch needs fuel gas at 4–6 psi.

Single-Stage Regulators

Single-stage regulators are the most common and least expensive pressure regulators. The balance of forces on each side of the diaphragm and attached stem perform the pressure regulation as shown in Figure 8-13.

There are four forces acting on the diaphragm and stem which work to open and close the regulator poppet valve. The combined forces of the *large upper spring* and *atmospheric pressure* act to *open* the regulator valve and admit gas into the regulator and hoses. Working in the opposite direction, the combined forces of the *high-pressure gas* on the lower side of the diaphragm and the *small stem spring* act to *close* the regulator.

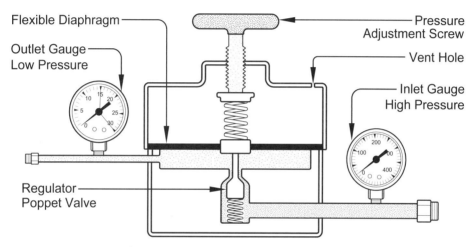

Figure 8-13. Single-stage pressure regulator.

When the pressure adjustment screw is unscrewed (or in the up position as in the above diagram), there is little pressure exerted downward on the diaphragm by the large spring, so the regulator stays closed. When the adjustment screw is tightened downward to increase regulator pressure, the increased pressure on the attached spring exerts more pressure on the flexible diaphragm and opens the valve, admitting high-pressure gas into the lower chamber and hose. As gas continues to enter this chamber, the pressure in the chamber rises. When it rises above the pressure called for, the high-pressure gas in the lower chamber partially or fully closes the poppet valve to maintain the desired pressure.

Two-Stage Regulators

A *two-stage regulator*, as shown in Figure 8-14, is basically two single-stage regulators connected in series inside the same housing. The total pressure drop is split across the two regulator stages. The first-stage pressure is factory-set and the second-stage pressure is user-set. The advantage of the two-stage regulator is that a higher volume of gas can be withdrawn from the cylinder with less pressure fluctuation at the torch than is possible with a single-stage regulator.

The combination of two regulators working in series maintains a very constant torch pressure over wide cylinder pressure changes. The disadvantage of two-stage regulators is cost. Two-stage pressure regulators are only essential when large volumes of gas are needed as when using multiple welding stations or when using rosebud tips.

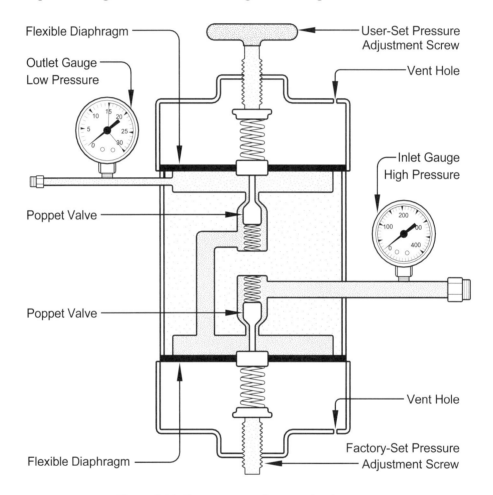

Figure 8-14. Two-stage regulators maintain a more
constant pressure at the torch as the cylinder empties.

Installing Regulators

Steps for installing oxygen and acetylene pressure regulators on full cylinders:

1. Put on welding safety equipment: tinted safety goggles or face shield (shade 2), cotton or wool shirt and pants, high-top shoes and gloves.

2. To prevent contamination, make sure the valves on old, empty cylinders are fully closed and their valve protection covers are securely screwed in place. Remove these empty cylinders from the work area and secure them from tipping during the wait for a refill shipment. Then, secure the *new*, full cylinders to a welding cart, building column, or other solid anchor to prevent tipping during storage or use, and remove their safety caps.

3. Momentarily open the oxygen cylinder valve to the atmosphere and quickly reclose the valve. This is known as *cracking* a valve. Cracking serves to blow out dust and grit from the valve port and to prevent debris from entering the regulators and torch.

4. With a clean, oil-free cloth, wipe off the cylinder valve-to-regulator fittings on *both* cylinders to remove dirt and grit from the connection faces and threads. Repeat this cleaning process on the threads and faces of *both* regulators. *Never* use oil on high-pressure gas fittings. Oxygen at high pressures can accelerate the combustion of oil into an explosion.

5. Check to see that both the oxygen and acetylene regulator pressure adjustment screws are unscrewed, then attach each regulator to its respective cylinder. Snug up the connections with a wrench. *Tip:* Oxygen cylinder-to-regulator threads are *right-handed*, as are oxygen hose-to-torch fittings. Acetylene cylinder-to-regulator threads and acetylene hose-to-torch screw fittings are *left-handed*. This arrangement prevents putting the wrong gas into a regulator or torch connection. *Another Tip:* The threads on MC-size acetylene cylinder valves are right-handed, an exception to the rule of left-handed threads for fuel gas fittings.

6. Standing so the cylinders are between you and the regulators, S-L-O-W-L-Y open the oxygen cylinder valve until the valve stem hits the upper seal. That's when the valve stops turning counterclockwise. Open the oxygen cylinder valve until it hits the upper valve stop and will turn no farther. Also, standing so the cylinders are between you and the regulators, gradually open the acetylene cylinder valve not more than one turn. If there is an old-style removable wrench on the acetylene cylinder, keep it on the valve in case you must close the valve in an emergency.

7. Make sure the high-pressure—cylinder side—gauges indicate about 225 psi in the acetylene cylinder and 2250 psi in the oxygen cylinder. Cylinder pressures will vary with ambient temperature. The pressures given above are for full cylinders at 70°F.

8. Separately purge each torch hose of air. Open the oxygen valve on the torch about three-quarters of a turn, then screw in the pressure control screw on the oxygen regulator to your initial pressure setting—about 6 psi. After several seconds, close the torch valve. Do the same with the acetylene hose. This is done for two reasons: (1) To make sure the torch is lighting on pure oxygen and acetylene, not a mixture with air, and (2) To set the regulators for the correct pressure while the gas is flowing through them. Caution: *Never* adjust the acetylene regulator pressure above 15 psi as an explosive disassociation of the acetylene could occur.

9. Recheck the low-pressure gauge pressures for each regulator to make sure that the working pressures are *not* rising. If the working pressure does rise with the torch valves turned off, the regulator valve seal is leaking, causing *regulator creep*. Immediately shut down the cylinders at

the cylinder valves. Continued leaking can lead to a regulator diaphragm rupture and a serious accident. Repair or replace the defective regulator.

10. Using an oil-free leak testing solution such as Leak-Tec, test the system for leaks at the cylinder-to-regulator fittings and at all hose fittings. Bubbles indicate leaks. Do not use soapy water for leak testing because it may contain fat that can decompose spontaneously on exposure to oxygen. This can cause an explosion.

Section V – Torches, Tips & Hoses

Torch Designs

The most common oxyacetylene torch is based on a torch body design on which welding torch tips, a cutting head, or a rosebud tip can be mounted. See Figure 8-15.

Here are the uses for these attachments:

- *Torch tips* with different orifice sizes provide a range of flame sizes.

- *Cutting heads,* also called *cutting attachments* (see *Chapter 10 – Cutting Processes*), are used for cutting steel.

- *Rosebud tips* produce much larger flames than welding torch tips and are used for heating metals prior to bending, for brazing large work, for preheating before welding or for heat treating.

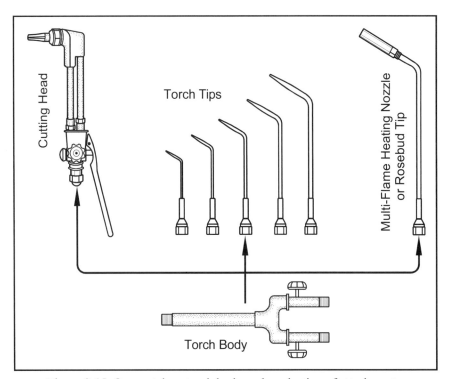

Figure 8-15. Oxyacetylene torch body and a selection of attachments.

Torches for welding, brazing, and bending are available in a wide range of sizes producing flames under an inch long to over 6 inches long. The choice of torch is determined by the range of flame sizes, the weight of the torch, and the convenience of the gas control valves. Figure 8-16 shows three different torches with tips for welding, brazing or bending.

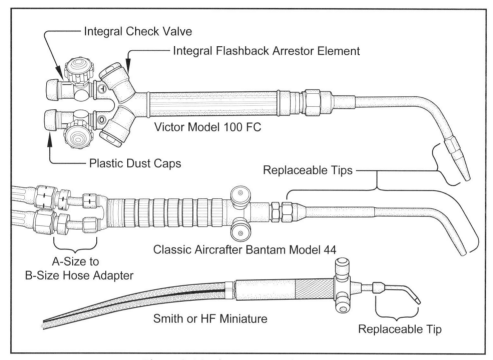

Figure 8-16. Three oxyacetylene torches.

Torch Tip Sizes

Matching flame size—and the resulting amount of heat—to the thickness of the metal in the weld or braze is important. Too much heat and the base metal around the weld melts, too little and there is inadequate heat to melt the weld metal for full penetration.

There is no industry standard for torch tip size; many torch manufacturers have their own numbering system although some share the same systems. Cross-reference tables compare each manufacturer's tip sizes with numbered drill sizes. Common tip orifices range from #71 to #26 drill sizes, or 0.026–0.147" diameter. Table 8-3 lists the orifice sizes from some major torch manufacturers.

Hoses

Hoses for oxyacetylene welding and cutting are coded red for acetylene or other fuel gases, and green or black for oxygen.

Caution: All possibility of permitting gas to enter the wrong hose and regulator must be prevented because it can lead to a deadly explosion. For this reason, each gas hose must be *separately*, not simultaneously, purged on shutdown.

Wire Drill №	Victor	Harbour Freight Micro Torch	Smith Equipment Little Torch	Harris	Linde ESAB Oxweld Prest-O-Lite	Meco Midget	Decimal Inch
97			2				0.0059
85		12	3				0.0110
80						00	0.0135
78		13			1		0.0160
76		14	4			0	0.0200
75	000			0			0.0220
74		15			2		0.0225
73						0.5	0.0240
71				1			0.0260
70	00					1.5	0.0280
69			5				0.0292
67						1.5	0.0320
65	0			2		2.5	0.0350
64					4		0.0360
63			6			3.5	0.0370
60	1						0.0400
58				3	6	3.0	0.0420
57							0.0430
56	2		7			4.0	0.0465
55				4	9		0.0520
54					12	4.5	0.0550
53	3			5	15		0.0595
52						5.0	0.0635
51				6			0.0670
50					20		0.0700
49	4					5.5	0.0730
48				7			0.0760
47						6.0	0.0780
45				8	30		0.0820
44						6.5	0.0860
43	5			9			0.0890
42						7.0	0.0930
40				10	40		0.0980
36	6						0.1060
35				13			0.1100

Table 8-3. Oxyacetylene torch tip size comparison for several different torch suppliers.

Section VI – Torch Operation

Torch Strikers

Use a striker to light torches; it will keep your fingers away from the flame. The strikers in Figure 8-17 have steel cups surrounding their flint and steel igniters. Light the torch by filling this cup with acetylene, and *then* squeezing the striker. The torch will light every time. Many inexperienced welders waive the striker in front of the torch tip and squeeze the striker. This procedure will not always work. The use of a butane cigarette or fireplace lighter is not a good method for torch ignition because it can cause a large fire ball or explosion with the potential power of a half-stick of dynamite.

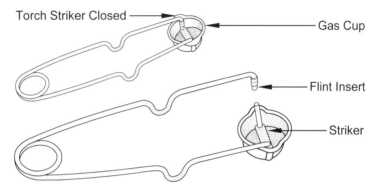

Torch Striker Closed ——— · Gas Cup · Flint Insert · Striker

Figure 8-17. Torch striker. Fill the gas cup with acetylene and then squeeze the striker.

Flames

Different ratios of oxygen and acetylene make three different types of flames:

- *Neutral flames* result when there is just enough oxygen to burn all the acetylene present. This flame has the least effect on weld pool metal because only carbon monoxide and hydrogen combustion products result. A neutral flame is most frequently used in welding common materials.

  Combustion in a neutral flame is a two-step process:

  1. First, the acetylene breaks down into carbon and hydrogen and the carbon reacts with cylinder-supplied oxygen to form carbon monoxide and hydrogen. This reaction takes place at the boundary between the extremely bright blue inner cone and the nearly invisible pale blue outer flame. The inner cone has sharp, well defined edges.

  2. The second stage of combustion occurs when the carbon monoxide from the first stage reacts, or burns, with the atmospheric oxygen drawn into the flame to form water. This secondary combustion process forms the nearly invisible outer flame.

- *Carburizing flames,* also called *reducing flames,* result when there is an excess of acetylene gas over the amount that can be burned by the oxygen present. The opposite of an oxidizing flame, carburizing flames add carbon to the weld pool and can change its metallurgy, usually adversely.

A carburizing flame can be used when *sooting* metal, that is, adjusting the torch flame with excess acetylene to produce intense carbon. This carbon, when deposited onto metal, can prevent braze metal from adhering to it. This is one of the ways to mask off areas where you do not want braze filler metal to stick.

Beginning with a neutral flame, if the proportion of acetylene is increased, a less intense pale blue outer cone forms outside the inner, brighter blue cone. And as the acetylene is further increased, the pale blue outer cone transitions to a white feather or ragged outer flame just beyond the inner cone. This white feather consists of incandescent particles of carbon that have not been burned in the inner cone. Further increases in acetylene eliminates both the inner cone and the white feather. A bright orange sooty flame results.

- *Oxidizing flames* result when there is an excess of oxygen over acetylene. This flame will change the metallurgy of the weld pool metal by lowering its carbon content as the carbon in the steel is converted to carbon dioxide. An oxidizing flame is often used in braze welding or in fusion welding of heavy, thick parts using brass or bronze rod. In these applications, weld pool contamination by carbon is not a concern. An oxidizing flame is significantly hotter than the other two flames, but it is less useful because it introduces more contaminants into the weld pool.

Beginning with a neutral flame, if the oxygen proportion is gradually increased, the intense pale blue inner cone will become brighter and smaller. With further increases, the flame will become noisy, sometimes called *angry*.

Adjusting for a Neutral Flame

With the typical shop torch there is no way to know the valve settings that will produce a neutral flame, so for safety, torches are lit on pure acetylene and then adjusted to a neutral flame, the most common flame for welding operations.

Here are the steps to light the torch and adjust it to a neutral flame:

1. After putting on safety equipment—safety glasses, long-sleeve cotton shirt, long pants—open the acetylene valve no more than $^1/_{16}$ turn and use a torch striker to ignite the gas coming out of the tip. A sooty, smoky orange flame will result as in Figure 8-18 (A). The falling bits of soot are known in the trade as *paratroopers*. These make a big mess inside the shop.

2. Continue to open the acetylene valve until the flame stops smoking and releasing soot. Another way to judge the proper amount of acetylene is to open the acetylene valve until the flame jumps away from the torch tip, leaving about a $^1/_{16}$" gap as in Figure 8-18 (B). Then close the valve until the flame moves back to the torch tip, closing the gap. Sometimes it is possible to add enough acetylene to eliminate sooting without the flame gap.

3. Open the oxygen valve *slowly*. As the oxygen is increased, the orange acetylene flame turns purple, and a smaller, white inner cone will begin to form, as in Figure 18-8 (C). With the further addition of oxygen, the inner cone goes from having ragged edges to sharp, clearly defined edges, as in Figure 8-18 (D). The flame is now neutral and adding more oxygen will make it an oxidizing flame, which is usually undesirable. Just beyond the inner cone is the hottest part of the flame. The inner cone is where the optimum mixture of oxygen and acetylene burn. Any unburned acetylene burns in the outer envelope of the flame with oxygen from the atmosphere. See Figure 8-19.

Should a larger flame be needed while keeping the same tip size, the acetylene can be increased and the oxygen further increased to keep the edges of the inner cone sharp. This process of increasing the acetylene, then the oxygen is usually done in several cycles before the maximum flame from a given tip is achieved.

Caution: Adjusting the flame below the minimum flow rate for the tip orifice permits the flame to ignite *inside* the nozzle. This is called *backfire,* for the popping sound it makes, and this is an extremely dangerous condition. If a smaller flame is needed, use a smaller torch tip. See *Section VII – Hazards & Safety Equipment* for more on backfires.

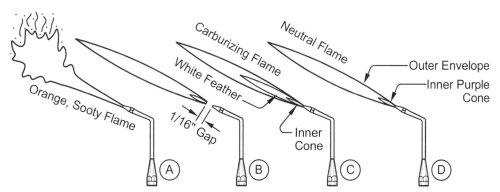

Figure 8-18. Steps in adjusting for a neutral flame. Torch is lit on pure acetylene (A), acetylene is increased until flame stops smoking, often flame will jump away from the torch tip and acetylene must be reduced slightly so flame reconnects with the torch tip (B). As oxygen is increased, the flame color changes from orange to bright white or yellow and the intense white oxygen feather develops from the tip (C). Finally, as the oxygen is increased further, a neutral flame develops, the white feather disappears and only the sharply defined inner purple cone surrounded by the outer envelope appears from the torch tip (D).

Caution: Extending beyond the tip of the flame's outer envelope, there is an invisible projection of very hot gas extending from 6–15" depending on the size of the tip and flame. It is important to bear this in mind because even though you may be working on the front edge of the workbench or welding table, this invisible hot gas stream has the ability to set fires and cause burns well beyond the torch's visible flame.

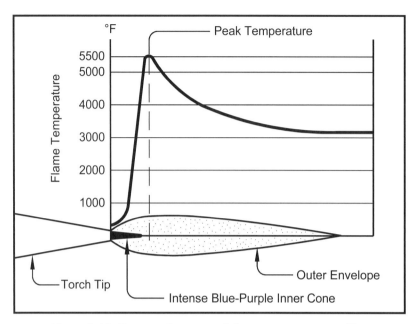

Figure 8-19. Oxyacetylene neutral flame temperature profile.

Flame Adjustment for Small Torches

Small torches, sometimes called *jewelers' torches*, require oxygen and acetylene pressures of 2–4 psi. Because these very low pressures are at the bottom end of the oxygen and acetylene hose-side pressure gauges, these pressures are hard to read and the gauges are usually inaccurate. These small torches benefit from another approach to setting their regulator pressures that completely avoids the use of the pressure gauges.

Here is how it's done:

1. After putting on the usual safety equipment, close the oxygen valve on the torch, and open the acetylene valve on the torch all the way.

2. With the oxygen regulator screw out—turned off—hold the torch so the tip points vertically about 6" away from your ear. Very slowly screw in the acetylene regulator screw until you hear a small hiss from the tip. This tells you that gas is flowing from the torch.

3. With the torch tip pointed away from you, use a torch striker to light the torch on acetylene.

4. Gradually, turn in the screw adjustment on the oxygen regulator, and using the pressure adjustments on *both* regulators, adjust for the desired flame.

This technique not only avoids the problems of reading a gas pressure on the low-end of a gauge's pressure range, it avoids the accumulation of pressure in the hose, which acts as a storage tank. This accumulation slows the changes at the torch end of the lines and makes it easy to undershoot or overshoot the desired pressure. Because pressure adjustment occurs at the regulator end of the supply hoses, this delay is eliminated.

Oxyacetylene Torch Shut-Down Steps

1. Using the *torch handle valves*, first turn off the oxygen and then the acetylene. Turning off the acetylene first can cause a flashback.

2. Turn off the oxygen and acetylene *cylinder valves*.

3. *Separately*, open and reclose the oxygen and acetylene valves on the torch handle to bleed the remaining gas in the hoses and regulator into the atmosphere. Verify that both the high-pressure and the low-pressure gauges on both regulators indicate zero.

4. Unscrew the *regulator pressure adjustment screws* on both cylinders in preparation for the next use of the equipment. The regulator screws should be loose, but not about to fall from their threads.

Section VII – Hazards & Safety Equipment

Backfire

If sparks from the weld puddle deposit carbon *inside* the torch nozzle or on the tip face, or if there is a momentary interruption of gas flow by contact of the torch tip against the work, this can cause the torch flame to go out with a loud pop, a snap, or a series of pops like a machine gun. As mentioned before, this is *backfire*. The torch can be relighted immediately, or it may relight itself if its gas stream is directed against hot metal.

The biggest hazard with backfire is that the detonation from the tip can blow molten weld metal 5–10' from the weld and burn someone. Also, a series of repeated, sustained backfires can overheat the tip, the torch or both, permanently damaging them.

However, if the torch backfires repeatedly without contact with the work, the cause must be investigated. Backfiring may be due to inadequate gas pressures which do not produce a high enough gas flow to keep the flame burning outside the torch. Backfiring may also be due to a loose torch tip or to dirt on the cutting nozzle seats.

Flashback

If the flame on the torch tip goes out and burns back inside the torch, there will usually be a loud hissing or squealing noise. This is called *flashback,* a potentially dangerous condition and a sign that there is something very wrong with the torch or your operation of it. Even if you only suspect flashback, turn of the torch immediately by shutting off the oxygen and then the acetylene.

Before relighting the torch after a flashback incident, allow it to cool for at least one minute, and check that the gas pressures are within the manufacturer's recommended range for the tip you are using. Then, flush the torch with oxygen to clear out any soot and relight the torch in the standard manner to continue working. If the torch has another flashback, remove it from service and send it out for repairs.

An unrecognized and extended flashback condition can allow the torch flame to begin burning back inside the hoses and possibly reach a regulator. This represents an extreme danger. Again, if you suspect this, shut of the oxygen, then the acetylene. *Burning in the hoses, regulators, or cylinders is likely to cause an accident with burns, a major fire, explosion, shrapnel injuries and death. Gases should only mix in the torch mixing chamber.* See Figure 8-20.

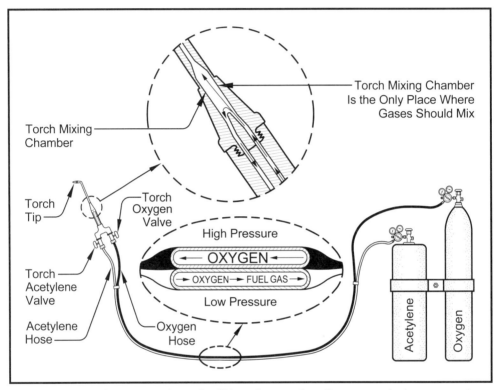

Figure 8-20. When oxygen forces itself into the acetylene lines, an explosion can result.

Flashbacks occur through operator error, such as turning on both the acetylene and the oxygen with the torch tip blocked, or through regulator failure. Either way, an explosive mixture of acetylene and oxygen is forced back toward the cylinders where it may enter:

- One hose, or
- One hose and one regulator, or
- One hose, one regulator, and one cylinder.

A caution worth repeating: If this happens, the stage is set for a catastrophic explosion. When the torch is lit, this explosive mixture will go off.

Torch Tip Cleaning

Torch tips should be cleaned whenever backfire occurs, when the flame splits, or when the flame no longer has a sharply defined cone. See the tip cleaner in Figure 8-21. Because a tip cleaning wire is really a small reamer, if used improperly, a tip cleaner can eventually cause bell-mouthing and destruction of the torch tip.

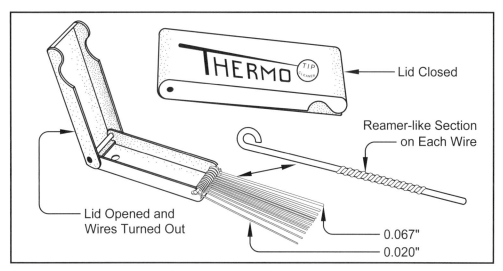

Figure 8-21. Tip cleaner. Unless carefully used, tip cleaners will do more harm than good.

To clean a torch tip, select the largest tip-cleaning wire that fits easily into the torch nozzle and use the serrated portion to remove any foreign material. Do not enlarge the existing hole. Then, touch up the face of the torch tip with a fine file or emery cloth to remove any adhering dirt, and finally, use compressed air or cylinder oxygen to blow out the torch tip. Never use a twist drill to clean a torch tip because it definitely will cause bell-mouthing.

Flashback Arrestor Locations

Flashback is easily prevented with the use of flashback arrestors. One arrestor is needed to protect each gas stream, and can be installed in any one of four locations:

- Many torches have *integral flashback arrestors* consisting of both a check valve and a flame arrestor. Refer to the torch in Figure 8-16 (top). This is an excellent safety enhancement, but it does increase torch weight. Many older torches do not have flashback arrestors and the same is true for very small torches, even the modern ones.

- Flashback arrestors may be *added to the hose end* of the torch when the torch does not have integral arrestors, but it makes the torch heavier and also clumsier.

- When there are long hose runs with a quick-connect connector between the two lengths, an arrestor can be inserted between them. This is a better location than on the regulator.

- Flashback arrestors are often *mounted on the cylinder regulator* between its output fitting and the welding hose. The arrestor in Figure 8-22 fits onto a Y-type fitting. The advantage of this mounting location is that the arrestor adds no weight to the torch itself, and the Y-fitting allows two torches to run from one regulator without changing fittings, but this mounting method does allow the flashback to get much closer to the regulator and cylinder.

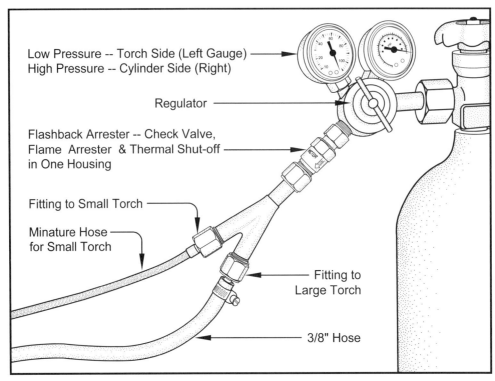

Low Pressure -- Torch Side (Left Gauge)
High Pressure -- Cylinder Side (Right)

Regulator

Flashback Arrester -- Check Valve,
Flame Arrester & Thermal Shut-off
in One Housing

Fitting to Small Torch

Minature Hose
for Small Torch

Fitting to
Large Torch

3/8" Hose

Figure 8-22. A flashback arrestor can be mounted between the regulator and the torch hose.
A Y-type fitting allows two torches to be run from one regulator without changing fittings.
This arrangement avoids having to fasten and unfasten hoses and fittings and protects two
torches with one arrestor, but it does allow potential danger closer to the cylinders than
if the arrestor was at the torch end of the hose.

Check Valve & Arrestor Designs

In the order of increasing protection from flashbacks and gas hose explosions:

- *Reverse-flow check valves* permit gas flow in one direction—from the cylinder to the torch. A ball bearing and a spring does the job. See Figure 8-23 (top). These offer some protection, but are not the best choice.

- *Reverse-flow check valves plus a flame arrestor* offer more protection than just a reverse-flow check valve. The flame arrestor element consists of a cylinder of stainless steel particles that have been compressed, heated, and fused together to form a porous cylinder. It allows gas to flow through it, but not a flame front. The flame-arrestor cylinder blocks fire by both lowering the temperature of the flame front by absorbing its heat and by forcing the flame through small passages. These devices are about the diameter of the gas hoses and about $1^{3}/_{4}$" long. See Figure 8-23 (middle).

- *Reverse-flow check valves, flame arrestor plus thermally activated, spring-loaded shutoff valves* are the best choice for flashback protection. The thermal shutoff valves in the arrestors close when sensing a fire. Figure 8-23 (bottom) shows one of these arrestors, and Figure 8-24 shows the type of information found on their labels.

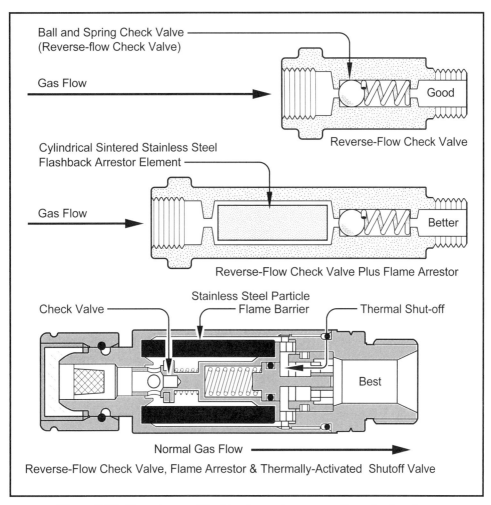

Figure 8-23. Three types of flashback arrestor reverse-flow check-valves.

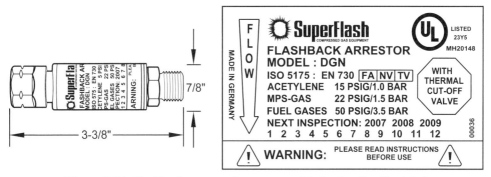

Figure 8-24. Flashback arrestor for oxygen with the details of its label.

Flashback on Rosebud Tips

The most likely cause of flashback when using a rosebud tip for heating metal prior to welding, bending, or brazing is low acetylene gas pressure. This low pressure does not push the oxygen/fuel mixture *out* of the tip faster than the flame can burn back on itself *inside* the tip. Increasing the gas pressures will solve this problem.

Section VIII – Oxyacetylene Welding

Mastering the Process—or Not

As other welding processes with higher deposition rates and lower skill requirements have become available, oxyacetylene welding has declined in importance. While oxyacetylene outfits are found in many shops, they are more often used for heating, bending, brazing, straightening, and cutting than for welding.

Here are the reasons for this decline:

- Oxyacetylene is the most difficult of all welding processes to master. Considerable hand-eye coordination is required. Besides having to manipulate the torch and filler metal, the welder must select the proper nozzle, adjust the torch flame, and set the gas pressures. Because the torch flame has invisible hot gases surrounding it, the welder must also make more subtle adjustments with the torch as he moves along the weld—and heat builds up in the work—than are needed in other welding processes. The average beginning welding student needs over 40 hours of practice to get basic control over the weld pool, and many more hours to learn vertical, overhead, and out-of-position welding. This is why there are relatively few new welders proficient in oxyacetylene welding. For these reasons many junior college welding courses no longer require oxyacetylene training. Although this training makes it easier to learn GTAW because it teaches weld pool control, compared with the other available welding processes, oxyacetylene is less useful and less industrially productive.

- Oxyacetylene has weld metal deposition rates much lower than GMAW and FCAW. These two processes can put down a lot of filler metal and make welds as sound as oxyacetylene, and require less welder training.

- Oxyacetylene's low deposition rate requires more heat time on the joint than electrically-based welding processes. This low travel speed, in combination with its large flame footprint, results in much higher heat input to the workpiece. This, in turn, increases the width of the HAZ, annealing more of the heat treatment in the base metal, weakening it.

Oxyacetylene Applications

Provided the welder has the skills, an oxyacetylene outfit can perform many manufacturing plant repair and maintenance operations.

- OAW can weld thin sheet, tubing, and small-diameter pipe. This includes auto body fabrication and repair, and tubular frames for race cars and light planes. These welds can also be performed by GTAW and GMAW.

- In-field operations for natural gas distribution systems remain one of the most common OAW applications. Not only can oxyacetylene weld gas lines, it can heat them red hot so they can be pinched closed with an Adams clamp while the internal natural gas pressure is on them.

- Although oxyacetylene was used for many years to weld auto exhaust systems, the risk of fire and insurance regulations have moved this work to GMAW, which has no open flames, making this work much safer.
- Off-the-vehicle custom fabrication of auto and motorcycle exhaust manifolds is one of the best oxyacetylene applications. Many fabricators cut, bend, and fit the exhaust tubing into place, then tack it with GTAW before completing the job with oxyacetylene. This technique has the advantage of annealing the welds and tubing, which prevents cracking under thermal cycling.

Poor Choices for Oxyacetylene

- OAW is not economical for welding thick sections as compared with arc welding, flux-cored arc welding or gas metal arc welding.
- Positioning and controlling the OAW torch flame inside a relatively small cavity can be difficult or impossible.
- Welding very small components together is better done with ultrasonic welding, spot welding or GTAW depending on the component size.

Metals Oxyacetylene Can Weld

- Copper
- Bronze
- Lead
- Low-alloy steels
- Cast steel

Aluminum and stainless steel can be welded provided one or more of the following steps are taken: preheat, postheat, use of fluxes, or special welding techniques.

Aluminum Welding Problems

- Aluminum does not change color prior to melting, so it requires extra welder skill to control heat input to avoid melting the work.
- Aluminum has *hot shortness*—lack of strength at high temperatures.
- Exposed aluminum has a very thin oxide layer that requires the use of flux. Also, this oxide layer does not let the welder see a wet-looking molten weld pool.

OAW Filler Metal Selection

Usually the filler metal is a close match to the base metal. Sometimes the filler metal has deoxidizers added which improve the weld more than just a base metal match. Rod diameters vary from $1/16$–$3/8$" diameter.

The prefix *R* indicates that a rod is for a non-electrical welding process. See Table 8-3.

AWS Rod Classification	Minimum Tensile Strength (ksi)	Elongation in 1" (minimum %)
R45	—	—
R60	60	20
R65	65	16
R100	100	14

Table 8-3. Gas welding rods for low-carbon steel.

For all metals, begin oxyacetylene welding by removing all surface dirt, scale, oxide, grease and paint.

Refer to Table 8-4 for technique, flux, flame and suggested welding or brazing method.

Metal Welded	Technique & Potential Problems	Flux Used	Flame Type	Suggested Rod
Aluminum	Tack joint before welding. Aluminum does not show color change before melting and has poor hot strength. Remove all flux after welding.	Al flux	SR	Match base metal
Cast Iron, Gray	Preheat to avoid cracking. Weld at dull red heat. Flux applied to rod by dipping hot rod into flux. Allow joint to cool slowly or it will crack.	Borax	N	Cast iron
Cast Iron, Malleable	Welds poorly. Better to braze weld using bronze rods.	Borax	—	Bronze
Steel, Low-Carbon	Weld or braze.	—	N	Steel
Steel, Medium-Carbon	Weld or braze.	—	SR	Steel
Steel, High-Carbon	Weld or braze.	—	R	Steel
Steel, Low-Alloy	Weld or braze.	—	SR	Steel
Steel, Stainless	Weld or braze.	S/S flux	SR	Match base metal

SR = Slightly Reducing   N = Neutral

Table 8-4. Methods for oxyacetylene welding common metals.

Carbon Content

Carbon content determines the weldability of steel and controls the steel's tendency to harden upon rapid cooling. The greater the carbon content, the harder the weld steel will become.

Butt Joint Preparation

Figure 8-25 shows the weld root spacing for $^1/_8$–$^1/_{16}$" butt welds, the simplest and most common oxyacetylene joints. Filler metal is nearly always used because it is very hard to make a full-strength weld by merely butting the pieces tightly, without spacing, and melting their edges together.

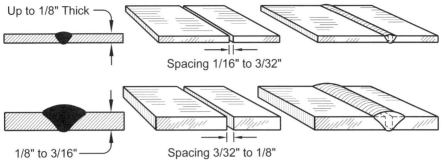

Figure 8-25. Preparation for OAW butt welds.

Weld Profiles

Figure 8-26 shows a correct butt weld profile and the most common defects.

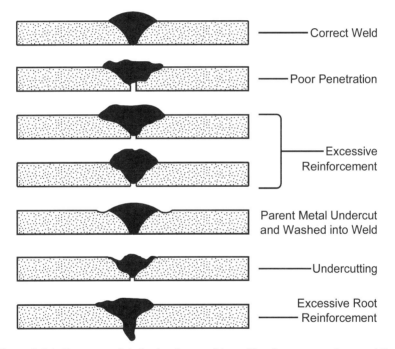

Figure 8-26. Correct and defective butt weld profiles for oxyacetylene welding.

Tips for Oxyacetylene Welding

- Keep the flame neutral. A few alloys may benefit from an oxidizing or reducing flame, but most like it neutral. If the weld produces more sparks than usual, the flame may have become slightly reducing and it must be readjusted.

- Always make secure tack welds to help control distortion and maintain the proper root spacing. Place at least one tack at each end of the bead and one more in the middle. On longer beads, several tacks may be needed.

- Be aware of cold *shuts*, or gaps, inside the weld. Usually they form between the root pass and the finishing, or cover pass, where there is incomplete fusion between the layers. These are hard to spot visually while welding, but nick and bend tests will reveal them.

- Keep the filler metal rod in the outer envelope of the torch flame, but not close to the inner flame. Keeping the rod in the envelope both preheats it for deposition in the weld puddle, and flame gases prevent the rod from oxidizing.

- Use both the filler metal rod and the torch flame to control puddle size. Should the puddle get too large, pull back the torch slightly and slow down the deposition of filler metal.

- If the filler rod gets stuck in the weld bead, melt it loose. Do not try to pull it out.

- Both safety and quality suggest clothes hangers should not be used for welding. Hangers are usually painted or plated and may release toxic fumes as they burn. From a quality standpoint, their metal content is unknown and unlikely to produce a good weld.

- Mastering oxyacetylene welding takes time and practice and cannot be learned in a day. Usually a week or more of full-time practice is needed just to gain control over the torch, filler metal, and puddle to make acceptable welds.

- The best way to learn oxyacetylene welding is from someone who already knows it. You need to see how it's done, not read how it's done. Trying to learn oxyacetylene welding from a book is like trying to learn to golf from a book. It just won't work. Find an experienced pro.

Safety Precautions for Oxyacetylene Equipment

- Never use oxygen in place of compressed air.
- Never use oxygen for starting engines or cleaning clothing.
- Store and use acetylene and propane cylinders valve end up.
- Secure cylinders to prevent them from being knocked over in use.
- Use valve protection caps on cylinders while moving them.
- Never leave a lighted torch unattended.
- When a cylinder is empty, close the valve and mark it *EMPTY*.
- Do not attempt to repair cylinder valves; return them to the gas distributor.
- Never use compressed gas cylinders as rollers.
- Never attempt welding on a compressed gas cylinder.
- Keep power and welding cables away from compressed gas cylinders.
- Prevent sparks from falling on other persons, combustible materials, or falling through cracks in the floor.
- Never carry compressed gas cylinders inside a car or car trunk. This presents a risk of suffocation and explosion.

Chapter 9

Controlling Distortion

People forget how fast you did a job—but they remember how well you did it.
—Howard Newton

What is Weld Distortion?
Welding heat induced shrinkage causes distortion which, in turn, causes permanent changes in the shape and dimensions of workpiece metal and leaves behind residual stresses. Dimensional changes can ruin a part and the residual stresses remaining inside can weaken it. Even if the part bears no external load, the residual stress acts as an initial load on top of what may eventually be imposed, reducing the total load-carrying capacity of the part.

Heating with & without Restraint
- *No Restraint* – First, look at the case where a steel block is slowly and evenly heated and cooled without any restraint. When heated, the metal atoms move apart from each other with great force. If these forces are unrestrained and the heating and subsequent cooling are gradual, the metal will expand when hot and then contract to its original size when cooled. No permanent changes in size and shape will occur. The unrestrained metal cube in Figure 9-1 is an example of this situation. Regardless of its shape, an unrestrained metal object that is gradually heated and cooled will return to its original dimensions on returning to room temperature.

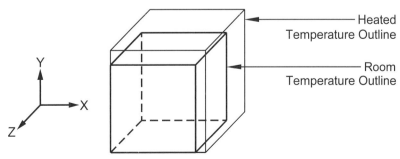

Figure 9-1. Exaggerated three-dimensional changes in an
unrestrained metal cube gradually and evenly heated and cooled.

- *Complete restraint in one dimension* – Figure 9-2 shows a steel cylinder restrained between the jaws of a vise. As the temperature rises, the cylinder expands and its volume increases. Since the cube cannot move horizontally—the x direction—due to the immovable vise jaws at either end, the cube must expand *more* in the y and z dimensions, where it grows radially, becoming fatter. Because expansion in the y and z directions is greater than the elastic properties of the metal, when the metal's yield strength is exceeded, the metal experiences plastic and permanent flow. We say the metal of the cylinder has been *upset*. Although some of the expansion forces were relieved and dissipated by upsetting the metal, some of these expansion forces will remain in the workpiece—like springs under tension—as permanent residual stress.

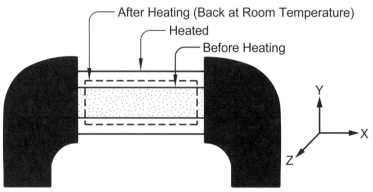

Figure 9-2. Exaggerated three-dimensional changes in
a steel cylinder completely restrained in one dimension.

- *Partial restraint in one dimension* – Figure 9-3 shows a steel cylinder that has been partially restrained by adding a spring between the cylinder and the vise jaw. When the temperature is cycled, partial restraint produces dimensional changes somewhere *between* the no-restraint case and the complete-restraint case. After temperature cycling, the cylinder is fatter and shorter, but does not show as much dimensional change as in the complete-restraint case. Some residual stress may also remain.

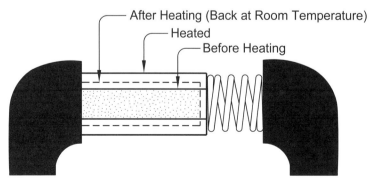

Figure 9-3. Exaggerated three-dimensional changes in a steel
cylinder partially restrained by a spring in one dimension.

Workpiece Restraints Causing Distortion

The examples of restraint forces in Figures 9-2 and 9-3 were caused by the vise jaws that were external to the work. In the following examples, because of uneven heating and cooling, a portion of the *work itself* causes the restraint, and this restraint results in weld-induced distortion.

- *Steel bar with uneven heating* – Figure 9-4 shows a steel bar that has been heated in one area on one side of the bar. This is another case of a change in dimension under partial restraint, similar to that in Figure 9-3, but here the restraint is caused by the cooler metal in the bar. After cooling, the heated side of the bar becomes slightly shorter while the unheated side remains its original length. The bar bends because of these uneven lengths. Some of the expansion force bends the bar and some remains as residual stress as symbolized by the spring in the bottom drawing.

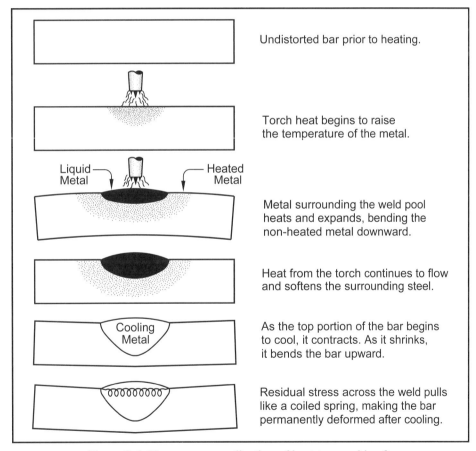

Undistorted bar prior to heating.

Torch heat begins to raise the temperature of the metal.

Liquid Metal — Heated Metal

Metal surrounding the weld pool heats and expands, bending the non-heated metal downward.

Heat from the torch continues to flow and softens the surrounding steel.

Cooling Metal

As the top portion of the bar begins to cool, it contracts. As it shrinks, it bends the bar upward.

Residual stress across the weld pulls like a coiled spring, making the bar permanently deformed after cooling.

Figure 9-4. How uneven application of heat to one side of a steel bar causes permanent bending or distortion.

- *Heated edge of sheet metal* – Figure 9-5 (left) shows a flat sheet metal panel before it is heated. Heating *one* edge of the panel makes it expand and soften while the cool edge does not. When the sheet cools back to room temperature, most of the heat-induced ripples disappear, but the sheet is permanently shorter along the once-heated edge. Uneven heating of the plate and the restraint imposed by its cooler side cause a dimensional change and upsetting. See Figure 9-5 (right).

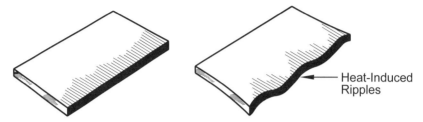

Figure 9-5. Sheet metal panel before heating (left) and rippling while hot (right).

Upsetting will be even more severe if a water spray is used to cool the sheet rapidly. This rapid cooling further prevents the unheated edge from heating and expanding as the heat flows across the panel. Note that what happens during the cooling period is seldom what happens during the heating period. The ripples must be controlled while they are hot, or they will prevent even joints and good welds.

- *Partial cut across a plate by flame cutting or plasma* – Because of differential heating and the restraint caused by the uncut portion of the plate, the *hinge effect* occurs. See Figure 9-6. If two parallel cuts are made simultaneously, the metal between the cuts shows little distortion because heating and expansion is balanced. Dual cutting torches are available to make parallel cuts that eliminate the hinge effect. Refer to Figure 10-12.

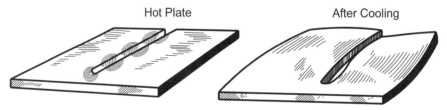

Figure 9-6. Hinge effect in partially cut steel plate.

- *Weld bead applied along a bar* – Figure 9-7 shows a single weld bead placed lengthwise along a straight steel bar. As the bead is applied, one side of the bar is heated and expands and the other does not.

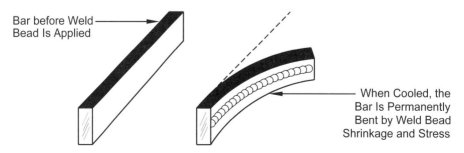

Figure 9-7. Effect of applying a weld bead on one side of a steel bar.

When the bar and the filler metal on top of the bar cool, they contract much more than the cooler metal on the bar's opposite side. Applying the weld bead makes the bar bend *toward* the side of the weld bead.

Types of Distortion

Figures 9-8 through 9-12 show the five major types of weld-induced distortion. Very often there is more than one type of distortion at work.

The types include:

- *Longitudinal distortion* – Figure 9-8 shows the distortion caused by shrinkage along the length of a butt weld on two plates. The weld could be either a single-V or a double-V.

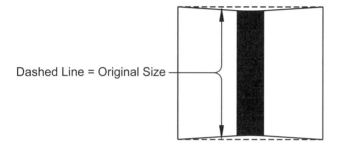

Figure 9-8. Results of longitudinal distortion in a butt weld.

- *Transverse distortion* – Figure 9-9 shows how transverse distortion in a single-V butt weld shrinks the width of the welded parts.

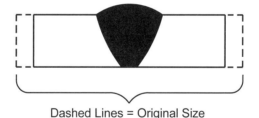

Figure 9-9. Results of transverse distortion on a single-V butt weld.

- *Angular distortion* – Figure 9-10 shows angular distortion between two plates causing them to dish upward. The greater mass of filler metal at the top of the joint causes the work to dish. In real life, several types of weld-induced distortion can occur simultaneously and all affect the workpiece.

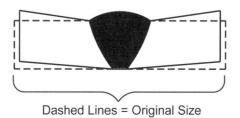

Figure 9-10. Angular distortion between two plates joined with in a single-V butt weld.

- *Fillet weld distortion* – Figure 9-11 shows the effects of fillet weld distortion pulling the vertical member of a T-joint off center.

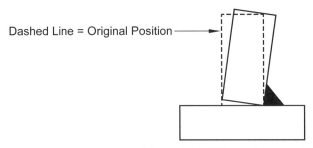

Figure 9-11. Fillet weld distortion.

- *Neutral axis distortion* – Figure 9-12 shows two sets of fillet welds on T-joints. Although the vertical member remains perpendicular to the base because the fillet welds exert balanced forces on it, the longitudinal shrinkage forces cause the welded members to bend. The location of the welds in relation to the neutral axis determines whether the bending is bowing or buckling.

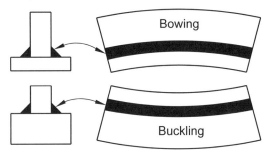

Figure 9-12. The pulling effect of welds above and below the neutral axis.

Predicting Transverse Shrinkage

Figure 9-13 shows that transverse shrinkage is directly related to the amount and shape of metal in the weld. In the same size plate, a double-V weld, because it is balanced and has less weld-metal volume, has about half the shrinkage of a single-V weld.

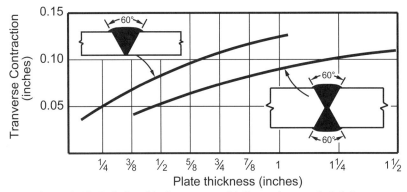

Figure 9-13. Relationship between weld dimensions and shrinkage.

Figure 9-14 shows a direct and linear (straight-line) relationship with the area of the weld for constant plate thickness. In general, we can estimate the transverse shrinkage of a weld to equal 10% of the average width of the weld's cross section, or

Transverse shrinkage = 0.10 × (Average weld width)

This indicates that minimizing weld size, while still retaining the required strength, is desirable to control shrinkage.

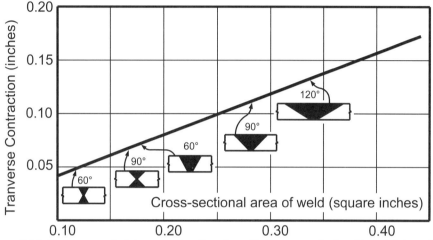

Figure 9-14. Transverse shrinkage varies directly with the amount of weld metal deposited.

Controlling Distortion

The forces of distortion cannot be prevented, but they can be controlled by employing the following shop practices:

- *Pre-set the parts* – Tack weld the parts slightly out of position and let residual forces bring them into proper position as in Figure 9-15. It may take several tries to determine how much out-of-position pre-set is needed.

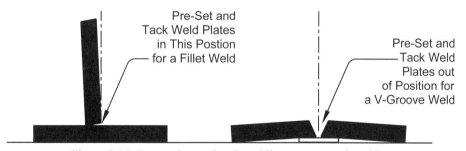

Figure 9-15. Pre-setting and tack welding parts out of position allows weld shrinkage to bring the parts back into alignment.

- *Pre-stress the parts* – Use clamps to bend the joint members in the opposite direction of the weld forces and let weld shrinkage bring the parts back into position. This method works well when a jig or fixture can be used and test runs can be made to determine the amount of pre-stress needed. See Figure 9-16.

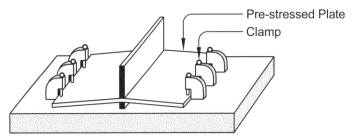

Figure 9-16. Pre-stressing a weld joint to compensate for residual stress.

- *Strongbacks* – By holding the weld joint *in the proper position* until the weld metal cools, strongbacks reduce weld-induced distortion. See Figure 9-17 for two different strongback designs.

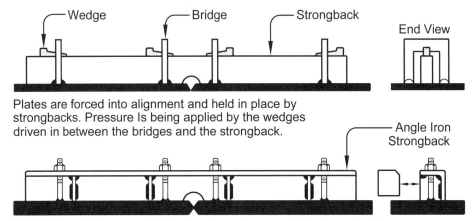

Plates are forced into alignment and held in place by strongbacks. Pressure Is being applied by the wedges driven in between the bridges and the strongback.

Temporary studs are welded to the plates to support the strongback.
Rectangular plates are welded to the angle iron strongback to prevent tipping.

Figure 9-17. Strongbacks hold the welded plates in position while the weld cools.

- *Clamps and wedges* – Figure 9-18 shows a clamp and wedge holding a V-groove in place for welding. The small temporary weld on the clamp arm is either snapped or ground off when the main weld is completed. This is common practice where there are long welded joints such as in tank building, truck trailer fabrication, and shipbuilding. Many clamps are usually needed at equal intervals along the weld bead.

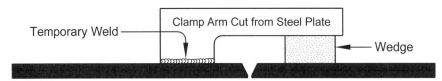

Figure 9-18. Temporary clamps across a V-groove weld permit horizontal movement, yet hold the plates in vertical alignment.

- *Chill bars* – Chill bars are steel or copper bars clamped beside and parallel to the weld bead. They draw heat away from the weld and reduce heat flow to the rest of the part. They also limit distortion from upsetting the metal close to the weld and eliminate ripples by exerting a clamping force.

A groove in the lower chill bar permits the weld to remain hot and not have its heat drained away by the chill bar. See Figure 9-19.

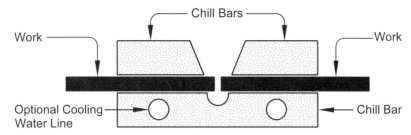

Figure 9-19. Chill bars reduce distortion by confining heat to the weld area and by preventing work from forming ripples when hot.

• *Balancing weld distortion forces* – Use equal distortion forces to balance each other by using two or more weld beads. This can be done by putting a fillet weld on both sides of a T-joint or using a double V-groove butt joint. See Figure 9-20.

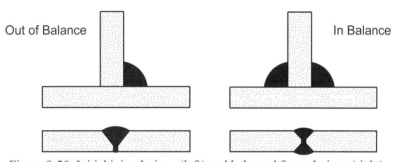

Figure 9-20. Initial joint designs (left) and balanced force designs (right).

• *Intermittent welds* – Chain intermittent or staggered intermittent weld beads, as in Chapter 3, not only balance weld shrinkage forces against each other, they also reduce the total amount of weld metal, which reduces the total residual force. See Figure 9-21. Even a single intermittent weld bead will have less distortion than a single continuous weld bead and can be used where the strength of a continuous bead is not needed.

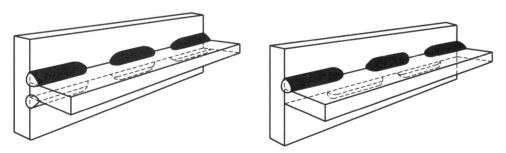

Figure 9-21. Using chain intermittent (left) or staggered intermittent welds (right) to balance forces and reduce total weld bead metal.

• Another balanced-force strategy uses a V-groove and a fillet weld in place of a fillet weld alone to balance residual stress. See Figure 9-22.

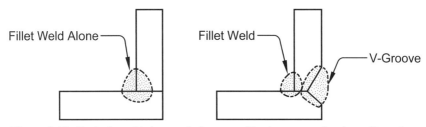

Figure 9-22. Redesigned joint can balance residual stress and reduce distortion.

- *Tack welds* – Use tack welds to restrain the part and control root spacing. Tack welding in a fixture is even better.

- *Backstep welding* – Apply short increments of beads in the direction opposite to the end point of the weld. Each weld increment has a small amount of shrinkage—small enough to be insignificant over the length of the entire weld. When applying multiple passes, start and stop the beads of each layer at different points. See Figure 9-23.

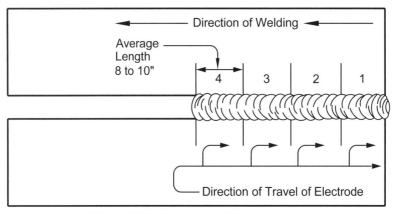

Figure 9-23. Backstep welding sequence.

- *Wedges control joint spacing* – Insert a steel wedge ahead of the weld bead to control joint spacing and move the wedge along the joint as the weld progresses. See Figure 9-24.

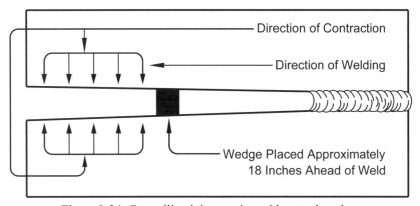

Figure 9-24. Controlling joint spacing with a steel wedge.

- *Peening* – Peening the weld metal, usually with a needle gun, slightly reshapes the metal and redistributes concentrated forces. Peening is essential in very large welds, such as those used to repair large castings where the filler metal is wide and deep. Needle gun peening is done after each welding pass. Though this method can be helpful, peening consistency is difficult to control and depends on the judgment and skill of the welder. Attempting to peen a weld with a hammer is more of a gesture than an effective step—and it takes a long time. Don't waste your time and energy trying.

- *Intermittent cooling* – When there are many welds on a relatively small workpiece there is a lot of heat input, which raises the temperature of the entire workpiece. By allowing the work to cool between welds, temporary weld-heat induced distortion dissipates and is not locked into place by subsequent welds.

- *Braze instead of weld* – Since brazing exposes the workpiece to much lower temperatures than welding, brazing can be used when the strength of welding is not required.

- *Sequence the joints in a complex structure to balance shrinkage forces* – In general, there is better balance if you perform diagonally opposite welds, not adjacent ones.

- *Preheating* – Raising the workpiece temperature several hundred degrees before welding begins can reduce distortion. This strategy works best when the part can be evenly and thoroughly heated in an oven. Preheating with a torch does not work well. Table 9-1 lists common preheat temperatures.

Alloy	Percent Carbon	°F Preheat
Mild Steel	0.05–0.3	250
Medium-Carbon Steel	0.30–0.55	600
High-Carbon Steel	0.55–0.75	700
Stainless Steel (18-8)	—	Not Effective

Table 9-1. Preheat temperatures for several steel alloys.

- *Postheating* – Heavy weldments are often heated to relieve residual stresses to prevent *further* distortion from occurring when machining removes additional metal. Removing metal from a workpiece or structure that has residual stress can lead to more distortion.

- *Mechanical straightening* – Distorted parts can be straightened using a hydraulic press or jacks. Sometimes flame straightening can be performed, but this technique requires considerable experience and is not suitable for production work.

Using two or more stress and distortion control steps together can even further reduce the effects of distortion.

Ten Rules for Minimizing Distortion

1. *Minimize heat input* – Choose welding processes that minimize heat input. For example, an oxyacetylene torch puts much more heat into the work than a GMAW or FCAW torch because these electrical processes concentrate the heat where it is needed to make the weld. The oxyacetylene torch has a large heat footprint to begin with and moves more slowly along the joint, heating much more workpiece metal. Faster travel speeds usually result in lower distortion than lower travel speeds.

2. *Minimize the number of welds* – Reduce the total number of welded joints because more weld metal means more shrinkage and more distortion.

3. *Balance welds around the neutral axis* – When possible, keep the welds close to the neutral axis of the work.

4. *Use intermittent welds* – Avoid long, continuous welds unless required for strength or function. Long welds are a major source of distortion.

5. *Balance weld forces* – Use one weld's shrinkage forces to balance another.

6. *Avoid overwelding* – Use the smallest groove angles and root openings that will result in adequate welding access and sound welds.

    - A smaller, steeper-angled V-groove requires less filler metal.

    - A narrow V-groove contains less metal volume than a U-groove.

    - A double V-groove causes less shrinkage than a single V-groove of the same angle.

7. *Select metals carefully* – If possible, select metals with low coefficients of expansion and high thermal conductivity.

8. *Balance the placement of welds* – Place welds on opposite sides on symmetrical workpieces.

9. *Anticipate shrinkage* – A couple of trial welds will determine the amount of pre-set required to counter the shrinkage forces.

10. *Plan your welding sequence* – Plan welds to counteract shrinkage forces.

Correcting Distortion after Welding

The shop project in Figure 9-25 shows a 22" long rack used to hold test leads. The rack is made from 1" × 1" × 0.23" square steel tubing. A series of 0.062" steel sheet metal plates are tack welded along the upper side of the steel tubing. Test lead wires slide between these plates and the connectors on the ends of the wires hold the test leads in place.

If the steel plates are welded onto the tubing without any distortion control steps taken, the rack will be badly bowed as shown in Figure 9-25 (A). This is caused by the amount of weld metal pulling the tubing out of line.

The solution, other than trying to remove the bow by bending, is to place one or more post-stress correction weld beads along the bottom of the tubing to compensate, as shown in Figure 9-25 (B).

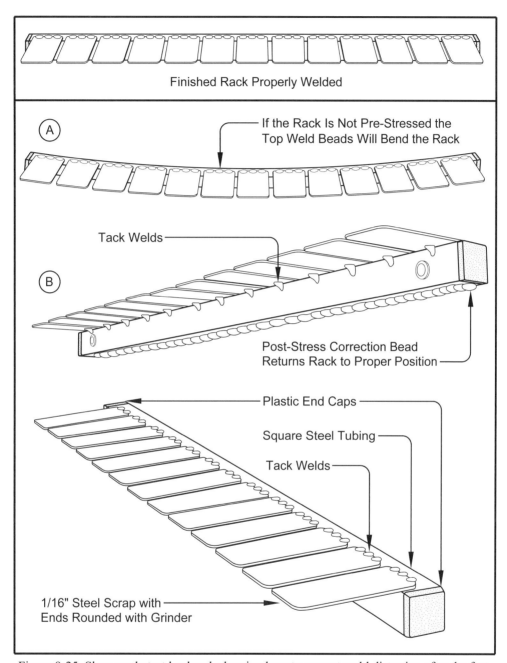

Finished Rack Properly Welded

(A)   If the Rack Is Not Pre-Stressed the
       Top Weld Beads Will Bend the Rack

Tack Welds

(B)

Post-Stress Correction Bead
Returns Rack to Proper Position

Plastic End Caps

Square Steel Tubing

Tack Welds

1/16" Steel Scrap with
Ends Rounded with Grinder

Figure 9-25. Shop-made test lead rack showing how to correct weld distortion after the fact.

Distortion in Carbon Steel

Most carbon steels rapidly loose strength above 600°F, and at 1100°F tensile strength falls to 30–40 percent of its room temperature value. Although the steel is far below its melting point of 2750°F, it is greatly weakened. For this reason, the higher the peak temperatures experienced by the steel under stress by expansion forces, the greater the deformation.

The physical properties of steel can change greatly with increasing temperature. Here is what happens:

- The stiffness or rigidity decreases as shown by the curve for the factor *modulus of elasticity*, also called *Young's modulus*.

- The *yield point* falls, the point at which the metal will suddenly increase in length without having experienced an increase in load.

- The *coefficient of expansion increases,* that is, with an increase in temperature, the steel expands at an increasing rate.

As the temperature of the metal increases, these three physical properties work together to increase distortion. Figure 9-26 shows these property changes for mild carbon steel.

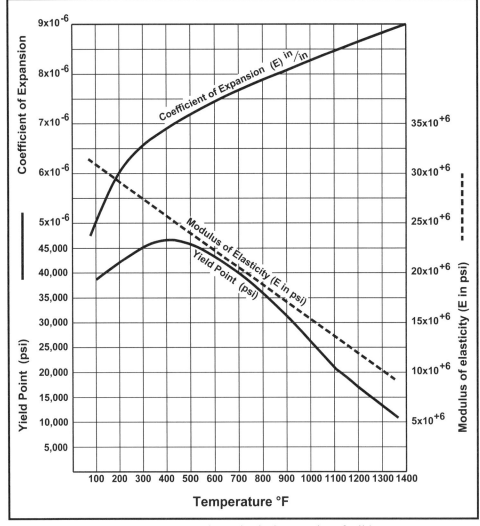

Figure 9-26. How three physical properties of mild carbon steel change at elevated temperatures.

Chapter 10

Cutting Processes

Practice is the best of all instruction.

—Aristotle

Section I – Oxyfuel Cutting

Introduction

Oxyfuel cutting is a family of cutting processes which heats the work metal to its kindling point, causing it to burn in a stream of oxygen. Common terms for these processes are *flame cutting*, *oxygen cutting,* and *burning*. The AWS abbreviation for the whole family of oxyfuel cutting processes is *OFC* and the most prominent member of this family is oxyacetylene cutting, abbreviated *OAC*. Oxyacetylene is used more for cutting than for welding, but natural gas, propane and propylene are also used for cutting. Oxyfuel cutting is an easy process to use, cuts in all directions, is portable, and it is inexpensive to add to an existing oxyfuel welding outfit. Oxyfuel can cut steel from under $^1/_{32}$" to over 12' thick. Today, with the decline in the cost of plasma cutting systems, plasma cutting has taken over some jobs once reserved for oxyfuel, but for many steel-cutting applications there still is no faster and more cost-effective process than oxyfuel cutting.

Equipment

A conventional oxyacetylene welding system is easily converted to perform oxyacetylene cutting (OAC) by replacing the welding nozzle on the torch handle with a cutting attachment head as shown in Figure 10-1.

The cutting attachment differs from an oxyacetylene welding torch because it also has a means to deliver a stream of pure oxygen to the cutting point. A cutting oxygen lever opens this pure oxygen stream when the welder depresses it. See Figure 10-2.

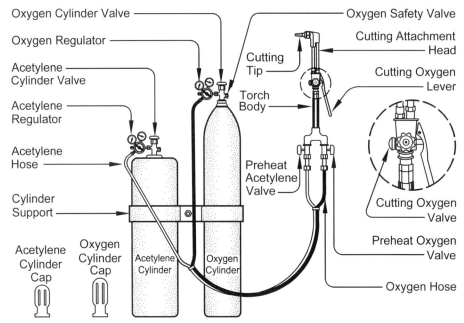

Oxygen Cylinder Valve

Oxygen Regulator

Acetylene Cylinder Valve

Acetylene Regulator

Acetylene Hose

Cylinder Support

Acetylene Cylinder Cap

Oxygen Cylinder Cap

Acetylene Cylinder

Oxygen Cylinder

Cutting Tip

Torch Body

Preheat Acetylene Valve

Oxygen Safety Valve

Cutting Attachment Head

Cutting Oxygen Lever

Cutting Oxygen Valve

Preheat Oxygen Valve

Oxygen Hose

Figure 10-1. Oxyacetylene (OAC) cutting outfit.

The advantages of a cutting attachment head over a one-piece cutting torch are that a cutting attachment head is less expensive than a one-piece cutting torch and it is quicker and easier to change back and forth between cutting and welding functions. A one-piece cutting torch, with its greater length, puts more distance between the cutting action and the welder, and can usually handle the greater oxygen flows needed for large jobs. Some cutting torches have cutting attachment heads set at a particular angle for a given task to help relieve operator fatigue. The position of the cutting head, though, is a matter of personal preference and varies by manufacturer.

The torch in Figure 10-2 (left) uses a mixing chamber to bring the oxygen and fuel gases together and is known as a *positive-pressure, balanced-pressure* or *medium-pressure torch*. The advantage of the mixing-chamber torch design is that it operates at *higher* fuel gas pressures and can supply more heat than the venturi design. Positive pressure is the most common torch design today.

The torch in Figure 10-2 (right) uses an injection chamber, or *venturi*, to draw the fuel gas into the oxygen stream and operates with the low fuel pressures of 6–8 oz/in^2. The venturi torch design is needed when natural gas from a gas main is used in place of acetylene for economy or for when acetylene is made on site with a gas generator, which is common in the third world.

Cutting thick steel requires more oxygen than thin steel, so a special oxygen regulator with the capacity of delivering more oxygen volume at higher than welding pressures may be needed to cut steel that is more than one inch thick. Larger diameter hoses are also required. The welding acetylene regulator is fine for cutting. Also, since in cutting there is much higher oxygen consumption and more rapid cylinder depletion than in welding operations, the typical cutting regulator has two-stages to maintain a constant working pressure as the cylinder gas dwindles. Gauges on the high-pressure side of oxygen regulators for cutting have higher pressure calibrations than those of welding regulators. Oxyfuel cutting operations on thick metals can require oxygen pressures as high as 100–150 psi.

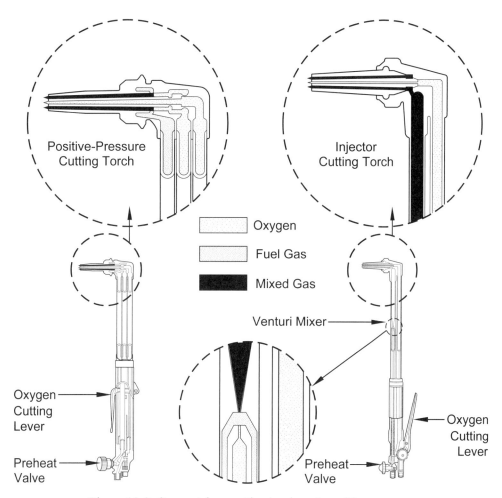

Figure 10-2. Oxyacetylene cutting torches. A positive-pressure cutting torch (left) and a venturi design injector cutting torch (right).

Oxyfuel Cutting Tips and Cutting Gases

The cutting tip is the single most important factor determining the quality of a cut. A clean, undamaged cutting tip provides a straight oxygen jet and a safe, stable flame, but because cutting tips are copper they are easily damaged if dropped. For a good cut, the exit end of the jets must be burr-free and perpendicular to the tip face. This is especially true for the oxygen jets. The seats in the base of the tip are also easily damaged either by dropping them or by tightening the tip when there is dirt on the seat. This damage is not usually repairable. In most cases, tips from one torch maker cannot be used in another manufacturer's torch.

If you have removed the nut that retains the torch tip, and the torch tip is stuck in the torch body, a gentle tap on the back of the torch head with a plastic hammer will usually release the tip.

Because of their proximity to the cutting heat, tips wear out and must eventually be replaced. Also, poor operating practices, rough handling and excessive tip cleaning further shortens the life of a cutting tip. Storing tips in a rack instead of rolling around loose will extend their lives. A wide variety of cutting tips are available to perform different jobs. See Figure 10-3.

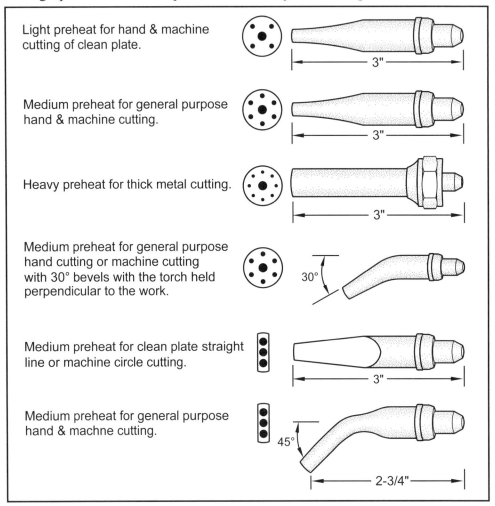

Figure 10-3. A selection of special-purpose oxyfuel cutting tips.

Besides acetylene, for economy and availability, natural gas and propylene are also used for preheating in the OFC processes. They are called *alternative fuels*. Torch tips designed for use with alternative fuels are frequently different because these fuels may be supplied at lower pressures, have different fuel-to-oxygen ratios and different burn-rate characteristics. Methylacetylene-propadiene, known as MAPP gas, was a common and effective alternative gas, but its production was discontinued in North America in 2008 and only less effective substitutes are now available.

Although acetylene always produces a higher preheat temperature, alternative fuels often offer significant cost savings. But, fuel selection is a complex matter involving material thickness, fuel and oxygen consumption, cutting speed, heat transfer, and performance on straight lines, curves and bevels. The availability of fuel, labor costs, the cost of preheat oxygen and the suitability of the alternative fuel to perform related processes like welding, bending, heating and brazing also influence total production costs.

A two-stage combustion process causes fuel gases to burn with a small, bright, hotter inner-flame cone close to the cutting tip, and a larger, dimmer, cooler outer-flame cone. All the fuel gases, including acetylene, have about the same heat content per pound, roughly 21,000 btu/lb, but as shown in Table 10-1, each fuel gas releases a different *proportion* of its heat between the inner and outer combustion cones. Fuels with a higher inner-cone heat ratio have a higher heat concentration, produce a higher flame temperature and also require less oxygen than fuels with more heat released in their outer cones. The hotter fuels—remember they release more heat in the inner cone—have a more complex structure than cooler fuels because they have double and triple carbon-hydrogen bonds.

The more heat released in the outer cone, the lower the flame temperature since the flame is cooled by the intake of atmospheric air with 20% oxygen and 80% non-combustible nitrogen. This mix results in a higher rate of cylinder oxygen consumption to achieve a given preheat input.

Fuel Gas	Neutral Flame Temperature with Oxygen		Ratio of Outer Cone to Inner Cone Heat	Oxygen-to-Fuel-Gas Combustion Ratio
	°F	°C		
Acetylene	5600	3100	34:66	2.5
Propane	4580	2520	10:90	5.0
Propylene	5200	2870	22:82	4.5
Natural Gas	4600	2540	99:1	2.0

Table 10-1. Cutting fuel gas properties.

At least two manufacturers offer systems that use gasoline as fuel. A small, pressurized tank, like those used for outboard motors, holds the gasoline, which remains in liquid form until leaving the torch tip. This system offers the convenience of eliminating the need for handling acetylene or other fuel gases, a big advantage in remote parts of the world.

Oxyfuel Cutting Process

To start a cut, the oxyacetylene—or alternative fuel—flame brings the steel up to its 1600°F kindling temperature. At this temperature steel readily burns in the presence of oxygen. When the welder presses the cutting lever to turn on the pure oxygen stream, the preheated steel burns, producing oxides of iron. This oxide mixture, called *slag*, has a melting point much lower than the melting point of the steel itself, which is 2600°F, and the slag runs out of the cut or kerf. The force of the oxygen stream provides additional help in clearing the kerf of molten oxides and molten steel. In addition to the preheat flame, the iron burning in the oxygen stream releases large amounts of additional heat. This heat aids in cutting action, particularly when cutting thick steel. Moving the torch across the work produces continuous cutting action and a cut line. Straight, curved or beveled cuts are readily made using this process. Because this is an oxidation process, cutting oxygen must be at least 99.5% pure, since a 1% decrease will reduce cutting speed by 25% and increase oxygen consumption by 25%.

Kerf & Drag

During flame cutting, the oxidation of the metal along the cut line removes a thin strip of metal called the *kerf*. In steel under 2" thick the kerf can be held to $^1/_{64}$" wide. For proper fit, when making patterns for parts to be flame cut from flat stock, allowance must be made for the kerf. See Figure 10-4.

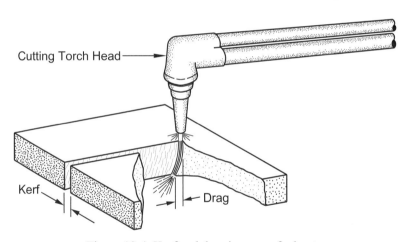

Figure 10-4. Kerf and drag in an oxyfuel cut.

Kerf width depends on the oxygen-orifice size and pressure, preheat-flame size, cutting speed and torch tip design. Cutting thicker steel requires more oxygen, which requires a larger oxygen-orifice size, greater oxygen-flow rates and a larger oxygen stream. This setup also produces a wider kerf.

The distance between the cutting action at the top and bottom of the kerf is called *drag*. If the oxygen stream enters the top of the kerf and exits the bottom of the kerf directly below, the drag is said to be zero. If the cutting speed is increased, or the oxygen flow decreased, oxygen in the lower portion of the kerf decreases and the kinetic energy of the oxygen stream drops, slowing cutting action in the bottom of the cut. This causes the cutting action at the kerf bottom to lag behind the cutting action at the top. Drag is expressed as a percentage of the thickness of the cut. Excessive drag can cause loss of cutting action in thick cuts, and restarting the cutting action can damage or destroy the part being flame cut. A 1" plate could have 25%, or $^1/_4$" drag.

OFC Chemistry

In OFC, iron oxidation occurs in three steps, producing a different iron oxide in each step:

$$Fe + O_2 \rightarrow FeO + \text{heat of 267 Kj (Kilojoules)}$$
$$3\,Fe + 2\,O_2 \rightarrow Fe_3O_4 + \text{heat of 1120 Kj}$$
$$2\,Fe + 1.5\,O_2 \rightarrow Fe_2O_3 + \text{heat of 825 Kj}$$

The second reaction above releases the most heat and helps sustain the cutting action. These equations show the ratios of oxygen to fuel (iron) needed. About 104 ft^3 of oxygen will oxidize 2.2 lb. of steel to iron oxide, Fe_3O_4.

OFC Advantages

- Lower in cost compared with mechanical cutting equipment, particularly because no cutting tools are dulled.
- Readily portable because no external electrical power is required.
- Steels usually can be cut faster than by conventional machining.
- Cutting direction may be easily changed.
- Angled cuts are readily made.
- Oxyfuel cutting is an effective edge preparation for groove and bevel weld joints.
- Large plates may be cut in place.
- Parts with unusual shapes and thickness variations, which are hard to cut with conventional machinery, are easily produced.
- Torch guidance is easily automated using tracks, patterns or computer generated programs.
- No other process cuts thick sections (6–168") as rapidly and as smoothly as oxyfuel cutting.

OFC Disadvantages

- Dimensional tolerance of oxyfuel cutting is dramatically poorer than with machine-tool based cutting.
- OAC process is commercially limited to steel and cast steel because other metals—high-alloy steels and cast iron—do not burn with enough heat.
- Both the preheat flame and the stream of molten slag in oxyfuel cutting present fire and burn hazards to personnel and facilities, and proper fume control is required.
- Hardenable steels may need preheat, postheat or both to control the metallurgy and the properties of the steel adjacent to the cut.
- Cutting must begin at the edge of the work or through a starter hole, otherwise ragged piercing results.
- Each time the oxy torch is set down and shut off, it involves a complete relighting and flame adjustment cycle, compared with plasma arc cutting which may be started and stopped at the pull of a trigger switch.

OFC Minimum & Maximum Cut Thickness

In OFC there is no practical limit to cut thickness. In heavy industry, steel 7 feet thick is routinely cut, and cuts up to 14 feet thick are not uncommon.

OAC's lower limit is 20 gauge (0.035") steel. Below this thickness the cut becomes ragged and irregular with uncontrollable melting. This steel can be cut with a large torch-tip-to-plate angle and fast travel speed, but laser or plasma cutters are better choices for cutting thin steel sheets.

Setting Up a Cutting Torch

To determine what cutting tip size and what oxygen and acetylene pressures to use on a given thickness of material, use the torch manufacturer's table to match metal thickness to tip size, starting oxygen pressure, and acetylene pressure. These tables are suggested starting pressure ranges and fine tuning of the pressures may be needed to get the best combination of speed and quality. Also, these tables usually show typical cutting speeds and gas consumption.

Steps to set up a cutting torch for $1/4$" carbon steel:

1. Inspect and clean the torch tip, if necessary, as explained in Step 6.

2. When cutting, always wear welding safety equipment: goggles with a filter lens, or tinted face shield, cap, high-top shoes, cotton or wool long-sleeved shirt, long pants and welding gloves. Avoid wearing trousers with cuffs when cutting because they can catch hot sparks and easily catch your pants on fire. *Do not wear synthetics, they melt.* For overhead cutting, leather skins or aprons are necessary to protect clothing from falling sparks. Goggles and face shields should be of Number 5 lens shade.

3. Firmly secure the oxygen and acetylene cylinders to a welding cart, building column, or other solid anchor to prevent tipping during storage or use. Non-flammable material must be used to secure the cylinders. *After* the cylinders are secured, the safety caps can be removed.

4. Verify the cutting torch has flashback arrestors and check valves installed.

5. Momentarily open each cylinder's valve to the atmosphere and quickly reclose the valve. This action, known as *cracking a valve*, blows out dust and grit from the valve port preventing debris from entering the regulators and torch. When cracking, stand on the opposite side of the cylinder from the valve port.

6. With a clean, oil-free cloth, wipe the valve-to-regulator fittings on both cylinders to remove dirt and grit from the connection faces and threads. Clean the threads and connection faces of both regulators. Remember, never use any oil on high-pressure gas fittings. Oxygen at high pressures accelerates the combustion of oil into an explosion.

7. Check to see that both the oxygen and the acetylene regulator pressure-adjustment screws are loosened, but not falling out of their threads, then screw each regulator to its respective cylinder. Snug up the connections

with a wrench. Caution: Oxygen cylinder-to-regulator threads are *right-handed*, as are oxygen hose-to-torch screw fittings. Acetylene cylinder-to-regulator fittings and acetylene hose-to-torch fittings are *left-handed*. This arrangement prevents putting the wrong gas into a regulator or torch.

8. Stand so the cylinder is between you and the regulators. Then, S-L-O-W-L-Y open the oxygen cylinder valve. Be sure to open the oxygen cylinder valve until it hits the upper valve stop and will not turn any farther.

9. With the cylinders still between you and the regulators, open the acetylene cylinder valve gradually and not more than *one turn*. If there is an old-style removable wrench on the cylinders, keep it in place in case you must quickly close the cylinder valve in an emergency.

10. Look for the high-pressure—or cylinder side—gauges to indicate about 225 psi in the acetylene cylinder and 2250 psi in the oxygen cylinder. These pressures will confirm that the cylinders are full. The pressures given above are for full cylinders at 70°F, but the actual pressures will vary with the ambient temperature of the cylinders.

11. Install the cutting torch on the hoses, or if using a combination welding and cutting handle, install the cutting attachment onto the torch handle.

12. Before lighting the torch, check the area for ignition sources other than your torch igniter. Next, separately purge each torch hose of air. Open the oxygen valve on the torch about three-quarters of a turn, then screw in the pressure-control screw on the oxygen regulator to your initial pressure setting. After several seconds, close the torch valve. Do the same with the acetylene hose. Note: This is done for two reasons, to make sure the torch is lighting on just oxygen and acetylene, not air, and to get the regulators set for the correct pressure while the gas is flowing through them. If the gas hoses are more than 50' long, a higher regulator setting will be needed to compensate for the pressure drop in the hoses.

13. Drizzle or spray leak testing solution at each joint to test the system for leaks at the cylinder-to-regulator fittings and at all hose fittings. Bubbles indicate leaks. Tighten the fitting when a leak is found and then repeat this step.

14. Light and adjust the torch as detailed in *Torch Lighting Steps* below.

Torch Lighting Steps

Here are the steps and safety procedures for lighting and adjusting a cutting torch for $1/4$" thick mild carbon steel:

1. Set the acetylene pressure to 6 psi and oxygen pressure to 40 psi for a 0.030–0.060" torch-orifice diameter. Never adjust the acetylene regulator pressure above 15 psi because a spontaneous explosive disassociation of acetylene can occur. The red portion of the pressure gauge indicates this explosive danger zone.

2. Open the cutting-oxygen valve all the way. It is located in the middle of the torch.

3. Re-check the low-pressure gauge to make sure that the working pressures are not rising. If the working pressure does rise, the regulator is leaking. The cylinders must immediately be shut down at the cylinder valves because leaking could lead to a regulator diaphragm rupture and a serious accident. This upward pressure creep is usually caused by the rubber components inside the regulators becoming hardened with age.

4. Prior to lighting the flame, put on a tinted welding face shield over safety glasses or use welding goggles with a Number 5 lens shade. To light the torch start by opening the acetylene valve on the torch handle 1/16th turn and light the acetylene using a sparker. A large, smoky, orange flame will result.

5. Increase the flame size by slowly opening the acetylene valve until most of the smoke disappears.

6. Open the oxygen-preheat valve on the lower end of the torch and adjust for a neutral flame.

7. Actuate the oxygen cutting lever and examine the preheat flame. Further adjustment of the oxygen preheat valve may be needed to keep the preheat flame large enough when the cutting oxygen is used. This is because the cutting oxygen can cause the hose pressure to drop so much that the oxygen to the preheat flame must be increased to keep a proper preheat flame.

8. You are now ready to begin cutting.

Cutting $^{1}/_{4}$" or Thicker Steel

The positions for holding a cutting torch for starting a cut and for cutting $^{1}/_{4}$" or thicker steel are shown in Figure 10-5. Here are the cutting steps:

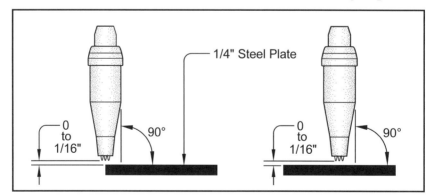

Figure 10-5. Position of cutting torch tip on ¼-inch and thicker
plate; for preheating and starting the cut (left) and for cutting (right).

1. Holding the cutting torch tip perpendicular to the metal, as in Figure 10-5 (left), start the cut at the edge of the stock by preheating the edge. Position the torch so the tips of the preheat flames just touch the work. For thicker material, the torch may be angled away from the direction of travel so the preheat flame strikes down the edge of the material, heating a larger

surface area. When the metal stock becomes a dull red, begin cutting by squeezing the oxygen cutting lever. Remember to hold the torch tip perpendicular to the surface of the stock when cutting action has begun.

Tip: Raising a burr on the edge of the stock using a slag hammer makes starting the cutting process easier. The burr heats more quickly than the solid base metal mass and begins burning faster. This starts a cascade effect leading to the work metal heating, melting and burning faster.

2. Move the torch along the cut line in a steady motion. For right-handed welders, cutting from right to left allows the welder to see the cutting line more easily. Left-handers will usually prefer cutting left to right.

Cutting Steel Less Than $^1/_8$" Thick

1. To cut thin sheet metal, use the smallest cutting tip available with two preheat flames. After starting the cut at about a 40° angle, hold the torch at a 15–30° angle to the metal surface to make the cut. This increases the length of the cut and makes cutting more controllable. Use the minimum preheat flame that permits cutting. See Figure 10-6.

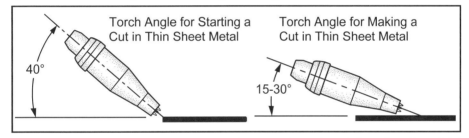

Figure 10-6. Torch position for cutting thin sheet metal, starting (left) and cutting (right).

2. If slag accumulates on the underside of a good sheet metal part, tipping the torch from 1–5° off the normal, away from the scrap side of the kerf, will keep slag off the good part. See Figure 10-7.

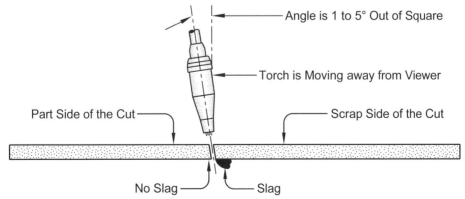

Figure 10-7. How to keep slag on the scrap side of a part when cutting very thin metal.

Shutting Down an Oxyacetylene Cutting Torch

1. Using the torch handle valves, turn off the oxygen and *then* the acetylene.

2. Turn off the oxygen and acetylene cylinder valves on the regulators.

3. One at a time, open and reclose the oxygen and acetylene valves on the torch handle to bleed to atmosphere the remaining gas in the lines and regulators. Bleed off the oxygen first to eliminate the possibility of providing oxygen to the remaining acetylene.

4. Verify that both the high-pressure and the low-pressure gauges on both cylinders indicate zero pressure.

5. Unscrew the regulator pressure-adjustment screws on both regulators in preparation for the next use of the equipment.

Unscrewing the pressure-adjustment screws on regulators when shutting down, in addition to shutting off the cylinder valves, is a good practice because it prevents shocking the regulator diaphragm with the sudden inrush of high-pressure gas when the cylinder valve is opened quickly. Omitting this step could lead to diaphragm failure and the escape of high-pressure gas from the cylinder.

Cutting Applications

Oxyacetylene cutting readily cuts the following metals:

- Mild steel, which is steel with a carbon content of less than 0.3% and low-alloy steels.
- Cast iron, though not readily.
- Titanium.

Oxyacetylene can also cut:

- Stainless steel, when carbon steel is introduced to produce additional heat.
- High-alloy steel, which must be preheated.

As the number and percentage of alloying elements increases, OFC becomes less effective and requires preheating. Unlike iron oxides, an alloy's oxides do not readily run out of the kerf to expose new iron to oxygen to keep the burning process going. This makes cutting alloys more difficult because the oxides of the alloying elements have a *higher* melting point than the alloying elements themselves. The oxides of iron have melting points *lower* than the melting point of iron so these oxides become fluid and easily leave the kerf as molten slag.

Oxyacetylene is *not* a good choice for non-ferrous metals such as aluminum, brass, copper, lead, magnesium, stainless steel and zinc.

The cutting of new steel plate, beams and pipes to size in steel mills, in fabrication plants, and on construction sites are excellent OAC applications.

The following are also excellent applications:

- Cutting risers, gates and defects from cast iron and steel castings.
- Cutting up old steel and cast iron equipment for removal and salvage.
- Removing rivets, bolts, and shafts from old equipment without damaging the surrounding steel.
- Removing damaged parts prior to welding new parts in place.

- Gouging the surface of steel plate edges in preparation for welding.
- Manufacturing steel parts by cutting them out of flat stock instead of machining them.

Stack Cutting

To make multiple parts in a single cutting pass, multiple sheets or plates are stacked and clamped or tack-welded together. To perform *stack cutting*, place several weld beads up the sides of the stack parallel to the flame direction. The weld beads can later be removed with a disc grinder to release the finished parts. Then proceed cutting either manually or, more likely, by machine. When the cutting is complete, the stack comes apart, leaving multiple flame-cut parts. Stack cutting also permits the cutting of thin stock which if cut individually would melt. Stack cutting can be used in place of shearing or die stamping when the production run does not justify the cost of making a die. Stack cutting also saves fuel and oxygen gas consumption, which is not directly proportional to the total cut thickness. Generally, the maximum thickness of plates in stack cutting must not exceed $^1/_2$ inch each. To achieve high-quality stack-cut parts, use clean, flat plates (or sheets) that, before tacking, are securely clamped in position with no air gaps between the plates. Air between the plates will extinguish cutting action and the parts will be ruined.

Tip: For rougher work that may introduce air gaps and allow the cutting flame to wander off the desired course, wet the plates before stacking them. The water and resulting steam will keep the cutting flame from entering or extinguishing in the gaps.

Torch Tip Cleaning

It's time to clean your torch tips when the heating flames are not of uniform height and shape, when they are unstable, when they lift off the torch tip, or when the kerf has rough sides. Cleaning tips when not indicated by inspection or poor torch performance shortens their working lives because the tip orifice becomes bell shaped, preventing good flame shape formation. Some cynics believe welding torch manufacturers give away tip cleaners to boost the sales of torch tips. And the cynics are probably right.

The method of torch cleaning used depends on the problem:

- If the torch backfires, one flame is *smaller* than the other flames, or a flame lifts off the tip face, a carbon deposit is the culprit and it must be removed from the orifice of the torch with a tip-cleaning tool.
- If one flame is *larger* than the others, its orifice has been *bell mouthed,* meaning it flares out at its opening. If the bell mouthing does not extend too far into the tip, repair it by filing or sanding the tip. To do this, remove the tip from the torch, hold it squarely against a medium file or emery cloth, and twist the tip to reface it. See Figure 10-8.

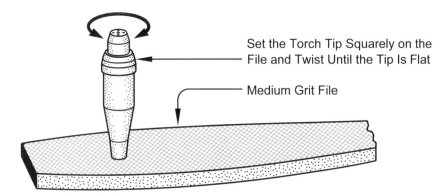

Figure 10-8. Refacing a bell-mouthed torch tip face by twisting it on a file.

- If an incomplete or offset flame comes from the torch, this is caused by a nick, ding, or carbon buildup on the tip face which has resulted in a restriction. Either use a tip cleaner or the filing and sanding method described above depending on the location of the buildup.

Marking the Line of Cut

Not being able to see the line of an OFC cut is a big problem. Welding heat melts the ink of most markers; so try the following methods:

- Mark lines with a welder's soapstone; it does not melt.
- Make a series of center-punch marks along the line of cut.
- Use an angle iron as a straight edge guide or as a bevel guide as shown in Figure 10-9.

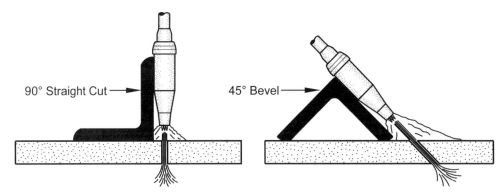

Figure 10-9. Angle iron used as a straight edge guide (left) and being used as a bevel guide (right).

Torch Attachments

- *Guide wheels* can be attached to the torch to keep the tip at a constant height above the work. This attachment helps to reduce operator fatigue. See Figure 10-10 (left).
- *Compass attachments* added to the torch top make near perfect circles. See Figure 10-10 (right).

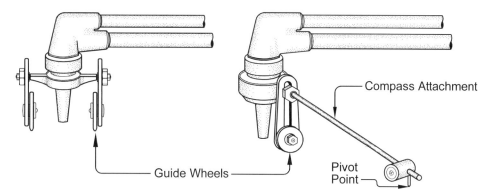

Figure 10-10. Torch attachment to keep the torch tip a constant height
above the work (left), and to make circular cuts (right).

- A *portable oxyfuel cutting machine*, which rolls along a pair of steel rails driven by a 120 VAC motor, can cut accurate bevels and chamfers for proper fit up. This machine can make straight-sided 90° cuts as well. See Figure 10-11.

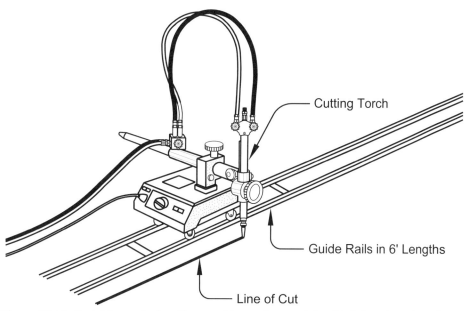

Figure 10-11. Portable oxyfuel cutting machine makes straight-sided, bevel or chamfer cuts.

- Oxyfuel cutting machines are often equipped with a *two-torch strip-cutting attachment*, also called a *twin torch*, that makes two parallel cuts simultaneously and produces a flat strip of metal with two parallel edges. Without two torches, the cut edge that has been subjected to cutting torch heat shrinks more than the uncut, unheated edge which causes the strip to curl. The solution to this problem is simple: use two torches and cut another strip the width of the kerf. This balances the heat and stress on both edges and prevents parts from curling. See Figure 10-12.

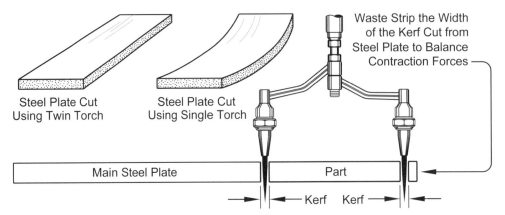

Figure 10-12. Two-torch strip-cutting attachment for a portable cutting machine.

- A *pattern tracer* is the next level of improvement for cutting torches. With a pattern tracer, a stylus follows the edge of a metal pattern, or a photoelectric eye follows a paper pattern, and a torch (or torches) is directly connected to the pattern tracing mechanism. This arrangement permits the torch to reproduce the pattern shape in steel. These cutting systems require heavy operator involvement, adjustment, and supervision.

- *Computer-driven cutting machines,* which store the path of the cutting torch in their memories, produce the most accurate and best quality cuts. Advanced machines control torch-to-work distance, adjust the torch speed on curves and corners, and adjust the preheat and cutting flames for starting and ending cuts. The most sophisticated machines require only loading the raw stock and removing scrap and the finished parts. These machines can also pierce holes to make inside cuts without operator assistance. Most cutting machines can maintain a $^1/_{32}$" tolerance to the desired cut line.

    Although there are several computer file formats for generating the pattern of the finished part, AutoCAD is one of the most popular. Once the AutoCAD file is submitted to the cutting shop, two important decisions must be made: the order in which the cuts will be made and the orientation of the important cuts with respect to the grain axis of the workpiece.

Starting & Finishing Heavy Cuts

- To start a heavy cut, tilt the torch toward the edge of the work to preheat the starting face. This technique exposes both the end and the surface of the workpiece to the flame heat and starts the cutting process more rapidly. See Figure 10-13.

- To finish a heavy cut, tilt the torch away from the direction of travel when nearing the end of the cut. This lessens the effect of drag and permits the bottom of the cutting action to proceed ahead of the top cutting action, which eliminates the premature breakout of the flame that leaves an uncut triangle at the end of the cut. See Figure 10-14.

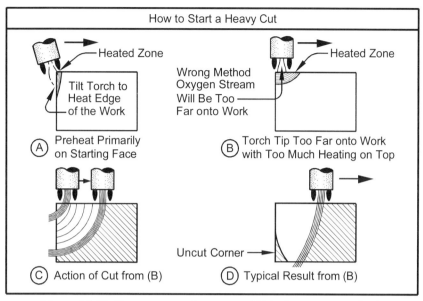

Figure 10-13. How to start a heavy cut. (A) is the correct method.

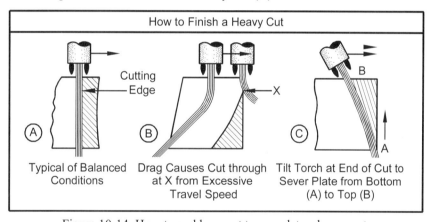

Figure 10-14. How to and how not to complete a heavy cut.

Removing Rivets or Bolts

Many rivets and bolts are extremely difficult to remove, particularly when they have rusted in place. To do this job, follow the steps in Figure 10-15, which apply to both rivets and bolts:

1. Preheat the rivet or bolt.

2. Cut a slot across the rivet or bolt head.

3. Cut off half the head.

4. Cut off the other half.

Sometimes the mass of the rivet and surrounding metal is so large in comparison to the torch flame that it is not possible to bring the rivet up to cutting temperature. The solution to this problem is to use a cold chisel to raise a burr on the top of the rivet and begin heating there. Once the smaller mass of the burr begins to burn, it will produce enough heat to extend the burning to the body of the rivet.

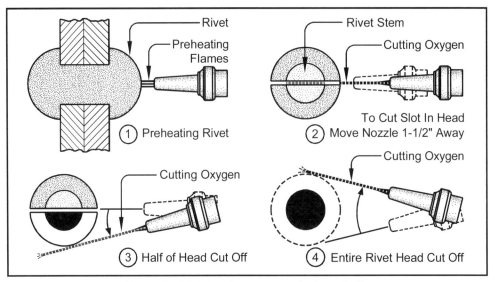

Figure 10-15. Steps to remove a rivet or a bolt.

Removing Countersunk Rivets or Bolts

1. Position the torch as in Figure 10-16 so its axis is parallel to the bevel edge of the rivet and begin preheating. When the starting spot becomes cherry red, press the cutting lever and burn away the countersunk edge.

2. Gradually move the torch *around* the rivet to remove the entire tapered edge. A layer of scale between the rivet and the base steel initially prevents the metal around the rivet or bolt from burning when the rivet burns, but keeping the torch in the same area after the rivet metal is flushed away will eventually burn the base metal. To avoid this, keep the torch moving and the torch axis parallel with the taper of the countersink.

3. After the tapered edge is cut away, position the torch perpendicular to the center of the rivet and remove the stem of the rivet.

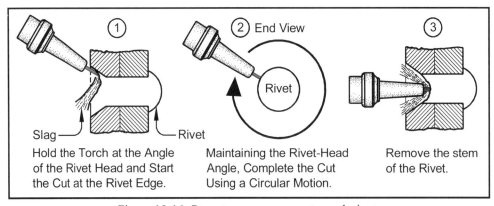

Figure 10-16. Steps to remove a countersunk rivet.

Piercing Steel with OFC

1. Holding the torch perpendicular to the metal, as in Figure 10-17, begin by preheating the pierce location to dull red.

2. When the metal becomes dull red, slightly raise the torch from the surface.

3. Now *angle the torch tip away from perpendicular*. This prevents the slag blown back from the surface of the metal from landing on or in the torch tip. Then, squeeze the oxygen lever to start cutting action.

4. As soon as the metal is completely pierced, if you are going to continue cutting, restore the tip to perpendicular with the preheat flame just above the surface and complete cutting the desired opening.

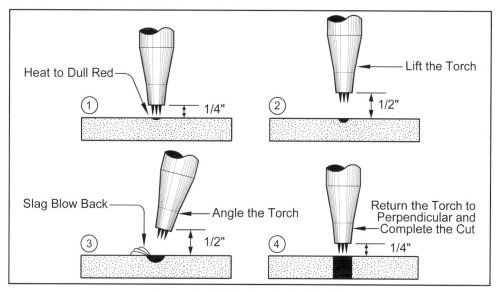

Figure 10-17. Piercing steel with OFC.

If a small hole is needed and the surrounding material must be protected from cutting action, drill a $\frac{1}{4}$" hole at the starting point, then begin the torch cutting action through this hole.

Cutting a Circular Opening with OFC

Start by piercing the material *inside* the circle, and when the cutting action is established, extend the cut into a spiral to begin cutting the circle itself. See Figure 10-18.

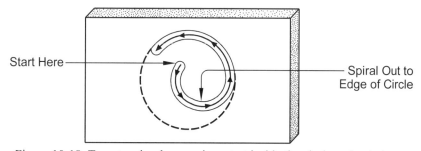

Figure 10-18. To cut a circular opening, start inside the circle and spiral out.

With small circles, to avoid damaging the finished edge, drill a $\frac{1}{4}$" hole in the center of the circle and cut through the hole, then spiral out to the edge.

Severing an I-Beam

Trimming an I-beam to length is one of the most common OAC tasks. To do this, first, mark the cut lines using the square and shop-made cutting guide in Figure 10-19, then, follow the numbered cut sequence in Figure 10-20.

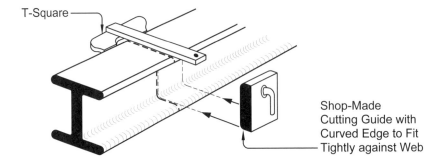

Figure 10-19. Marking an I-beam for a square cut.

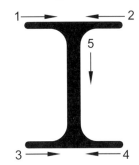

Figure 10-20. The proper sequence of cuts for severing an I-beam.

Bell-Mouthed Kerf & Defective Edges

Two major welding problems are bell-mouthed kerfs and defective edges. As in Figure 10-21, bell-mouthed kerfs are caused by excessive oxygen pressure. To fix this problem, simply lower the oxygen pressure. To diagnose a defective edge, compare the edge with the defective edge drawings in Figure 10-22, then to fix the problem, follow the recommendations in the drawing.

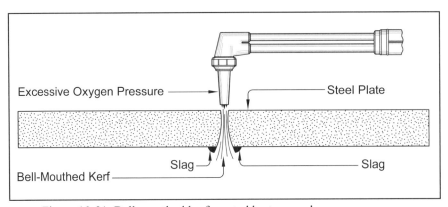

Figure 10-21. Bell-mouthed kerf created by too much oxygen pressure.

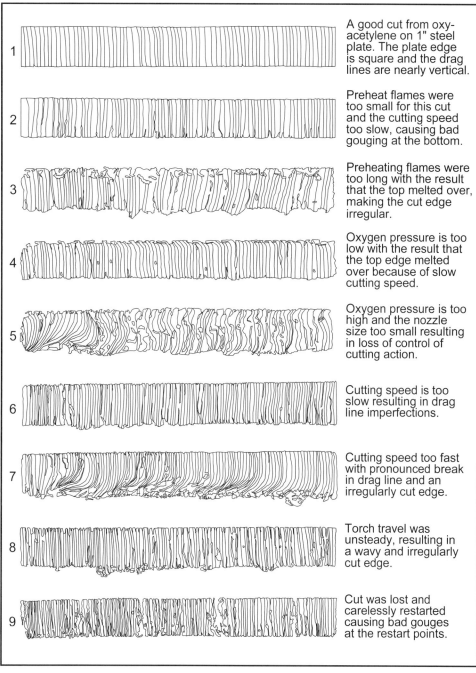

1	A good cut from oxy-acetylene on 1" steel plate. The plate edge is square and the drag lines are nearly vertical.
2	Preheat flames were too small for this cut and the cutting speed too slow, causing bad gouging at the bottom.
3	Preheating flames were too long with the result that the top melted over, making the cut edge irregular.
4	Oxygen pressure is too low with the result that the top edge melted over because of slow cutting speed.
5	Oxygen pressure is too high and the nozzle size too small resulting in loss of control of cutting action.
6	Cutting speed is too slow resulting in drag line imperfections.
7	Cutting speed too fast with pronounced break in drag line and an irregularly cut edge.
8	Torch travel was unsteady, resulting in a wavy and irregularly cut edge.
9	Cut was lost and carelessly restarted causing bad gouges at the restart points.

Figure 10-22. Oxyacetylene cutting problems and their causes.

Section II – Plasma Arc Cutting

Introduction

Plasma arc cutting, AWS designation *PAC*, is a common and important process when a work metal thickness is below $1\frac{1}{2}$ inches. In many applications PAC is superior to OFC in cost savings, convenience and cutting speed. Unlike oxyacetylene cutting, PAC easily cuts stainless steel, cast iron, aluminum and non-ferrous alloys. Equipment costs continue to come down, and a small plasma arc cutting system with integral air compressor capable of cutting metals up to $^{3}/_{4}$" now costs as little as $1000. A larger unit that cuts steel or stainless steel to $^{7}/_{8}$" and aluminum to $^{3}/_{4}$" costs under $4000. PAC is also very effective for *gouging*, that is, cutting a groove or a bevel, or for removing an existing weld bead.

As costs of PAC systems decline, its popularity increases. In many cases PAC has replaced OFC because PAC quickly cuts both ferrous and non-ferrous metals, avoids the long starting cycle of oxyacetylene cutting, needs no starting hole, is easy to use, and works particularly well on aluminum.

How Plasma Cutting Works

The three common states of matter are solid, liquid and gas. *Plasma* is a fourth state and it exists when matter has been subjected to very high energy input. The most common examples of plasmas seen on earth are lightning bolts, electric sparks, neon signs and fluorescent lamps. The surface of the sun is also plasma.

Here is how cutting plasma works:

When additional energy from an electric current or laser is applied to a gas, this energy strips electrons from the gas atoms and forms a combination of free-moving ions (positively charged particles) and free electrons. The energized gas is now plasma and a good conductor of electricity. When the external energy source is removed, the plasma cools and returns to one of the other three states of matter depending on its temperature.

PAC cuts metals by melting them with a hot jet of ionized gas delivered from a constricting orifice. After melting the metal, the high-velocity plasma, which approaches the speed of sound, mechanically blows away the molten material, completing the cut. Cutting plasma has a temperature of 24,000°F and will melt any metal. Both hand-held and machine-mounted torches are available.

Plasma Cutting Equipment

The components of a PAC system are:

- Constant-current power supply.
- Torch and its cables.
- Power and work leads.
- Plasma gas regulator and solenoid.
- Cutting gas hoses and gas supply.

Figure 10-23 shows a small, 120 VAC plasma cutter that includes an air compressor inside the same case as the power supply and a gas solenoid. Larger plasma cutters require an external source of compressed air or gas. Also, many larger PAC systems have a water system for torch cooling that recirculates the water between the torch and a fan-cooled radiator.

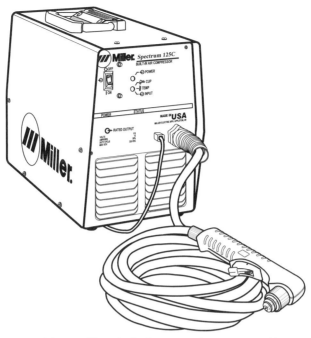

Figure 10-23. A Miller 125C plasma cutting system with an integral air compressor operates on 120 VAC 20 A outlets.

PAC Power Supplies

PAC requires a constant-current power supply with DCEN (direct-current electrode-negative) polarity. Small plasma systems, like those used in sheet metal fabrication, maintenance, and vehicle repair, provide 25–60 A to the torch, larger portable units provide up to 100 A, and high-power units for machine-controlled cutting supply up to 1000 A.

Unlike other welding power supplies, an open-circuit voltage, which is roughly *twice* the operating voltage, is needed to *initiate* the arc. Since operating voltages range from 50 to over 200 volts, open-circuit voltages run from 100 to over 400 volts. Because of hazardous open-circuit voltages, higher capacity torches must be machine operated. This limits the cutting capacity of hand-held torches to $1^1/_4$" steel.

Only the smallest portable cutting systems can be powered from a 20 A, 110 VAC receptacle. Larger units require 220 VAC, and many units need three-phase power.

Special Features of PAC Power Supplies

- Electronics that start the plasma arc and then transfer the arc to the work.
- A power level control.
- Interlocks to shut off the power supply and protect the torch head from damage should the cutting gas or cooling water supply fail.
- Safety interlocks to prevent plasma injuries to the operator.

PAC Gases

While compressed air is adequate for cutting carbon steel, using other gases improves PAC performance. See Table 10-2 for a comparison of gases.

Work Metal	Cutting Gas
Carbon Steel & Low-alloy Steel	Compressed Air, Nitrogen, Argon-Hydrogen Mix
Stainless Steel	Nitrogen, Argon-Hydrogen Mix
Aluminum & Aluminum Alloys	Nitrogen, Argon, Argon-Hydrogen Mix
Gouging	Argon + 35–40% Hydrogen

Table 10-2. Gases for plasma arc cutting and gouging.

Filters keep the gas free of oil, moisture and particles. Particle contamination shortens electrode and nozzle life, and water causes an immediate failure from the steam created. If consumables wear out quickly or black burn marks appear on the work, this suggests a contaminated gas supply.

Torch Construction

A basic plasma torch consists of a handpiece, or *torch body*, a copper *electrode* and a surrounding copper *nozzle*, sometimes called the *cutting tip*, and a *ceramic insulating cup*. See Figure 10-24. The electrode and nozzle are copper plated to prevent spatter adhesion.

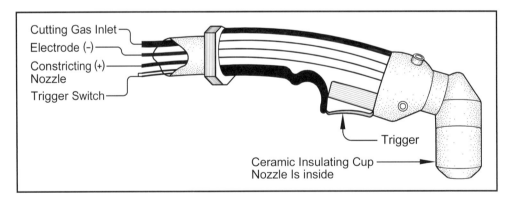

Figure 10-24. A plasma cutting torch handpiece.

As shown in Figure 10-25, when the torch trigger is squeezed, cutting gas flows into the *plenum chamber*—the annular space between the electrode and the nozzle—and out the *cutting orifice*. The orifice is about 0.030" diameter on a low-power cutting torch, and the gas attains supersonic velocity as it is forced through this orifice. The gas cools the torch as well as being the gas that forms the plasma. A ceramic insulating cup surrounds the cutting tip and prevents electrical contact with the work or with a cutting template.

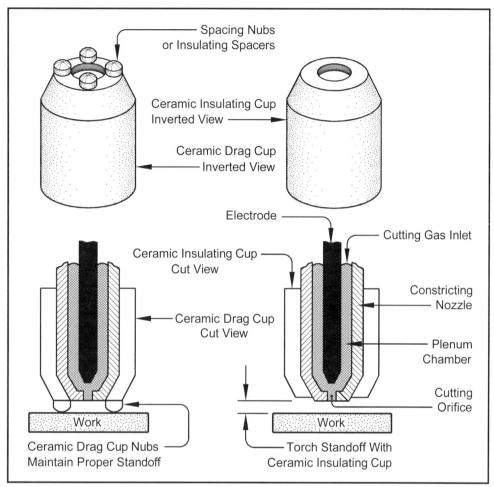

Figure 10-25. Ceramic cups for a plasma cutting torch: a drag cup (top left), an insulating cup (top right) and cross-sectional views of the cups and torch interiors (bottom row).

Plasma Cutting Process

Plasma must flow *from the negative electrode to the work*. Because thousands of volts would be needed between the electrode and the work to establish this plasma path, and this would be very dangerous, cutting plasma is initiated in a two-step process.

First, a *pilot arc* is established between the electrode and the cutting tip *inside* the torch. This is relatively easy to accomplish at much lower and less hazardous voltage than trying to establish the cutting arc in one step. While the pilot arc is established, the work metal is not part of the electrical circuit. Second, since plasma exiting the orifice is conductive, applying a voltage between the negative electrode and the positive workpiece establishes a new electrical path, and the plasma is transferred to the work and cutting begins. Power supply electronics automatically turn off the pilot arc. This process uses a high-voltage, low-current circuit to start the pilot arc, and a low-voltage, high-current circuit to maintain the cutting arc.

Initiating the Pilot Arc

There are two common methods to start the pilot arc:

- The power supply electronics applies a momentary high-frequency voltage between the electrode and the cutting tip until the pilot arc plasma forms.
- The electrode and cutting tip touch when the torch is off, and pop apart when cutting gas begins to flow between them, making a spark that ignites the pilot arc. Because this starting method avoids the use of high-frequency voltage, it also eliminates the chance of an uncomfortable electrical shock during the starting cycle.

Double Arcing

This occurs when *both* the pilot arc and the main cutting arc exist simultaneously. This condition should exist very briefly as the plasma transitions between the nozzle and the work, but if double arcing exists longer, it can damage the electrode and the nozzle. Double arcing can also occur when the nozzle touches the work. And remember, if not stopped, double arcing will quickly damage or destroy the electrode and nozzle.

PAC System Consumables

In PAC systems the cutting gas, electrode and nozzle are consumables. The outer protective ceramic insulating cup will also eventually need replacement. The electrode and nozzle pair should be replaced at the same time. Roughly 1000 starts and cuts may be expected from an electrode and nozzle pair depending on arc current, double arcs and operator skill.

Standoff Distance

Too much standoff produces a wide kerf, a rounded top edge, and *dross* on the bottom edge. Dross is a mixture of iron oxides and other impurities that develop when the workpiece metal is melted. Too little standoff reduces the working life of the nozzle. Optimum standoff distance is a compromise between these two extremes. For best results follow the torch manufacturer's recommendations.

Drag Cups

Drag cups are ceramic cups with insulating spacers, or nubs. Drag cups fit over the nozzle and keep the torch the proper distance above the work and do not allow the metal of the nozzle to touch the work. Refer back to Figure 10-25 (top left). If the nozzle is allowed to touch the work, double arcing occurs, shortening the life of the electrode and the nozzle. Drag cups effectively prevent double arcing, but because they increase the torch-tip-to-work distance, they reduce the thickness of metal the torch can cut when the cut is not at right angles to the work. For angled cuts, nozzles without the projecting nubs of drag cups are used.

Controlling Kerf Size

Table 10-3 shows the principal factors that affect kerf size.

Factor	Relationship
Electrode & Nozzle Tip	Wear and damage widen kerf and degrade cut quality.
Gas	Travel speed, power, and plasma-concentration changes affect kerf width and smoothness.
Orifice Diameter	Larger orifice increases kerf.
Plasma Swirling	Torch tip designs that make the plasma swirl, cut a smaller, smoother kerf.
Power Setting	Using a power setting above or below the optimum power setting increases kerf.
Standoff Distance	Reducing standoff distance reduces kerf.
Travel Speed	Increasing travel speed decreases kerf, but may increase kerf bevel and increase dross on the bottom of the cut.

Table 10-3. Factors affecting kerf size. Usually the kerf is 1.5–2 × the orifice diameter.

Common PAC Variations

Figure 10-26 shows three different plasma cutting methods:

- *Dual gas cutting* cools the torch and focuses the arc.
- The *water shrouding* and *water injection* cutting methods reduce smoke and improve cut quality.
- *Under water cutting* captures smoke and particulates and reduces noise.

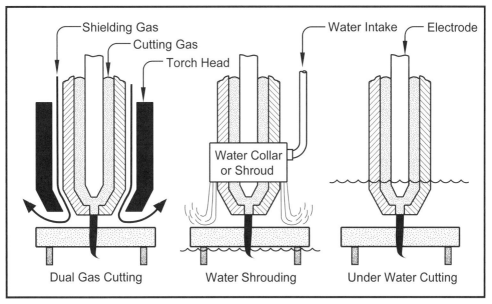

Figure 10-26. Common PAC process variations.

Process Capabilities

PAC will cut any conductive material or non-conductive material with a conductive coating. PAC has the greatest economic advantage over other cutting methods on carbon steels under 1 inch, and on aluminum and stainless steel under 3 inches thick. High-current PAC systems cut $^1/_8$" thick metal with a 100 inch/minute travel speed, and 0.050" thick metal with a 200 inch/minute travel speed. PAC cuts expanded metal screening which, with its frequent starts and stops, OAC cannot cut. PAC is especially convenient for sheet-metal fabrication and for auto body work because it rapidly cuts metal that is too thin for OAC. For example, PAC is used to cut openings in the roofs of cars to install moon roofs.

Setup Procedure for PAC

1. Position and secure the work so cutting sparks will not start fires and the work will not move by operator or arc action.

2. Set up cutting guides, templates, or cutting lines.

3. At a minimum, put on tinted lenses and leather welding gloves.

4. Use ear protection, ventilation or personal air supply and other safety equipment as needed.

5. Position the power supply convenient to the cutting location, and provide electrical power. Insure that operator electrical shock hazards are not created by sweat, moisture, or water puddles. Standing on a rubber mat or a piece of dry wood is good safety practice whenever water is present.

6. Connect the cutting gas supply to the power supply and, if gas cylinders are used, secure them with a non-flammable material such as steel chains or strapping so they will not tip over.

7. While pressing the purge button on the power supply, adjust the gas to the recommended pressure, then release the button. Do not change the pressure regulator setting when the gas pressure rises after the purge button is released. The gas pressure is now set to the proper pressure during gas flow.

8. Attach the work lead—grounding cable—to a clean area on the work. You are now ready to cut.

Plasma Arc Cutter Operation

*   The torch should never be in contact with the work metal since this will cause double arcing and drastically reduce the consumable electrode and nozzle life. Hold the torch $^1/_{16}$–$^1/_8$" above the work or use a drag cup.

*   Many PAC systems have an arc current control. What usually works best is to begin with 95% of the rated arc current and then drop to the lowest current that produces a quality cut. With experience you will learn just what power setting to use.

*   Traveling at the right speed produces the best cut. Using the proper speed causes the dross to shoot out the bottom of the kerf at a 15–20° angle in the direction of travel. Moving too slowly creates molten dross build up on the kerf bottom, while moving too rapidly causes dross to accumulate on the upper work surface which may later require grinding to remove.

Torch Positions

- *Cutting* – Position the torch nozzle just over the edge of the work metal to start the arc *before* moving it over the work metal. Hold the torch so the arc will be at right angles to the work. Squeeze the torch trigger. The gas pre-flow begins, the pilot arc lights, and the main arc ignites. Slowly move (or drag, if using a drag cup) across the work maintaining a distance of $^1/_{16}$–$^1/_8$" from the work. Move slowly enough to allow the arc to pass completely through the work. When near the end of the cut on the opposite edge of the work, angle the torch slightly toward the end of the cut and finish cutting. This technique cuts away the bottom edge first which otherwise can be left at the end of the cut. When the trigger is released the post-flow gas will continue briefly to cool the torch.

- *Piercing* – Hold the torch at a 30–40° angle to the work and squeeze the trigger. When the main arc begins, rotate the torch so the arc is at right angles to the work and complete the hole. Holding the torch at an angle to the work prevents molten metal formed by the start of piercing from spraying back and hitting the nozzle. You can pierce up to half the maximum cutting thickness provided by the machine.

- *Gouging* – This process is used to remove a defective or no longer needed weld. Gouging is also valuable to perform the edge prep when plates have been tacked in place without edge preparation. For gouging, tilt the torch 30–45° from the work and hold the torch $^1/_8$–$^3/_{16}$" above the work. When gouging, it is better to make several shallow passes than one deep pass.

Tips for Better Plasma Arc Cutting

- When you can see the arc coming through the bottom of the cut metal, your travel speed is correct.
- Bad work-lead connections, insufficient arc current, wrong torch angle, or too rapid travel speed cause poor kerf quality or incomplete cuts.
- Minimize pilot arc time to extend nozzle and electrode life.
- Always keep the torch moving or turn it off.
- Poor cuts or cracking will result if the work metal is below 70°F, so preheat may be necessary in cold conditions.
- Periodically check the cutting gas filters and replace them if necessary.
- A dirty compressed air supply may require multiple in-line air filters.
- Use the recommended air pressure. Higher air pressures do not lead to better cutting.
- Keep the return lead connection close to the cutting action.

Many torch designs swirl the cutting gas (or compressed air) for a tighter plasma column. As shown in Figure 10-27, this swirling makes one side of the kerf squarer than the other. When the swirl is clockwise, the kerf is closer to a right angle on the right-side of the cut as seen from the direction of travel. If you are cutting a circle from a plate and want the circle cut-out to have a near-vertical edge, then make the cut clockwise.

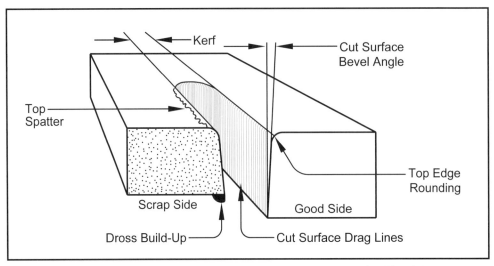

Figure 10-27. Plasma swirl improves cut wall quality on the right side of the cut.

Guides, Templates & Circle Cutters

Cutting precise straight-line, curved and circle cuts can be made easier by using the following guides, templates and circle cutters:

- *Straight-Line Cuts* – Angle iron secured to the work helps make better cuts. Either clamps, tack welds, or magnets work well to secure the angle iron.

See Figure 10-28.

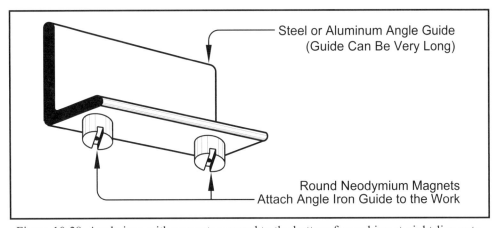

Figure 10-28. Angle iron with magnets secured to the bottom for making straight-line cuts.

- *Curved-Line Cuts* – Aluminum angle that is $1" \times {}^3/_4" \times {}^1/_{16}"$ and has a series of relief cuts can be formed to any curve. See the curve guide in Figure 10-29. Round neodymium magnets secured along the bottom of this aluminum angle holds it in place on the work. This technique also works for angle iron.

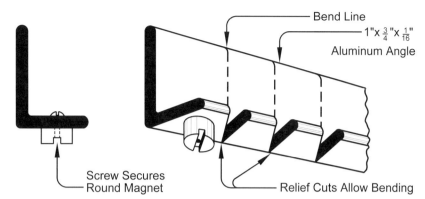

Figure 10-29. To cut curves, make an angle iron or aluminum angle cutting guide with relief cuts to allow bending. Secure the guide to the work with magnets, then make the curved cut.

- *Circle Cuts* – Compass-like devices similar to those used on OAC and OFC torches are available for plasma torches. Refer back to Figure 10-10 (right). For smaller diameter cuts, as shown in Figure 10-30, pipe sections work well as guides. Each pipe section can produce circles of two different diameters:

   - *Inside cuts* are the diameter of the pipe minus the radius of the torch.

   - *Outside cuts* are the diameter of the pipe plus the radius of the torch.

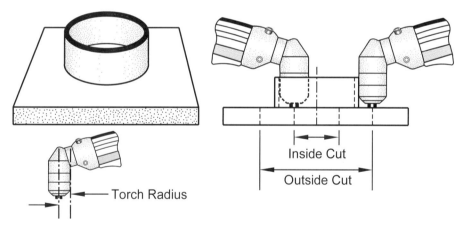

Figure 10-30. Typical PAC pipe section guides for cutting circles. A pipe section can be used for ID and OD cuts for two different diameter circles.

- *Templates* – Plywood, Masonite, and aluminum are the most commonly used template materials because they are easy to cut. Most modern PAC torches have an insulating cup which also allows the torch to be used with a metal guide or template. Some older torches, though, do not permit this because their nozzles are not insulated on their sides. When unsure if your torch is insulated, check your manufacturer's instructions. Unlike OAC or OAF, templates of materials that burn work well for PAC and can be reused many times. Figure 10-31 shows a template designed for installing moon roofs on car tops. This one is held in place with suction cups, but magnets can also be used.

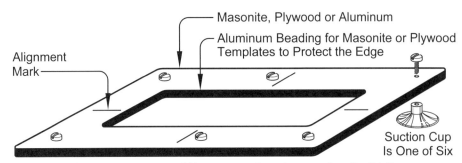

Figure 10-31. Automobile moon roof cutting template for PAC.

An experienced installer can make this cutout in less than a minute. When the compressed air is properly adjusted, there is no damage to the car, including the car roof lining fabric.

Precise Saddle Cuts with PAC

There are two methods to make saddle cuts:

- *For small openings in large pipes*, as in Figure 10-32 (left), a steel or aluminum cutting template is held in place on the work with magnets.
- *For end cuts*, use a pipe larger than the work as a pattern as in Figure 10-32 (right). Pipe-cutting templates must be positioned to compensate for the offset caused by the plasma coming from the middle of the torch head while the torch rides along the edge of the template.

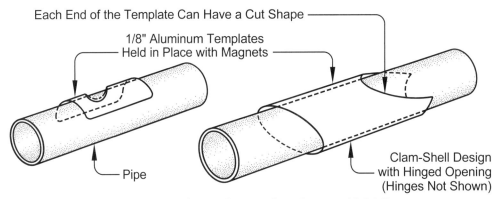

Figure 10-32. Pipe-cutting templates for use with PAC.

Plasma Arc Cutting Advantages

- PAC cuts all metals, has a narrow kerf, and requires no preheat cycle or preheat fuel when performed at normal room temperature.
- Material from thin sheet metal to metal several inches thick can be cut.
- Cutting speed is usually $10 \times$ faster than OAC for steel under $1/2$" thick.
- There is a smaller heat-affected zone than in most other cutting processes.
- PAC pierces metals cleanly without the starting hole needed by OAC, making it ideal for cutting parts under computer-driven control.
- Its 24,000°F plasma cuts materials with melting points too high for OAC.

- Since PAC has a smaller heat-affected zone than OAC, welding can often be done over plasma-cut edges in aluminum and stainless steel without further edge preparation. The contaminating oxides and carbon deposits of OAC do not occur in PAC.
- The plasma arc cuts in any direction.
- Surface smoothness of the cut edges is equal to or better than those cut with OAC.
- PAC costs less than a mechanical/hydraulic shear for the same thickness of metal because it uses less metal stock to cut a part. For example, when a rectangular piece is needed from a stock plate, only the section required can be cut out with PAC leaving the remaining stock for other uses. A shear used to cut the same rectangular piece would require two cuts that would sever the stock plate into three pieces.
- Slag particles from the kerf are smaller in diameter and smaller in volume than with OAC. This makes cleanup easier and damage to the surrounding area is more limited.
- PAC is much simpler to adjust for quality cuts than OAC, is easy to use, and requires no special training.
- Wood, plywood, Masonite, and aluminum cutting templates work well.

Plasma Arc Cutting Disadvantages

- PAC is limited to metal just a few inches thick, whereas OAC can cut steel up to 12 feet thick.
- On steel under $^1/_2$" thick, PAC equipment is roughly 30-50% more expensive than a similarly capable OAC setup. However, for steel *over* $^1/_2$" thick, PAC equipment is 5–10 times more expensive than OAC.
- PAC generates intense light and high noise levels, so eye and ear protection must be worn.
- Hi-powered plasma cutting produces large volumes of hazardous fumes and particulates that must be controlled.

Plasma Arc Cutting Hazards

There are many hazards related to PAC:

- Plasma arcs, including the pilot arc, easily penetrate welding gloves making accidental torch ignition a serious hazard. Keep your hands away from the nozzle at all times and insure that all power is turned off when replacing torch consumables. Do not assume it is off. Check.
- Electrical shock hazards exist from input power lines as well as the high open-circuit voltage between the torch nozzle and the work. To avoid this hazard, wear dry insulating gloves. Ground fault interrupters (GFIs) on the primary or input power side of the power supply will not protect the operator from electric shock from the output voltage between the PAC torch and the work metal.
- Fire and burn hazards exist because the torch throws sparks and slag.

- Intense arc radiation is both visible and invisible (infrared and ultraviolet), making eye protection essential. Also, wear dark, tightly woven long sleeve shirts made from non-synthetic materials. Arcs produce a severe sunburn risk and with just a few hours of exposure, third-degree burns are possible. Repeated burn cycles increase your chances of skin cancer.
- PAC produces smoke and fumes. Keep your head out of the smoke plume by staying to one side of the torch. To insure good ventilation when high-power cutting, either work outside, use an exhaust system, or wear an air-supplied respirator. Take extra precautions to avoid fumes from metals plated with cadmium, chrome, or zinc (galvanized); these are toxic. See *Chapter 2 – Safety* for more on the toxic effects of heavy metals.
- Over time the noise from high-power cutting damages hearing, so ear protection is required.
- For the hazards related to compressed gas cylinders, refer back to *Chapter 8 – Oxyacetylene*.

Section III – Shielded Metal Arc Cutting

Introduction

Shielded Metal Arc Cutting, AWS designation *SMAC*, is sometimes called *hot rodding*. *SMAC* severs metals by melting them with the heat of an arc between a metal electrode and the work. It performs cutting, grooving, piercing, beveling and gouging and uses an SMAW (stick welding) power supply and electrode holder. No compressed air or cylinder gas is needed.

This process is important because adding SMAC electrodes to an SMAW outfit instantly gives it cutting capability. SMAC is used for repair work and for the last minute fixes needed to proceed with construction welding, not for production.

Typical SMAC Cutting Applications

- Beveling plate edges, gouging and removing old welds, bolts, and rivets.
- Piercing holes in I-beams and automotive leaf springs.
- Dismantling welded structures including towers, sign supports, pipe, and sheet piling.
- Trimming and removing hardfacing and high-alloy steel plates on earth moving equipment.

SMAC Equipment

- The preferred power supply for SMAW is a constant-current DC welding machine with DCEN, but an AC constant-current machine may also be used. Arc currents are in the 150–300 A range. See the SMAC setup in Figure 10-33.
- Heavy-duty electrode holder and cutting electrodes.
- Cables and work lead.

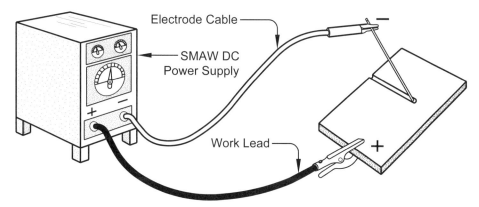

Figure 10-33. SMAC cutting setup.

SMAC Cutting Electrodes

SMAC rods, also called *cutting electrodes*, run at higher current levels than comparably sized rods used for welding. SMAC rods melt the work metal and depend on gravity to remove the molten metal. SMAC cutting electrodes burn more rapidly than their coverings, which results in the electrodes actually burning inside their coverings. This concentrates the arc by forcing it out the end of the electrode. Besides concentrating the arc, the electrode covering serves two other purposes: to keep the electrode from shorting-out to the sides of the cut when inserted into the kerf, and to stabilize the arc with the gases produced as the electrode burns. See Figure 10-34.

Soaking regular welding electrodes in water prior to use will enhance their cutting ability because the steam produced forces the molten metal out of the cut. Typical cutting electrodes are $^3/_{16}$" or larger, but smaller electrodes are also available. E6010, E6012 and E6020 rods are commonly used, but there are proprietary SMAC electrodes designed specifically for cutting. These proprietary electrodes will give better cutting performance than standard welding electrodes.

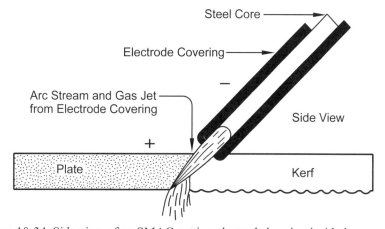

Figure 10-34. Side view of an SMAC cutting electrode burning inside its covering.

Cutting, Gouging & Piercing with SMAC

- *Cutting* – Use an up-and-down sawing motion while holding the electrode at a 45° angle to the work and pointing in the direction of travel. The down motion uses the force of the arc to displace molten metal, and the up motion to expose more metal to arc heat. See Figure 10-35.

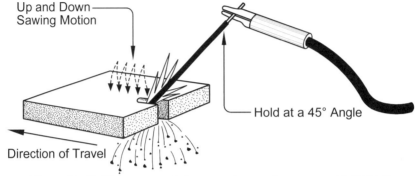

Figure 10-35. Use an up-and-down sawing motion to cut with SMAC.

- *Gouging* – Tilt the cutting rod to point its tip in the direction of travel to direct the force of the arc into the intended groove and keep the rod at an angle of 5° or less to the work surface as in Figure 10-36.

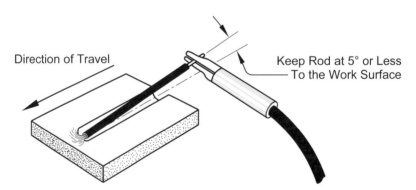

Figure 10-36. Gouging performed with SMAC.

- *Piercing* – Use a small circular motion and draw a long arc over the spot to be pierced. When the metal surface is molten, force the electrode tip down through the metal. Trim the size and shape of the hole with an up-and-down sawing motion.

SMAC Advantages

- Fast cutting process.
- Very convenient for cutting and weld preparation when OAC or PAC equipment is not available and SMAW equipment is already in place.
- Excellent for making a last-minute cut or weld bevel needed before welding starts.
- Avoids the handling of the compressed gases needed for OFC.

SMAC Disadvantages

- Requires more operator skill to produce acceptable grooving than with other processes.
- Generally, the cut quality is not as good as with OAC and PAC, and grinding may be needed to achieve a smooth surface.

Section IV – Air Carbon Arc Cutting

Introduction

Air Carbon Arc Cutting, AWS designation *CAC-A*, uses heat from a carbon arc to melt the work metal and a compressed air jet to blow the molten metal away. This versatile process can cut, bevel, groove, gouge, pierce, or resurface all metals in a technique called *plate washing*.

CAC-A is important because it removes existing or defective weld bead metal faster than *all* other processes. Also, it is ten times faster than abrasive grinding and less expensive. In addition, since it is not an oxidation but a melting process, air carbon arc cutting can cut most metals including cast iron.

CAC-A Applications

- Beveling and gouging for weld preparation and weld removal are the most important applications of air carbon arc cutting. No other weld removal method can remove a weld bead on an inside corner without damaging the surrounding work metal. See Figure 10-37.

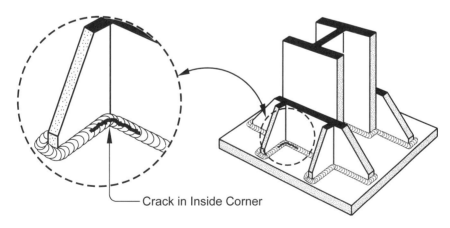

Figure 10-37. CAC-A is the best method for removing
a defective weld bead on an inside corner.

- Repair operations to prepare work for welding or dismantling. This is usually performed in heavy industry, shipyards, and in boiler shops.
- Air carbon arc cutting is used in cast iron foundries and steel mills for cutting *risers*, and for resurfacing (plate washing) castings where risers and defects were removed.
- CAC-A can be used with automated beveling equipment.

- Although CAC-A can be used for cutting, OAC, OAF or plasma are often better choices.

CAC-A Equipment

- SMAW power supply up to 500 A.
- Carbon-graphite SMAC electrodes.
- Electrode holder and cables.
- Compressed air supply.

CAC-A Power Supplies

Any three-phase DC welding machine or DC generator with the requisite current capacity will work. DC machines with DCEP offer the widest range of electrode diameters and current capacity and are preferred for air carbon arc cutting, but AC machines can sometimes work. Single-phase AC machines, though, are not a good choice because the 60 cycle/second reversal of the current flow through the plasma reduces the effect of the cutting current. See Table 10-5 for a comparison of electrodes and power supplies.

Electrode Diameter (inches)	Current Range (A)		
	DC Electrode DCEP	AC Electrode on AC	AC Electrode on DCEN
$1/8$	60–90	—	—
$5/32$	90–150	—	—
$3/16$	200–250	200–250	150–180
$1/4$	300–400	300–400	200–250
$5/16$	350–450	—	—
$3/8$	450–600	350–450	300–400
$1/2$	800–1000	400–800	400–500
$5/8$	1000–1250	—	—
$3/4$	1250–1600	—	—
1	1600–2200	—	—

Table 10-5. Suggested current ranges for commonly used CAC-A electrodes.

CAC-A Electrode Holder

The copper electrode contacts on a CAC-A holder contain one or more compressed air-jet openings or holes. These holes direct air along the underside of the electrode and blow away the molten metal that has been heated by the arc. Most electrode holders are air-cooled and the air stream runs along the electrode just as water tends to run along the side of a knife held under a faucet. The compressed air supply is controlled by a lever on the torch. There is an optimum electrode stickout length, too long and the air stream breaks away from the electrode and looses strength, too short and melting is retarded. See the CAC-A electrode holder in Figure 10-38.

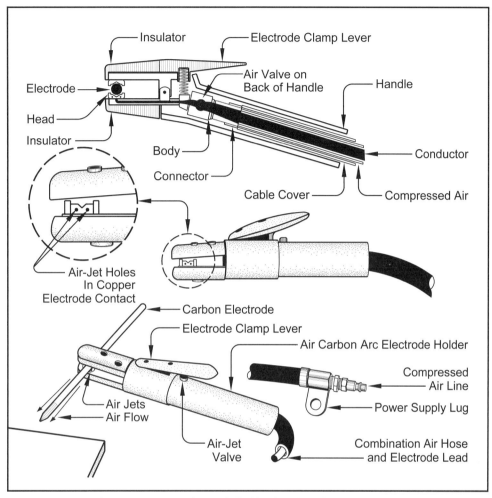

Figure 10-38. An electrode holder for air carbon arc cutting.

CAC-A Electrode Types

- *DC copper-coated electrodes* run cooler and last longer than the plain, uncoated electrodes. They provide a stable arc and a uniform groove size because the copper coating prevents oxidation from reducing the electrode's diameter *before* it gets to the arc. These electrodes are also available *jointed*, that is, with a female socket and a male tang. This arrangement allows a replacement electrode to be connected to the electrode in use and its stub to be burned down into the replacement electrode, which eliminates all stub loss. Both round and flat—also called rectangular—electrodes are available to make shaped grooves.
- *DC plain electrodes* are made like the coated ones except they have no covering and burn much faster.
- *AC copper-coated electrodes* have rare earth elements added to stabilize the arc.

Compressed Air Requirements

- Pressures run 60–100 psi, but light duty torches run as low as 40 psi.
- Air consumption typically is 25–33 ft^3/minute, but higher operating currents require higher compressed air pressures.
- Air pressures over those recommended will not improve metal removal. Though pressures that are too low may appear to work, they often leave slag and carbon deposits in the kerf which may require grinding.
- Air supply hoses must be at least $^3/_8$" diameter to assure adequate volume.
- Never use oxygen in place of compressed air because this can cause a dangerous explosion.

CAC-A Setup & Operation

1. Set up the welding machine the same as for SMAW. See pages 84–85.

2. Adjust the power supply to the correct current for your electrode diameter.

3. Start the air compressor and adjust the regulator to the correct air pressure. Use just enough air pressure to blow away the molten metal. Remember, more pressure is not better.

4. Insert the electrode into the holder. Extend the carbon-graphite electrode 6" beyond the holder. Use a 3" extension for aluminum. Ensure that the electrode point is properly shaped, usually sharply pointed.

5. Position the electrode holder so that the electrode tip points in the direction of travel.

6. Open the air-jet valve on the electrode holder, then strike the arc. Do not draw out the arc when it is struck. Maintain a short arc.

7. The depth and contour of the cutting groove are controlled by the electrode angle, travel speed, and by the current setting. The width of the groove is governed by the diameter of the electrode and the cross-sectional shape of the electrode. For pad or plate washing, use an electrode with a rectangular cross section to speed metal removal. These rectangular electrodes are also used for some grooving work. When cutting or gouging a shallow groove on the surface of a piece of metal, position the electrode holder at a very flat angle in relation to the work. This process may be used to cut or gouge metal in the flat, horizontal, vertical, or overhead positions. See Figure 10-39.

8. Control the arc and the speed of travel according to the shape and the condition of the cut desired. As metal is removed, move fast enough to maintain a short arc. Always cut away from the operator as molten metal sprays some distance from the cutting action.

9. When cutting is complete, leave the compressed air on until the carbon electrode is no longer red hot.

Tip: Do not soak carbon electrodes in water because they may shatter. If carbon electrodes become damp before use, bake them for 10 hours at 300°F in a rod oven.

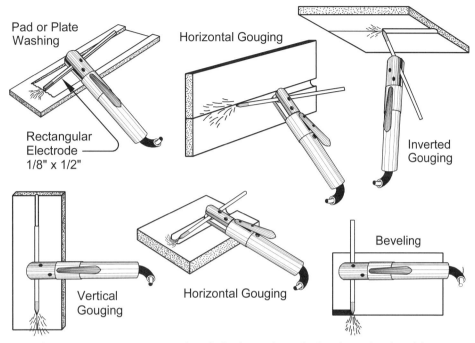

Figure 10-39. CAC-A operations in horizontal, vertical and overhead positions.

Gouging Electrode Recommendations

See Table 10-6.

Metals & Their Alloys	Gouging Electrode Recommendations
Carbon Steel, Low-Alloy Steel, & Stainless Steel	DC electrodes with DCEP.
Cast Iron	$1/2$" or larger DC electrodes at highest rated current, use 70° push angle, do not exceed $1/2$" depth/pass.
Copper Alloys (60% Cu and under)	DC electrodes with DCEN at highest electrode rating.
Copper Alloys (60% Cu and over)	DC electrodes with DCEN at highest electrode rating, or use AC electrodes on AC.
Aluminum Bronze, Aluminum Nickel & Bronze	DC electrodes with DCEN.
Nickel Alloys (80% Ni & over)	AC electrodes on AC.
Magnesium Alloys	DC electrodes with DCEP. Wire brush the groove before welding to remove oxides.
Aluminum	DC electrodes with DCEP or DCEN. Use stainless steel wire brush before welding. Do not exceed electrode extension of 3 inches.
Titanium, Zirconium, Hafnium & Their Alloys	Surface layer must be mechanically removed before beginning a new weld.

Table 10-6. Gouging electrode types and use recommendations.

CAC-A Advantages

- Removes metal very fast, making it ideal for when a large volume of metal needs to be removed.
- Process is easy to learn and to control and requires relatively low welder skill.
- Few adjustments are required.
- Suitable SMAW power supplies are usually already on hand, so adding a CAC-A torch costs just a few hundred dollars.
- Cuts *all* metals.
- Has a lower heat input than oxyacetylene cutting and a smaller heat-affected zone.
- Uses compressed air rather than oxygen and fuel gas in cylinders.

CAC-A Disadvantages

- Throws sparks and molten metal up to 35 feet, so non-flammable plastic or metal shielding may be needed.
- Welding hood, gloves and long sleeves are required.
- Produces *very* high noise levels so ear protection is required.
- May produce toxic smoke and fumes depending on the work metal.
- May not produce as smooth a cut as other processes.
- No low-current AC electrodes are available, so this process cannot be used with the common AC *buzz boxes*.
- This equipment is more expensive than OFC.
- CAC-A performs best at arc currents between 350–700 A and is used very little at lower currents because most welders do not have power supplies available that can supply these high arc currents.

Section V – Water Jet Cutting

Introduction

Water jet cutting refers to two versions of this process: *Pure water jet cutting* and *abrasive water jet cutting (AJC)*. Pure water jet cutting is for soft materials such as paper, bread, foam, diapers, gaskets and automotive interior rugs. Abrasive jet cutting adds abrasive particles to the water jet and cuts hard materials such as metal, glass, marble, structural laminate, printed circuit boards and plastic.

Here's how it works:

When the high-velocity water jet strikes the work, supersonic erosion tears away microscopic particles, making a cut. Since we are concerned with cutting metals, not diapers, this chapter focuses on abrasive water jet cutting.

Because of its versatility, high cutting speeds, low cutting forces, lack of heat input and dimensional accuracy, AJC is the best choice for many cutting tasks. In many applications it is the only choice.

Abrasive Water Jet System

Figure 10-40 shows how the components of an abrasive water jet cutting system work together.

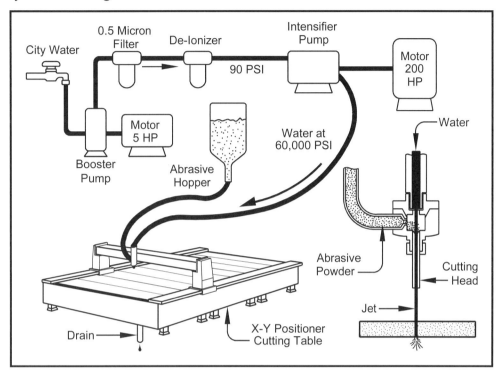

Figure 10-40. An abrasive water jet cutting system.

Abrasive Water Jet Process

Incoming tap water is filtered, de-ionized and sent to a booster pump where its pressure is raised to 90 psi. This booster insures that the next pump in line, the *intensifier pump*, receives a steady flow of water and never runs dry. The intensifier uses a 20–200 hp electric motor driving a mechanical gear pump to raise hydraulic oil to 3000 psi. This high-pressure oil drives a piston pump that raises the incoming water pressure to 60,000 psi. This high-pressure water is piped to the cutting head, blended with the cutting abrasive, and forced through the cutting nozzle.

Cutting nozzles are made of sapphire, ruby, or diamond and are typically 4–10 thousandths of an inch in diameter. Forcing the water and abrasive mixture through the cutting nozzle converts the high-pressure water into a cutting stream with a velocity of twice the speed of sound. The work is positioned in a tray to catch the water and recover the abrasive. Sometimes cutting is done underwater to reduce noise. Most ACJ systems use NC positioners on the cutting head, but a few systems are operated like a manual bandsaw.

AJC Applications
- Cutting parts to final size from all metals.
- Cutting parts to near-finished size to reduce final machining time.
- Trimming printed circuit boards, Kevlar and carbon-carbon composites.
- Hole piercing.

Abrasive Water Jet Advantages
- Edges are smooth and square, and in many cases parts can be used without further cleanup.
- Abrasive water jet cutting does not introduce distortion and is especially good on thin, complex parts.
- No cutting heat, so no heat-affected zone.
- Because of the narrow kerfs—between 0.004–0.010 inches—parts can be closely nested to save material.
- Capable of cutting very complex shapes to high tolerances and may replace hard tooling on shorter production runs.
- Cuts many materials: metals, plastics, rubber, laminates, paper and glass.
- Cuts soft, light materials such as diapers, fiberglass insulation, paper and gasket materials without damage.
- Very low force on the work, around 2 lbs, requires only simple fixturing.
- Very fast cutting, without fumes.
- Unattended operation is possible.

Abrasive Water Jet Disadvantages
- Cutting machine capital costs, run time, and consumables are more expensive than other cutting methods such as PAC and OAC.
- AJC is not portable and cannot be used in the field.

Section VI – Oxygen Lances & Burning Bars

Introduction
Oxygen lances, AWS designation *LOC*, and *burning bars* produce high enough temperatures to melt through *all* materials including concrete.

Oxygen lances and burning bars are important because they quickly cut materials not readily cut by other processes and they can also cut thicknesses of many materials which are otherwise impossible to cut. Oxygen lances and burning bars are primarily used in steel mills and foundries for trimming ingots and castings, for heavy machinery demolition, and for building collapse rescue work. Small burning bars are useful for removing frozen shafts and large bolts without damaging the surrounding parts.

LOC Equipment
The typical oxygen lance system shown in Figure 10-41 consists of:

- *Oxygen source*, either manifolded oxygen cylinders or a liquid oxygen cylinder and vaporizer. These are needed to supply the high volume of oxygen required because a single oxygen cylinder is not adequate.
- *High-volume oxygen regulator* capable of 40 ft^3/min at 150 psi (10 bar) minimum.
- *Oxygen lance hose* with a $^3/_8$" diameter minimum. A $^1/_2$" diameter hose is needed for hose lengths over 100 feet.

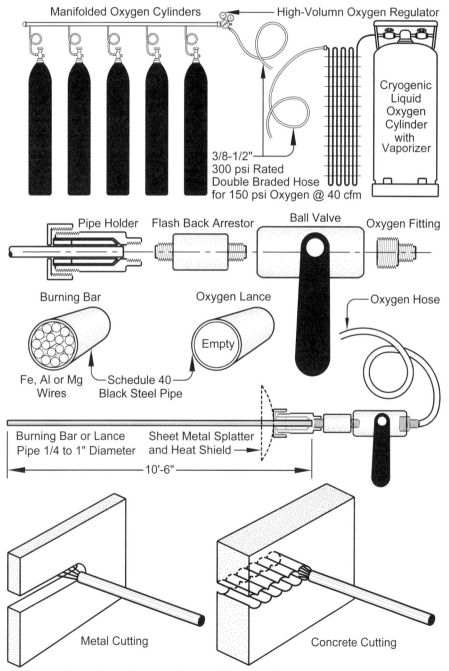

Figure 10-41. Oxygen lance and burning bar cutting equipment.

- *Lance pipe*, which is typically Schedule 40 black steel pipe, from $^3/_{16}$–1 inch OD, depending on the application. The lance pipe length is usually about 10.5 feet, but may run from 3–21 feet.
- *Valve and pipe-holder assembly,* usually consisting of a ball valve and hardware to connect the valve to the lance pipe. In addition, there may also be a heat shield and a flashback arrestor.
- A *means of igniting* the oxygen lance is also needed. Usually an oxyacetylene torch is used, but smaller lances sometimes use a battery and a copper striker plate. The lance is drawn across the plate at a 45° angle and the resulting sparks ignite the lance.

LOC Process

Oxygen lances are most often used for cutting cast iron and steel in foundries and steel mills where the materials to be cut are *already* red hot from processing and need no additional preheating to begin lancing. There are many other production and maintenance applications in foundries and steel mills where the work metal is not red hot. For example, if a failure in the production equipment allows molten metal to cool in a ladle, an oxygen lance can cut up the solidified metal so it can be removed in pieces without damaging the ladle. When the material to be cut is *not* already red hot, a second welder usually preheats the start of the cut with an oxyacetylene torch. When the starting point is red hot, the lance operator positions the lance over the preheated spot and opens the oxygen valve. The steel lance pipe begins burning in a self-sustaining exothermic (heat releasing) reaction and releases heat that melts the work. If the work material itself burns, as with steel, then even more heat is released, accelerating both the burning and melting processes.

Oxygen Lances vs. Burning Bars

An oxygen lance uses a length of *empty* steel pipe to contain and direct the oxygen stream and to provide heat from the oxidation of the pipe steel to the work. A burning bar, more correctly called an *exothermic burning bar*, is supplied with iron, aluminum, or magnesium rods, wires or hollow tubing *inside* the steel pipe. These rods provide substantially more heat to the work than an oxygen lance and cut much more rapidly. Burning bars will cut virtually any metal, concrete, or refractory (fire brick). Temperatures of 6600–8000°F have been recorded on burning bars, and up to 12,000°F in high-performance burning bars. See Table 10-7 for melting points of materials commonly cut with oxygen lances and burning bars. The same oxygen supply equipment works for both lances and burning bars, but burning bars require oxygen pressures as high as 250 psi, so a special double-braided oxygen hose with a rated working pressure of 300 psi is required.

Burning Bar/Material	Output Temperature or Melting Point (°F)
Oxygen Lance	5000
Exothermic Burning Bar	6600–8000
Exothermic High-Temperature Burning Bar	12000
Steel	2850
Copper Alloys	1985
Nickel Alloys	2650
Concrete	5200

Table 10-7. Melting point comparison for burning bars and oxygen lances versus the materials they are designed to cut.

Oxygen lances work better on iron and steel that is already red hot from processing, while burning bars work better cutting cold metals and concrete. Both cut metals in a continuous line, but sever concrete, masonry and refractory material by melting a series of overlapping holes much like chain drilling in metal.

A typical 10.5-foot burning bar consumes about 100 ft^3 of oxygen in 4–4$^1/_2$ minutes. In normal operation it will use 1200 ft^3/hour. A $^3/_8$" diameter burning bar will melt through a foot of concrete per minute, or 24–30 inches of 2-inch diameter holes. The same size burning bar cuts about 17 feet of 2-inch carbon steel, or 14 feet of 3-inch stainless steel. Reinforcing rods in the concrete present no problems, they actually speed up the cutting action because they provide iron to burn in the oxygen stream.

Lances and burning bars actually oxidize iron and steel and blow away the oxides in the form of slag. Other materials like copper and concrete are cut by melting them and blowing the melted liquid material from the cutting zone.

In general, oxygen lances cut faster than an oxyacetylene cutting torch. In many applications burning bars are the best solution from both a time and total cost standpoint.

Burning Bars in Machine Shop Applications

Burning bars are excellent for removing frozen axels, shafts, dowels, taper pins and large bolts that are rusted in place. See Figure 10-42.

Here's how to unfreeze a rusted axle or shaft:

1. Using a $^1/_4$" or $^3/_8$" diameter burning bar, pierce a hole through the center of the frozen axel or shaft. The burning bar heat first expands the shaft and then allows it to relax and shrink slightly when it cools. The heating and subsequent cooling by the burning bar temperature-cycles the shaft or axle and breaks the bond between the rusted surfaces.

2. Now the shaft can be driven out and the rusted bolts unscrewed.

3. If the axle, shaft or pin is in a blind hole and cannot be driven out, weld a stub to the accessible end and use a slide hammer to remove it.

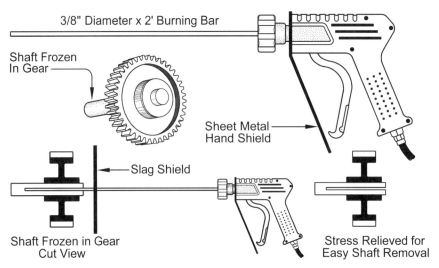

Figure 10-42. Using a burning bar to free a frozen axle or shaft.

A similar application is the removal of a propeller that is frozen onto its shaft. Usually the shaft is bent or the propeller damaged and one of the two can be salvaged using a burning bar. If the shaft is stainless steel, a burning bar is the very best way to remove the propeller.

Small burning bars usually have a sheet-metal *hand shield* secured in front of the handle, but most experienced welders add a *second* shield on the burning bar called a *slag shield*. To make a slag shield, cut a slit in a square of a used rubber tire and slip the square over the burning bar, positioning it close to where the burning bar enters the work. This second shield keeps smoke, sparks and slag away from the handle and the welder.

LOC Advantages

- Cuts thick stainless steel – A burning bar or oxygen lance is the best choice for cutting *thick* stainless steel sections. In fact, there is no practical limit to the depth of cut since burning bars and oxygen lances can have additional lengths of pipe added to extend their reach.
- High-speed cuts – Burning bars cut at high-speed and with no mechanical vibration, both essential in demolition and rescue work. In some cases, there is no other effective way to cut large, and sometimes tangled, masses of material.
- Little training is required – To successfully use this process, just a few hours of training is needed.

LOC Disadvantages

- Lances and burning bars consume large volumes of oxygen. In heavy industry, where oxygen is purchased in bulk and is relatively inexpensive, oxygen consumption is not an issue.
- Generates lots of heat, light, sparks and fumes.

Chapter 11

Brazing & Soldering

*There is nothing more useless as doing efficiently
that which should not be done at all.*

—Peter F. Drucker

Section I – Brazing Basics

Brazing Basics

Brazing joins metals with the addition of *braze filler metal,* also called *brazing alloy,* which melts at temperatures above 840°F. Often two different metals are joined by brazing.

Here are the steps to braze a joint:

1. Be sure that the joint surfaces are designed or modified for good fit with clearances of 0.001–0.003 inches. This provides the best capillary attraction to draw filler metal into the joint to assure maximum joint strength.

2. Surfaces to be brazed must be cleaned of oil, paint, rust and dirt. Often an alcohol or acetone wipe-down is used to remove remaining oils.

3. Flux is usually added to chemically clean—and sometimes etch—the joint surfaces to prepare them for the braze filler metal. Additionally, by creating a protective atmosphere, flux prevents both the filler and work metals from oxidizing during the heating process.

4. The parts are positioned for joining and can be held in a fixture. Two flat parts can be merely placed one on top of the other.

5. The joint is heated slightly above the melting point of the filler metal. The melting temperature of the filler metal is lower—sometimes substantially lower—than the melting point of the workpiece metal. *Capillary attraction* draws the melted filler metal into the joint. Inside the joint, the filler metal *wets* the base metal forming *intermetallic compounds* or *alloys* between the base and filler metals at their interface. See Figure 11-1.

6. When the filler metal cools and solidifies, the joint is complete. Atomic attractive forces hold the joint together at the braze metal and base metal interfaces. This is called *adhesion*.

7. The joint is then cleaned to remove flux, which is corrosive and could weaken the joint and affect its appearance.

Wetting & Capillary Attraction

Wetting action between the filler and base metals is facilitated by the ability of the filler metal to alloy with the base metal at their interface. For example, pure lead does not readily wet copper or steel or adhere to either metal, but a tin-lead alloy readily wets both copper and steel. This preference of filler metal for atoms other than its own causes the *wetting action* of the base metal. Although wetting is often called *tinning*, this term is misleading because wetting action occurs between many different metals, not just tin. If filler metal does not wet the base metal, and instead balls up to form small spheres, this is usually caused by a dirty base metal surface or the lack of a proper flux.

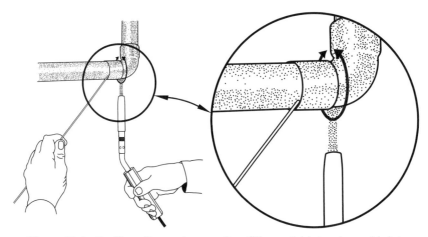

Figure 11-1. Capillary forces draw molten filler metal into a brazed joint.

In summary, capillary forces draw the filler metal into the joint and when the filler metal cools and solidifies, interatomic forces hold the joint together.

Joint strength is greatly affected by the condition of the brazed surfaces. In addition to surface cleanliness, *surface roughness* influences brazed joint strength. A rough surface provides more surface area for the filler metal to bond to, forming a stronger joint. Also, a roughened surface often has a jagged contour that traps and locks the filler metal in place, further strengthening the joint mechanically. Brazed joint strength results from *both* atomic and mechanical forces. To achieve the required strength, the joint surfaces may be roughened mechanically or chemically.

Soldering vs. Brazing

The distinction between brazing and soldering is the temperature at which these processes are performed. Brazing takes place *above* 840°F and soldering *below* 840°F, but otherwise the two processes are quite similar. Brazed joints are considerably stronger than soldered joints because the strength of brazing filler metals is greater than the strength of solders. However, the joint strength of brazed joints on non-ferrous metals and steels can be greater than the tensile strength of the filler metal itself because of the thinness of the joint and the interatomic adhesion forces at work. On stainless steels, joints with tensile strength greater than 130,000 psi are possible. Brazing often achieves nearly the strength of a welded joint without the problems of heat distortion and, because the seam line is thin, the joint can be concealed.

Brazing vs. Braze Welding

Brazing uses capillary attraction to draw filler metal into the mating joint, while in *braze welding* the filler metal is *deposited* in grooves or fillets at the points where needed for joint strength. With braze welding capillary attraction is *not* a factor in distributing the filler metal since the joints are open and exposed to the welder. Wetting of the base metal by the filler metal results in atomic bonds which are the same for brazing, braze welding, and soldering.

Braze welding is *not* a brazing process, but a welding process that uses braze filler metal. Joint designs are similar to those for the oxyacetylene welding of V-groove butt joints, lap joints, T-joints, fillets and plug joints. Braze welding is an important and effective repair method for cracked or broken cast iron and aluminum parts, and many large machinery castings can be successfully repaired this way. For example, large areas of damaged aluminum outboard propeller blades can be built up or replaced using a low-temperature solder in a fashion similar to braze welding.

In one instance, a new hydraulic shear in a production department was misused by a maintenance man on a Saturday when no supervisor was present. The mechanic attempted to shear the maximum thickness for steel, but in stainless steel. The side of the shear casting snapped and was repaired with braze welding—a repair that lasted for more than 20 years.

As with brazing, braze welding does not melt the base metal and is performed at a lower temperature than welding, resulting in much less distortion of the work. Also, since braze welding is performed only on a small area of the part, the entire part does not need to be brought up to braze temperature at once. This is a big advantage when repairing large castings. See *Section IX, Repairs Made with Braze Welding*, page 315.

Metals Joined by Brazing & Soldering

Most common metals can be brazed including: aluminum, bronze, brass, cast iron, copper, stainless steel, carbon steel, titanium, some tool steels and tungsten carbide. Nearly all metals can be soldered. If two different workpiece metals can be wetted by the same filler metal, they can be brazed or soldered together.

Process Temperature Selection

Temperatures are selected so that the braze or solder metal is completely liquid, which allows it to readily flow into the joint and quickly wet the surfaces. This temperature, though, must be as low as possible so as not to affect the work metal, burn the flux, or burn the surrounding work. When using the correct flux and correct process temperature, both the capillary attraction and the wetting action occur in less than a second.

Brazing Advantages

- *Low temperature process* – The components being joined, such as semiconductors and other electronic components, are less likely to be damaged since the base metals do not reach their melting temperatures.

- *Ability to join dissimilar metals* – Steel is easily joined to copper, cast iron to stainless steel, and brass to aluminum.

- *Able to join non-metals to metals* – Ceramics and glass are easily joined to metals or to each other.

- *Joins parts of widely different thicknesses* – Either thin-to-thin or thin-to-thick parts may be joined without burn-through or overheating, which can be a serious problem when welding.

- *Excellent stress distribution* – Many of the distortion problems of fusion welding are eliminated because brazing has lower process temperatures, even heat distribution, and more gradual temperature changes.

- *Economical for complex assemblies* – Many parts can be joined in a single step. Often complex parts are more economically made by brazing several pieces together rather than machining the part from a single piece of metal. This method results in a savings of both raw material and machining time.

- *Good for joining precision parts* – Using proper jigs and fixtures, parts can be very accurately positioned.

- *Parts can be temporarily joined* – After being temporarily joined, parts can undergo other manufacturing processes and then be separated without damage.

- *Parts can be assembled rapidly* – Processes are readily adaptable to utilize batch brazing as well as automatic assembly operations.

- *Mistakes are easily fixed* – A misaligned part is simple to reposition.

- *Ability to make leak-proof and vacuum-tight joints* – Many tanks and vessels are soldered or brazed. High-power radio transmitter vacuum tubes and integrated circuits with metal to ceramic joints are also brazed.

- *Joints require little or no finishing* – With proper process design, brazed or soldered joints can be nearly invisible.

- *Combined brazing and heat treatment cycles* – When protective-atmosphere brazing is used, the brazing process may be incorporated into the heat-treatment cycle.

Brazing Disadvantages

- Brazing processes are rarely as strong as fusion-welded joints.

- The brazed parts and filler metal may have a poor color match.

Section II – Joint Design & Cleaning

Joint Design

Well designed braze and solder joints start with fundamental butt, lap and scarfed joints as shown in Figure 11-2 (top & center). Scarfed joints are stronger than if the same materials were butted together because scarfed joints provide more surface area to which the filler metal can adhere. The bottom of Figure 11-2 shows a detail of a brazed lap joint.

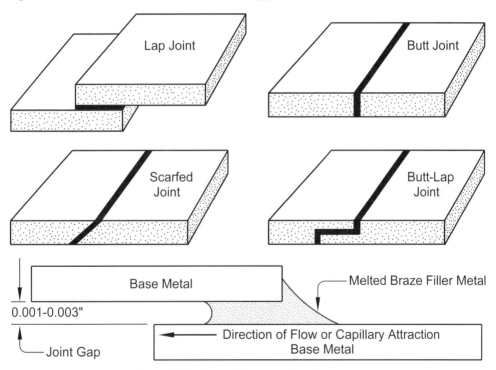

Figure 11-2. Typical braze and solder joints.

The maximum strength of a simple lap joint can be increased by an overlap of three times the thickness of the base metal (3T). This is sometimes called the *Rule of Threes*. More overlap without additional refinements will not improve joint strength, but tapers or smooth transitions in thickness, as shown in Figure 11-3 (left, bottom two joints), make stronger joints because they spread out the stress over a greater area.

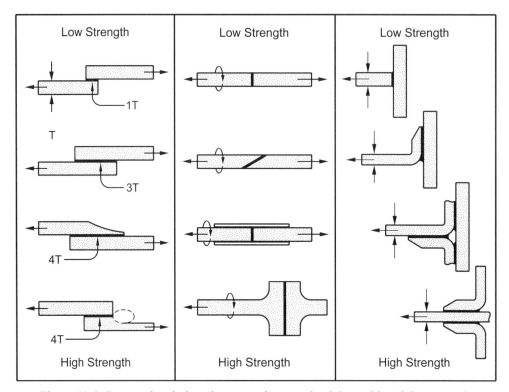

Figure 11-3. Progressive design changes to increase lap joint and butt joint strength.

Factors in Joint Design

- *Filler Metal Selection* – Base and filler metal alloys should have similar coefficients of thermal expansion. At brazing temperatures, joints between metals with different coefficients can cause too much or too little joint clearance. Dissimilar metals may also lead to the formation of an electrolytic cell (sort of like a battery) that leads to corrosion.

- *Effect of Flux on Clearance* – Flux must enter the joint *ahead* of the braze filler metal, then be displaced by it. But when joint clearance is too small, the flux may be held in the joint by capillary forces. This prevents proper braze filler entry and leaves voids. More about flux later in this chapter.

- *Joint Clearances* – Joint clearances range from 0.002–0.010" because within this range capillary attraction is most effective. Assuming that the joint clearance is adequate to admit braze filler material, the lower the joint clearance, the stronger the joint. Too much clearance reduces joint strength, too little permits voids in the joint. Joints in the 0.001–0.002" range often have a tensile strength 4–5 times higher than that of the filler metal because of surface tension between the filler metal and the joint sides. See Graph 11-1. Another example of this phenomena is the attraction between two smooth glass plates with a few drops of water between them, despite the fact that the water itself has no tensile strength.

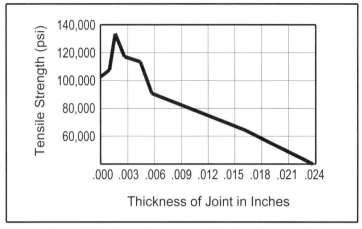

Graph 11-1. Joint clearance vs. joint tensile strength.

Joint Surface Cleaning

Grinding, filing, wire brushing, bead and sand blasting are the most common surface preparation methods used to remove dirt, paint and grease so the filler metal completely wets the base metal. Some other surface preparation methods include solvent cleaning with acetone or trichloroethylene, vapor degreasing with perchlorethylene, alkaline cleaning, electrolytic cleaning, salt baths and ultrasonic cleaning.

The blasting media used in joint surface cleaning must be chosen so that the particles do not embed themselves into the base metal and are easily removed after blasting. For this reason, blasting media like alumina—made from bauxite or synthetically produced aluminum oxide—zirconia and silicon carbide should be avoided since they leave residual particles that inhibit wetting and reduce joint strength.

The wire brushes used in surface cleaning must be free of contaminating materials and selected so none of the wire wheel material is transferred to the part being cleaned. A carbon steel wire brush is fine for steel, but on most other materials a stainless steel wire brush is a better choice. While a stainless steel wire brush could be used on ferrous metal, it should not be later used on stainless steel because it will transfer iron particles from the ferrous metals to the stainless steel. This can cause a blemish and inhibit wetting action. Label brushes for stainless steel use only and prevent them from touching other metals.

Clean joints just before brazing. Do not clean joints one day and expect good wetting results when they are brazed the next day.

Many joint cleaning processes used for brazing are also used for soldering. However, in a non-production situation, mechanical cleaning, especially with emery cloth, commercial abrasive pads, or by filing is effective for soldering. Getting down to fresh, bare metal is the objective. As with brazing, complete the soldering immediately, before the base metals have a chance to re-oxidize.

Section III – Filler Metals & Fluxes

Essential Properties of Brazing Filler Metals

- While the melting point of the filler metal or solder must be below the melting point of the workpiece metal, equally important is the temperature at which the filler or solder actually *flows* into the joint. It is common for the flow or *liquidus* temperature to be 100°F or more *above* the melting temperature. Remember that the melting temperature can leave the filler metal in a pasty or slushy condition and at this temperature it will not flow into the joint. Usually the liquidus temperature is the more important number when comparing similar brazing alloys. See Figure 11-4 for a comparison of the melting points of braze filler metals and solders.

- Brazing filler metals contain alloys whose composition *does not* allow separation of the filler metal into its alloy components during brazing. This metal separation process, called *liquation*, is necessary when extracting metals from ore, but not when brazing.

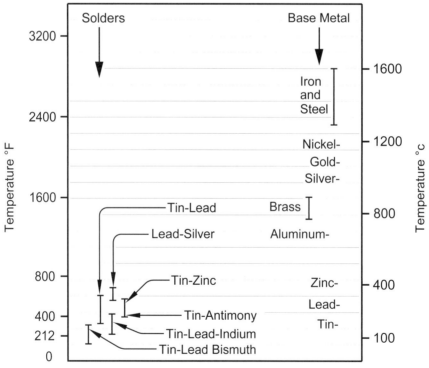

Figure 11-4. Melting points of braze filler metals and
solders are below the melting point of most base metals.

Melting Points of Pure Metals & Alloys

Because pure metals have an abrupt melting point, their solidus and liquidus temperatures are the same. However, in an alloy of two or more metals there is both a range of temperatures and a range of compositions at which both solid and liquid phases of the alloy coexist. The state between solidus and liquidus is often described as mushy, slushy or pasty.

A *phase* or *constitutional diagram* shows how changing the alloy's mix affects its solidus and liquidus temperatures and its pasty range. See the silver-copper constitutional diagram in Figure 11-5.

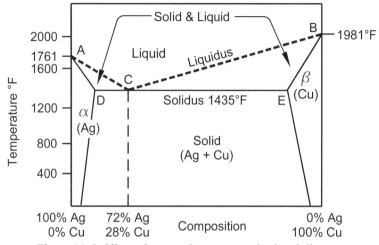

Figure 11-5. Silver–Copper phase or constitutional diagram.

This phase diagram shows:

- The *solidus* line, ADEB, indicates the temperature at which the alloy begins to melt for compositions of silver-copper.

- The *liquidus* line, ACB, indicates the temperature above which the alloy is completely melted.

- For a particular mix of the two metals, the melting point is *lower* than the melting point of either pure metal making up the alloy, or of any other mixture of the alloy. For a silver-copper alloy, the minimum melting point is 1435°F and occurs at 72% silver–28% copper (Point C). This is called the *eutectic temperature* and *eutectic composition.* Note that copper melts at 1481°F and silver at 1761°F, both well above the 1435°F eutectic temperature.

- For alloy mixtures other than the eutectic, there is a range of temperatures in which both solid and liquid phases of the alloy exist together (area ADC area CEB). In these areas of temperature and composition, the alloy is mushy or slushy, while at the eutectic temperature, it has a sharp melting point and is as fluid as a pure metal.

- Using a eutectic alloy produces the minimum brazing (or soldering in the case of tin-lead or tin-antimony alloys) temperature to have a fluid composition that can easily make its way into the joints.

- By using a non-eutectic alloy, we can achieve an alloy that is more slushy or less fluid than at the eutectic temperature. The wider the difference between the solidus and liquidus lines in the constitutional diagram, the more sluggish the alloy is in this temperature range. This is helpful where too fluid an alloy would not stay in place as with an inverted joint where we want capillary attraction to prevail over gravity. A good example of this is sweating a copper tubing fitting or seam upside down.

While the silver-copper constitutional diagram accurately represents a two-component alloy in two dimensions, many brazing alloys contain three or more metals. The constitutional diagram for a three-component system is a three-dimensional surface, and a system with N components has an N-dimensional surface—a complex situation!

Silver Braze Alloys

Silver brazing, commonly and incorrectly known as *silver soldering* or *hard soldering*, is a brazing process that uses a silver-based alloy filler metal. There are hundreds of these alloys with different percentages of silver and other metals, such as copper, zinc, phosphorus and cadmium. Many alloys are needed to meet cost, processing temperature, corrosion, vibration, tensile strength, electrical conductivity, gap filling and wetting characteristics. These alloys are supplied in rods, wire, paste and powder form. Silver-braze filler alloys can be grouped into three categories:

- *Silver-braze alloys without cadmium* typically contain 0–50% silver in 5% increments and the balance of the alloy is copper and zinc. In general, the lower the percentage of silver, the higher the melt and flow temperatures.

- *Silver-braze alloys with cadmium* typically contain 20–50% silver and about 15% cadmium and the balance is copper and zinc. While cadmium is toxic and must be handled carefully, these alloys wet base metals very easily. For joints that will be repaired by remelting them, such as tungsten carbide cutting tools, adding cadmium lowers the remelt temperature which facilitates the installation of a new carbide cutting edge.

- *Silver-braze alloys with phosphorus* are principally used on copper, brass and bronze, but cannot be used on ferrous alloys because they are subject to cracking. With their fluidity and attraction to copper, these alloys get into tight joints, resist vibration and do not require flux. A typical alloy would contain 6% silver, 6% phosphorus and the balance copper. Fittings put together with these alloys cannot be reheated and separated because the filler metal forms a new alloy with the workpiece metal making the joint no longer a simple braze, yet not quite a fusion weld.

Low-Fuming Bronze or Brass-Based Braze Alloys

Low-fuming bronze is typically 60% copper and 40% zinc with small traces of tin and iron. Properly applied, low-fuming bronze has a tensile strength of 56,000–60,000 psi. Rods are available both bare and flux covered and commonly come in $^1/_{16}$–$^1/_4$" diameter with $^1/_{16}$" increments. Not all major rod suppliers offer all rod sizes. These rods are useful for oxyacetylene brazing of steel, copper alloys, cast iron, nickel alloys and stainless steel, and are an essential shop supply. When someone talks about brazing rod and it does not involve silver brazing, this is the filler metal they are most likely talking about.

With low-fuming bronze or brass-based braze alloys, solidus is 1590°F and liquidus 1630°F. At these temperatures the base metal turns a dull red.

Aluminum Brazing

Several rod manufacturers offer aluminum brazing rods, some are uncoated and must be used with separately applied flux, some are flux coated, and some have an internal flux core. Because the melting point of these rods is about 50°F below that of the aluminum workpiece itself, experience and skill are needed to avoid melting the base aluminum. When joining aluminum, for the same level of difficulty, welding is a better choice than brazing whether with oxyacetylene, SMAW or GTAW since the welding rods and wire are less expensive and the tensile strength is higher. Additionally, since a lot of aluminum sheet metal work is for cars and aircraft, which requires shrinking and stretching to achieve the complex shapes needed, welding is often a better choice because during shaping processes filler metal in the joints behaves the same as the base metal. This is because the welding rod *is* base metal and not modified as braze filler metal must be to have a lower melting point.

The selection of rods and number of manufacturers is much smaller for brazing rods than for other metals, so relatively little aluminum brazing is performed. One major rod manufacturer has a $150 minimum order, which buys you one pound of rods, and the rods are only sold either direct to customers by phone or on the Internet, not in welding supply stores. Not a very attractive choice, especially if your job is small.

Aluminum Soldering & Solder Welding

Several manufacturers offer uncoated solder in rod form that meets military specification MIL-R-4208 for repairing aluminum, zinc, and white metal. Some of these rods consist of 93% zinc, 4% aluminum and 3% copper, while others are mostly zinc with a few percent copper. Because these rods melt in the 720–732°F range, nearly 100°F below the minimum temperature for brazing, they *do* perform soldering and solder welding. *Solder welding* is the solder version of braze welding, which is not welding at all. Despite the claims of several promoters hawking them at county fairs and swap meets, *these rods do not and cannot perform brazing or welding.* Look for them next to the ShamWow booth and enjoy their lively demos!

Joints with a 3:1 overlap can be soldered with these rods, however butt joints and T-joints are relatively weak and not recommended. In spite of their weaknesses, these rods are excellent for repairing aluminum outboard motor propellers that have serious blade damage. The blades are solder welded— really *drip melted* using a propane torch—to replace missing blade sections. Because the working temperature of this solder is too low to activate the fluxes needed to break up the aluminum surface oxides, no fluxes are used. To repair an aluminum propeller, follow the steps in Figure 11-6.

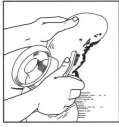 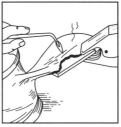 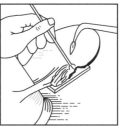 

1. Wire brush thoroughly to break up any surface oxide and to remove paint. Grind the damaged edges to a 45° bevel.

2. Heat metal hot enough to flow rod without the aid of the flame. Tin the flat side of the blade and attach a piece of carbon or copper to support the repair temporarily.

3. Turn and tin the beveled surface, building new metal until slightly larger than its original size. Remove temporary support with minimal heat.

4. Let the repair cool, then grind to proper pitch standards. You now have a complete repair without porosity ready to balance and paint.

Aladdin Welding Products, Inc.

Figure 11-6. Steps to repair a damaged propeller with Aladdin 3-in-1 rod.

Lead-Containing or Common Solders

Tin-lead alloys are the most common solders supplied as wires, pastes, or ingots. They can be used to secure the components on PC boards, in auto body work, in gasoline tank fabrication and in many other applications. With solder it is customary to indicate the tin percentage first, then the lead content. A 40/60 tin-lead solder is 40% tin and 60% lead. Tin-lead solders 35/65, 40/60 and 50/50 are popular because of their low liquidus temperatures. Tin-lead solders 60/40 and the 63/37 eutectic are used when low processing temperatures are needed. The 63-37 eutectic alloy is not only the lowest melting point tin-lead alloy, this mixture has a single melting point and no slushy region. See Table 11-1.

The tin-lead constitutional diagram shape in Figure 11-7 is quite similar to the silver-copper diagram, but with much lower temperatures. The horizontal line CD shows that the solidus temperature is the same for all these alloys, and the sloping line EA shows how the liquidus temperature increases as the lead content increases. In general, the greater percentage of tin, the greater tensile strength and hardness of the alloy.

Tin-Lead (%-%)	Solidus (°F)	Liquidus (°F)
25-75	361	511
35-65	361	465
40-60	361	460
50-50	361	420
55-45	361	379
60-40	361	371
63-37	361	361

Table 11-1. Solidus and liquidus temperatures for common tin-lead solders. Note that 63-37 as the eutectic has the lowest melting point of all mixtures.

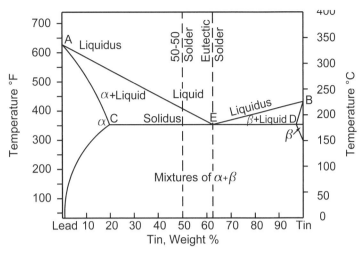

Figure 11-7. Tin–Lead constitutional diagram.

Lead-Free Solders

Tin-silver, tin-copper-silver and tin-antimony alloys are used where lead must be eliminated for health reasons as in stainless steel fabrication for kitchens, food processing equipment, and copper potable water systems. *Never* use lead-containing solder on potable water systems. These lead-free alloys are not as easy to use as their tin-lead cousins because of their poor copper wetting and flow characteristics. Dozens of lead-free alloys are available for electronic and semiconductor devices. They may contain tin, antimony, silver, copper, bismuth or indium. They all cost more than the older tin-lead solders and often present other problems such as a very narrow slushy temperature range between solidus and liquidus, poor wetting and weak bonds.

Brazing & Soldering Fluxes

Fluxes perform many duties. In addition to cleaning the base metal's surface after the initial chemical or mechanical cleaning, flux prevents the base metal from oxidizing while heating and promotes wetting by the braze filler metal or solder by lowering the surface tension and assisting capillary attraction.

Activated by the brazing heat, flux flows into the joint ahead of the filler metal. Since the flux has a *lower* attraction to the base metal's atoms than the filler or solder, when the filler metal or solder melts, it slides *under* the flux and adheres to the clean, unoxidized base metal surface where it is needed. Fluxes will not remove oil, dirt, paint or heavy oxides, so the joint surface must already be clean for them to work.

Brazing fluxes usually contain fluorides, chlorides, borax, borates, alkalis, fluoroborates, wetting agents and water. A traditional, still common and effective flux, is 75% borax and 25% boric acid (borax plus water) mixed into a paste. Alcohol is sometimes used instead of water. Heat activates their cleaning action. After applying the flux, braze the work promptly before new surface oxides form.

When activated by heat, brazing fluxes and some electrical fluxes contain acids or compounds that release acids such as hydrochloric or phosphoric acid. These fluxes leave a residue of the acid or its salt. This acid-salt combination is highly corrosive and must be promptly removed. The fumes these fluxes produce when heated are health hazards and can damage any tools in the shop on which they condense. For safety, either work with forced ventilation or outside.

Although there are dozens of fluxes and flux specifications, most are for special situations. Just three fluxes will handle most brazing jobs: white flux for silver brazing, white flux for brass-based brazing, and black flux for brass-based brazing of cast iron. Electrical and electronic soldering fluxes are usually less aggressive and contain *organic fluxes, inorganic fluxes*, or *rosin-based compounds.*

Stopoff

Stopoff is a liquid or paste that dries to a paint-like solid and is applied by brush, tape, spray or hypodermic needle. Metal oxides of titanium, calcium, aluminum and magnesium in a water or alcohol base are common stopoffs. Outlining areas *not* to receive braze metal or solder with stopoff prevents flux from entering that area, which prevents braze filler metal or solder from adhering. After brazing or soldering is complete, washing or brushing removes the stopoff. Great care must be taken to avoid getting stopoff into the braze area.

Soot from an isopropyl alcohol lamp has traditionally been used by clockmakers as another form of stopoff. Usually the area for the soot is masked by a thin sheet of metal with openings in the shape of the areas to be sooted. An old-fashioned metal eraser shield works well for masking. *Potters slip* thinned with water can also be painted on the work and performs the same function as stopoff.

Flux Application Methods

* Flux can be applied by brushing, rolling, spraying or dipping.

* When the flux is a fine dry powder, it may be adhered to the end of a brazing rod by heating the end of the rod with a torch and then dipping the rod into the flux container through a small hole in its top.

* Sheets, rings, shims and washers of flux and filler metal, called *preforms*, can be inserted into the joint *before* assembly. See the preforms in Figure 11-8. Preplacing filler metal permits the parts to be brazed or soldered in an oven or on a turntable without the need of human attention to feed in the filler metal at the correct time and place. Because with preforms just the right amount of filler metal is positioned inside the joint, all the filler metal remains inside the joint, leaving the seam line of the joint nearly invisible.

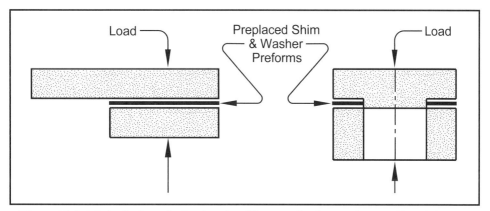

Figure 11-8. Method of preplacing brazing filler metal using preforms. Shim (left), and washer, (right). Sometimes both filler metal and flux are preplaced inside the joint.

• Some aluminum brazing rods have an internal core that contains flux. Generally, the ends of these rods are melted shut to keep oxygen away from the flux. Once the ends are opened, the rods cannot be stored for later work, but must be used promptly. Other brazing (and braze welding) rods come from the factory with flux already applied to their outside.

• Special guns can inject flux directly into the joint.

• Many wire solders have flux cores, so no separate fluxing step is needed.

• Using a gas fluxing unit, flux can be dissolved in alcohol and supplied in the fuel gas stream to the braze, eliminating the manual operation of adding flux. This process automatically controls the amount of flux applied. See the gas fluxing unit in Figure 11-9.

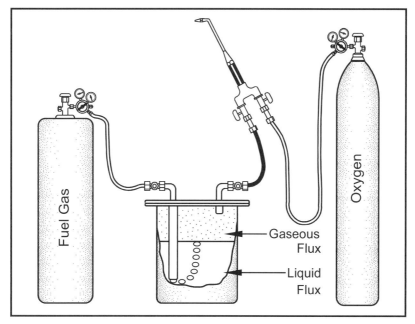

Figure 11-9. Gas fluxing unit for oxyfuel brazing. The fuel gas and oxygen stream carry the right amount of gaseous flux to the torch flame.

Section IV – Torch Brazing & Soldering

Introduction

Though there are many industrial brazing processes that require special equipment, *torch brazing* requires minimal equipment, is easy to learn, is portable, and produces excellent results.

Here are some torch brazing guidelines:

- Torch tip size and filler rod diameter must match the work metal thickness. Table 11-2 provides a starting point for tip selection. The torch tip must be large enough to put adequate heat into the work to raise it to brazing temperature rapidly to melt the filler metal before the rod reaches the joint. Gas pressure is used to make fine adjustments to the flame size.

- Joints require more heat when the torch is first applied than is needed after the first filler metal melts. Torch heat, and the torch flame, advance ahead of the immediate work area and begins heating areas well ahead of the torch. This heat is stored in the work metal. The welder needs to remove the torch from the work on a regular cycle to prevent overheating the work. There will be a regular rhythm to torch time on and off the joint. Remember that the torch flame temperature is 5600°F and most brazing needs only 840–1750°F, so it is easy to apply too much heat. Practice and experience are important factors for achieving good brazes.

Material Thickness (inches)	Filler Rod Diameter (inches)	Victor Torch Tip Size	Orifice Size		Gas Pressures (psig)		Inner Flame Cone Length (inches)
			Drill Number	Inches	O_2	C_2H_2	
$1/32$	$1/16$	000	75	0.022	3–5	3–5	$\geq 1/32$
$3/64$	$3/16$	00	70	0.028	3–5	3–5	$1/64-3/64$
$5/64$	$3/32$	0	65	0.035	3–5	3–5	$1/32-5/64$
$3/32$	$1/8$	1	60	0.040	3–5	3–5	$3/64-3/32$
$1/8$	$1/8$	2	56	0.046	3–5	3–5	$1/16-1/8$
$3/16$	$5/32$	3	53	0.060	4–7	3–6	$1/8-3/16$
$1/4$	$3/16$	4	49	0.073	5–10	4–7	$3/16-1/4$
$1/2$	$3/16$	5	43	0.089	6/12	5–8	$1/4-1/2$
$3/4$	$1/4$	6	36	0.106	7–14	6–9	$1/2-3/4$
$1 1/4$	$1/4$	7	30	0.128	8–16	8–10	$3/4-1 1/4$

Table 11-2. Braze workpiece thickness determines the filler rod diameter, the torch tip size, and the gas pressure. PSIG (pounds/in^2 gauge) stands for psi *above* atmospheric pressure.

Basic Brazing Technique

- When brazing, not the flame but the heated work should melt the braze metal. An experienced welder will heat the joint with the torch, remove the torch flame and touch the joint edge with the filler rod. After several torch application cycles, the work metal will be hot enough to melt the filler metal and it will run into the joint. An *inexperienced welder* will start heating the work, keep the filler metal in the flame, and get a piece of the filler metal to melt so it balls up on the joint but does not flow into it. Then the welder goes back with more heat hoping to melt the short segment of filler into the joint. Wrong technique. You can always spot a beginning brazer. He picks up the braze filler metal and the torch at the same time he begins to heat the part.

- Torch location and joint shape determine the optimum starting point of the joint braze. The following six cases illustrate how to braze successfully:

  - *Case I – Brazing a pipe to a plate* presents the fewest problems because the torch flame tends to follow around the work and make the heating of the joint quite even. If the pipe is not heavy enough to remain in position during brazing, place a non-flammable weight on top of it.

  - Here's how to braze a pipe to a plate:

    1. Start by placing the initial tack on one side of the joint. See Figure 11-10 (1).

    2. Then, begin brazing on the opposite side of the pipe, running the seam completely around the pipe without stopping. The stream of very hot invisible gases, which extends 6–18" beyond the torch flame, preheats the joint. See Figure 11-10 (2).

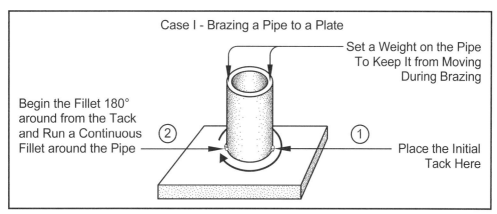

Figure 11-10. Case I – Brazing a pipe to a plate.

  - *Case II – Brazing a thin plate to a thicker plate* runs the risk of melting the thinner plate before the thicker one reaches brazing temperature. See Figure 11-11. To avoid melting the thinner plate, start at one end of the joint and concentrate torch heat on the thicker part. When the filler metal starts to melt, begin your fillet. Because the torch flame and its heated gas runs far ahead of the actual brazing point, once the braze is started, begin a rhythm of removing the torch and adding braze metal to the fillet. Repeat this torch, heat, filler-metal sequence to work your way across the fillet.

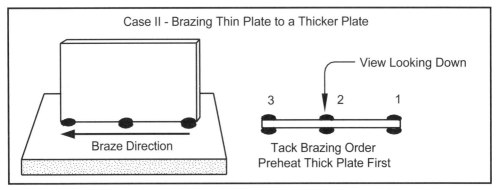

Figure 11-11. Case II – Tack order for brazing a thin plate to a thicker plate.

- *Case III – Brazing an angle iron to a plate* is shown in Figure 11-12. Placing the first tack in the inside corner of the angle iron pulls the angle iron flat against the plate and the remaining tacks prevent further movement. Run additional fillet tacks as needed.

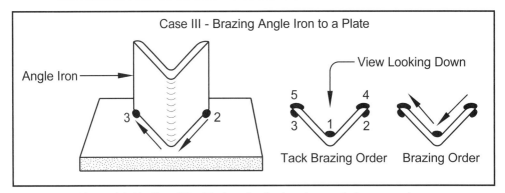

Figure 11-12. Case III – Tack order for brazing angle iron to a plate.

- *Case IV – Brazing an outside corner to a plate* is slightly more difficult than an inside corner. Here's how to do it:
  1. First, braze the two vertical plates together by laying them over an angle iron or other fixture and make this joint while the plates are horizontal. See Figure 11-13 (1).
  2. Then, place the brazed plates on the horizontal plate and apply the tack brazes. By working from the outside ends toward the center, you can apply the extra heat needed at the ends to get the braze started. To prevent overheating, apply the flame in a regular rhythm while applying the braze metal continuously. See Figure 11-13 (2 & 3).

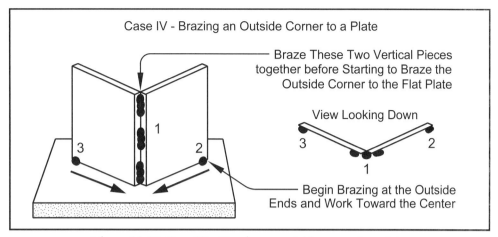

Figure 11-13. Case IV – Brazing an outside corner to a plate.

- *Case V – Brazing an inside corner to a plate* presents the most problems because inside corners tend to deflect the flame and braze metal away from the corner. To avoid this, start at the inside corner and work toward the outer ends as shown in Figure 11-14. By starting at the inside corner the heat is concentrated at the start where it is needed. As much as $^1/_3$ more heat is needed to raise an inside corner to brazing temperature. The trouble is that the blast of the torch gases often makes it hard to get braze filler metal into the corner, but here are three ways to solve this problem:

  • Heat the base and vertical plates to melt the filler metal, then remove the torch heat and apply the filler metal. This gets the torch blast out of the way.

  • Apply the torch to the outside of the corner. This will both raise the temperature of the work to melt the filler metal and draw the filler metal into and under the corner.

  • Tin or wet the corner area of the base plate with braze metal before placing the upper two corner plates.

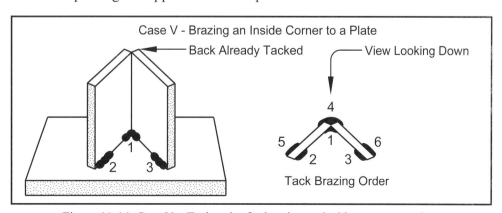

Figure 11-14. Case V – Tack order for brazing an inside corner to a plate.

- *Case VI – Brazing a fillet on two plates* requires a steel backer block clamped to the workpieces to keep them square. Tack fillets placed on both sides of the work prevent the plates from moving and keep them square. Figure 11-15 shows the order in which to place the tack fillets.

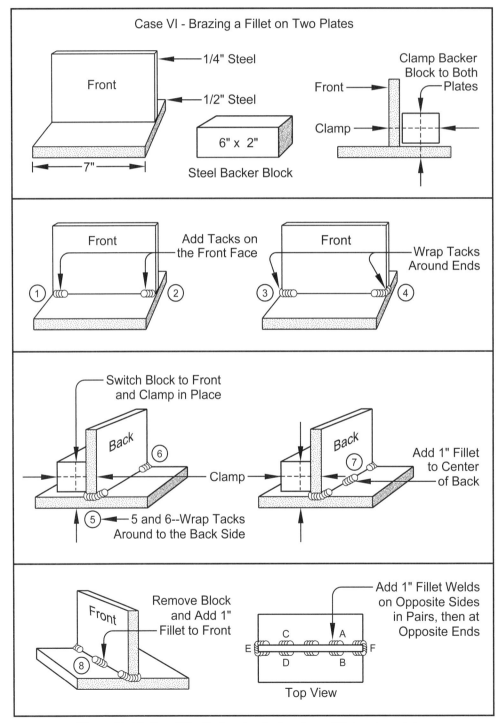

Figure 11-15. Case VI - Tack order for brazing a fillet on two plates.

Positioning Work Accurately

When the two parts being brazed are very different in size and shape, as in Figure 11-16 (left), the larger part requires so much heat to bring it up to brazing temperature that the smaller part would melt. The solution is to position the smaller part where it is to be brazed, and locate this position with a V-block as in Figure 11-16 (center). Remove the smaller part as in Figure 11-16 (right), and heat the base. When the base is up to temperature, replace the part against the V-block, remove the V-block and braze the parts together. Naturally, the V-block used for welding and brazing is degraded by torch heat, so it is no longer useful for accurate machining work. Many welders keep an old V-block just for this purpose. Remember to mark it *For Welding Only*.

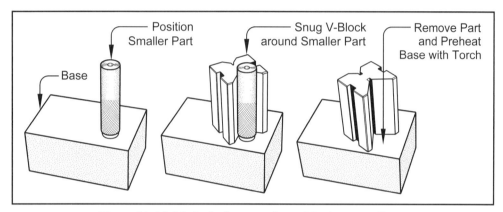

Figure 11-16. Method of accurately positioning a small part
so it can be removed while a large part is being preheated.

Torch Soldering

This is very much like torch brazing, but done at a lower temperature. Usually propane, air-acetylene—a plumber's torch—or natural gas burning in air supplies the heat. While widely used in manufacturing and maintenance, torch soldering is also used in plumbing to join copper tubing for potable water. When used in plumbing, torch soldering is called *copper sweating*. For more information on copper sweating, see *Preparations for Soldering Copper Tubing* starting on page 299.

Section V – Advanced Brazing Techniques

Adding Filler Metal Chips to Flux

Small pieces of filler metal can be mixed in with common brazing fluxes for hard-to-wet materials. The small size and sharp edges of these chips allows them to melt quickly, which promotes a cascade effect that accelerates wetting. This technique works with all filler metals, but is more often used with silver braze and brass braze. When added to brass-based braze filler metal, these pieces are called *spelter*. This approach can be used on all metals, but is especially useful on workpieces that are hard to wet. Mix the ground-up filler metal with brazing flux at the moment it is needed because it will not keep more than a few hours. One way to produce small chips of metal from braze filler metal without creating a mess is shown in Figure 11-17.

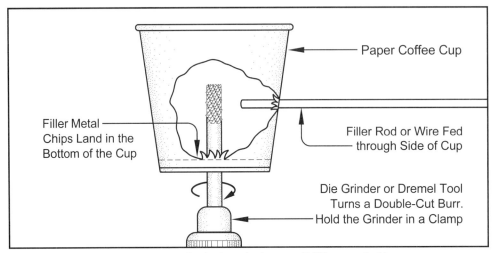

Figure 11-17. Method of producing small filler metal chips.

Commercial paste that contains both flux and solder alloy is widely used in production and in hand soldering. Unlike flux-alloy pastes for brazing which contain aggressive flux ingredients, solder pastes are stable and are sold ready-mixed. Solder pastes can be stored for long periods as long as they remain dry.

Using Braze Metal Chips for a Shop-Made Socket Wrench

The project shown in Figure 11-18 is a close-quarters socket wrench that can be turned with your finger tips. Making this wrench requires annealing brass, cutting a chamfer and a registration step, and brazing.

Here are the steps:

1. Because the $\frac{1}{2}$" diameter brass base must be knurled, it has to be annealed to easily accept the straight knurls. If this step is skipped, the knurling pressures will be too high and could damage the lathe. The brass base is drilled and chamfered in the lathe while it is still part of the longer stock bar, after which it is cut to length, then annealed by heating it to a dull red and quenching it in water. Then apply the knurls.

2. Next, the desired length is cut from a socket wrench extension in a lathe or bandsaw, a step is machined on the length both to remove the chrome plating and to set the registration, which is the depth the extension enters the brass base.

3. To attach the extension, first flux both parts and insert the extension into the base. Then, place filler metal chips in the chamfer between the brass base and the extension. Finally, heat only the brass base until the filler metal melts. The heat applied to the socket wrench extension must be

minimized so the ball-detent spring is not annealed. A heat sink can be clamped to the drive end of the extension to limit its temperature rise.

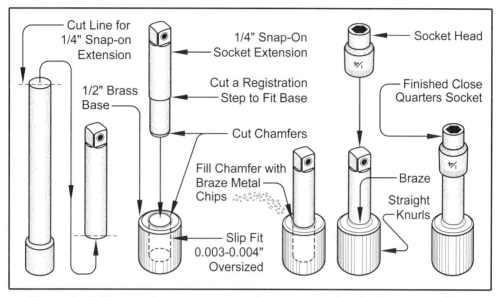

Figure 11-18. Shop-made close quarters socket wrench made using braze metal chips.

Joining Two Pipes or Tubes at 90°

Figure 11-19 shows where to add another V-cut to a standard V-block to accurately position two pipes or tubes at right angles for brazing. To do this, tack the tubes together in the tack order shown, then remove the V-block and run a fillet around the joint.

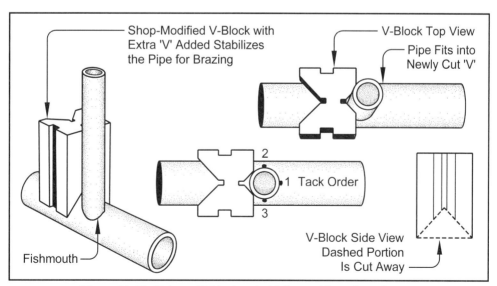

Figure 11-19. Using a V-block to hold the position of small parts.
A bail, the U-shaped clamp used to hold work securely in the block,
is not shown for clarity. The bail holds the vertical tube to the V-block.
The workpieces are usually tubing or pipes, but could also be rod stock.

Quality V-blocks are hardened and must be annealed before trying to make the V-cut in a mill. To anneal a hardened V-block, heat it to a dull red in a furnace or a with torch, and allow it to cool slowly in sand, vermiculite, or in an oven. The cut can be made in a surface grinder, but since the block will be degraded anyway by the torch heat when brazing, you might as well anneal the V-block and cut it in your mill. Inexpensive V-blocks are not hardened and are perfect for this application.

Making Smaller Diameter Brazing Rod

Brazing rods and wire come in standard diameters, and usually $^1/_{16}$" is the smallest diameter available. When performing very small silver braze jobs, $^1/_{16}$" rod is too large to readily melt against the work. The solution is to make the existing brazing filler metal rod smaller. There are a couple of methods:

- Put the braze filler metal on an anvil and hammer it flat, then using a pair of tin snips, cut the flattened filler metal in half lengthwise. Because the filler metal will pick up contamination from the steel hammer and anvil, wipe the flattened filler metal down with acetone before using it. When flattening the filler metal it will often split in two because the wire or rod was cut from a flat ribbon before it was drawn down further. If this occurs, use this to your advantage and further flatten each of the two separate pieces. To see this flattening method, go to Figure 11-23.

- Use a set of ring rollers to flatten the filler metal so it can be cut into thin strips which will melt faster. As above, contamination from the steel rolls must be removed with acetone. Also, the final desired thickness cannot be achieved in a single pass through the rolls, so several passes will be necessary.

Controlling Flux Flare-Up with a Flux Trough

Granular white flux for brass-based brazing is usually applied to the brazing rod by heating the rod and dipping it into the flux, which adheres the flux to the rod.

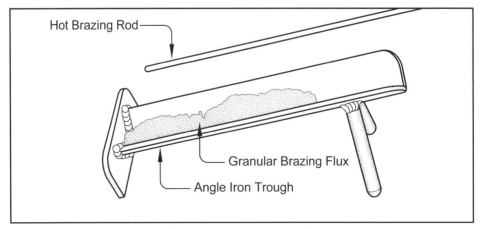

Figure 11-20. A shop-made granular flux trough.

The problem with this method, though, is that the flux momentarily flares up when it enters the torch flame, causing the welder to lose sight of the braze. The solution to this is problem is to adhere flux *only to the bottom* of the rod where it will do some good and not to the top. Fill the rod trough in Figure 11-20 with granular flux, heat the rod in the torch and lay the rod in the flux on its side to pick up flux. The result is no flux on top of the rod and no blinding flare-up. The shop-made angle iron trough is approximately 6" long and can be brazed or GTAW welded.

Improving Joint Strength & Shaft Centering

When a shaft or axle must be centered in a hole, pressed in place and brazed, the hole in the part must be large enough to hold *both* the shaft and the braze metal. This oversized hole can result in poor centering. The solution is to knurl the section of the shaft to be brazed and force it into the hole. The knurling both centers the shaft and provides a path for the flux and filler metal. Strips of 1–2 thousandths of an inch shim stock could also be used, but they are not as convenient as knurling. See Figure 11-21.

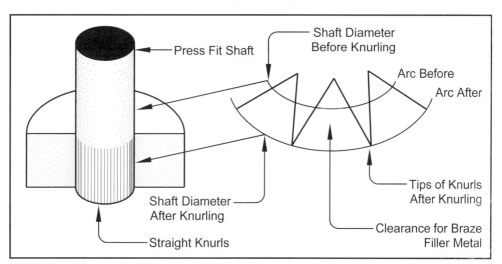

Figure 11-21. Using knurling to improve joint strength and centering.

Accurately Centering Small Tubing

The example in Figure 11-22 shows a medical device part that needs a threaded assembly to hold hypodermic tubing.

This device has two requirements:

- The hypodermic tubing must be coaxial with the threaded base assembly.
- The tubing must have a liquid-tight seal with its threaded base.

Here is how it's done:

1. Drill and ream a hole in the stainless steel nozzle fitting with a slip fit for the hypodermic tubing. This hole will align the tubing with the stainless steel nozzle fitting and hold the nozzle in position.

2. Counterbore the hole drilled in Step 1 with a larger hole that is 0.002–0.004" oversize so the hypodermic tubing can be silver brazed to form a liquid seal. This larger hole is needed to admit the solder or braze metal which seals the nozzle to the fitting. The initial hole fits snugly around the tubing and serves as a positive bottom stop.

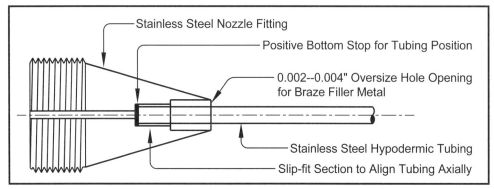

Figure 11-22. Attaching small metal tubing for a medical device by silver brazing.

Brazing Thin Tubing to a Large Base

The challenge in brazing a small, thin part to a much larger base is that the thinner part will melt before the larger one reaches brazing temperature. The solution is to heat only the larger part and allow its heat to transfer to the smaller part and to the braze metal.

Here are the steps to braze the parts in Figure 11-23:

1. Drill the hole into the brass base 0.006-0.006" oversize to provide space for the braze filler metal between the tubing and the base.

2. Chamfer the end of the hole in the base to allow easy insertion of the preformed braze wire. This chamfer also helps transfer heat from the base to the preform.

3. Clean the tubing with emery cloth or a finishing wheel.

4. Flush both the tubing and the hole in the brass base with acetone, alcohol, or carburetor cleaner to remove any remaining oil.

5. Flux both the hole in the base and the end of the tubing.

6. Make a filler metal preform, that is, a ring of braze filler metal that will fit snugly around the tubing and in the chamfer in the brass base. Because the braze filler metal is 0.062" diameter, it is too large for the job and a smaller diameter preform is needed to melt rapidly. To make the preform, hammer the braze wire on an anvil. As mentioned before, the stresses from making this flat strip usually cause the wire to split into two thinner strips. If not, cut two strips with a tin snips. After splitting the wire, wipe the pieces with acetone to clean off the iron particles from the hammer and anvil. Then form a ring, or preform, out of one piece of split wire that will fit around the tubing by bending it around a mandrel.

7. Slip the tubing into the base and the preform around the tubing and seat the preform in the chamfer.

8. Play the torch on the base, not the tubing, until the braze is complete.

9. When the part is cool, remove all traces of flux from the part, usually by boiling the part in water.

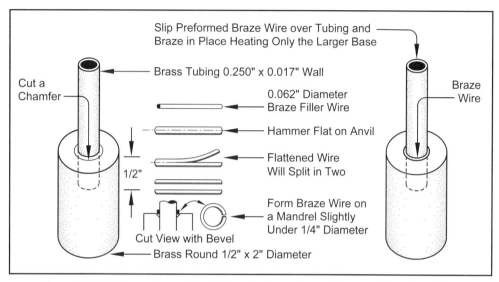

Figure 11-23. How to braze thin tubing to a large base without melting the tubing.

Section VI – Principal Industrial Processes

Furnace Brazing

In this process the parts are cleaned, brazing filler metal is placed inside the joints, and the parts are assembled using fixtures to hold them in proper position. The preplaced brazing filler metal can be filings, foil, paste, powder, tape, or special preform shapes that fit the joint. In this process, both batch and continuous conveyor furnaces are used. Figure 11-24 shows how furnaces have multiple heat zones for preheat, brazing, and cool down.

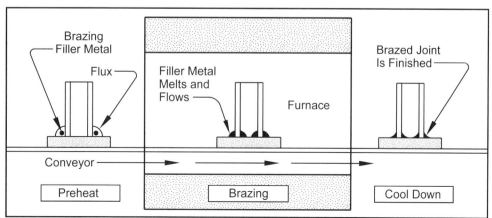

Figure 11-24. Furnace brazing is a continuous process using a conveyor in a furnace.

Flux is used in furnaces with an air atmosphere, but flux can be eliminated by protecting the work while in the furnace by using argon, helium, or a vacuum. If flux is not used in the brazing process, it will not have to be removed in a later step—a significant advantage. Furnace brazing creates lower distortion than torch brazing and can also perform heat treating. An excellent example of the great strength of this process are the jaws of Vise-Grip pliers which are secured to their handles using furnace brazing. *Furnace soldering* is similar to furnace brazing, but it is performed at a lower temperature and in an air atmosphere.

Induction Brazing

This process depends on inducing an alternating current into the part. As this induced current flows inside the part, it generates heat from the resistance of the part itself and brings the part up to brazing temperature. In induction brazing, a solid-state, or vacuum-tube oscillator, generates alternating current from 10–500 kHz. This current is fed to a coil of copper tubing that usually surrounds the part. This copper coil acts as the primary winding of a transformer and the parts themselves act as the secondary winding. The copper-tubing coil is kept from melting by cooling water flowing through it. Power from one to several hundred kilowatts is used. Induction coils are designed in many shapes and sizes that maximize the transfer of current to the assembly being brazed. Figure 11-25 shows a selection of brazing coils.

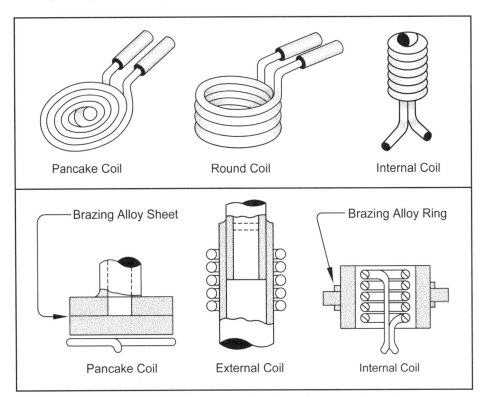

Figure 11-25. Different shaped brazing induction coils (top)
and the same coils in place on brazing work (bottom).

Here are the steps to perform induction brazing:

1. Start by cleaning the parts.
2. Insert the brazing filler metal and flux into the joints and assemble the parts. Some induction brazing processes utilize a vacuum and do not use flux.
3. Put the work in or on the induction coil.
4. When the coil is energized, heat induced in the part performs the brazing.

This brazing process, which can be automated, is very fast, usually measured in seconds. It is used to make parts for consumers and for the military.

Infrared Brazing & Soldering

Infrared brazing is a form of furnace brazing where high-intensity quartz lamps supply long-wave heat of up to 5 kW each. Concentrating reflectors focus the heat onto the parts. This process is sometimes performed in a vacuum and is usually done in a conveyor-fed production process.

Infrared soldering is similar to infrared brazing, but performed at a lower temperature. This process is essential when small, surface mount electronic components must be soldered onto printed circuit boards. Traditional wave soldering would literally wash the components away during soldering, but infrared soldering only heats them with radiated heat and does not disturb their positions.

Resistance Brazing

In *resistance brazing*, electric current flowing through the joint provides brazing heat. See the resistance brazing process in Figure 11-26.

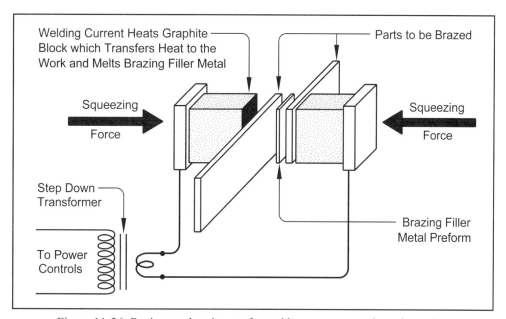

Figure 11-26. Resistance brazing performed between two carbon electrodes.

To begin this process the joint is cleaned, fluxed, and braze filler material placed inside the joint in the form of wire, washers, shims, powder or paste. Then the joint is placed between two electrodes, squeezed together, and electricity is applied. The source of electricity is usually a step-down transformer which provides from 2–25 volts. Current runs from 50 A for small jobs, to thousands of amperes for large jobs. The electrodes are carbon or graphite blocks, or tungsten or molybdenum rods. Most of the heat is produced in these electrodes raising them to incandescence. This heat flows into the joint to complete the braze. The resistance of the joint alone is not usually an adequate heat source. The brazing cycle time varies from one second to several minutes depending on the size of the part. Although industrial processes use purpose-built equipment for resistance brazing, carbon rods salvaged from dry cells and an automobile battery for a source of heat have been used on small parts with great success.

Wave Soldering

This process solders electronic components onto printed circuit boards. A conveyor belt draws printed circuit boards with components inserted into them over a fountain (or *wave*) of solder. This solders all the components in place in a single step. Wave soldering machines are available which can flux, dry, preheat, solder and clean the flux off a finished board on a single conveyor line. See Figure 11-27.

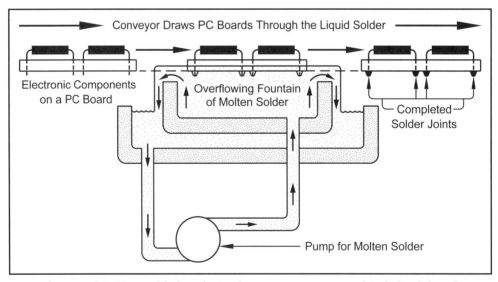

Figure 11-27. Wave soldering electronic components onto a printed circuit board.

Iron Soldering

Most soldering irons today, such as the ones in Figure 11-28, are heated electrically. The copper tip stores and carries heat to the solder joint. This transfer is made possible by the solder applied between the soldering iron's heated tip and the joint, which form a metal-to-metal bridge. After the joint is raised to soldering temperature, the solder is applied to the joint itself, which wets the entire joint. Flux core solder is used for electronic work. This solder has been formed concentrically around a core of one or more strands of flux. In sheet metal and other non-electrical work, the flux may also be in the solder core, or the flux can be applied as a paste or a liquid.

Soldering irons are available from just a few watts for electronic work to 1250 watts for heavy roofing sheet metal work. Many irons for electronic work have temperature-controlled tips and earth grounds to avoid static electricity damage to sensitive electronic components.

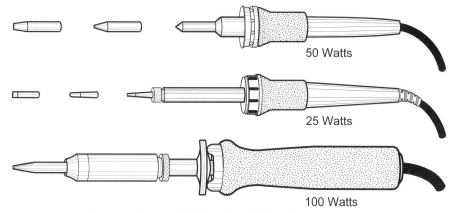

50 Watts

25 Watts

100 Watts

Figure 11-28. Typical electric soldering irons. Many irons
have copper tips which can be ground into shapes to fit the work.

Section VII – Soldering & Brazing Copper Tubing

Potable Water Solders
By U.S. Federal law, only lead-free solders, pipe and fittings may be sold and used in drinking water systems. These solders are commonly 95-5 tin-antimony, but may include a variety of other alloying elements. These lead-free solders can cost 4–8 times as much as the tin-lead alloys they replace. While it is good that these solders are lead-free, they have a narrow pasty temperature range so they are harder to work with than the traditional tin-lead solders. They also do not wet as nicely as the traditional tin-lead solders.

Solders for Non-Drinkable Water or Other Fluids
Lead-containing solders may be used for non-potable water. These solders are popular because they work well and cost less than the lead-free alloys. The most common of these solders are the 50-50 tin-lead and the 60-40 tin-lead alloys.

Copper-Phosphorus Brazing Alloys
Although considerably more expensive than the tin-lead or lead-free solders, this braze filler metal does not require flux or the careful cleaning of the tubing and fittings the way soldering alloys do. Using an oxyacetylene torch, copper-phosphorous brazing alloys form a stronger bond than solders, so any critical copper tubing joint is a candidate for this filler metal. The U.S. Navy

uses this type of product on all shipboard copper tubing including urinal waste lines. Even though copper-phosphorous joints do not always completely fill the fitting socket, because this filler alloys with the copper, these joints are exceptionally strong, fluid tight, and vibration resistant. These joints cannot be disassembled by reheating because the filler metal alloys with the copper tubing forming a permanent joint. Joints must be cut apart and a new section spliced into the gap.

Torches for Sweating Copper Tubing

Air-acetylene and propane torches all work well for sweating copper tubing. Oxyacetylene torches are too hot for sweating copper tubing except for copper-phosphorus alloys. The BernzOmatic torches in Figure 11-29 burn propane gas. The torch version with a separate regulator, 48" hose, and handpiece is especially convenient because the torch does not stall out when the cylinder is inverted as the single-piece torch does. The hose-based torch can also put heat into tight quarters.

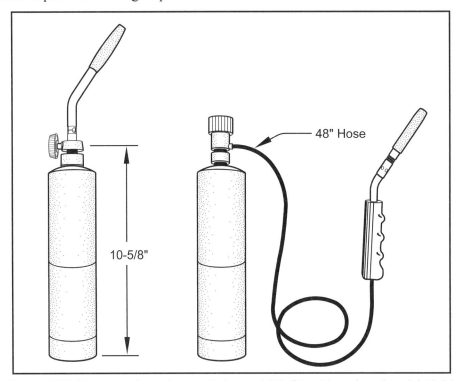

Figure 11-29. BernzOmatic torch-on-cylinder model (left) and hose-based model (right).

Flameless Heat Source

Where open flames or compressed gas cylinders are a hazard, electrical resistance soldering works well. A step-down transformer supplies a high current through a pair of cables to a pliers-like handpiece. This handpiece clamps carbon blocks against opposite sides of the copper tubing fitting. High current from the transformer flowing through the copper fitting's resistance generates most of the heat, the rest comes from the resistance of the carbon blocks.

Solder is applied to the fitting as with a torch. This process is fast, clean and flameless. For copper tubing, electrical resistance soldering is a complete replacement for torches, hoses and gas cylinders. See Figure 11-30.

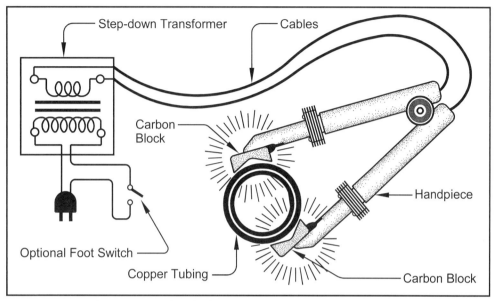

Figure 11-30. Electrical resistance soldering of copper tubing.

Preparations for Soldering Copper Tubing

To successfully solder copper tubing, a process which is also called *sweating*, follow these steps:

1. Measure the copper tubing length for cutting. The tubing must be long enough to reach the bottom of the fitting cup, but not so long that it causes stress in the completed piping.

2. Cut the tubing, preferably with a disc-type tubing cutter to insure square ends. These copper tubing cutters come in all tubing sizes. A hacksaw, an abrasive wheel, or a portable or stationary bandsaw may also be used.

3. Remove burrs from inside the tubing ends with a round file, half-round file, or a reamer. Many copper tubing cutters carry a triangular blade for inside reaming. Remove outside burrs with a file because these burrs will prevent seating of the tubing into the fitting cup. A properly reamed tube end provides an undisturbed surface through the entire fitting for smooth, laminar flow and minimum pressure drop.

4. Use emery cloth, nylon abrasive pads like 3M Scotch-Brite, or male and female stainless steel brushes sized to fit the tubing to remove the dirt and oxide from the end of the tubing and the inside mating surfaces of the fitting. See Figure 11-31. An electric drill can drive the male stainless steel internal brush and save a lot of elbow grease on a large job. The goal is to get down to fresh, shiny metal. Clean the outside of the tubing from the end of the tubing to about $^3/_8$" beyond where the tubing enters the fitting. The capillary space between the tubing and its fitting is about

0.004 inches. Filler metal fills this gap. Removing too much metal from either the tubing or the fitting will prevent the proper flow of solder around the tubing by capillary forces and weaken the joint. Do not touch the cleaned area with bare hands or oily gloves. Skin oils, lubricating oils, and grease impair the adherence of filler metal.

Figure 11-31. Male stainless steel brush fits into a hand-held electric drill for cleaning inside copper fittings (left) and a female brush for cleaning the outside ends of copper tubing (right).

5. Select the flux to match the solder, since a mismatch can cause problems. Use a flux that meets ASTM B 813 requirements.

6. Using a disposable acid brush, apply a thin coating of flux to the ends of the tubing sections and to the fitting's interior mating surfaces. The soldering flux will dissolve and remove traces of oxide from the cleaned surfaces to be joined, protect the cleaned surfaces from re-oxidation during heating, and promote wetting of the surfaces by the solder metal. Be sure to keep the flux off your hands because chemicals in the flux can be harmful if transferred to the eyes, mouth or to open cuts.

7. Insert the tubing end into the fitting with a twisting motion. Make sure the tubing is properly seated in the fitting cup. If using a paste flux, use a clean cotton rag to wipe any excess flux off the tubing from the exterior of the joint. Caution: Do not leave a cleaned and fluxed joint unsoldered overnight. If you must stop work before soldering, disassemble the joint and remove all the flux. On starting work the next day, perform the cleaning and fluxing process from the beginning.

8. Most of the time there are two or three tubing lengths going into a fitting, so insert all the tubing lengths into the fitting so they can all be soldered in one operation. This will save time and torch fuel. Make sure the tubing lengths and fittings are supported or braced so they remain at the bottom of their respective fitting cups. You are now ready to solder the fitting.

9. Begin by heating the copper tubing around the bottom and sides about one cup length away from the fitting as in Figure 11-32. This brings the initial heat into the fitting cup and provides even heat to the joint area. If the joint is vertical, be sure to heat the tubing around its entire circumference. If the joint is horizontal as shown, heat the bottom and sides of the tubing. To avoid burning the flux, do not heat the top of the tubing. The natural

tendency of heat to rise preheats the top of the assembly and brings sections of the tubing up to temperature. The larger the joint, the more heat and time will be needed for preheating. Experience determines the amount of preheat time needed. Large diameter tubing is best soldered with two torches or a multi-orifice torch.

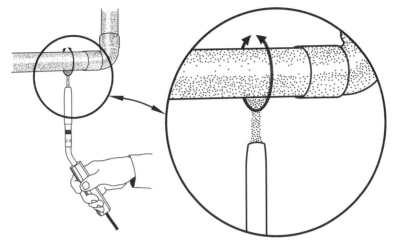

Figure 11-32. Preheat the tubing around the bottom and the sides about one cup length away from the fitting. The torch heat will rise and heat the top of the fitting.

10. Now, move the flame onto the base of the fitting cup and sweep the flame back and forth between the base of the fitting cup and along the tubing sides to a distance equal to the depth of the fitting cup as in Figure 11-33. Preheat the circumference of the assembly as described above. Again, do not heat the top during this preheating to prevent burning the flux.

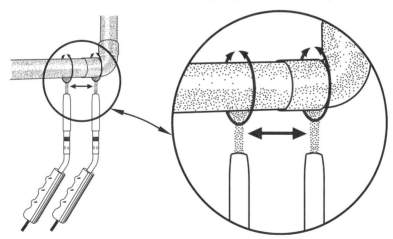

Figure 11-33. Preheat the fitting starting from the base of the cup and sweep the flame back and forth between the base of the fitting cup out to the copper tubing.

11. With the flame positioned at the base of the fitting cup, *touch* the solder to the joint at the point where the tubing enters the fitting as in Figure 11-34. Keep the torch flame from playing directly on the solder. If the solder does not melt, remove it, and continue preheating. When the solder melts

when touched against the fitting and tubing, soldering can begin. Remember: Do not overheat the joint or direct the flame onto the edge of the fitting cup. Overheating could burn the flux, destroying its effectiveness and preventing the solder from properly entering the fitting.

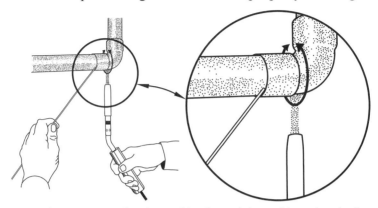

Figure 11-34. When to stop preheating and begin applying solder using the "touch test."

Soldering Horizontal Joints

1. Start applying the solder slightly off-center at the bottom of the joint, as in Figures 11-35. When the solder begins to melt, push it into the joint while moving the torch upward along the base of the fitting and slightly ahead of the point of application of the solder. When the bottom portion of the fitting fills with solder, a drip of solder will appear at the bottom of the fitting. Continue to feed solder into the joint while moving the solder up and around to its top, or 12 o'clock position, and at the same time move the flame so it slightly leads the solder up to the top of the joint.

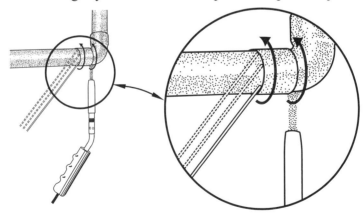

Figure 11-35. Soldering up the side of the fitting.

In general, solder dripping off the fitting bottom is not coming from the bottom of the joint. As the joint fills, excess solder runs down the face of the joint and drips off the bottom. This is a good indication of using the proper amount of solder and a full joint. This will allow the solder in the *lower* portion of the joint to become pasty, form a dam as in Figure 11-36 (A) and (B), and support the solder applied above it.

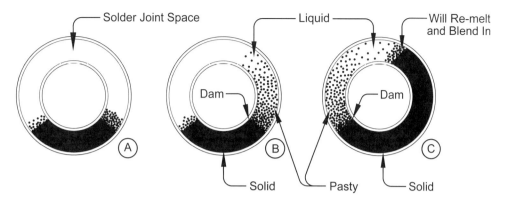

Figure 11-36. Sectional view of a solder fitting showing how cooler solder in the base of the fitting forms a dam to hold pasty solder in place until it cools.

2. Move the torch heat and solder to the other side of the fitting and, overlapping slightly, proceed up the uncompleted side to the top and over, once more overlapping slightly. See Figure 11-36 (C). Again, while soldering, small solder drops may appear behind the point of solder application. This indicates the joint is full to that point and will take no more solder. Because these drops show that solder in the upper part of the joint is above the pasty temperature range and in the full liquid state, we want to cool the joint slightly to get back into the pasty temperature range. To do this, relocate the flame to the base of the fitting and apply more solder. Adding this solder will also cool the joint. Throughout this process you are using all three physical states of solder: solid, pasty, and liquid. Remember that you want to control the state of the solder: cooler solidified solder at the bottom of the fitting, pasty transitional solder above the solid, and liquid solder at the point of application to allow the solder to be drawn into the fitting. Beginners often apply too much heat and cannot get the solder to stay inside the fitting because it is too liquid and runs out.

Soldering Vertical Joints

1. After preheating, make a series of overlapping circular passes feeding in solder and starting wherever is convenient. Stop applying solder when you can see the joint is filled and it will take no more solder. Vertical joints are the easiest to learn because gravity helps.

2. Since vertical joints are the easiest to make, try to plan the job so the maximum number of joints are in the vertical position with the joint cup pointed up. Plumbers often pre-assemble sections of tubing and fittings on a bench or in a vise where it is more convenient and comfortable to work.

Soldering Fittings with Horizontal or Cup-Inverted Joints

1. Begin soldering the bottom-most joint first since the heat applied to it will rise and preheat the joints above it. If you solder the upper joints first, you will melt the solder out of them when you begin soldering the lower joints. By soldering the lowest joint first, you not only preheat the joint(s) above

it, but you have total control of the heat input to this joint. If you overheat this joint, the solder will be too thin and runny to be held in place by capillary attraction and it will flow out. Just the right amount of heat will let the solder be drawn up into the joint.

2. After the lowest joint is done, the side and top joint will then be ready to solder. Apply a little more heat to the joint and run the solder around the ring where the tubing meets the fitting on the side, then the top joint.

3. In all cases, trying to improve the integrity of a soldered joint by loading additional solder where the tubing enters the fitting is pointless. The strength of the joint is the solder bond *between* the inside of the fitting and the outside of the tubing inserted into the fitting. If the joint was clean, properly fluxed and heated when the solder was applied, it will hold.

4. Carefully remove the excess solder while the joint is still hot, but be gentle, wiping the joint while the solder is still molten can lead to joint cracking. Figure 11-37 shows what a perfect male joint should look like.

5. To complete the joint, allow the assembly to air cool without disturbing it. Do not spray it with water or dip the fitting in water because it may crack or you may jiggle the joint when it is not quite solid, resulting in a *cold solder joint*.

6. Once the joint has reached room temperature, take a clean, cotton rag dipped in water or alcohol and wipe the flux residue from the joint.

7. Finally, test the completed—and cooled—joint for leaks, and flush the tubing lines to remove the remaining flux.

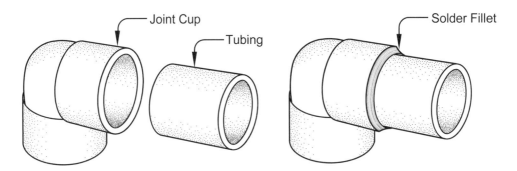

Figure 11-37. Parts of a male joint (left) and a perfect male solder joint (right).

Soldering Valves

Soldering on valves must be done with the valve in the open position. Also, the valve stems must be removed to prevent exposing the packing and washers to torch heat. Most ball valves can be soldered without disassembly because they have Teflon PTFE seals which can withstand soldering temperatures for a few seconds.

Controlling Residual Water in Tubing for Soldering & Brazing

Soldering can only be done in tubing and fittings that are free of water. Sometimes in-service pipes with both horizontal and vertical runs prevent the complete removal of the remaining water and just enough water remains in the line to prevent successful soldering. When this happens, torch heat turns some water to steam, disturbing the remaining water column, bringing water into the joint, and preventing soldering. Although you can repeatedly attempt to solder the joint, there will always be more water coming down the pipe. Usually the best solution is to apply compressed air to flush out the remaining water. Whenever you see steam rising from a fitting after sweating, there is a very good chance that water in the lines has spoiled the joint. Take it apart, fully drain the lines, and begin again.

Here are some other methods to dry a pipe when the line has been in service:

1. Open the taps above and below the joint to help the tubing drain.

2. Remove any pipe straps on each side of the joint to permit bending the tubing down to let water run out.

3. On vertical lines that contain residual water, use a short length of $1/4$" hose to siphon out the water so the water level inside the line is at least 8 inches below the joint.

4. Using paper towels and a stick, dowel, or long screwdriver, remove all moisture and water drops within 8" of the soldering. When finished, be sure to remove the paper towel.

5. Valves on the lines to be soldered may not shut off completely, or it may be impossible to drain the line enough to prevent all water from entering the soldering area. To keep this water away, stuff fresh white bread into the line or lines to form a plug and push it 8 inches back into the line away from the fitting. Be sure to cut the crusts off the bread because they dissolve slowly. Then assemble the copper tubing to the fitting and complete the solder joint. Flush out the bread when the joint is complete.

Heat Shields

When sweating copper tubing in tight quarters, the surrounding wood and building structure must be protected from torch heat otherwise a fire will start. There are three ways to protect this area from torch heat:

• Although no longer commercially available, a slab of $1/4$" or $3/8$" asbestos insulation works best. Many shops still have these as NOS—new old stock.

• A commercial woven glass mat can be cut to fit around tubing and curve around corners. See Figure 11-38.

• Steel plate $1/4$" or more in thickness makes a good heat shield.

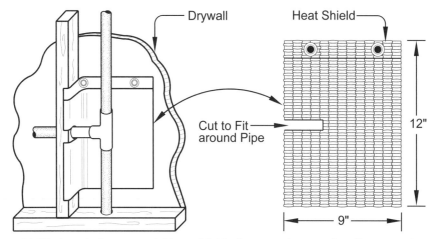

Figure 11-38. A typical commercial heat shield of woven glass mat bending around a pipe.

Section VIII – Step-by-Step Brazing Examples

Materials Needed for Silver Brazing Bandsaw Blades

Many times bandsaw blade stock is purchased in bulk and must be cut to length and then spliced end to end. In addition, if an interior, or island, section of material must be cut in work, a hole is drilled in the work, the bandsaw blade threaded through the hole, and then the splice is made. After the island material is cut out, the blade is broken so it can be removed from the workpiece.

Here is everything required to silver braze bandsaw blades:

- A shop-made saw blade brazing fixture such as the ones in Figures 11-39 and 11-40, an oxyacetylene torch with a #0 tip, regulators, hoses, torch sparker and gas cylinders.

- A white borax-based brazing flux for silver brazing on steel.

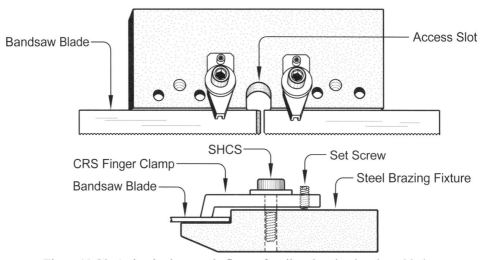

Figure 11-39. A simple shop-made fixture for silver brazing bandsaw blades.

- Thin wooden stir sticks for flux application—flux brushes are far too large.

- 0.035" or 0.045" diameter silver braze wire containing 45% silver. From some suppliers this wire is available with cadmium, which has better wetting characteristics and a wider fluid temperature range than the braze alloys without cadmium. Using 0.062" silver braze filler metal is a poor choice because its large size makes it difficult to initiate melting.

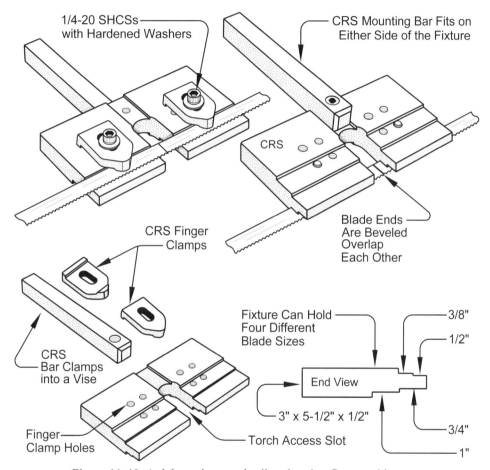

Figure 11-40. A deluxe shop-made silver brazing fixture with steps that can hold four different widths of bandsaw blades.

Silver Brazing Procedure for Bandsaw Blades

1. If the saw blade has been spliced before, trim the blade $^{1}/_{4}$" away from each end of the previous splice. Stack the two blade ends so they are parallel and the teeth are on the same side as in Figure 11-41 (left).

2. Using a pedestal, table, disc or belt grinder with an aluminum oxide abrasive, grind the ends of the two blades square. Make sure that both ends stop at a gullet so there are no partial teeth on the blade ends. Then, holding them together, grind a 20° bevel on the blade ends as in Figure 11-41 (middle). By grinding the two blade ends at the same time, when the

blades are matched up in a continuous band, the bevels will be identical and the blades will butt up tightly as in Figure 11-41 (right).

3. Remove all burrs from the blade ends and lightly grind the flats of the blades $^3/_8$" back from the ends on both the top and bottom down to fresh metal.

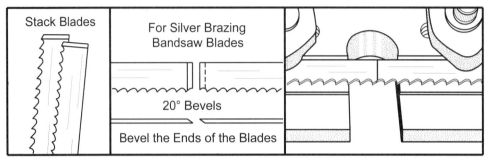

Figure 11-41. Aligning bandsaw blade ends for beveling before silver brazing (left). Ground beveled edges (middle) and blade ends in brazing fixture ready to be brazed (right).

4. Wipe down the blade ends with acetone or alcohol to remove all grease and oils. Do not touch the cleaned ends with your fingers.

5. Your silver brazing flux should be a paste. If it has dried out, add distilled water and remix it into a paste. Apply the flux in a *thin* layer over the beveled ends of the blade using a thin wooden stir stick. Avoid getting flux on the flats of the blade because this will only put silver braze metal where it is not needed and will have to be removed.

6. Secure the brazing fixture in a vise so the fixture will not move when pulled on by the weight of the blade ends.

7. Secure the blade ends in the brazing fixture:

    -   If you are splicing the blade *through* a workpiece, make sure you have the teeth running in the correct direction when the work sits flat on the bandsaw table. Also, make sure that the marked cut lines on the work face up when the workpiece is on the saw table.

    -   Face the teeth outward away from the brazing fixture.

    -   Insure that the back edge of the blade is snug against the back ledge of the brazing fixture.

    -   When the blades are butted, the upper beveled blade should exert a little force on the lower beveled blade. The two bevels should join evenly.

8. Cut off about 10–12" of silver brazing wire and straighten it.

9. Light the oxyacetylene torch and adjust it for a neutral flame, then increase the acetylene slightly for a mildly carburizing flame with a $^3/_4$" long inner cone. The flame should be neither wispy—likely to go out if the torch is waved back and forth—or hissing. The torch should show a $1^1/_2$" diameter flat heat area when played against a flat plate.

10. In preparation for heating the blade, position the torch upside down inside the torch access slot in the fixture so the tip of the blue inner cone is level with the bottom of the saw blade.

11. Move the torch up and down each side of the braze line several times. Remember that the torch flame is about 5600°F and the silver braze metal will flow at 1200–1400°F. The blade will come up to the brazing temperature within a few seconds. Note that the silver braze metal's data sheet specifies a melting point of 1100–1200°F, but it will not *flow* until it gets 150–200°F hotter. Melting is of no help here, what we need is flow.

12. Watch for the three phases brazing flux goes through when heated:

   - *White powder* – From the paste it becomes a dry, white powder.

   - *Semi-transparent spheres* – From a white powder it transforms into a series of small semi-transparent spheres.

   - *Glassy coating* – From the spheres it becomes a milky, glass-like coating. When the flux reaches this phase, it has done its work of chemically cleaning the steel's surface to prepare it to accept the silver braze alloy, and the steel is hot enough to melt and flow the alloy on contact. *At this time, touch the silver braze metal to the joint.*

13. In a second or less, the braze metal will melt and flow, and a silver line will appear in the braze joint. Do not apply additional braze metal. The joint is complete. Very little braze metal is actually needed; a $^1/_2$" blade requires only 2–4 *pinheads* of filler metal for a solid joint.

14. Allow the joint to cool for 3–5 minutes and remove the blade from the fixture. Remember that the brazing fixture will still be hot.

15. A well-made joint has almost no braze metal outside of the joint, but if there is any, remove it by grinding or filing.

16. Stop. You are done. No annealing cycle is needed because of the lower temperatures used in brazing.

Tips on Blade Splicing

- Determine the maximum length blade your bandsaw will accept, and make your blade this length. By doing this you will be able to make the maximum number of splices before having to add in a second length of saw blade. Remember, each splice requires two $^1/_4$" sections of blade to be trimmed around the splice. This loss of blade length can be important if you must break a blade and resplice it through workpieces to saw out island sections.

- Measuring and marking off the length of a saw blade by painting lines on the shop floor eliminates having to repeatedly measure off saw blade stock when making up new blades. This easy method will also save you some cuts.

Brazing Twist Drill Extensions

Sometimes only a jobber-length drill is available and a longer drill is needed. Here are two methods to extend the length of a drill:

Method 1 for drill diameters equal to or larger than the extension rod diameter – If the drill diameter is relatively large, chuck it in a lathe with the point-end inside the chuck or headstock. Trim the shank of the twist drill square, center drill it, and then drill the socket in the shank for a piece of drill rod. Drill shanks are usually not hardened and are easily machined. For maximum joint strength there should be between 2–3 thousandths of an inch space for solder around the drill rod. Too close a fit and the solder will not enter the clearance space, too great a space reduces the joint strength. See Figure 11-42 (A, B, C & D). Grind a small flat on the drill rod extension to let air escape and to let the solder into the joint. Finally, silver braze the drill and drill rod together.

Method 2 for drill diameters smaller than the extension rod diameter – Trim the extension rod so it is square and center drill the rod to accept the twist drill shank. Grind a flat on the drill shank for air exit and filler metal to enter.

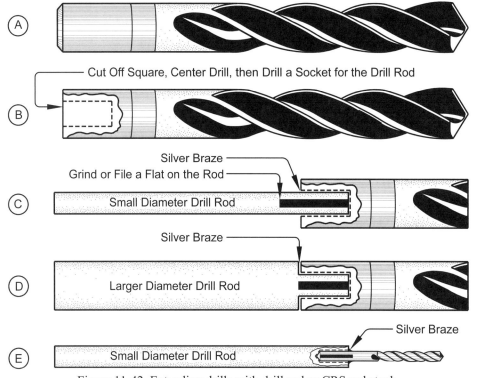

Figure 11-42. Extending drills with drill rod or CRS rod stock.

Flux the drill and the hole, insert the drill into the drill extension and wrap the flutes in a damp rag so brazing heat does not anneal the drill, then heat the drill shank. When the silver braze melts when touched to the drill metal without the torch flame on the braze metal, feed metal into the joint and allow it to cool. Clean the joint of flux. See Figure 11-42 (E).

Extending a Twist Drill with a Scarfed Joint

Another method of making extensions for twist drills is to use a scarf joint made in the fixture shown in Figure 11-43. This method is useful on smaller drills where drilling a hole into the back end of the drill for the extension is not feasible. Scarf joints are considerably stronger than butt joints because there is more area available on which the filler metal can adhere. Also, the forces across the joint are compression, tension and shear, somewhat better than shear alone.

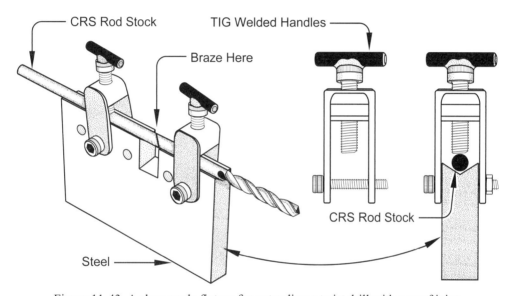

Figure 11-43. A shop-made fixture for extending a twist drill with a scarf joint.

Silver Brazing Carbide Tool Bits

Tungsten carbide cutters—small chips or pieces—are silver brazed onto a square or rectangular steel bar that fits into a lathe toolholder. See the cutters in Figure 11-44.

Carbide inserts are small separate pieces of metal that fit into matching toolholders. No silver brazing is needed with these replaceable carbide insert cutting tools. They are held in place by screws and clamps. See Figure 11-45.

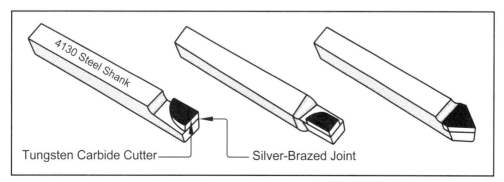

Figure 11-44. Standard, commercial, low-cost brazed carbide lathe tools.

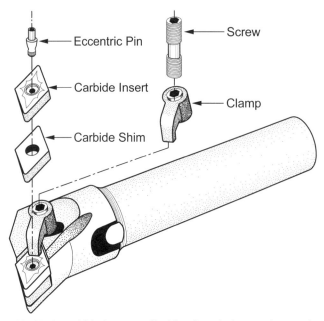

Figure 11-45. A carbide insert toolholder for a lathe requires no brazing.

However, there are times when the ability to silver braze a carbide insert onto steel offers a substantial advantage. These inserts, shown in Figure 11-46, though originally designed for use in a carbide toolholder, can be used in several other ways:

- When a carbide cutter with a custom profile is required, these inserts can be brazed to a piece of steel and used to form male and female grooves, V-shapes, ogives or other complex shapes in a single cutting engagement.

- If a boring bar or trepanning tool is needed and a commercial one is not available or does not fit the job, making one by brazing an insert to a steel bar is a quick and easy solution.

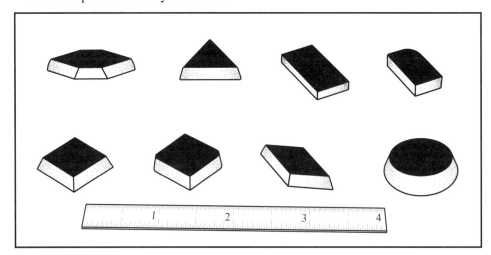

Figure 11-46. Some of the hundreds of designs of carbide inserts. Many inserts have a screw hole to better secure them in their toolholders, but others do not. These were selected without holes because they provide more surface area for braze filler metal to grip.

Silver Brazing Carbide Cutters

Tungsten carbide can only be cut with *wire EDM* and diamond grinding wheels. *Green* or *silicon carbide* grinding wheels can be used to shape tungsten carbide and is often used for roughing in the shape to save wear on diamond grinding wheels.

While the inexpensive brazed tungsten carbide cutters mounted on steel shanks can be "touched-up" or slightly modified with green or diamond grinding wheels, allowing the steel shank to touch these grinding wheels damages the grinding wheels by loading them with steel. For this reason, as well as the ability to reach all parts of the carbide insert for grinding, inserts are usually ground to shape, then brazed to a steel shank. See Figure 11-47.

Any of the following torch and gas combinations will work:

- Oxyacetylene with slightly reduced oxygen.
- MAAP gas.
- Air-acetylene, also known as a plumber's torch.
- Propane.

While propane works fine, use the torch model with a hose, not the torch-on-tank model because its flame reacts to the tank position and can stall when liquid fuel enters the torch as the tank is tilted. Refer to Figure 11-29.

The following flux-filler metal combinations work well:

- Stay-Silv white brazing flux.
- Stay-Silv 15% silver braze filler wire in 0.062" diameter. In general, the lower the silver content, the higher the joint strength, but the poorer the braze metal flows into the joint. Also, using too small a silver filler wire diameter allows the wire to melt when near the flame instead of on the work. Use small diameter wire only on small work with a small torch.

Here are the steps to silver braze tungsten carbide inserts onto a steel base:

1. Clean the mating surfaces by sandblasting, stainless steel wire brushing, or by filing. Do not touch the cleaned surfaces before soldering because finger oils are a contaminant.

2. Prepare flux supplied as a paste. Remove a quarter teaspoon with a clean spatula to a clean mixing surface. Add distilled water to the paste so it can be thinned and painted onto the mating surfaces. Always start with fresh flux from the jar and fresh mixing implements and a new acid brush for applying the flux.

3. Paint the flux on both mating surfaces. Avoid getting flux outside of the mating surfaces as the braze metal will follow the flux to unwanted areas.

4. Put the mating parts together. Unless steps are taken to keep the carbide part in place, it will tend to float out of position on the layer of liquid flux and the braze metal. Usually a single, pointed tool—sometimes called a

third hand or welder's helper—holding the carbide part in place works well.

5. Begin heating the assembled parts from the bottom with a feathered flame. Adjust the flame size to envelop the entire area under the carbide cutter within the flame and avoid allowing the flame cone to touch the carbide.

6. Use a flame large enough to heat the part, but small enough to permit you to see how the flux is changing with heat.

7. As described before, the flux goes through three stages when heated:

   ▪ *White powder* – The initial heat turns the liquid or paste to a white powder when all the water content is removed.

   ▪ *Semi-transparent spheres* – More heat turns visible bits of flux along the edge of the work into small glass-like spheres.

   ▪ *Glossy Coating* – Finally, the flux turns into a milky-white, glass-like coating. This is when to apply the braze filler metal.

8. Touch the braze filler metal to the spot where the flux has turned milky-white and continue to apply heat. A small bit of braze filler metal will melt off forming a small ball. A bit more heat and the ball disappears as the braze metal adheres to the work surface. Now the work metal is ready to receive the rest of the braze metal.

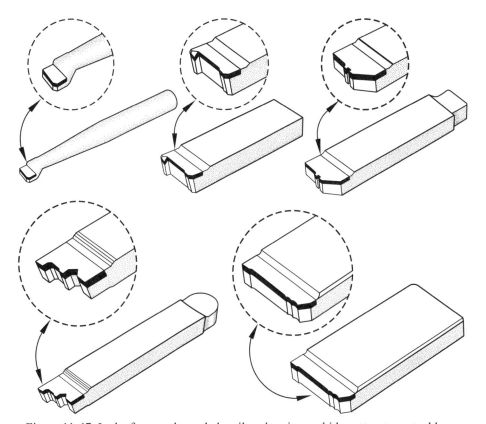

Figure 11-47. Lathe form tools made by silver brazing carbide cutters to a steel base.

9. Continue to apply heat and feed the braze filler metal into the metal adjacent to the seam between the parts. Move the heat away from the initial ball area and insure that the more distant areas of the part reach soldering temperature. Remember that the braze metal follows the heat.

10. When you can see braze metal at the edges of all joints, brazing is done. Allow the part to air cool.

Section IX – Repairs Made with Braze Welding

Braze Welding a Casting

As shown in Figure 11-48, a large casting has broken and must be braze welded to repair it.

Here are the steps:

1. Remove all oil, grease, paint and dirt from the crack faces and 2" back from each face of the casting break. See Figure 11-48 (A).

2. Grind a V-groove on the top and bottom joint edges, but do not go all the way through to the middle. Leave $^1/_3$ of the broken face in place in the center of the casting thickness to provide precise joint alignment. See Figure 11-48 (B).

3. Preheat the entire casting to 500–900ºF, as in Figure 11-48 (C). One or more rosebud tips will be needed for this. This heating step reduces the chances of warping and cracking. Temperature sensing crayons, thermocouples or non-contact heat guns may be used to check the work temperature. When the work is up to temperature, apply borax-boric acid flux to the V-grooves. A flux containing brass spelter (zinc particles) will facilitate wetting (or tinning) the joint faces. See Figure 11-48 (D).

4. Begin at one end and heat the joint to a dull red, then add bronze filler rod. Make sure the joint faces are thoroughly tinned and work your way along the joint to the other end. Several braze passes may be needed for thick castings.

5. Alternate from one side to the other when adding filler metal until all layers are built up. Use $^1/_8$" thick passes to build up the V-groove. See Figure 11-48 (E).

6. Complete the repair by reinforcing, or crowning, the joint so it is about $^1/_2$" above the face of the casting. This crown is added for reinforcement. Cool the part slowly either burying the casting in sand, cooling it in an oven, or covering it with a heat blanket. Not doing so risks cracking.

Thoroughly remove all flux remaining on the casting after it cools to prevent future corrosion.

See the completed repair in Figure 11-48 (F).

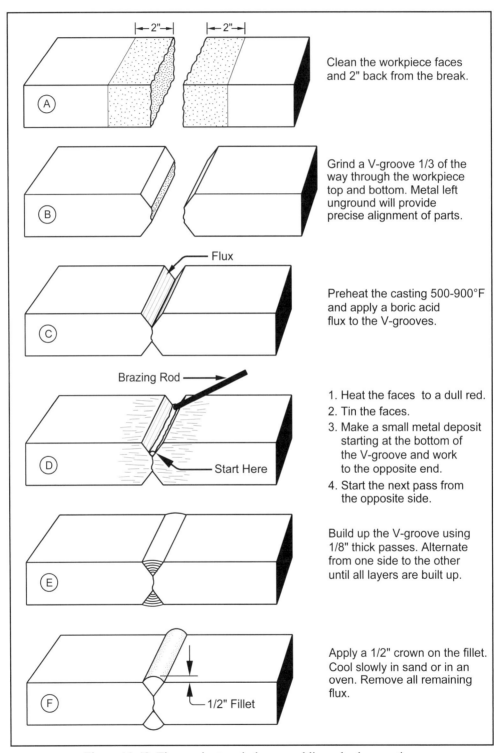

Clean the workpiece faces and 2" back from the break.

Grind a V-groove 1/3 of the way through the workpiece top and bottom. Metal left unground will provide precise alignment of parts.

Preheat the casting 500-900°F and apply a boric acid flux to the V-grooves.

1. Heat the faces to a dull red.
2. Tin the faces.
3. Make a small metal deposit starting at the bottom of the V-groove and work to the opposite end.
4. Start the next pass from the opposite side.

Build up the V-groove using 1/8" thick passes. Alternate from one side to the other until all layers are built up.

Apply a 1/2" crown on the fillet. Cool slowly in sand or in an oven. Remove all remaining flux.

Figure 11-48. The repair steps in braze welding a broken casting.

Chapter 12

Common Problems & Solutions

*Creative thinkers make many false starts, and continually waver
between unmanageable fantasies and systematic attack.*

—Harry Kepner

Introduction

As mentioned in the opening of this book, there are few genuine welding
secrets, but there are many valuable and little known techniques, methods and
procedures that can make any welding job go smoother. Collectively called
Know-How, these time, money, and aggravation-saving tips can be the
difference between success or failure, profit or loss; between removing that
snapped drill and saving a part or giving up and throwing the part away. Many
of these tips are based on science, and others on pure experience. You've
probably seen some of the following welding problems, and with this
chapter—you'll now have the solutions.

Section I – Removing What's Stuck

Frozen and Broken Bolt Removal Methods

When a rusted, seized or broken bolt or tap is stuck and cannot be removed,
besides using a traditional screw extractor, sometimes called an *easy out*,
there are several other solutions.

- If the assembly holding the bolt will tolerate heat without damage, use an
  oxyfuel torch to heat the bolt head to just below red heat. A rapid water
  quench or compressed air stream will further help with the screw removal.
  This method works because the heating and cooling will not occur evenly
  between the bolt and the part, which results in a differential expansion and
  contraction that breaks the bonds between the parts. Two or more heating
  and cooling cycles may be needed.

- If a slotted head or Allen cap screw socket is damaged or missing, place a
  nut over the bolt head, or the remaining stub end, clamp this nut in place,
  and fill the inside of the nut with weld metal. This weld will join the nut to
  the bolt stub. Then, put a wrench or socket on the nut and back out the
  broken bolt. This method simultaneously provides a new gripping point
  and applies heat to the fastener.

See Figure 12-1. SMAW, FCAW, GMAW and GTAW may be used on fasteners of $^1/_2$" diameter or larger. GTAW is needed for smaller fasteners because it provides better control.

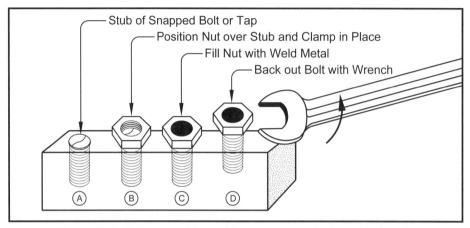

Figure 12-1. Bolt removal by welding a nut onto the frozen bolt stub.

- When the tap or fastener is snapped off *below* the workpiece surface, GTAW can be used to extend a column of metal from the broken off fastener to the surface of the workpiece. A nut can then be attached to the broken fastener. See Figure 12-2. The GTAW tungsten electrode must be held coaxially with the hole axis so it does not attach weld metal to the sides of the hole, but just to the broken tap or fastener.

Filler metal does not easily bond to the internal threads for two reasons:

- The threads are much cooler than the weld metal.

- Capillary attraction of the weld metal to itself makes it relatively easy to form a column up to the top of a threaded hole without attaching weld metal to the threads.

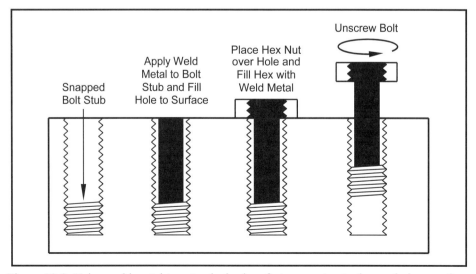

Figure 12-2. Using weld metal to extend a broken fastener or tap to the workpiece surface.

Figure 12-3 shows the types of fasteners and taps that can be removed using this welded-on nut extraction method.

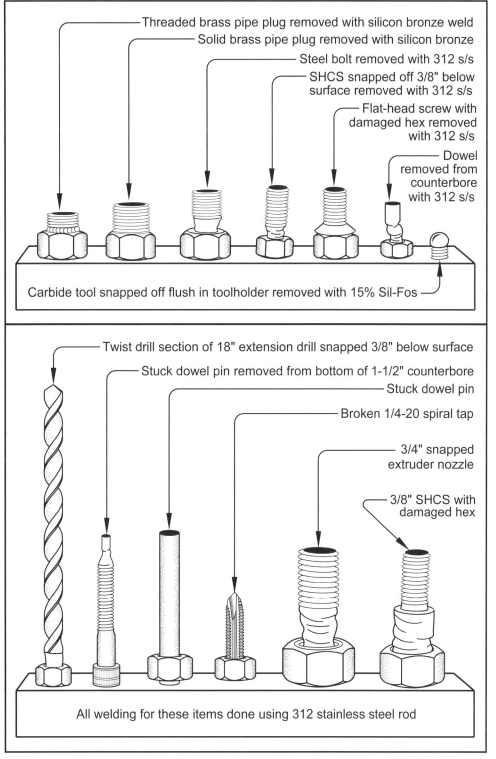

Figure 12-3. Frozen or damaged items removed from work using GTAW.

Removing Dowel Pins without Welding

There are several removal techniques that, though they do not use welding, every welder should know.

For dowel pins that are stuck in blind holes, the following approach avoids exposing the workpiece to the welding heat of GTAW and instead uses a piston and hydraulic force to free the dowel. Here are the steps:

1. Center drill and then drill a hole through the center of the stuck dowel pin. For a $^1/_2$" diameter dowel, drill a hole about 0.015" *less* than $^1/_4$" diameter to prepare for reaming. Use a milling machine and a twist drill with brazed carbide tips. A solid carbide drill could also be used, but it is likely to snap because solid carbide drills are very brittle. See Figure 12-4 (A & B).

2. In a mill, ream this hole to $^1/_4$" diameter. See Figure 12-4 (C).

3. Using a syringe, fill the reamed hole in the stuck dowel pin with grease. Leave a little length of the reamed hole empty of grease to give the $^1/_4$" dowel pin good starting alignment. See Figure 12-4 (D).

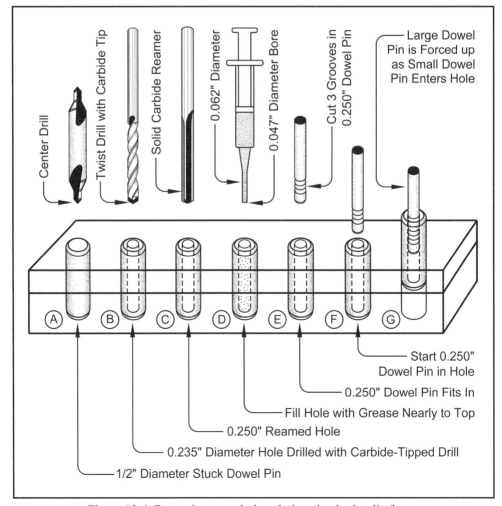

Figure 12-4. Removing a stuck dowel pin using hydraulic force.

4. Prepare a $^1/_4$" dowel pin by cutting three 0.020" deep rings, or grooves, just back from one end of the pin using a lathe and a carbide cutter. These rings reduce grease leakage around the pin. See Figure 12-4 (E).

5. Insert the smaller dowel into the hole drilled into the larger dowel pin. See Figure 12-4 (F). Use an arbor or hydraulic press to force the smaller dowel through the larger one.

6. The stuck dowel pin will be forced out of its hole and can be removed with a pair of Vise-Grip-style pliers. See Figure 12-4 (G).

Removing a Snapped Extension Twist Drill

This problem involves a steel plastic-injection mold. Because the machinist failed to clear the $^1/_2$" × 18" long extension drill, the twist drill section at the bottom of the hole snapped off from its $^1/_2$" shank. See Figure 12-5 (A & B).

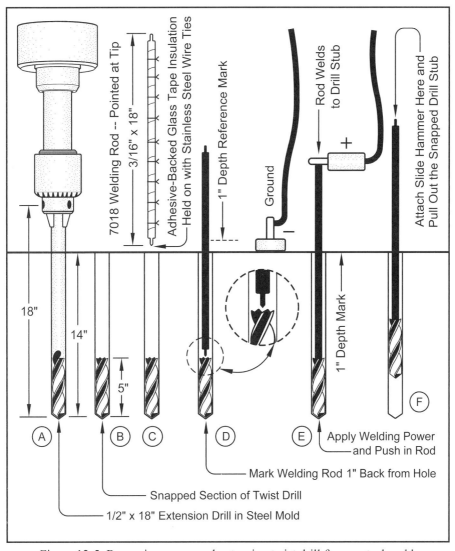

Figure 12-5. Removing a snapped extension twist drill from a steel mold.

Here are the steps to remove the stuck drill tip:

1. Grind a point on a $^3/_{16}$" diameter 7018 SMAW welding rod. This will get the arc started since a *scratch start* is not possible inside the hole. Starting one inch back from the point, wrap the welding rod with an adhesive-backed fiberglass tape and secure the tape with fine stainless steel wire ties in 8–12 locations along the rod. Bend the twisted section of the wire ties so they lie flat against the rod coating. The stainless steel ties keep the fiberglass tape in place when the rod is hot. The taped welding rod will slide freely into the $^1/_2$" diameter drilled hole. See Figure 12-5 (C).

2. Slide the rod into the hole so it bumps the shank of the snapped twist drill and make a depth reference mark on the fiberglass insulation tape one inch up from the surface of the hole. See Figure 12-5 (D).

3. Connect only the positive terminal of an SMAW power supply to the exposed end of the welding rod. See Figure 12-5 (E).

4. Set the SMAW constant voltage welding power to supply 250 A DC.

5. Turn on the welding power supply and hold the negative power supply terminal in your left hand.

6. Touch the negative power supply terminal—the ground line—to the steel mold, then push in the welding rod so it arcs against the stuck drill inside the mold. The reference mark on the welding rod shows when the rod has burned down one inch. This takes 2–3 seconds. Then remove the negative terminal to stop the arc.

7. Disconnect the positive terminal from the rod and turn off the SMAW welding supply.

8. Attach a slide hammer to the outside end of the welding rod and pull out the rod with the snapped drill stub welded to it. See Figure 12-5 (F).

Rusted Nut Removal

The problem is that a rusted nut must be removed from bolt threads, but heat cannot be used.

Here's how to remove it:

1. Position a diamond-point chisel just inside the edge of the rusted nut. See Figure 12-6 (A).

2. Using a bronze hammer, drive the chisel into the nut. A bronze hammer has just the right softness to transfer most of its energy to the chisel. A steel, lead or brass hammer will not work as well.

3. Reposition the chisel to the right of the first cut and make the next vertical cut. See Figure 12-6 (B).

4. Place the chisel to the left of the first cut for the final vertical cut. See Figure 12-6 (C).

5. The nut now has a wide gap cut into it. Use a cold chisel to free the nut from the bolt threads by striking the nut sideways. See Figure 12-6 (D).

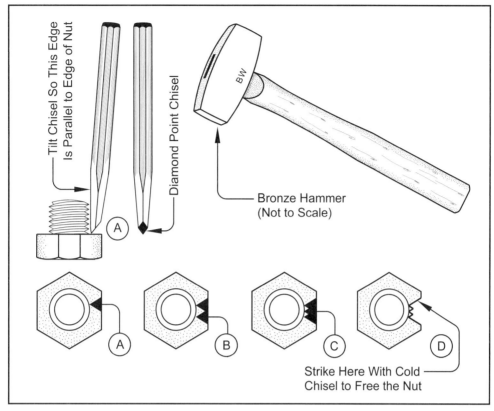

Figure 12-6. Using a diamond-point chisel to remove a rusted nut.

Removing a Stuck Steel Bearing

A bearing stuck inside a motor or machine casting can often be removed by placing a weld bead on the inside circumference of the bearing as in Figure 12-7. The combination of the shrinkage of the weld bead, which reduces the bearing diameter, and the heat of the welding process should free the bearing. For example, a 4" diameter steel bearing will shrink about 0.050" across its diameter if the bead runs completely around its circumference.

Stuck ball bearings can also be removed using this same technique, but the inner race and balls must be removed first to provide access to the inside of the outer race. This weld-bead method is good for when a part is too large or too heavy to fit into a press.

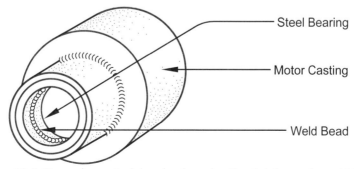

Figure 12-7. Removing a stuck bearing by using the shrinkage of a weld bead.

Section II – Securing Nuts, Bolts & Pins

Securing a Nut on a Bolt or on All-Thread

Figure 12-8 shows four ways to prevent a nut from being removed from a bolt or a threaded rod.

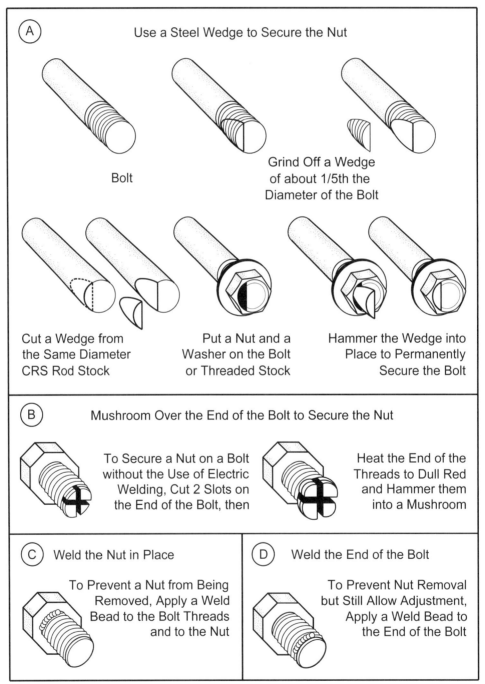

Figure 12-8. Ways to secure a nut: (A) Use a steel wedge, (B) Make hacksaw cuts in the shaft and mushroom the bolt end, (C) Apply a weld bead between the nut and its threads, (D) Apply a weld bead to the thread ends to permit nut adjustment, but prevent its removal.

Securing Pins

Here are the steps to permanently secure a pin in a plate:

1. Locate, center punch, and center drill the pin position in the plate.

2. Drill a hole that the pin can slip or be driven into.

3. Chamfer the bottom end of the pin and insert it in the hole so the pin is $^1/_{16}$" below the surface of the plate.

4. Make a plug weld on the recessed end of the pin. The plug weld may be ground flush with the plate for better fit and appearance. See Figure 12-9.

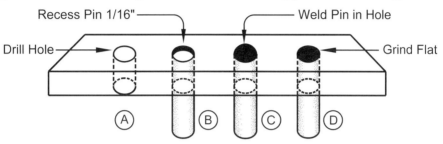

Figure 12-9. Securing a pin in a plate using a plug weld.

Permanently Securing a Bolt to a Plate

It is easy to permanently secure a bolt to a plate. There are two methods:

- *Method 1* – Weld or braze a large-diameter bolt with its head down onto the plate. Place a weld bead completely around the bolt head. It may be necessary to preheat both the bolt and the plate as their combined size draws too much welding heat away from the weld. See Figure 12-10 (left).

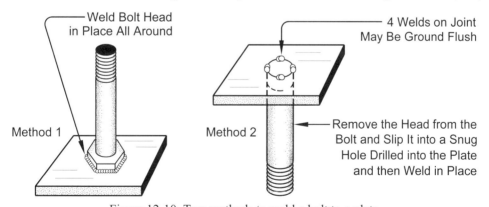

Figure 12-10. Two methods to weld a bolt to a plate.

- *Method 2* – After removing the head from the bolt, drill a hole in the plate to fit the shank of the bolt and then insert the bolt through the plate. Weld the bolt to the plate as shown in Figure 12-10 (right). The inverted bolt provides a large diameter thread to secure a hollow object without having to cut threads or drill a large diameter hole in the mounting plate.

If torch preheating, bolts between $^3/_8$" and $^5/_8$" diameter can be attached to a $^1/_2$" thick steel plate using a 130 A GMAW/FCAW welding machine.

Section III – Adding Threads, Lift Rings, Tie Points & Jacks

Adding Threads to a Thin-Walled Tube

Because most tubing walls are too thin to accept threads, a threaded insert can be placed inside the tubing and secured in place with one or more plug welds. This is a common practice in automotive suspensions and aircraft control rods. These insert plugs are commercially available in both male and female, left or right-handed threads. They can also be shop-made. See Figure 12-11.

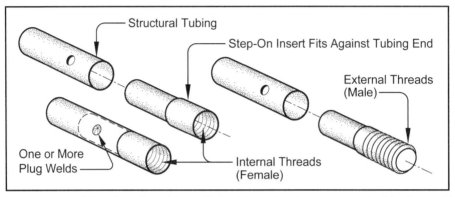

Figure 12-11. Adding threads to thin-walled tubing using inserts secured with plug welds.

Adding Threads to a Plate

To add threads to a plate or thin sheet metal, tack weld a nut onto the work. Here is how it's done:

1. Drill a clearance hole in the plate or sheet metal that needs threads.

2. File or grind off any zinc or cadmium plating on the nut prior to welding to avoid contaminating the weld with the plating metal and releasing toxic plating fumes into the air.

3. Clamp the nut in place using another nut and bolt to draw the first nut flat and hold it securely against the plate when welding.

4. When the work cools, remove the non-welded clamping bolt and the extra nut. All four steps are shown in Figure 12-12.

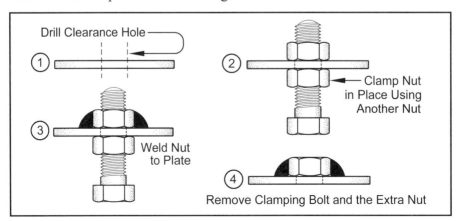

Figure 12-12. Welding a nut over a hole to add threads to a plate.

Threaded Plugs for Installing Lift Rings

Many heavy machine parts must be moved with a chain hoist or a crane and require the addition of threads for installing a lift ring. If the part is hardened, it can be drilled with a carbide drill, but it *cannot* be tapped for threads. The solution is to drill a hole in the part, insert a threaded plug into the hole, and weld the plug in place. Now there are threads where they are needed.

As shown in Figure 12-13, here's how it's done:

1. At a balance point, drill a hole in the heavy machine part to be lifted.

2. Make a threaded plug to fit into the drilled hole. The plug should be made from a high grade steel, such as 4130 or 4140. A readily available source of suitable steel is the shank of a Grade 5 or a Grade 8 bolt. To use a bolt, put the bolt shank in a lathe, turn a section to size, then drill and tap it.

3. Chamfer the edge of the hole in the part and the edge of the lift ring insert plug. These chamfers give the final weld bead a place to go. Though it is best to chamfer both the plug and the hole as in Figure 12-13 (bottom left), sometimes only the lift ring insert plug can be chamfered, as in Figure 12-13 (bottom right).

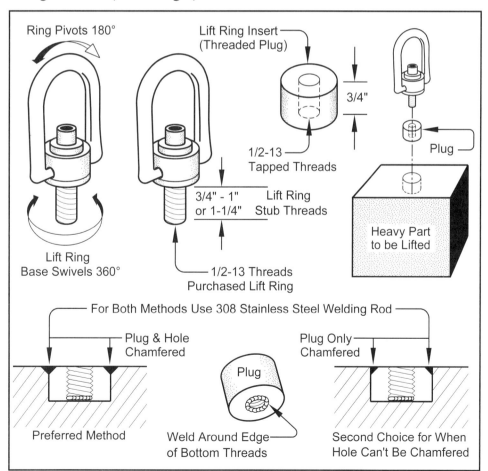

Figure 12-13. Making a threaded plug insert for installing a lift ring.

4. Weld around the bottom of the threaded hole so that a bolt screwed into these threads cannot act as a jack to force the insert plug out of its hole. This weld forms a stop for the bolt before it exits the threaded plug.

5. Weld the threaded plug into the hole with a bead around its top edge and screw in a purchased lift ring.

Tip: Because lift rings with the same stub threads are available in several lengths—for example $^3/_4$-, 1-, and $1^1/_4$-inch lengths—a stub can be longer than a plug is deep. If this happens, add spacer washers or, as described previously, the screw will act as a jack and place an additional load on the weld holding the plug in place. This added load can lead to load release.

Making a Hasp or Tie Point

Shop-made hasps are easy to fabricate. Here's how it's done:

1. Cut a link from a steel chain using a hacksaw, bandsaw, or a Sawzall-type reciprocating saw so the ends of the link are parallel.

2. Drill two holes in the part where the hasp is needed. Make sure the holes fit the position and diameter of the cut link ends.

3. Chamfer the ends of the links so they enter the holes more easily.

4. Insert the link into the holes and, from the back side, secure them in place with plug welds. See Figure 12-14.

If there is no welding access on the back of the part on which the hasp is to be placed, the hasp can be secured onto a small plate and then the plate welded to the part.

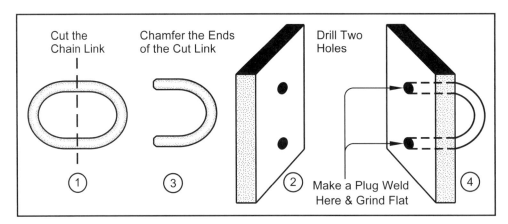

Figure 12-14. Making a hasp or tie point from a chain link.

Securing Chain Tie Downs

One solution to securing heavy loads to truck floors and ship decks is to chain them in place using flame-cut cross-shaped holes in the deck. These cross-shaped holes, called *tie-down holes*, provide a secure, convenient means to attach tie-down chains. A steel pan is welded underneath each tie-down hole to prevent water, fire and fumes from making their way to the deck below. See Figure 12-15.

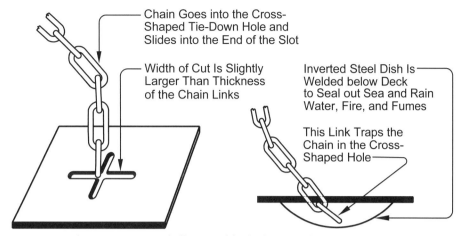

Figure 12-15. Truck floor or ship deck cargo tie-down method.
The actual plate is much larger than the one shown.

Adding Cleats to a Plate

An integral lifting cleat can be added to a plate by using a plasma torch to cut the C-shape hole shown in Figure 12-16.

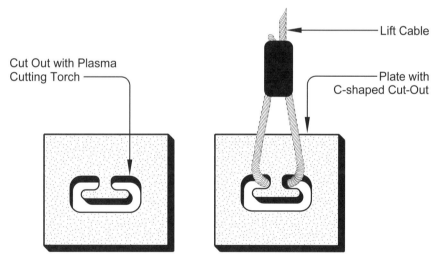

Figure 12-16. Lifting cleat plasma-cut into a steel plate.

Leveling Jacks

Here is how to add the leveling jacks in Figure 12-17 to a table or machine:

1. Drill clearance holes in the table or machine to be leveled.

2. Using a $^5/_{16}$" × 3" hex bolt, grind down the hex bolt head so that the bolt head force-fits into the hole of a 1-inch washer.

3. Weld the washer to the bolt head to form the foot of the leveler.

4. Weld a 3" piece of $^1/_4$" rod perpendicular to the bolt for a turning handle.

5. Affix a nut to the top of the clearance hole in the table to form threads.

6. Screw the leveling jacks into the base of the table or machine and then adjust the height of the jacks.

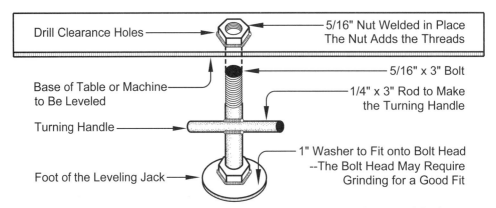

Figure 12-17. A shop-made leveling jack. Nut can go on top or bottom of the base.

Section IV – Stubbing Out & Building Up Shafts

Stubbing Out Shafts

Many times when a keyway on a large machine has been torn out of its shaft, the machine and the shaft are too expensive to replace. Luckily, the shaft can be repaired by cutting off the damaged end section and adding on a new steel repair stub. Here are the steps:

1. Machine the replacement repair stub shown in Figure 12-18 (right). The rounded corners at the bottom of the stub reduce stress concentrations.

2. Place the damaged shaft in a lathe with a steady rest supporting the shaft on the lathe tailstock end. This arrangement provides easy access to the damaged end of the shaft.

3. Center the shaft in the steady rest using a dial test indicator.

4. Remove the damaged section of the shaft using a cutoff tool and lubricant. Alternatively, the damaged section may be cut off with a bandsaw before going into the lathe for machining.

5. Prepare the shaft's damaged end for its new stub by boring a center hole and chamfering its edges to help the stub slide into place. To provide a space for trapped air when the stub goes in, make the hole in the shaft at least $\frac{1}{4}$" deeper than the repair stub is long. Round the corners at the bottom of the hole to reduce stress concentrations. See Figure 12-18 (left).

6. Bevel the outer diameter of both the repair shaft and the damaged shaft to allow for a weld which will hold the new stub in place.

7. Remove the damaged shaft from the lathe and block it up to secure the new stub. Hold and position the shaft so the new stub can be driven in with a sledge hammer in the next steps.

8. Heat the damaged shaft with one or two oxyacetylene rosebud torches while cooling the repair stub in dry ice. This takes more than one person.

9. Once the heated and cooled parts are put into position, the repair stub must be driven into place without delay.

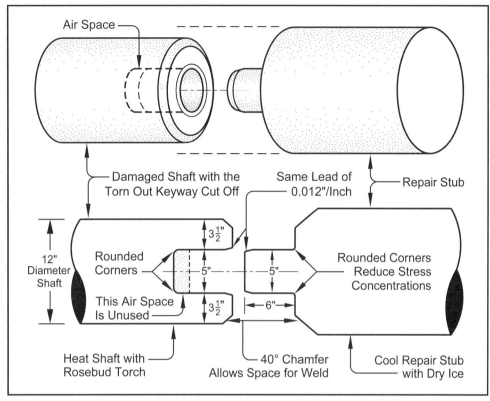

Figure 12-18. When a keyway is torn out of a machinery shaft, by making
a repair stub, a new section of shaft can be added and a new keyway cut.

10. While one welder inserts the repair stub into the hole in the shaft and
    holds it in position, one or two other welders drive the repair stub into
    place with sledge hammers. The repair stub is larger in diameter than the
    shaft so that, if the repair stub is not perfectly seated, it can still be turned
    down to match the outer diameter of the original shaft.

11. Tack weld the new stub and original shaft at the 3, 6, 9 and 12 o'clock
    positions. Next, weld the shaft all-around and then turn it down in a lathe
    so that the two shafts are the same diameter.

12. Cut the new keyway in the new stub, usually with a milling machine.

Building up a Worn Shaft

A badly worn or undersized shaft can be built up using FCAW, GMAW, or
GTAW beads. There are four points to remember to get good results:

• Place weld beads *parallel* with the axis of the shaft.

• Put down one bead, rotate the shaft 180º, and then place the next weld
  bead as *Method 1* shows in Figure 12-19 (left). This weld sequence will
  balance weld-stress forces and virtually eliminate heat-induced distortion.
  Placing sequential beads next to one another will cause the shaft to curve
  into a banana shape. Building up a worn shaft is best done using welding
  rollers to make handling the shaft easier.

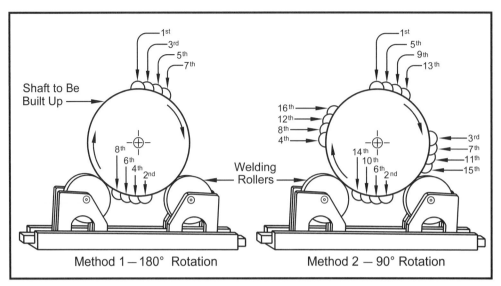

Figure 12-19. Building up a worn or undersized shaft with weld metal.

- Weld beads must be placed tightly *onto* one another with a 30–50% overlap to provide a smooth surface after final machining.

- SMAW and FCAW will require thorough flux removal by brushing and chipping between each bead.

- It is also possible to add a weld bead every 90°—at the 3, 6, 9 and 12 o'clock positions. This further reduces the effects of distortion as shown in *Method 2* of Figure 12-19 (right). In some applications, such as building up a bronze or copper part, adding braze metal may be better than welding because less heat means less distortion.

Section V – Making Holes & Sealing Holes

Making Holes in Spring Steel & Hacksaw Blades

Spring steel and hacksaw blades are difficult to put holes through because these materials are hardened, but this task can easily be accomplished if you know how.

Here are two methods:

- *Method 1* – Drill the holes in the spring steel. To do this, set the drill press to its slowest speed, place an aluminum block under the spring steel as a heat sink so the steel will not be annealed, securely clamp in place, and then, using an HSS cobalt drill with a 135° point, drill the work. Be sure to apply cutting fluid. Considerable drill pressure may be needed to get the drilling started. Remove the burrs around the hole using a grinding wheel. Step drill holes over $^3/_8$" in diameter.

- *Method 2* – With this method holes are made using a GTAW torch. Figure 12-20 shows this unusual technique which rapidly produces smooth, round, burr-free holes. This method will even work with larger spring steel stock such as truck springs.

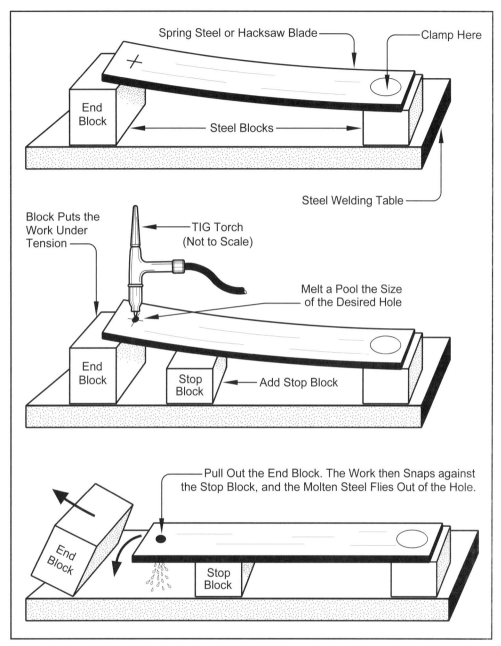

Figure 12-20. Using a GTAW (TIG) torch to make round,
smooth, burr-free holes in spring steel or hacksaw blades.

Sealing Closed Vessels

The problem is that when welding or brazing to seal a float or hollow part, the final end of the weld bead keeps blowing out from the hot air trapped inside the vessel. The solution is to drill a $^1/_{16}$" diameter pressure-relief hole in the float or hollow part to vent the weld-heated air to atmosphere, and then weld all the seams closed. To finish, allow the part to cool, and then seal up the drilled hole with a small weld. See Figure 12-21. In addition to closed vessels, use relief holes when welding structural pipe and tubing with trapped air.

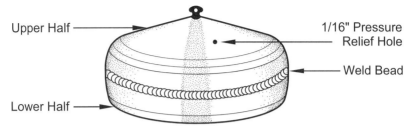

Upper Half

1/16" Pressure
Relief Hole

Weld Bead

Lower Half

Figure 12-21. Sealing a float. Weld up the relief hole after all other welding is complete.

Caution: Welding on a closed vessel can be dangerous. Make sure the interior of the vessel, pipe, or tube is clean and free of flammable or explosive vapors before starting to weld.

Closing Tubing Ends

When the open ends of square tubing must be closed off for appearance, safety, or weather-proofing, there are two ways to do this:

• The easiest way is to insert a plastic plug or cap that is sized for this tubing, as in Figure 12-22 (left). These plugs are available in round, square, and rectangular shapes. There are two drawbacks to plastic plugs. First, most designs and sizes are only available in black, and second, if the product is exposed to the outdoors, the plastic plugs will not protect the edges of the tubing from rust.

• Another approach is to cut a steel cover or cap for the tubing end, and weld it in place. See Figure 12-22 (right). This takes more time, but this method will protect the tubing ends from the weather.

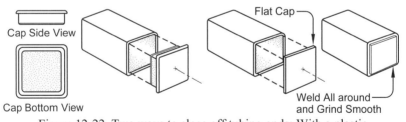

Cap Side View

Cap Bottom View

Flat Cap

Weld All around
and Grind Smooth

Figure 12-22. Two ways to close off tubing ends: With a plastic end cap (left) and with a welded steel-plate cover (right).

Section VI – Odd Problems & Clever Solutions

Extending the Capacity of a Welding Machine

Here is the problem: You have two steel parts to join with FCAW or GMAW, but one or both of the parts are just a little too thick for the maximum available current from your welding machine.

The solution is to first preheat the metal in the joint area, then use a propane, MAPP gas, or an acetylene torch to heat the weld area of the two parts to 300–500°F. Now you can make the weld. Preheating the metal in the weld area prevents the otherwise cold metal from draining heat away from the weld zone and preventing proper fusion. Preheating gives the effect of having a larger amperage welding machine.

Extension of the Welding Current Rule: Every 100°F the workpiece temperature is over 200°F is equivalent to 20 A of additional welding current.

Stretching Metal to Flatten Parts

A metal part that has been distorted can be stretched so it will once again lie flat. For example, Figure 12-23 (top row) shows a small machine part—a sewing machine throat plate—that has been fractured and repaired with TIG welds. In this repair, metal was added to the "fingers" of the throat plate and now the plate no longer lies flat, a critical issue with this part. The solution is simple and fast—stretch the part slightly and the fingers will once again lie flat as in Figure 12-23 (bottom right). To stretch the part, place a row of center-punch marks along the outer edges of the part. These punches stretch the part's outer edges enough to allow the repaired section to drop into its proper place, but not so much that the part no longer fits.

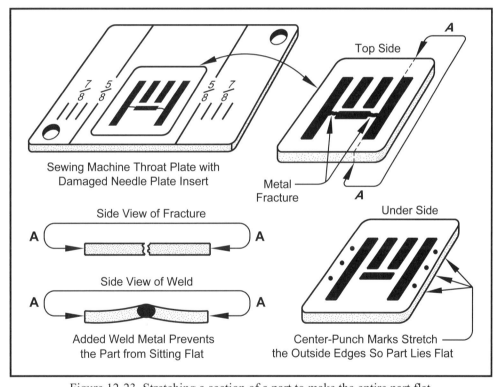

Figure 12-23. Stretching a section of a part to make the entire part flat.

Using Plug Welds

When a steel pad is welded to the surface of a steel plate, the fillet welds around the outer edge of the pad tend to force the center of the pad to lift and pull away from the steel plate. See Figure 12-24 (top). This separation complicates machining and threading operations and interferes with fit. To flatten the steel pad, drill a hole in the pad and make a plug weld through the hole to pull the pad back into place against the steel plate as shown in Figure 12-24 (bottom).

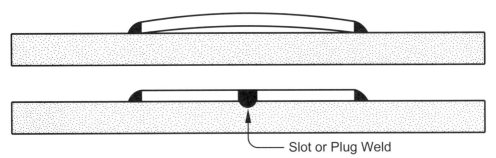

Figure 12-24. Using a plug or slot weld to pull a steel pad down against its base plate. Clamp the bowed plate flat before making the plug weld.

Stopping Crack Propagation in Plates

When tank or ship plating develops a crack, further propagation can be stopped by a two-step process. First, drill a hole at each end of the crack to distribute the end stress over a wider area, and then add the trapezoidal-shaped padding just beyond the holes, as in Figure 12-25. This padding adds strength to the section of the plate where the crack is headed. Ideally, the drilled holes should be *magnafluxed* to insure that the crack enters only one side of the hole and does not cross to the other side to continue the crack.

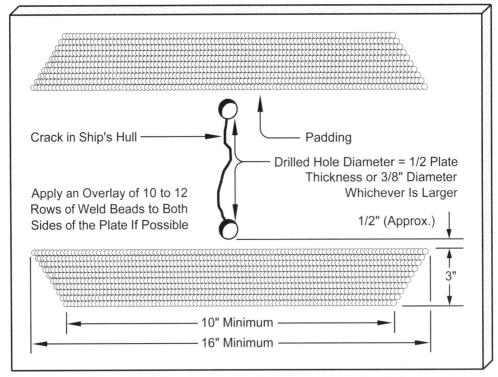

Figure 12-25. How to stop a crack in a plate using drilled holes and padding to distribute the stress and strengthen the plate.

Welding Thick to Thin Parts

Here's the problem: When using GMAW or FCAW to weld a thin sheet-metal cap onto the end of a much heavier gauge steel tube, you cannot set the current level properly. If the current level is set low enough to avoid burning through the cap, it will not weld on the heavier steel tube, and if it is set high enough to weld on the tube, it burns through the cap. Here's two solutions:

- Set the welding current so as not to burn through the thinner material, then preheat the heavier metal with a torch and make the weld as if both materials were the same, thinner gauge.

- Set the welding current for the heavier gauge material. When performing the weld, keep the arc on the heavy metal 90% of the time and take short excursions into the thinner material. This technique takes practice, but works well when mastered.

Adding Thickness

Whenever an area of a panel must be thicker than the panel itself, place another, thicker piece of metal on both the front and back sides of the panel where added strength is needed and secure the add-ons by welding all around. Such add-ons will provide the thickness needed to perform subsequent machining, boring, or drilling, and can replace a much heavier one-piece panel or a casting. This technique can also be used for repairs.

See Figure 12-26.

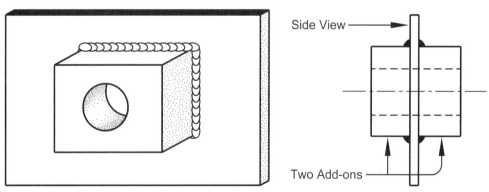

Figure 12-26. Adding a thick plate onto a thinner panel for additional strength and rigidity.

When applying two add-ons, a good method is to drill one add-on *before* welding the two add-ons to the panel, and then, after welding, use the drilled add-on as a guide to drill the panel and the other add-on. Another method is to drill a hole through the panel, and through the add-ons, then use a bolt to hold both the add-ons in place to weld them. After welding, remove the bolt.

Stiffening Flat Panels

The standard way to stiffen panels to resist loads is to weld angle iron onto the panels vertically. It might seem logical to weld a flat L-portion of the angle iron to the panel, but placing the 'L' of the angle on the outside helps to stiffen the panel even more. See Figure 12-27.

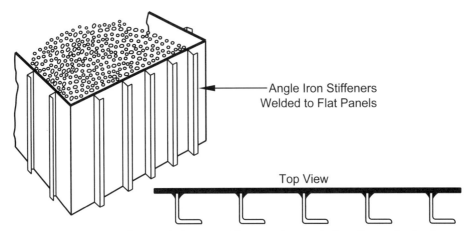

Figure 12-27. Adding angle iron to stiffen panels to resist bending under load.

Reducing Noise and Vibration

Sheet metal is used for thunder sound effects, but most of the time we don't want this noise. There are several ways to reduce the noise and low-frequency vibration caused by thin panels:

- Add stiffeners in the form of creases, flanges, or corrugations.

- Break the panel into smaller sections to reduce the size of the unsupported lengths. This will raise the resonant frequency of the panel and lower the noise level.

- Use a sprayed-on bituminous coating, which is commonly applied in automobile manufacturing to dampen noise.

- Adhere a layer of sound-dampening felt or a paint-on coating to the panel.

- When vibration occurs at a relatively low frequency, adding the metal stiffeners in Figure 12-28 often works to dampen noise.

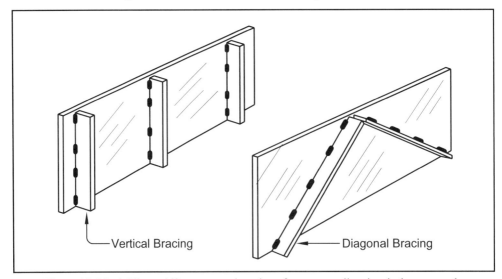

Figure 12-28. Adding stiffeners to reduce low-frequency vibration in large panels.

Welding Screen or Wire Mesh to a Frame

The problem is that when you try to weld screening or expanded metal to a frame using GMAW, FCAW or GTAW, the screening burns through and the weld is incomplete.

The solution is to use the *washer method*. Place bare steel washers over the steel screening (or expanded metal) and clamp the washers, screening and frame together. Vise-Grip Model 9R welding pliers work well for this task. Do not use cadmium plated or galvanized washers because their fumes are toxic. See Figure 12-29 (A).

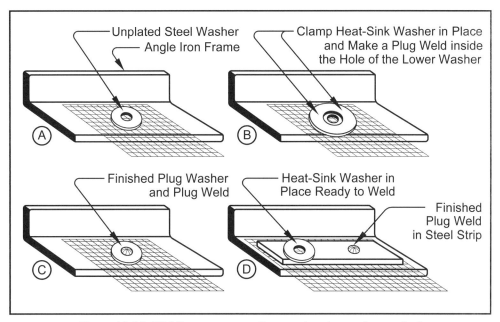

Figure 12-29. Welding screen to a frame using the *washer method*.

Then, as a heat sink, place another larger washer over the washer to be welded in place. This top washer should have a larger hole than the bottom washer to avoid welding *both* washers to the frame. Make your plug weld *through* the two holes of the washers and weld only the bottom washer to the frame. Some tweaking of the welder may be needed to get enough heat to perform the weld, but not so much as to burn away the surrounding screening. See Figure 12-29 (B & C).

Another approach to welding screening is to use a steel strip with holes at regular intervals either in addition to or in place of the washers. See Figure 12-29 (D).

Chamfering Welded Repair Plugs

When stepped plugs are used to repair holes in angle plates or other tooling, the stepped side of the plug should be placed so the forces on the plug pull against the plug so it cannot be pulled through the hole. With this method very little force is seen by the weld. However, by chamfering the plug on both ends, the welds can have better penetration and strength that would be needed should the forces on the plug be reversed. See Figure 12-30.

Tip: Place the first weld on the plug so it pulls the plug tight into the repair hole. Placing the first weld in the wrong order will prevent the plug from seating properly against its step.

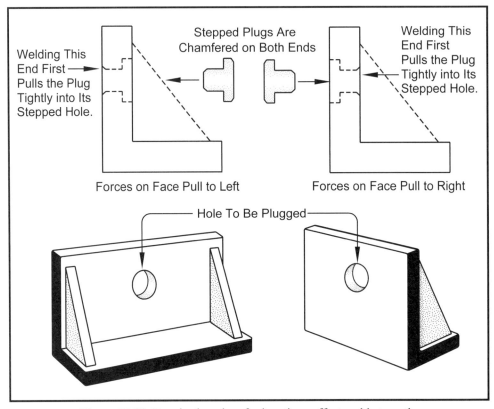

Figure 12-30. Repair plug chamfer locations affect weld strength.

Chapter 13

Design Tips

Success is the result of countless failures you've done in order to attain it.
—Mark Aaron A. Corrales

Introduction

Like a chain, a part is only as strong as its weakest link. To assure the quality of a part, keep the function of the part in mind when designing welds and remember that welding is not the answer to every metal joining problem. Try to avoid unnecessary welds by incorporating small castings, forgings, or standard sections whenever possible, and use bending, rolling and flanging to add strength without adding weld metal. Also, place welds in sections with lower stress concentrations and make sure the weld design has no stress-inducing notches which could lead to fatigue failure.

Good Weld Characteristics

A good weld design meets the following four criteria:

- *Strength* – A weld should satisfy the strength and stiffness requirements of the part, but must not be *over designed*. If in doubt, have engineers check the part for safety. They may discover that the stiffness requirements are set too high; an error which costs money in extra material, welding time, handling and shipping. Over design may also impose added long-term costs on the end user in fuel consumption and maintenance.

- *Rigidity* – Use thick sections to resist bending. Symmetrical sections are more efficient for bending resistance.

- *Appearance* – Specify the appearance required on the welds to avoid unnecessary grinding and finishing. Appearance for its own sake usually increases cost and is not necessary when welds are completely hidden from view. The welder is not likely to know which welds are critical appearance-wise and which are not unless the print specifies appearance.

- *Code & Legal Issues* – If the product must be fabricated to a code, check to determine that the most economical method currently allowed is used.

Methods to Add Strength

The proper use of stiffeners will provide strength and rigidity with less weight. Here are several ways to add strength:

- *Closed sections* are used for torsion resistance. Torsional resistance of a frame is approximately equal to the sum of the resistance of its individual parts. Sections that are closed are often several times more torsion-resistant than open sections. See Table 13-1.

Angle of Twist Indicates Torsion Resistance					
	A	B	C	D	E
All Loadings Identical	t = 0.060 $3\frac{1}{2}$	t = 0.060 $2\frac{1}{8}$ 3/4	t = 0.060 1.15	t = 0.060	t = 0.060
Actual Twist	9°	9.5°	11°	Too Small to Measure	Too Small to Measure

Table 13-1. Five steel shapes and their measured angle of twist when subjected to the same torsional load.

- *Diagonal bracing* is much more effective than longitudinal or straight-across bracing in resisting torsion. The diagonally braced frame in Figure 13-1 is 36 times more resistant to torsional twist, yet uses 6% less metal.

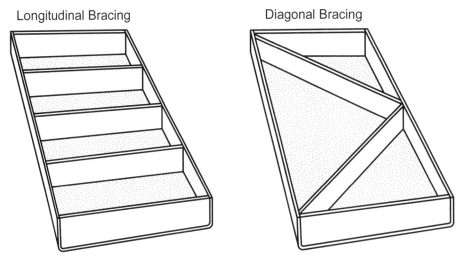

Longitudinal Bracing   Diagonal Bracing

Figure 13-1. Diagonal bracing increases torsional rigidity much more than longitudinal, or straight-across, bracing.

- *Vertical stiffeners vs. horizontal stiffeners* – As shown in Figure 13-2, vertical stiffeners are not as effective in resisting compressive loads as horizontal stiffeners. The horizontal stiffeners provide more support along the length of the box. This reduces the length of the intervals along the sides of the box not supported by stiffeners.

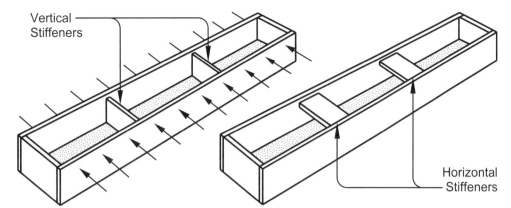

Figure 13-2. Vertical stiffeners (left) are not as effective in
resisting compressive loads as horizontal stiffeners (right).

- *Vertical bracing* is not as effective as diagonal bracing. Vertical or longitudinal stiffeners must be used in castings because of coring constraints, while horizontal stiffeners can be used in a welded design. Figure 13-3 shows two welded steel machine bases. When both bases are subjected to torque of 1000 in-lb, the base on the left with vertical bracing twists 1.84° while the base on the right with diagonal bracing twists less than 0.001°.

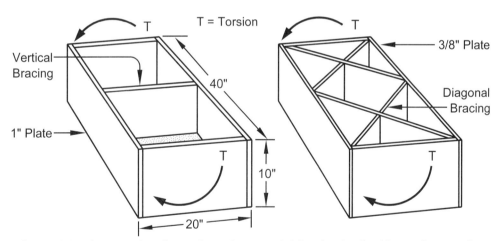

Figure 13-3. These two box frames have the same rigidity despite the thinner plates used to make the diagonally reinforced box on the right. Diagonal bracing is often used in machine bases because it is more rigid than vertical bracing.

Construction Considerations

With a little planning, parts cannot only be made stronger, lighter and quicker, they can also cost less and be easier to maintain. Here are some examples:

- If only the surface properties are needed, such as wear-resistance on a high-priced or difficult-to-weld material, consider using a mild steel base and *hardfacing*—which means adding hard-as-welded filler metals in critical areas only.

- Adding *hardened parts,* such as dowel pins, in critical areas only is an economical alternative to an entirely hardened part. See Figure 13-4.

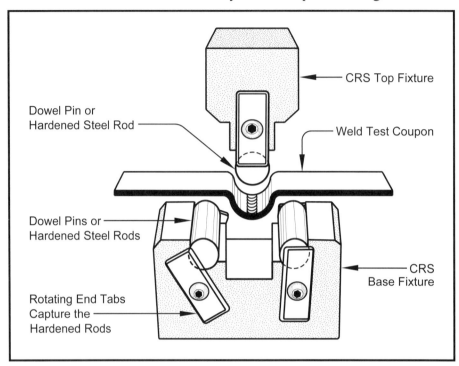

Figure 13-4. Adding hardened stock to only the critical areas of this weld-test fixture—the areas that really require extra hardness—saves on materials and heat-treatment costs.

- Dimension parts so that the plate and bar sizes can be *easily obtained* from your in-shop stock or from a vendor's in-house inventory. Do not specify a special-order size unless absolutely necessary. Try not to design parts that require *unobtainum.*

- *Round parts can replace square ones*, as in Figure 13-5, so that a rotary welding table can be used. Welding on a rotary table has one starting and stopping point and no corner welds, so it is not only easier on the welder because torch movement is minimized, it reduces the number of potential failure points where weld defects can develop.

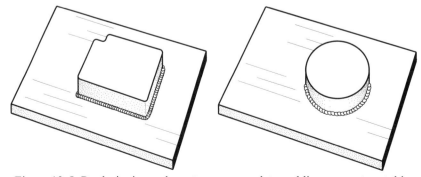

Figure 13-5. Re-designing a shape to accommodate welding on a rotary table.

- Be sure to *provide maintenance accessibility*. Do not bury a bearing support or other critical wear point within a closed-box weldment. The same applies to electrical wiring, hydraulic lines and other components which may need repair or replacement at a later time.

Layout Design Considerations

- *Bending & Folding* – Designing your part to contain the fewest number of pieces reduces layout and assembly time and the amount of welding needed. Consider layout and design alternatives such as folding or bending rather than welding parts together as shown in Figure 13-6. The bending method is much more cost effective.

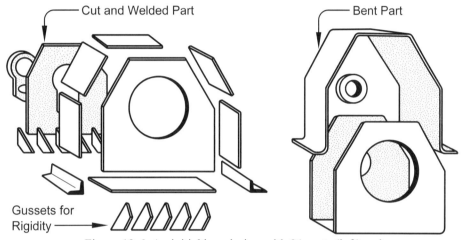

Figure 13-6. An initial box design with 21 parts (left) and
the improved design with four parts (right).

- *Changing weld location* – Figure 13-7 shows an example of design changes that save welding time and materials. Review your design carefully to see if it can be improved without affecting the strength of the end product.

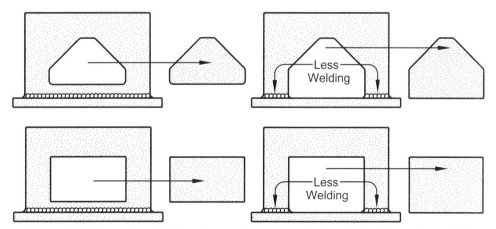

Figure 13-7. Examples of design changes that save on both welding time and materials.

- *Cutting & nesting* – The cost of material, cutting, welding and the cost-saving alternative uses for the cutout—excess or scrap material—must be considered before deciding between the three different layout approaches shown in Figure 13-8.

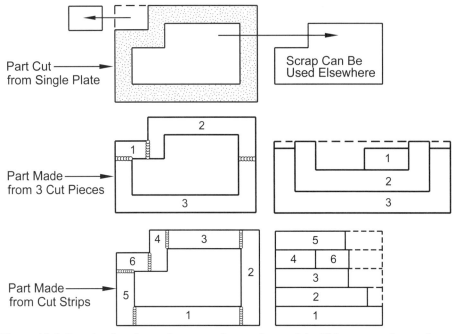

Figure 13-8. Imaginative alternatives save time and materials. This part can be cut from a single plate (top), assembled from three cut parts (middle) or assembled from strips (bottom).

- *Three methods for rings* – When fabricating rings, remember that they can be cut from a single plate, as in Figure 13-9, or welded from sections nested on a plate. Part dimensional tolerances, material, cutting and welding costs, and the alternative uses of the scrap must be calculated before the best layout plan is known. If the delivery of new material is a problem, cut segments might get the job done without having to wait for more plate.

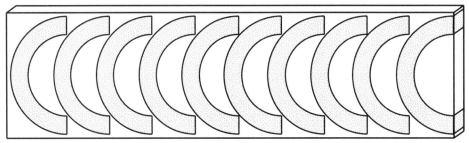

Figure 13-9. To make rings from thick plate, cut nested segments to reduce material cost or to improve delivery time.

When tolerances permit, cut strips from bar stock, bending them into rings and then welding them closed instead of cutting the rings from thick plate or billets. Material waste will be reduced as in Figure 13-10.

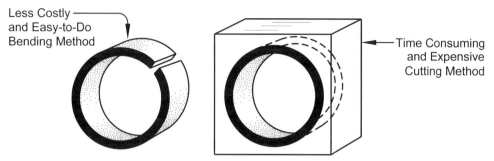

Figure 13-10. Cut and roll rings from bar stock and weld them
closed (left) instead of cutting the rings from heavy plate stock (right).

If a number of rings are required for a job, try this cost saver: roll a plate into a cylinder, weld up its seam, and then flame cut the cylinder into rings. The cylinder can be any length. The one in Figure 13-11 is for a short run.

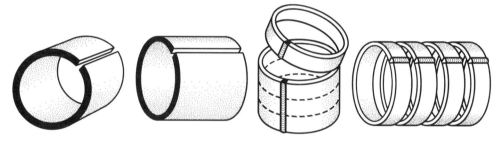

Figure 13-11. Making rings from plate stock by rolling a cylinder, welding, and cutting.

- *Designing Complex Parts* – Very complex parts can be fabricated by welding together several components, which saves on weight, materials and machining time. In addition, this method can replace cast parts, such as the hub of the pulley shown in Figure 13-12, and it eliminates the need for costly molds with their long lead times. This method is also excellent for making a prototype or replacement part in a hurry.

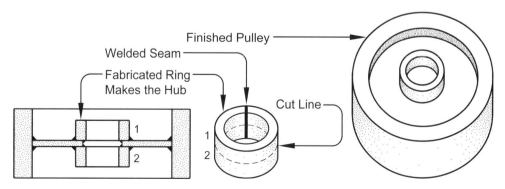

Figure 13-12. The hub of this pulley is rolled from flat stock,
welded into a ring, sawed in half horizontally and welded in place.

- *Adding stiffness to flat plates* – Extra stiffness can be added to a flat plate or panel by pressing in either a vertical or a horizontal crease—or flange—with a press brake. See Figure 13-13. This technique can also be used to help hide or straighten ripples in a large sheet metal panel as in Figure 13-13 (left).

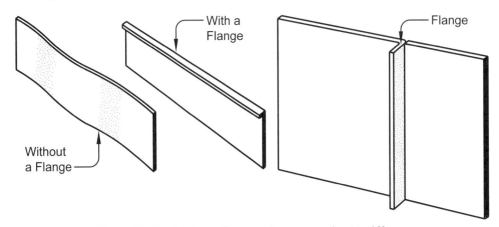

Figure 13-13. Adding a flange to increase a plate's stiffness.

For another method to add extra stiffness, try pressing creases into a flat panel. Figure 13-14 shows a low-cost way to add stiffness that uses a press brake. To do this, place the panel diagonally in a press brake and press in one crease, then rotate the panel to press in the second diagonal crease. A slight dome will form in the center of the panel where the creases cross each other.

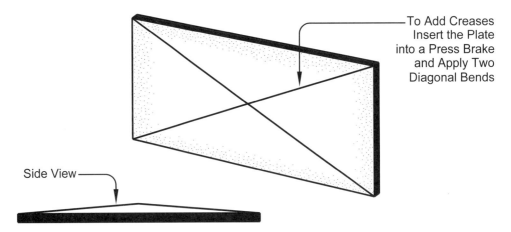

Figure 13-14. Adding creases in a flat panel is a low-cost way to increase its stiffness.

- *Weld location and fatigue failure* – Figure 13-15 shows how the location of a weld seam can adversely affect the strength of a part. Make sure that the weld seam is at the optimum location based on the particular welding and fabrication process.

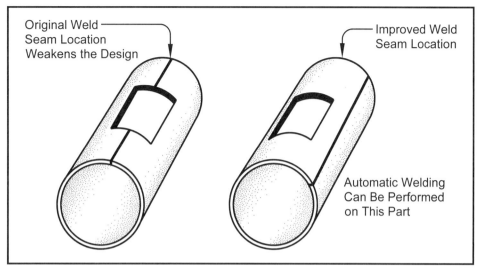

Figure 13-15. Moving a weld seam to its optimum location can strengthen a design.
It can also make possible the use of automatic welding equipment.

Many design choices affect fatigue life. One of the most important design decisions is the selection of *grain orientation* of rolled sheet goods and plates. For longest fatigue life, the grain direction of the sheet or plate should be in line with the force on the part. Another good anti-fatigue idea is to have at least the bottom third of a sheet being made into a tank run lengthwise with the tank as in Figure 13-16 (B), but if possible, run a half or more of the grain direction lengthwise with the tank. Figure 13-17 shows seven more ways to help avoid fatigue failure.

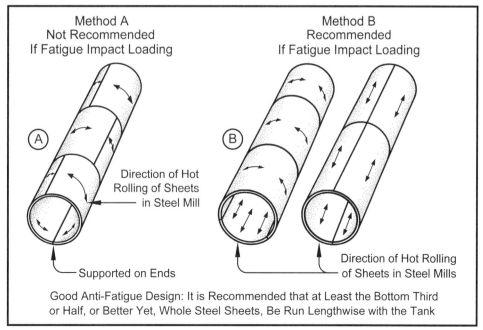

Figure 13-16. For maximum fatigue life, choose the
grain direction to run in line with the force on the part.

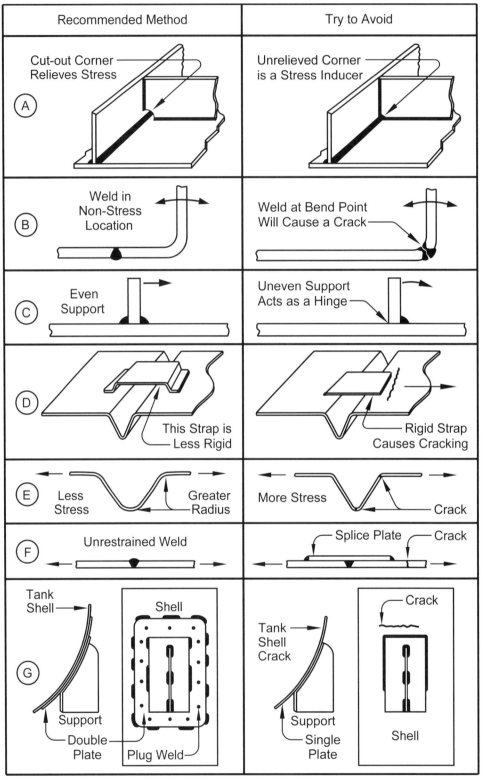

Figure 13-17. Seven design tips for avoiding fatigue failures. The example on the right side of "F" shows how welding a splice plate near a stress point where flexing occurs can do more harm than good.

Welded Joint Design

Avoid joints that create extremely deep grooves. One example is the joint formed by the meeting of a piece of round stock or tubing with a flat surface. This type of joint presents two procedural problems: getting the proper fusion to the root as shown in Figure 13-18 (left) and not burning through the thin wall of the tubing while filling the joint with weld metal. Sometimes these problems can be avoided by simply rotating a part as in Figure 13-18 (right).

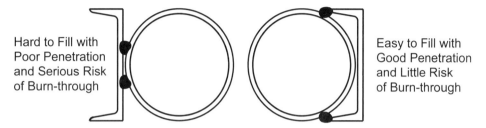

Hard to Fill with
Poor Penetration
and Serious Risk
of Burn-through

Easy to Fill with
Good Penetration
and Little Risk
of Burn-through

Figure 13-18. Avoiding hard-to-fill joints will
sidestep poor fusion and burn-through problems.

When choosing weld designs, keep the following criteria in mind:

- Be sure the weld's design has adequate strength.
- Use a minimum amount of weld metal.
- Do not design in burn-through problems for the welder. Figure 13-19 shows ways to avoid burn-through.

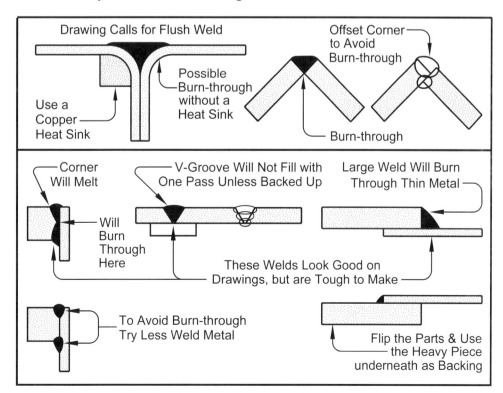

Drawing Calls for Flush Weld

Offset Corner
to Avoid
Burn-through

Possible
Burn-through
without a
Heat Sink

Use a
Copper
Heat Sink

Burn-through

Corner
Will Melt

V-Groove Will Not Fill with
One Pass Unless Backed Up

Large Weld Will Burn
Through Thin Metal

Will
Burn
Through
Here

These Welds Look Good on
Drawings, but are Tough to Make

To Avoid Burn-through
Try Less Weld Metal

Flip the Parts & Use
the Heavy Piece
underneath as Backing

Figure 13-19. Choosing the proper weld design to avoid burn-through.

The Penetration Rule: About 60% penetration is all that can be safely obtained with one weld pass without using a backing piece on a joint that has no gap, and less than 50% penetration when a gap is present. See the penetration rule in Figure 13-20.

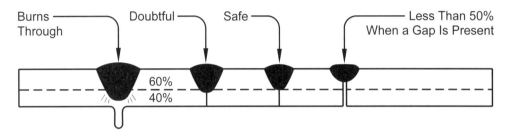

Figure 13-20. 60% penetration rule for avoiding burn-through.

To avoid weld distortion, remember that the larger the volume of the filler metal in the joint, the greater the weld distortion from shrinkage when the weld metal cools. As in Figure 13-21, use minimum root openings and included angles in order to reduce the amount of filler material required.

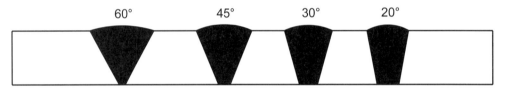

Figure 13-21. Minimum root openings and included angles minimize welding metal and time. Smaller joints help reduce weld-induced distortion.

Combining Joints

Sometimes a single joint can be used to join three parts with one weld as in Figure 13-22. Remember to leave enough gap between the top two horizontal plates so the weld fusion reaches the bottom angled plate.

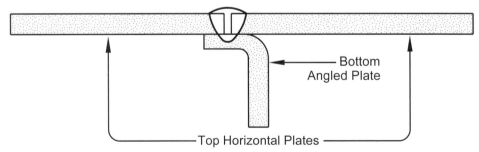

Figure 13-22. Joining three parts with one weld. The gap between the top two plates allows for better fusion among all three parts.

Access to Welded Joints

Check to see that the joint location in your design allows easy access for making the weld. The examples shown in Figure 13-23 show poorly thought out welds with difficult access.

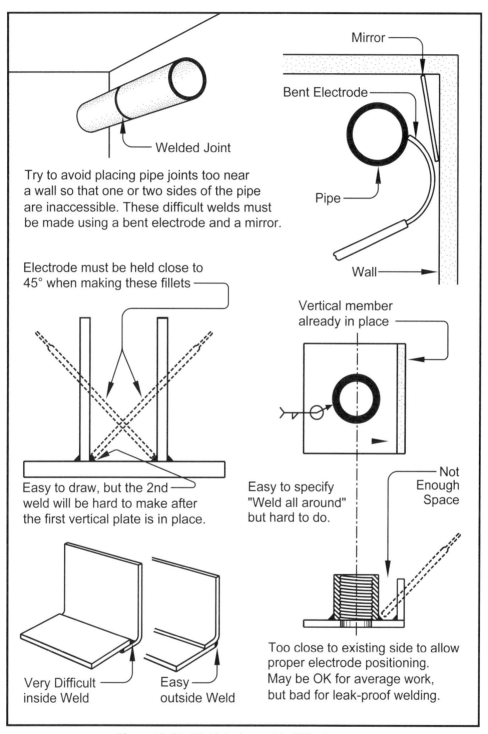

Try to avoid placing pipe joints too near a wall so that one or two sides of the pipe are inaccessible. These difficult welds must be made using a bent electrode and a mirror.

Welded Joint

Mirror

Bent Electrode

Pipe

Wall

Electrode must be held close to 45° when making these fillets

Vertical member already in place

Easy to draw, but the 2nd weld will be hard to make after the first vertical plate is in place.

Easy to specify "Weld all around" but hard to do.

Not Enough Space

Very Difficult inside Weld

Easy outside Weld

Too close to existing side to allow proper electrode positioning. May be OK for average work, but bad for leak-proof welding.

Figure 13-23. Weld designs with difficult access.

Determining Weld Size

• As mentioned before, be sure to use the correct amount of welding filler metal—not too little and not too much. Excessive weld size is costly and causes weld-induced distortion. See Figure 13-24.

- Specify by print or *Standard Shop Practice* that only the needed amount of weld filler metal should be furnished. The weld specified by the designer has a built-in safety factor. Don't add still another safety factor.

- Remember that the leg size of fillet welds is especially important since the area or amount of weld filler metal required increases as the square of the increase in leg size. As in Figure 13-24, the *Leg-Size Rule* states: Doubling the leg size increases the weld filler metal volume four times.

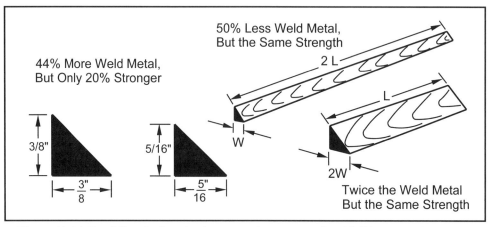

Figure 13-24. Doubling the leg size increases the amount of weld filler metal four times.

- Sometimes under light-load or no-load conditions, an intermittent fillet weld can be used in place of a continuous weld of the same leg size.

- Place the weld in the workpiece section with the least thickness and base the weld size on the thinner piece.

- Stiffeners do not need much welding and are often over-welded. To avoid this waste of time and materials, if possible, reduce the weld leg size or the length of the weld.

Assembly Tips

- Clean work of oil, rust, and dirt *before* welding.

- Check fit-up. Gaps are costly to remedy.

- Clamp work into position to hold it in place.

- For proper fit-up, use jigs and fixtures to hold parts and to maintain alignment during welding.

- Pre-set joints to offset the expected weld contraction.

- Pre-bend the work to offset any expected distortion.

- Use strongbacks to reduce distortion.

- Where possible, break the weldment into natural sections so the welding of each section can be balanced around its own neutral axis.

- Before final welding of an assembly, weld the more flexible sections together first because they can be more easily straightened.

Welding Procedure

- Deposit the greatest amount of filler metal in the shortest possible time.

- For groove joints, use backup bars on the first pass to increase the speed of the welding.

- Use manual electrodes down to a 2" stub.

- If possible, weld in the flat, down-hand position. Overhead and vertical welds are more expensive and more difficult to perform.

- If possible, position fillet welds in the flat (trough) position for the highest welding speed.

- Position fillet welds at an angle of 30° from the horizontal to obtain greater penetration into the root of the joint. See Figure 13-25.

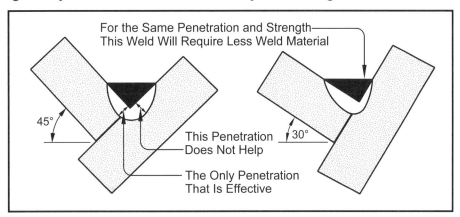

Figure 13-25. Position the joint to minimize weld
size without affecting penetration or strength.

- To add weld filler metal faster, consider using larger electrodes at higher currents. Be sure to adjust for optimum travel speed and appropriate current/voltage settings.

- Weld toward the unrestrained portion of an assembly.

- Use a welding procedure that eliminates arc blow.

- Joints that may have the greatest contraction as they cool should be welded first and allowed to cool before going on to the remaining welds.

- Use semi-automatic or fully-automatic welding where possible to take advantage of its deeper penetration and uniform deposit.

Cleaning & Finishing

- Reduce cleaning time by using iron powder electrodes on SMAW and GMAW.

- Use anti-spatter films applied parallel to the weld line for wire feed welds.

- Do not grind the surface of a weld smooth or flush unless required for a reason other than appearance. This is a very costly operation and usually exceeds the cost of welding and makes a mess to clean up.

Two Big Mistakes

Figure 13-26 shows a layout for cutting parts for a propeller from sheet metal. This layout contains two common design oversights:

- Because the same shape parts are cut both *with* and *across* the grain, the grain, or rolling direction of the sheet metal, has been ignored. The propeller blades *cut with* the grain direction are less susceptible to metal fatigue in their long direction than those cut across the grain. While fatigue failure will not occur immediately, one day in service it will fail suddenly.

- The three rivet holes are placed in the top edge of the blades in a straight line instead of being staggered. This straight-line placement weakens the part much like the perforations in paper towels or postage stamps. The lined-up holes—no matter what their direction relative to the grain—will cause fatigue failure.

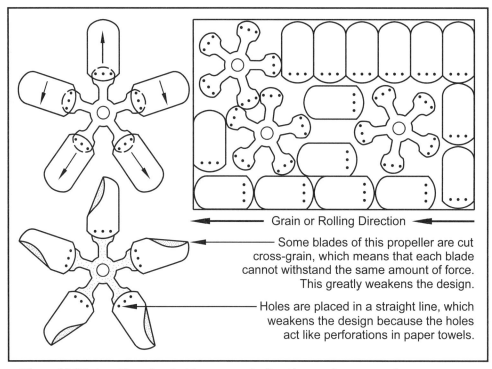

Figure 13-26. A cutting plan that ignores grain direction produces parts that are prone to fatigue failure. This same layout places rivet holes in a straight line instead of staggering them, making fatigue failure more likely.

Chapter 14

Fabrication Tips

Everyone is a genius at least once a year.
A real genius has his original ideas closer together.

—G.C. Lichtenberg

Section I – Frames & Brackets

Fabrication Steps

Many a good weld design is ruined by mistakes made in fabrication. This chapter will help you avoid the most common mistakes, and also a few uncommon mistakes. Though not all of the following steps are used on all projects, the typical weld fabrication steps are:

- Get or make a fabrication sketch or drawing.
- Develop a well thought out step-by-step procedure.
- Gather tools and materials.
- Make patterns, jigs, templates and fixtures, if needed.
- Put together a cut list.
- Lay out and cut the materials.
- Make edge preparations and clean the metal areas to be welded.
- Position and clamp materials prior to welding.
- Tack weld assemblies, check dimensions, setup and squareness.
- Place the final welds and assemble the final fabrication.
- Grind welds smooth only if necessary.
- Paint the fabrication, if needed.

Angle Iron Frame Corner Designs

There are three common methods for making corners on angle iron frames: mitering, notching, and notching and bending a single length of angle iron. Figure 14-1 shows mitering and notching.

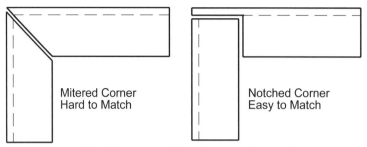

Figure 14-1. Two corner joint designs using angle iron.

Both methods work, but with notching it is easier to get good results and this technique is more dimensionally tolerant because the joint gaps between the angle irons' length can be adjusted to bring the frame square and the side lengths equal. After welding and grinding, both methods will look equally good and be equally strong. In general, use mitered corners when you have a bandsaw or a notching tool to cut perfectly matching corners.

The third approach for making square and rectangular frames from angle iron lends itself to production work because it requires notching and bending, which is best done on a machine like an *Ironworker*. These versatile machines can perform the functions of a press brake and a bending fixture, such as bending and notching angle iron. As shown in Figure 14-2, getting the correct bend-allowance gap is critical because this gap provides the extra material needed to go around the outside corner when the bend is made. To make these mitered and bent corners, begin by setting the bend-allowance gap to slightly less than the thickness of the angle iron and go from there. *This method only works if corners are bent by machine.* Heating the corners and manually freehand bending them will produce rounded corners—and scrap.

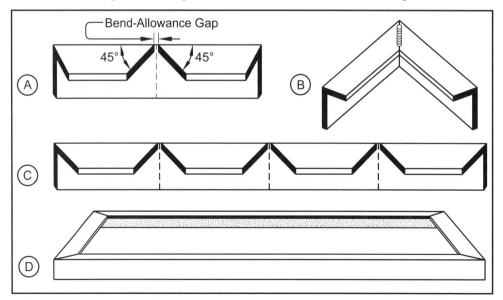

Figure 14-2. Notching and bending to make a single-piece frame: (A) corner detail before bending, (B) corner detail after bending, welding, and grinding, (C) notched angle iron frame ready for bending, and (D) the completed frame.

Checking for Squareness

There are several ways to check frames for squareness:

- When welding a very large L-shape, where a square is too small and there are no diagonals to measure, use a 3-4-5 triangle. Here's how it's done:

  1. Measure off four units on one leg, or member, of the frame.

  2. Measure off three units on the other leg.

  3. Adjust the hypotenuse by moving either leg of the L-shape until the hypotenuse measures exactly 5 units. Following this procedure makes a perfect right triangle. See Figure 14-3.

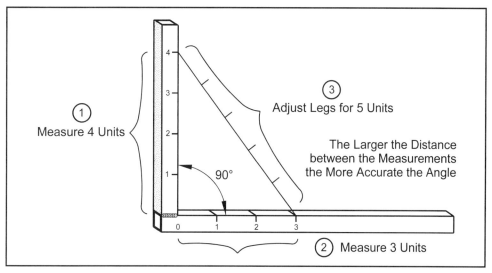

Figure 14-3. Using a 3-4-5 triangle to set members at a right angle. Remember to reduce the overall length of the frame sides to allow for additional joint root spacing, otherwise your frame will be oversized.

- Check for equal diagonals between opposite frame corners using a steel measuring tape. This method is used in Figure 14-7.

- On large frames, check the squareness using a carpenter's square, and on smaller frames, check squareness using a machinist's square.

- If the sides of the frame are to be plumb and level, a large level can be used.

Improving the Odds of a Welded Frame Being Square

In *decreasing* order of effectiveness:

- Secure all members in a rigid fixture, tack them, weld them, and let them cool down in the fixture. This is the best method.

- Clamp members to a steel table and then tack and weld them.

- Use a fixture to hold members for tacking, then weld the tacked members *outside* of the fixture. This fixture can be as simple as a sheet of plywood with wood blocks fixed to it to hold the work in place while the tack welds are made. For an example of this type of fixture, see Figure 14-4.

- When tacking is complete and you have checked the frame for squareness, weld one corner, and then weld the opposite corner. Weld the same relative corner in the exact same sequence on all four corner joints. Next, weld all outside faces, then all top corners, and finally all bottom faces. Make each weld in the same relative direction and give each weld time to cool before starting the next weld.

- Begin by tack welding each of the corners together using a Bessy-type clamp each time, then check for squareness. If needed, bend the part back into squareness. If the tack welds are not too large, with moderate force you will be able to straighten the frame by hand without using hydraulic jacks. After tacking, begin your final welds at *opposite* corners.

   The Around-The-World Rule: Do not start welding at one end and travel sequentially using a corner clamp—the last two corner pieces of the frame probably will not meet.

- Use magnetic corner tools. These are effective only for light sheet metal and light angle iron because they lack the strength to resist weld-induced distortion—but they will allow you to place initial tack welds.

How to Weld a Rectangular Steel Tubing Frame

The following instructions are for fabricating a rectangular frame made of rectangular or square steel tubing for use as a gate, a door, or a table. The challenge is to get square corners and a flat, non-twisted frame with all the tubing on the same plane.

Corners may be mitered or butted up square. Mitering requires accurate corner cuts and produces a finished look. Butted joints leave four tubing ends open that must be closed with welding or plastic caps to produce a finished look. Take your choice, but remember, for outdoor installations, using the plastic caps will allow the steel to rust.

Perform this welding fabrication on a $^3/_4$" thick plywood fixture on a flat surface. Thinner plywood is not stiff or strong enough to hold the parts rigidly. The frame will only be as flat as the plywood sheet. The plywood will scorch, but this sheet can be used several times.

Here's how to weld the frame:

1. Cut wood stops for the inner and outer faces of the tubing as shown in Figure 14-4. A minimum of eight pairs of stops are required to hold the tubing on its outer faces. Four to eight more pieces on the inner faces are helpful too. To make the stops, use 1" × 1", 2" × 2" or 2" × 4" lumber such as pine, not plywood. Lumber accepts nails better.

2. Before using the stops to secure the tubing for welding, pre-drive two nails into each of the eight outer stops nearly all the way, but not through the stops. This will make it easier to accurately position them on the plywood when nailing.

3. Cut the four sides of the frame to length and, if desired, miter the corners. Remove all burrs so the tubing will lie flat on the plywood.

4. Lay up the four frame sides on the plywood and secure them in place with the eight wood stops on the *outside* of the tubing. The frame will be square when the diagonal measurements are equal. Keep the wood stops away from the corners so they do not interfere with welding access.

5. After checking the frame for squareness, add the 4–8 internal stops. Note: tilt the nails away from the tubing.

6. Place two small tack welds on the *outside* edges of each of the four corners in 1-3-2-4 order. Check for squareness and correct if necessary. Correcting for squareness after a complete weld has been made will be impossible. If the frame is not square, make any corrections now by removing the tack weld, repositioning the tubing, and re-tacking it.

7. Place a vertical-down weld along the *inside* corners of the tubing in 1-3-2-4 order. This is a complete weld, not a tack.

8. Place a complete vertical-down weld on the four *outside* corners over the initial tack welds in 1-3-2-4 order.

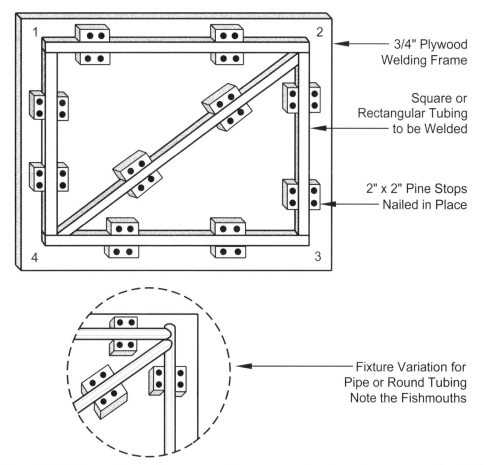

Figure 14-4. Using a plywood fixture to weld up a rectangular frame from square tubing (top) and from round tubing (bottom). The round tubing is *fishmouthed* for a tight fit.

9. If using mitered corners, prepare to weld the top mitered corners by making practice welds to insure you know how to make this weld without burning through the steel. The outside corners are the most vulnerable to burn-through, so start the welds at the inside corners and weld outward. Perform these welds in 1-3-2-4 order.

10. Remove the frame from the stops, turn it over and weld the remaining corner joints, inside to outside in 1-3-2-4 order.

Mounting Table Legs

To mount table legs to an angle iron frame, follow the steps in Figure 14-5.

1. Put the table frame upside down on a flat surface and attach two clamps to lightly secure a leg to both sides of the angle iron frame corner.

2. With a carpenter's square, adjust the leg so it is perpendicular to the frame, then using a length of steel or wood, apply two clamps to brace the leg to bring it into square. See Figure 14-5 (A).

3. Repeat this squaring/bracing/clamping for the other right angle as in Figure 14-5 (B). Fully tighten the two clamps holding the leg to the frame.

4. Tack the leg in place on the horizontal section of the base. This makes it easier to grind out the weld if the leg must be repositioned.

5. Re-check for squareness in both directions, then weld the leg to the frame as shown in Figure 14-5 (C). Repeat Steps 1–5 for each leg.

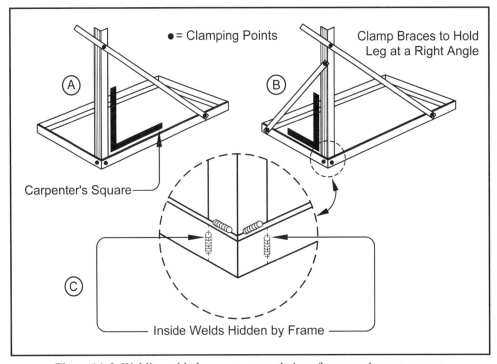

Figure 14-5. Welding table legs onto an angle iron frame so they are square.

Flattening a Rectangular Angle Iron Frame

If a frame does not lie flat, the steps in Figure 14-6 show how to bend the horizontal face of the frame to flatten it using only an open-end wrench.

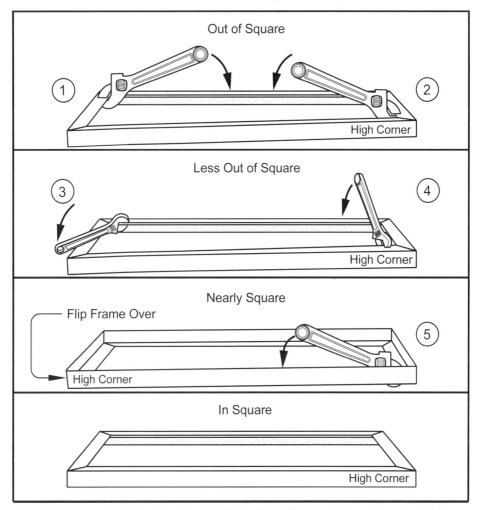

Figure 14-6. Using an open-end wrench to adjust a bent angle iron frame to lie flat.

Making Box Frames

To build a box frame, start by making the upper and lower frames shown in Figure 14-7 using one of the methods shown in Figure 14-2, then follow these steps:

1. Use clamps to secure the four vertical legs to the lower frame and make the legs square to the lower frame as shown in Figure 14-5.

2. Place the upper frame over the legs as in Figure 14-7 (top), and drop it into place.

3. Make whatever adjustments are needed to the verticals to make them squarely meet the upper frame. Some tweaking may be necessary. Note that all opposite diagonals, such as dotted line X-Y in Figure 14-7 (bottom), will be the same length in a *rectangular* box.

4. Clamp each of the four legs to the upper frame.

5. Tack all joints and check for squareness and fit.

6. Weld all joints.

This method works equally well with angle iron or rectangular tubing.

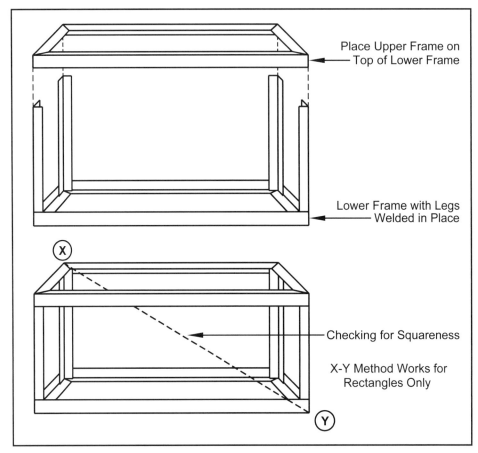

Figure 14-7. Making a box frame. Attaching the upper frame
to the legs (top), and checking for squareness (bottom).

Right-Angle Brackets

Right-angle brackets are often needed to strengthen structures or to mount additional components onto parts or machinery. There are many types of brackets and many ways to fabricate them. See Figures 14-8 through 14-11.

When you need a way to secure an object to a frame member, yet make the object easily removable, make the hollow tube bracket in Figure 14-9. Start by welding a short length of rectangular tubing to the frame member, then insert a bracket that slip fits into the tubing. Using round tubing and a rod will permit the bracket to swivel, if desired. Standard steel tubing and square stock works well for this application. Because the square or round tubing being welded to the base is usually much thinner than the base metal, to achieve a solid weld, yet avoid burn-through, place a nesting solid square or round rod inside the tubing as a heat sink.

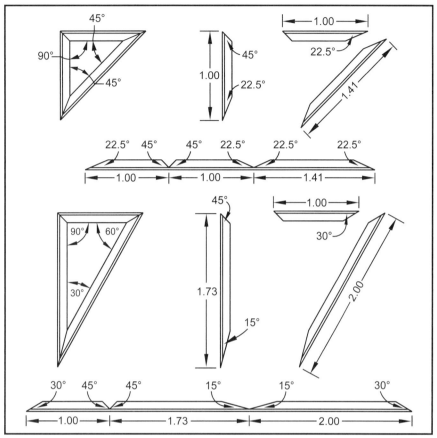

Figure 14-8. Plans for a 45-45-90-degree right-angle bracket and a 30-60-90-degree right-angle bracket. These dimensions can be scaled to make any size bracket from angle iron, tubing, or pipe.

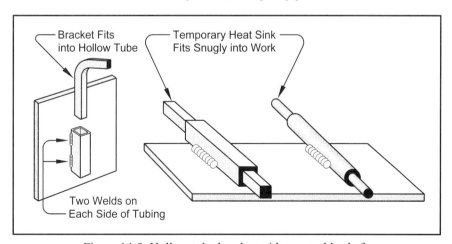

Figure 14-9. Hollow tube bracket with removable shaft.

Figure 14-10 shows three ways to fabricate a right-angle bracket. The first two are welded and the third is made by cutting an I-beam. This last design offers a significant advantage: cutting an I-beam on an angle produces two strong brackets from one piece of stock without welding.

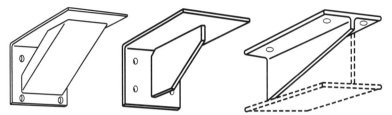

Figure 14-10. Three ways to fabricate a sturdy right-angle bracket.

Many product designs evolve in production such as the bracket casting in Figure 14-11 which was redesigned to reduce both cost and weight.

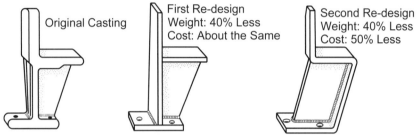

Figure 14-11. A bracket originally made as a casting (left)
evolves into a weldment that saves on cost and weight.

Section II – Other Fabricated Parts

Machine Feet & Pillow Block Designs

Welding offers many ways to fabricate machine feet and pillow blocks. See Figures 14-12 and 14-13. Pillow blocks hold bearings or shafts in place.

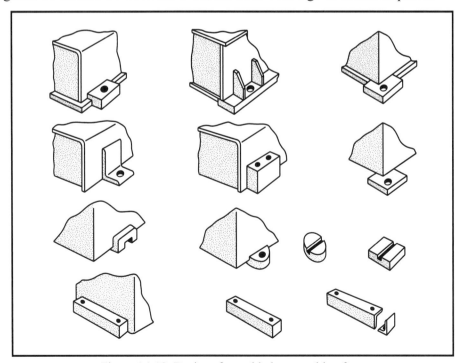

Figure 14-12. Designs for welded-on machine feet.

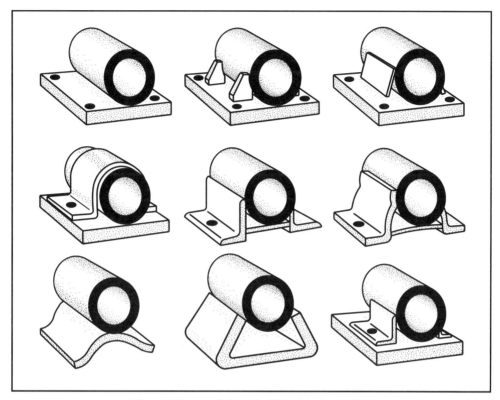

Figure 14-13. Fabricated pillow block designs.

Stand-Off Spacer Design

Undercutting the center area of a stand-off spacer or equipment foot allows it to be pulled up tight. In addition, on an uneven surface, this stand-off design helps prevent the equipment from rocking. See Figure 14-14.

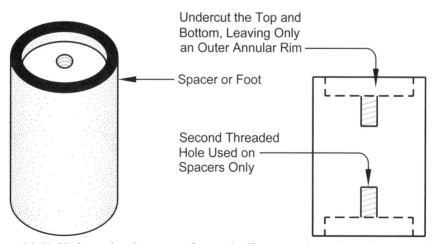

Figure 14-14. Undercutting the center of a stand-off spacer reduces its tendency to rock.

Enlarging an Existing Hole with a Hole Saw

Enlarging an existing hole with a hole saw in sheet metal or plate is easy with a centering guide. See Figure 14-15.

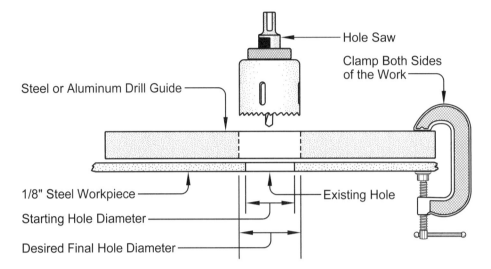

Figure 14-15. Enlarging an existing hole in sheet metal or plate. The drill guide holds the hole saw in position by its rim since there is no place to secure its center drill.

Extending Hose Clamps

When existing hose clamps are not long enough for a job, there are several ways to extend them: splice a length of stainless steel taken from another hose clamp or attach steel strapping bands to the ends of the existing clamp. Secure the extension to the existing clamp ends by making a plug or rosette weld through $^3/_{16}$" holes drilled into the extension. A copper plate will keep the lower extension piece from burning through during welding. GMAW, GTAW with stainless steel filler, GTAW with silicon bronze filler, or silver braze will work well. Fusing the edges of the bands together without additional filler metal—autogenous welds—on the band edges will also work. Other joining methods are pop rivets and conventional rivets. See Figure 14-16.

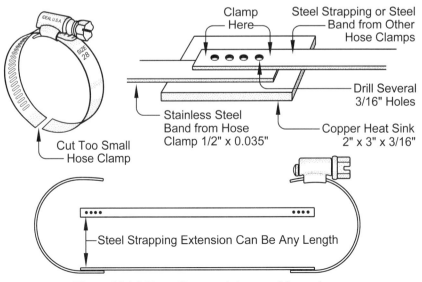

Figure 14-16. Extending a stainless steel hose clamp.

Using Piano Wire for Measuring Straight Edges

When you need to check the straightness of a long workpiece, say 40 feet or more, using tightly stretched piano wire as a guide works well. Piano wire, though, is very hard and has a high tensile strength, so it is difficult to secure and pull tight, but there are a couple of ways to do it.

The arrangement in Figure 14-17 shows a typical method to check the straightness of long steel bars when the bars are being straightened in a hydraulic press. First, steel tubing vertical supports about 8 inches tall are welded to the ends of the bar being straightened, then the piano wire is stretched between the supports and tensioned by one of the methods shown in Figure 14-18. Next, measurements are taken between the bar and the piano wire to determine where corrective bending forces must be applied. Because the piano wire stretches, it can be left in place during the press cycle and remain undamaged.

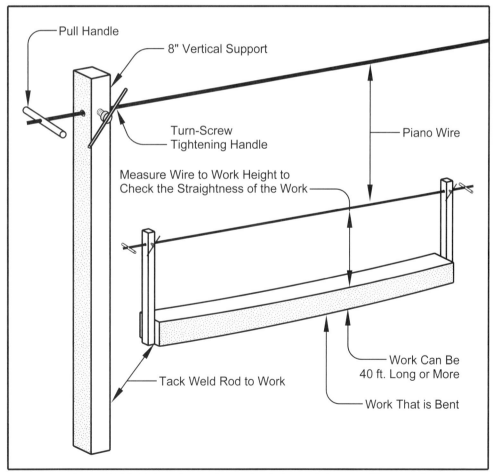

Figure 14-17. Using piano wire to check the straightness of long work.
Note the pull handle and the turn-screw tightening handle. A detail
of this arrangement is in Method 2 of Figure 14-18.

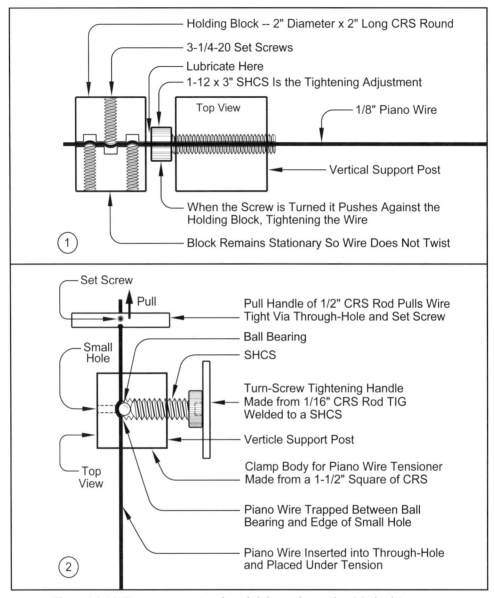

Figure 14-18. Two ways to stretch and tighten piano wire. Method 1 uses set screws in holding blocks to tension and secure the wire. Method 2 uses a pull handle and a turn-screw tightening handle.

Making Round Corners

If a metal or plastic base plate must have rounded corners with identical radii, as in Figure 14-19, here is a good way to do it:

1. Select a piece of drill rod whose radius matches the radius desired on the base plate.
2. Chuck several inches of this drill rod in a lathe and cut off several $^1/_8$-inch lengths using the cutoff tool.
3. Harden these coin-sized pieces by using a torch. Bring them up to bright red, and then quench them in air, oil or water, depending on the rod.

4. Position and clamp two of these hardened drill rod coins to form a template for filing each corner. When using these templates, a disc or belt sander can easily apply the corners.

5. After removing most of the corner waste material with a disc grinder or hacksaw, use light pressure on a file and let the hardened drill rod rounds guide the file to make the final radius cut.

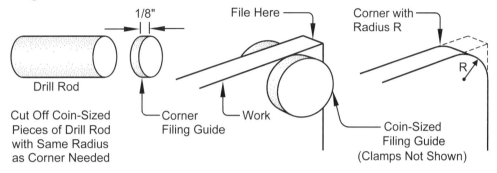

Figure 14-19. Using coin-shaped sections of hardened drill rod as guides to round corners.

Holding Ball Bearings & Spheres

Many times before welding a ball bearing or a sphere, it needs to have a flat or hole drilled into it. Figure 14-20 shows how two nuts can be used to capture the sphere and hold it securely while performing these tasks. For even better results with less chances of marking the sphere, cut slight chamfers on the inside diameter of the nuts. Note how a bottom spacer provides stability and raises the sphere to allow better access.

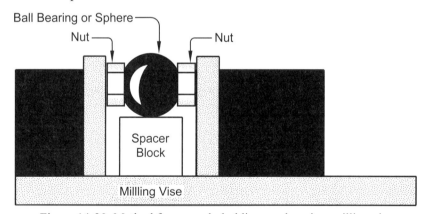

Figure 14-20. Method for securely holding a sphere in a milling vise.

Annealing, Drilling & Tapping Ball Bearings

Ball bearings are difficult to anneal without a furnace because, when heated, their alloy hardens easily, and with their small size, they cool too rapidly to remain annealed. Figures 14-21 and 14-22 show how to prepare ball bearings for drilling and tapping. With this method a lead bath is used instead of a heat-treating oven. The mass of the heated lead slows the cooling rate enough for the ball bearing to remain annealed. The ball bearing can remain in the lead for drilling and tapping, then be removed by melting the lead.

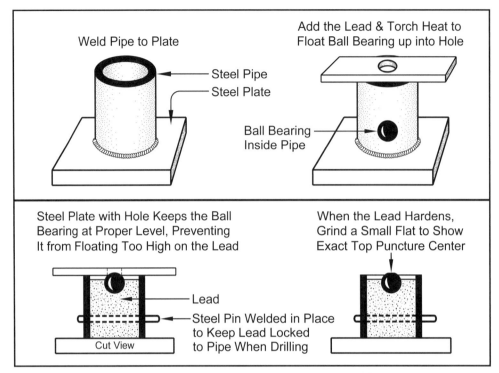

Figure 14-21. Annealing a ball bearing in a lead bath for drilling and tapping.

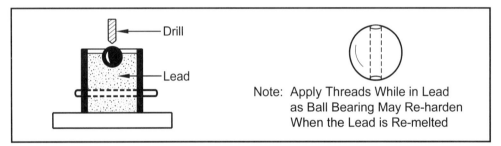

Figure 14-22. Drilling and tapping a ball bearing held in an annealing lead bath.

Pipe Cleaning & Abrasive Burr Removal

Figures 14-23 through 14-25 show two shop-made tools that hold abrasive cloth to clean the interior of pipe or tubing. Both of these tools are held in an electric drill.

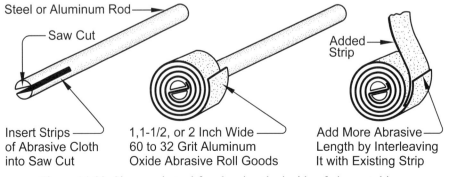

Figure 14-23. Shop-made tool for cleaning the inside of pipe or tubing.

The diameter of the pipe determines the length of the abrasive strip needed. When the outside section of the abrasive cloth becomes worn from use, insert another abrasive strip under the first strip, which will hold it in place.

The arrangement in Figures 14-24 and 14-25 has the advantage of removing interior burrs from the pipe as well as enlarging its diameter. If the pipe is welded, the interior weld seam can be smoothed, but not completely removed. To mount the abrasive cloth on the mandrel, use a drive punch on a lead block to make a center hole through the abrasive cloth. The drive punch should be the diameter of the mandrel.

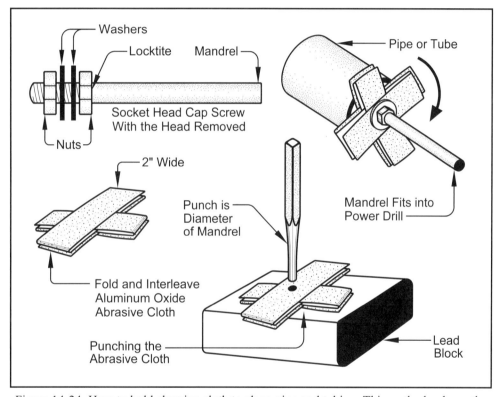

Figure 14-24. How to hold abrasive cloth to clean pipe and tubing. This method reduces the pipe's inside diameter, smoothes the interior weld seams, and removes the burrs remaining after cutting the pipe.

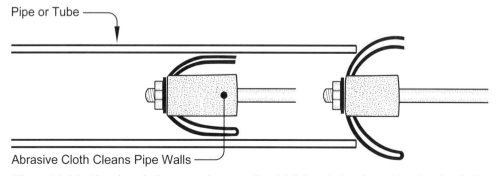

Figure 14-25. Abrasive cloth mounted on an arbor (right) and cleaning tubing interior (left).

Section III – Rolled Steel Shapes

I-Beams

The three most common structural I-beam shapes are:

S-beams, also called *American Standard Shape I-beams,* are the traditional and the oldest beam shape. S-beams are made of carbon steel and are used in building structural steel frames.

W-beams, also called *Wide Flange I-beams,* are frequently used in buildings for structural applications. W-beams carry loads more efficiently than S-beams on a weight-for-weight basis because they have a higher percentage of total metal in the flanges which makes them better able to resist loads. These beams are also popular because more sizes of W-beams are available than S-beams, giving designers more choices.

H-beams are most often used for bearing piles and for shoring. They are also used to carry the exceptionally heavy loads held by the columns in high-rise buildings. They are particularly useful in resisting seismic loads because they offer more equal resistance to bending forces, both in line and perpendicular to the webs, than other I-beam shapes. As in Figure 14-26, H-beams are different from S- and W-beams because the flange and the web thicknesses are approximately equal, and the beam height and width are also approximately equal. Figure 14-27 shows the parts of an I-beam and its key dimensions.

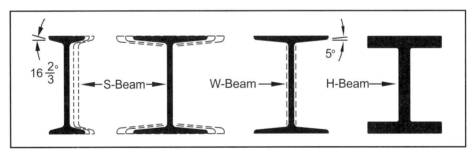

Figure 14-26. Common I-beam shapes: S-beam, W-beam and H-beam. At the mill, adjusting the distance between the rolls makes S-beams of different web thicknesses and strength.

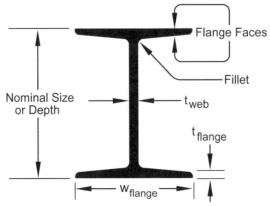

Figure 14-27. Parts of an I-beam.

Common Steel Sections

- *Ts, or T-sections, angles,* and *channels* are the three most common steel sections. Large structural Ts are made by cutting an I-beam in half, which leaves the beams with a flat edge on the bottom of the T-section. Ts are identified as either ST-sections or WT-sections depending on whether they were cut from an S-beam or a W-beam. Small T-sections, typically with legs of 4" or less, are initially rolled as Ts and have rounded bottoms. See Figure 14-28.

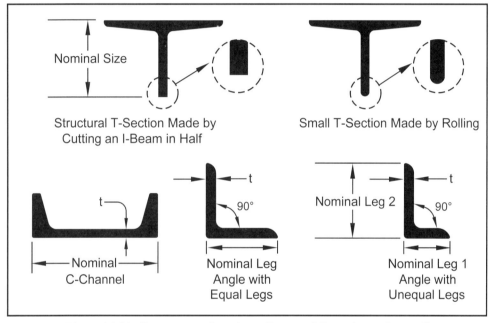

Figure 14-28. Common steel sections: Structural T-section and a small
T-section (top row), C-channel (bottom left) and angles (bottom center and right).

- *Tubular steel* is another common type of steel section. Tubular steel members are used for door frames, table legs, gates, brackets, braces and light support columns. See Figure 14-29.

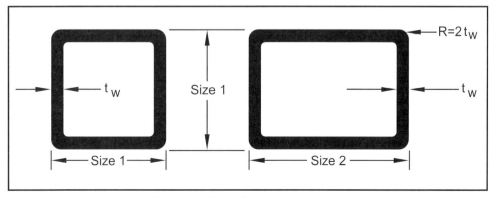

Figure 14-29. Tubular steel sections.

Hangers for Rolled Shapes

Threaded rods on structural steel shapes support lights, pipes, ducts and signs and avoid the need for welding because these rods can hold light loads. Figure 14-30 shows several ways to hang threaded rods from rolled structural shapes without welding.

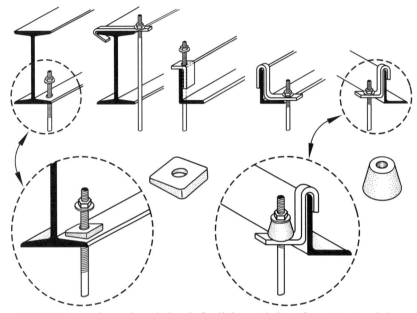

Figure 14-30. Ways to hang threaded rods for lights and signs from structural shapes. The detail drawings show a wedge to distribute forces evenly over the rod and its nut (left). Washers and bushings must be placed under the nut on brackets (right).

When a support rod is run through a hole in an I-beam flange, a wedge-shaped washer should be placed under the nut to distribute the load evenly over the nut and its threads. Washers and bushings must be placed under the nut on the threaded support rod to distribute the load over the bracket and prevent them from deforming. See Figure 14-30 (bottom).

Hooking Welds around Corners

When welding on structural steel, there are often questions about whether to hook fillet weld beads around a corner at the end of the bead.

Here is the general rule:

If bringing the weld around a corner maintains the size of the weld cross section, then carry the bead around the corner. If not, don't. This rule is important because weld failures are most likely to begin at their smallest cross-sectional point where they are weakest.

The seat-angle connection pictured in Figure 14-31 (top) is designed to flex and give. Tests have shown that carrying the weld bead down the side of the angle for about one-quarter the length of the angle provides the greatest strength and movement before failure. Other examples of the application of this rule are also shown in the *Do* and *Don'ts* of Figure 14-31.

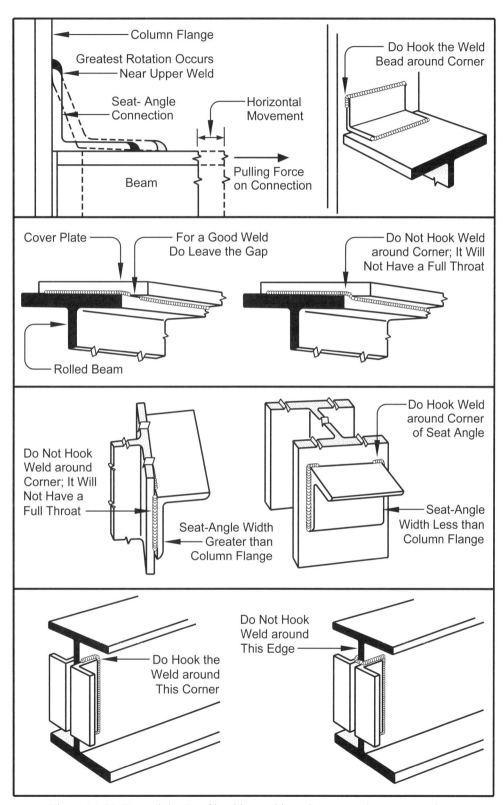

Figure 14-31. Do and don'ts of hooking welds on beam to column connections.

Weld Cracking on Thick Plates

When placing fillet welds on thick plates, the welds sometimes crack, but this cracking can be avoided. On thick plates with large welds, if there is metal-to-metal contact prior to welding, as shown in Figure 14-32 (left), this contact prevents the possibility of plate movement. This is not a good situation because as the welds cool and contract, all of the shrinkage stresses must be taken up in the welds. In cases of severe restraint, the welds may crack, especially in the first pass on either side of the plate. By allowing a small gap between the plates, the plates can "move in" slightly as the weld shrinks. This reduces the transverse stresses in the weld. Heavy plates should always have a minimum $1/32$" gap between them, and if possible a $1/16$" gap.

This gap can be obtained by several means:

- Insertion of spacers made of soft steel wire placed between the plates as in Figure 14-32 (center). The soft wire will flatten out as the weld shrinks and the plates will usually fit tightly together after the weld has cooled. If copper wire is used, care should be taken that it does not mix with the weld metal.

- A deliberately rough flame-cut edge. The small peaks of the cut edge keep the plates apart, yet can squash down as the weld shrinks.

- Upsetting the edge of the plate with a heavy center punch. This acts in a similar manner to the rough, flame-cut edge method.

After using any of these methods the plates will usually be tight together after the weld has cooled as in Figure 14- 32 (right).

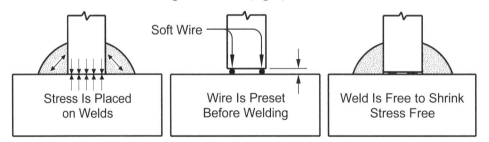

Figure 14-32. Using soft wire as a spacer to prevent weld cracking on thick plates.

Expanded Beams

Expanded beams are made by cutting an I-beam through its web, adding a spacer to the web, and welding it all back together. Figure 14-33 (A) shows a beam cut along the middle of its web, and the finished expanded beam after the welding of an additional piece of steel into its web. This modification deepens the beam, increasing both its stiffness and its load-carrying ability.

If a beam is expanded by cutting the I-beam web on an angle, a tapered beam results as shown in Figure 14-33 (B). This beam has the greatest bending strength where it is most needed—in the center of the span. Such a design also lowers the total steel load required to support the beam weight on the lower members of the building's frame.

If the web is cut in a zig-zag pattern along its center line and welded back together offset, an open-web beam results as in Figure 14-33 (C). This beam is deeper, stronger, and stiffer than the original beam. Another variation on this is the tapered open-web beam shown in Figure 14-33 (D). All of these designs are easily made using an oxyacetylene cutting torch and a template. Plasma arc cutting is also suitable.

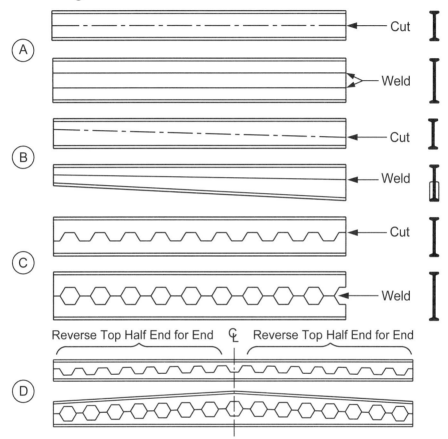

Figure 14-33. Four ways to expand a beam by adding height to its web.

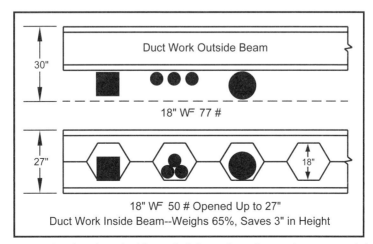

Figure 14-34. Steel and vertical beam height savings from using open-web beams.

For additional savings in steel and vertical height, use the openings in beams to run pipes, electrical conduit, and ductwork as in Figure 14-34. With this time-saving method, there is no wasted material.

Base Plate Designs

Base plate designs are determined by the height of the structure, its floor loading, the underlying soil, and foundation strength, as well as wind and seismic forces. A structural steel engineer is needed to determine which base plate design is best for the project. See the selection of base plate designs in Figure 14-35.

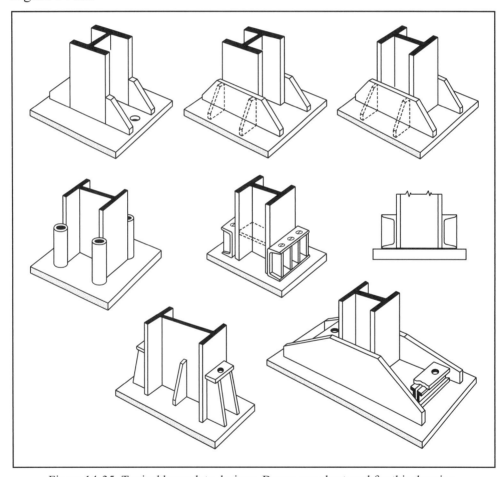

Figure 14-35. Typical base plate designs. Beams are shortened for this drawing.

Beam-to-Column Connections

Many factors determine the optimum beam-to-column connection design. The strongest connections, such as the one in Figure 14-36 (left), require welding in the field. Often, though, it is possible to perform most of the welding in the shop and make the final field connections with high-strength structural-steel nuts and bolts as in Figure 14-36 (center and right). Welding in the shop is convenient because it speeds field work and avoids the weather-related welding problems encountered on the job site.

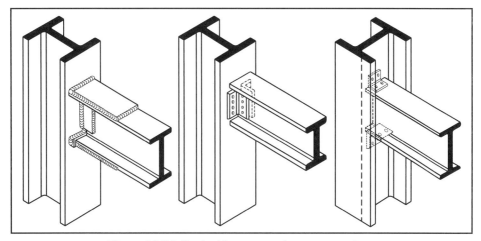

Figure 14-36. Typical beam-to-column connections.

Column Splice Designs

Columns can be spliced to each other using many different methods. The choice of method depends on several important factors, including the building floor, wind, and seismic loads. Some connection methods avoid field welding and instead use bolts. See Figure 14-37.

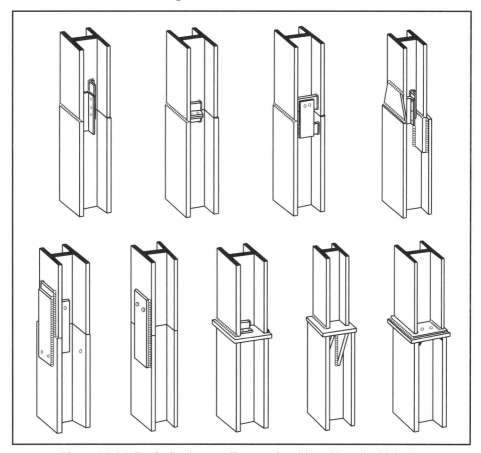

Figure 14-37. Typical column splices made with welds and with bolts.

Column Supports and Guy Wire Attachments

Figure 14-38 shows some effective ways to provide guy wire attachment points for columns.

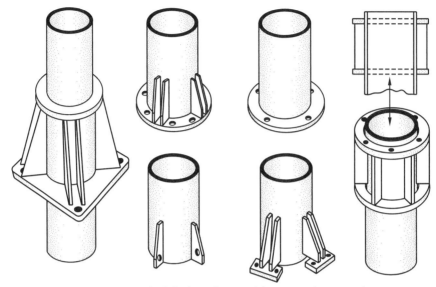

Figure 14-38. Typical designs for attaching guy wires to columns.

Weld Access Holes

Weld access holes serve two purposes: First, they provide the welder access to the weld joint, and second, the weld access hole prevents the interaction of the residual stress field of the flange and the web. This is important because the interaction of the longitudinal shrinkage of the web and flange weld, as well as the transverse shrinkage of the flange weld, creates tri-axial stress that can crack the flange weld. The weld access hole eliminates this tri-axial stress and so reduces the chances of weld cracking. See Figure 14-39.

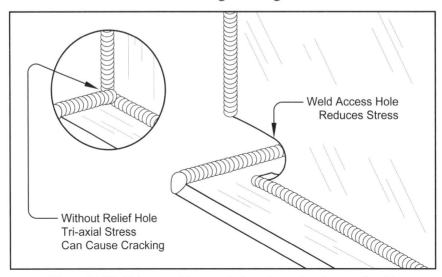

Figure 14-39. Using a weld access hole reduces the chance of weld cracking by eliminating tri-axial stresses on the flange weld.

Bolting Beams End to End

In a fabrication shop positioning bolt holes accurately is easy, but in the field, without templates or digital drilling equipment, it is much harder to put holes in a beam so that they match up with holes on other beams.

Here is a solution to this problem:

It would seem logical to weld the tab first and then bolt the I-beams together, but without specialized equipment, performing the task in that order will guarantee misalignment. The correct order is: drill the hole in the I-beam on the ground, bolt the two beams in place, and then weld on the tab. Doing the welding last allows the most wiggle room and produces the best alignment. See Figure 14-40.

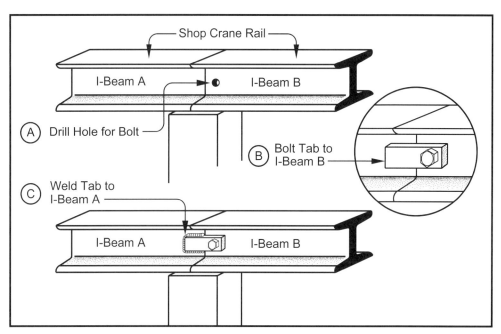

Figure 14-40. Attaching I-beams by first putting in the bolt and then welding the tab.

Mounting Plates on Pipe Column Ends

There is a simple way to position end plates onto the ends of a structural column in preparation for welding. To assure that the upper and lower plates properly align, follow these steps:

1. Support the pipe column on pipe jacks and inspect the pipe ends for squareness. If the pipe end is only slightly out of square, mark the high side with an X and use this mark for the first weld tack location. If the pipe end is seriously out of square, trim and grind it to make it square.

2. Mark the layout on the end plate according to the prints. See the layout in Figure 14-41 (A).

3. Cut a V-plate guide from $^3/_8$" steel plate. It should be 6" wide and should project about 3" beyond the base plate when positioned on the column.

Mark a center line on the V-plate guide and note the exact dimension. See Figure 14-41 (B and C).

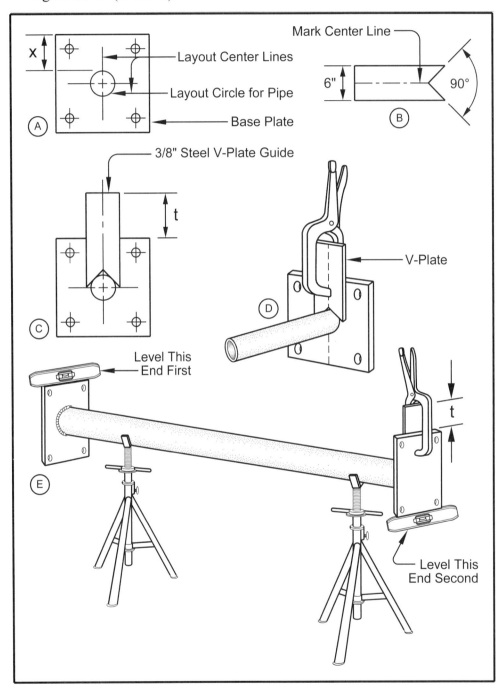

Figure 14-41. Steps in mounting base plates onto a structural pipe.

4. Mark a center line on the base plate, then position the V-plate so its center line lies over the center line of the base plate and the V-plate's top edge projects the distance t above the base plate as in Figure 14-41 (C). Clamp the V-plate to the base plate as shown in Figure 14-41 (D).

5. Hang the base plate over the end of the column using the V-plate guide to position and to tack the plate in place, then apply the final weld.

6. The next objective is to tack the unwelded base plate onto the other end of the pipe column so that the top and bottom plates are aligned, not rotated with respect to one another. To do this, put a torpedo level on the top edge of the previously welded base plate as in Figure 14-41 (E), and rotate the column to bring this edge into level.

7. Repeat Step 4 with the remaining base plate and hang it in welding position. Use a torpedo level to bring its top edge into level.

8. Tack the second base plate and then apply the final weld.

Placing Joints in Low Stress Areas

In a rigid beam, the bending moment passes through zero twice along its length at its *points of inflection*. At these points the bending stresses are zero so a joint in this location does not require much welding, just enough to sustain the shear load. This shear load is taken by a small clip welded to the bottom of the cantilevered sections of the beam. For example, the cross beam in Figure 14-42 (A) is frequently fabricated in three sections, as shown in Figure 14-42 (B). This offers three advantages:

•   It simplifies the handling and fitting of the cross beam so it can be welded to the supports at each end.

•   Very little welding is required to join the three beam sections, yet the beam deflects no more than the one-piece beam under the same load.

•   The center section of the beam is removed by undoing just two bolts.

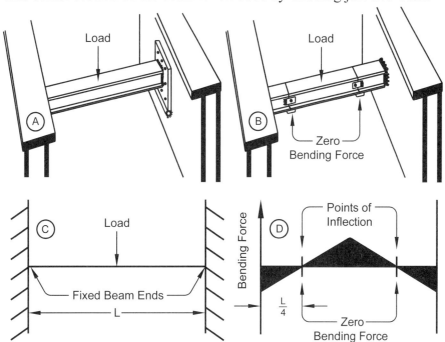

Figure 14-42. Weld location determines both the type and the magnitude of forces on a weld.

Section IV – Vehicle Welding

Vehicle Frame Repairs

There are prominent labels on the C-channel frames of modern tractors and heavy trucks that warn against cutting or welding on their frames. This is because to save weight manufacturers use a thinner, lighter steel for their C-channel frames, and then use a special heat treatment to provide extra strength. Welding and torch cutting on these frames destroys the strength of the factory heat treatment. If a frame has not failed, do not weld, flame cut or drill on it. If you have to mount something onto the frame, use the extra existing holes put in the frame at the factory. However, if C-channel frames must be repaired, try to minimize welding on them.

To repair a C-channel frame use the following preliminary steps:

1. Clean the repair area. Steam clean and scrub the entire area surrounding the weld. This is particularly important for waste hauling vehicles.

2. Use an oxyfuel torch to dry this area and remove remaining mill scale.

3. Wire brush the area down to shiny metal.

4. Compare your failure with those shown in Figure 14-43 to determine which Case your frame failure best matches and then follow the repair steps for that Case.

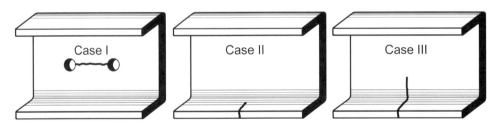

Figure 14-43. Three typical truck frame C-channel cracks.

Case I – Horizontal crack along the web between factory-drilled holes.

Here are the repair steps:

1. On the inside of the C-channel in Figure 14-44 (A), grind a V-groove to within $^1/_{16}$–$^1/_8$" of the thickness of the web steel along the path of the crack and extend this groove 2" beyond the initial crack on each end as in Figure 14-44 (B).

2. Clamp a copper backing plate to the back of the V-groove to protect the back of the weld from atmospheric contamination. Then, using SMAW low-hydrogen or iron powder electrodes, fill the V-groove with weld metal. Be sure to use enough current for a full penetration weld. See Figure 14-44 (C).

3. Grind the weld flush on the outside of the channel if necessary to make it flat. Be sure to leave the ground surface as smooth as possible. Any irregularities or scratches are stress raisers and can cause more cracks.

4. Cut and fit a $^{1}/_{2}$" thick carbon steel reinforcement plate on the inside of the web extending at least 6" beyond the ends of the weld repair. Round the corners of this plate on the lower and upper inside edges so it fits *tightly* against the web and edges of the flanges for the entire length of the reinforcement plate. If there are factory-drilled holes suitable for holding the reinforcement plate, use them. Otherwise drill two holes for the plate. Drill the holes in the reinforcement plate to mate with the holes in the weld as in Figure 14-44 (D). Holes are usually $^{1}/_{2}$", $^{9}/_{16}$", or $^{5}/_{8}$" diameter. Use a washer under each nut as in Figure 14-44 (E).

5. Stop. The repair is complete. No additional welding is needed.

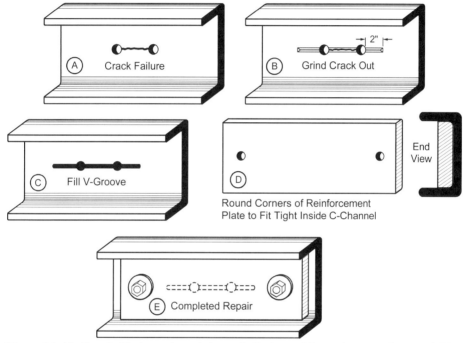

Figure 14-44. Case I: Horizontal crack in truck C-channel frame between factory-drilled holes in the web. This is a common case and cracks as long as 10" can occur.

Case II – Crack on the bottom flange perpendicular to the web only.

Here are the repair steps:

1. Grind a V-groove half way through the thickness of the flange in Figure 14-45 (A) along the path of the crack. See Figure 14-45 (B).

2. Using SMAW with a low-hydrogen or iron powder electrode, fill the V-groove with weld metal and grind it flush. Use enough current for full penetration of the flange metal. See Figure 14-45 (C).

3. Grind the weld flush (on the inside of the flange too if necessary to make it flat) making sure to leave the ground surface as smooth as possible. Again, any remaining surface imperfections are stress raisers.

4. Cut a $^{1}/_{2}$" × $1^{1}/_{2}$" reinforcement bar from mild carbon steel 12–15" long. Center it on the crack.

5. Using SMAW with a low-hydrogen or iron powder electrode, weld this bar onto the middle of the flange. The $1^1/_2$" dimension of the bar is vertical. See Figure 14-45 (D).

6. With a grinder, gouge a bevel groove through the unwelded side of the reinforcement bar to weld metal on the other side as in Figure 14-45 (D).

7. Place a fillet weld in the gouged groove using SMAW with a low-hydrogen or iron powder electrode to secure the other side of the reinforcement bar. See Figure 14-45 (E).

8. Stop, you are done. Do *not* make welds perpendicular to the length of the channel at the ends of the reinforcement bar.

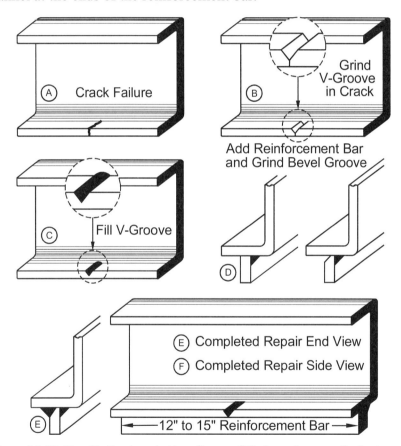

Figure 14-45. Case II: Crack on bottom flange of C-channel perpendicular to web.

Case III – Crack on the bottom flange perpendicular to the web and extending up into the web.

Figure 14-46 (A) shows what happens when Case II is left un-repaired and becomes Case III. Here are the repair steps are:

1. Grind out the crack with a V-groove halfway through the thickness of the flange along the path of the crack. See Figure 14-46 (B).

2. Drill a $^3/_8-^1/_2$" diameter hole at the end of the crack in the web to relieve stress as in the top of 14-46 (B).

3. Using SMAW with a low-hydrogen or iron powder electrode, fill the V-groove with weld metal and grind it flush. Next, use the reinforcement methods of Cases I and II to add both a bottom reinforcement bar and a reinforcement plate inside the C-channel web.

See Figure 14-46 (C through F).

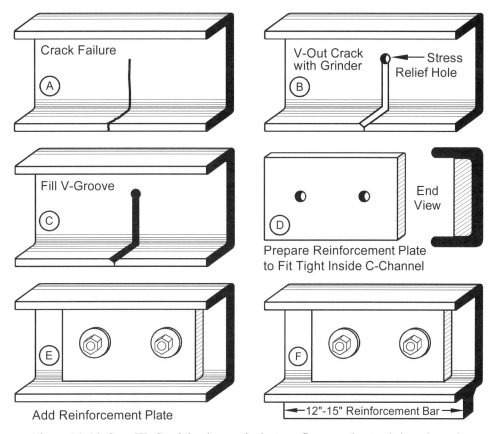

Figure 14-46. Case III: Crack begins on the bottom flange and extends into the web.

Another, more traditional C-channel repair, is to weld reinforcement plates to the web instead of bolting them. Also, a reinforcement bar can be welded along the bottom flange, but this last method is less commonly done today. See Figure 14-47.

If you choose welding instead of bolting for C-channel web repair, be sure to place welds *parallel* to the channel. Do not place any welds perpendicular to the channel. Welds perpendicular to the channel concentrate stresses on just one section of the weld. This is because the end welds on the patch plate prevent beam stress from being distributed evenly along the weld length. These welds themselves become new stress raisers and will result in near-term failure.

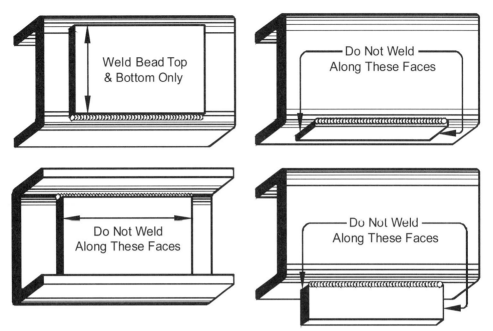

Figure 14-47. Welding reinforcement plates to C-channels.
Welds parallel to C-channels are acceptable; perpendicular welds are not.

Tip: Remember that these failures occurred in the first place because the vehicle frame was stressed beyond its design capacity by excessive loads and fatigue. Dump truck action stresses, hydraulic cylinder loads, road vibration, and truck overloading all contribute to failure.

Failure is likely to happen again, usually in the next weakest location, if the frame is subject to the same load conditions that caused the initial failure.

Section V – Other Vehicle Welding

Automotive Sheet Metal

Although the sheet metal in older cars can be repaired with oxyacetylene welding, the high-strength sheet metal in newer model cars cannot because the welds will crack. However, this special alloy steel, which is used to save weight, can be successfully GMAW (MIG) welded.

Begin the weld bead on the *outside* edge of the crack and work toward the *inside*, which will keep the inherent weakness of the bead-ending crater away from the metal's edge where it would act as a stress raiser and lead to a new failure.

On galvanized body parts, ER70S-3 electrodes should be used because they contain less silicon than ER70S-6 electrodes. This silicon, when mixed with zinc, contributes to weld cracking. Use a copper heat sink on the back of the sheet metal being welded as in Figure 14-48. This will prevent the welding heat from melting the work.

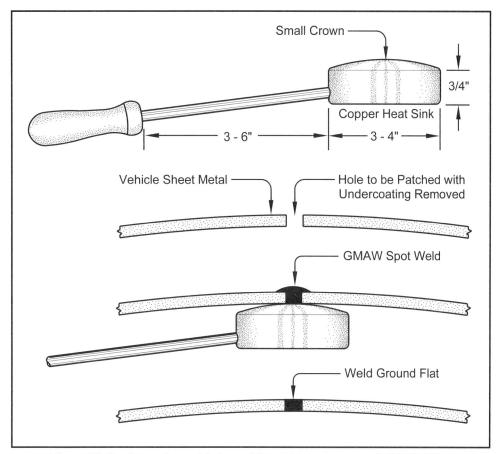

Figure 14-48. Copper heat-sink for welding vehicle sheet metal with GMAW.
This tool can be purchased or shop-made.

Unibody Designs & Roll Cages

While unibody design provides a strong and rigid vehicle frame, because it is made of relatively light sheet metal, it cannot support the forces that roll cage tubing ends can exert on it. If you need to mount a roll cage, a good solution is to use GMAW to first weld the roll cage tubing to a mounting plate and let the mounting plate distribute the forces over a wider area than the tubing end alone.

Either an all-around fillet weld or several $1/2$" diameter plug welds are suitable to hold the mounting plate to the unibody box beam. For best results, be sure to use ER70S-3 electrode wire. See the all-around welding technique in Figure 14-49 (left).

When roll cage tubing supports must be mounted to vehicle flooring, a stiff $1/4$" mounting plate is required to distribute forces over the thinner sheet metal flooring. This floor-mounted plate may be welded all around or bolted sandwich-style to the vehicle flooring as shown in Figure 14-49 (right).

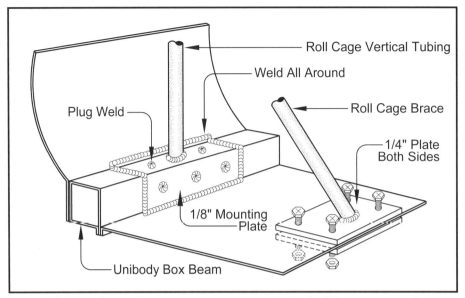

Figure 14-49. Mounting roll bar tubing to a unibody vehicle. Welding a support plate to a box beam (left) and bolting a mounting plate to sheet metal when welding is not permitted (right).

Truck Step

Figure 14-50 shows how to mount a truck step that is rigid enough to step on, but flexible enough to bend if the vehicle it is on backs into something.

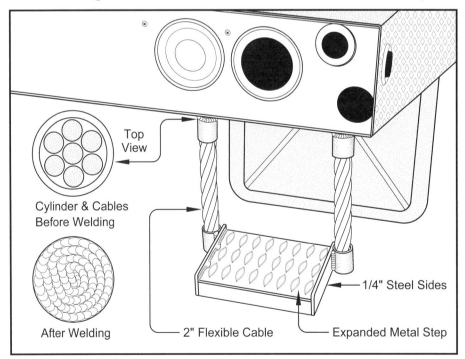

Figure 14-50. Flexible truck step added for ease of access to the back of the truck.

The short lengths of steel cable fit into cylinders and are welded in place. This welding not only secures the cables to the cylinders, it keeps them from unraveling. GTAW, SMAW or GMAW processes can be used for this job.

Railing Pinch Points

Figure 14-51 shows a truck railing, also called a tie-down bar, made from steel pipe. Because it is not possible to put a right-angle bend in steel pipe without specialized hydraulic bending equipment with internal mandrels, the fabricator had to settle for the tapered bend in the right-hand top of the figure. This design has a nasty pinch point that anyone grabbing the end of the railing will discover as their fingers slide down the pipe.

There are two solutions to correct this design flaw:

• Change from the stronger steel pipe to the less strong steel tubing which can be bent on a shorter radius with inexpensive tubing benders.

• Use forged steel elbows with the steel pipe to make the right-angle bends.

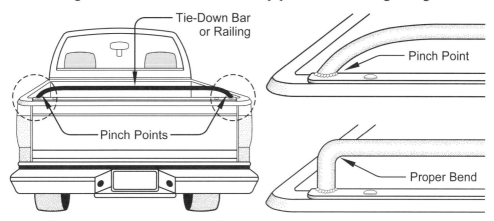

Figure 14-51. Railings with a shallow bend at their ends contain a pinch point.

Right-Angle Bends in Steel Pipe

Welded steel pipe fittings can be used to replace right angle bends in steel pipe railings. Welding these elbow, or right angle fittings, in place and grinding the welds flat makes a professional job, yet retains all the strength of the steel pipe. Another benefit of this approach is that all pipe lengths are straight and easily measured. No bend allowances need to be calculated. See Figure 14-52.

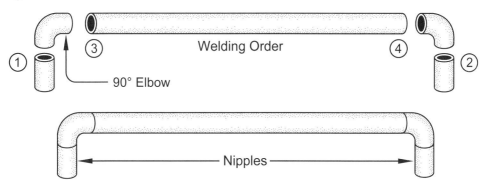

Figure 14-52. Welded elbows are the easy way to put right-angle bends in steel pipe.

The welding sequence of adding right-angle fittings to the pipe lengths is important. By adding the short pipe lengths to each right angle fitting *first*, it is easy to grind the weld bead flat in a disc or belt grinder. The longer pipe length that fits between the right angle fitting can be welded before installation and then also ground flat in a stationary disc or belt grinder. If the welding sequence is reversed, the grinding must be done with a hand-held grinder which is somewhat slower. Finally, the nipples are welded to the railing.

Avoiding Bend Allowances in Tubing

The additional length of tubing needed to compensate for the material in the radius of the bend is known as the *bend allowance.* Several tries, some experimenting, and some scrapped tubing may be needed to determine the bend allowance for a particular tubing diameter and bend radius combination.

Figure 14-53, though, shows a way to completely sidestep this problem. Here are the steps:

1. Make the bends in two lengths of pipe whose combined lengths are *slightly longer* than the finished railing.

2. Overlap the pipes so that the center-to-center distance of the pipe ends corresponds to the desired final length and mark the cut line.

3. Cut one of the pipes and weld them together.

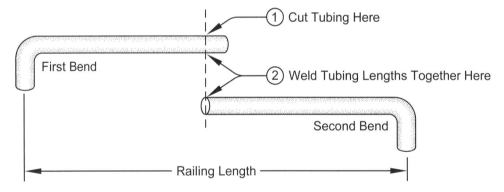

Figure 14-53. Making steel tubing railings by welding two lengths of steel pipe together to produce the exact length of pipe railing needed without calculating a bending allowance.

Chapter 15

Tools & Tooling

The more I want to get something done, the less I call it work.
—Richard Bach

Section I – Shop-Made Tools

Subtle Workpiece Marking

Because the same part may be worked on by several different welders or even several different shops, many welders inconspicuously mark the section of the part they repaired. This avoids the question of who made the repairs. To do this, marking punches can be made from drive pin punches of $1/8$" diameter or less which are modified to produce a distinctive mark. A welder usually only reveals his marking code when a customer suggests that his work was done by someone else. See Figure 15-1.

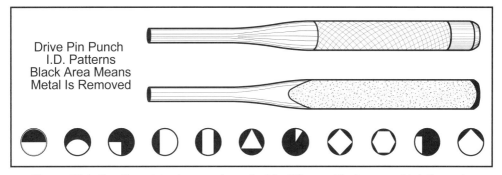

Drive Pin Punch
I.D. Patterns
Black Area Means
Metal Is Removed

Figure 15-1. Small unobtrusive punch marks identify a welder's or machinist's work.

Fire Pot

Figure 15-2 shows a shop-made fire pot fabricated from two sections of steel pipe, a steel angle bracket, and a nut and bolt. The concentrated flame from this pot can be used to heat lead or to bring work up to red heat for bending. The tip of an oxyacetylene torch is positioned in the small pipe on the side of the fire pot to get optimum flame swirls around the inside of the pot. The torch tip is locked into place by the nut and bolt on the side of the small piece of tubing. The firepot has no bottom, it rests on a firebrick.

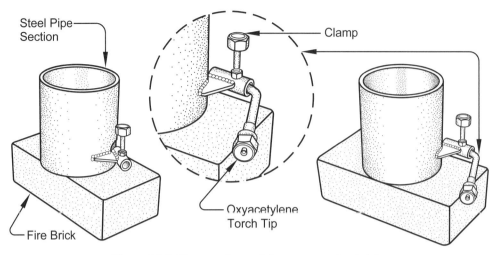

Figure 15-2. Shop-made steel fire pot on a fire brick.

Air Wrench Tools

The majority of electric- or air-driven drills turn too fast for larger drills or countersinks, but the shop-made air-wrench tool in Figure 15-3 solves that problem. To make this tool, use a little GTAW welding to join a countersink or a drill chuck to a cut-down impact socket. This method uses the high-strength and shock-resistant steel of the socket and its square drive to fit onto the air wrench. The advantage of the air wrench is that it has lots of torque and a slow speed, ideal for larger drills and countersinks.

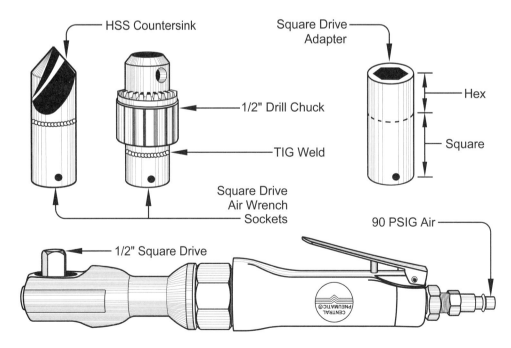

Figure 15-3. GTAW joins a square drive socket to
a countersink and a drill chuck for use in an air-wrench.

Single-Lip Carbide Milling Machine Cutters

Figure 15-4 (bottom) shows the welding fixture used to make the single-lip milling cutters shown in Figure 15-4 (top). The advantage of these cutters is that they are inexpensive, are easily sharpened many times on a green grinding wheel, and will cut steel up to R_c 60 with ease.

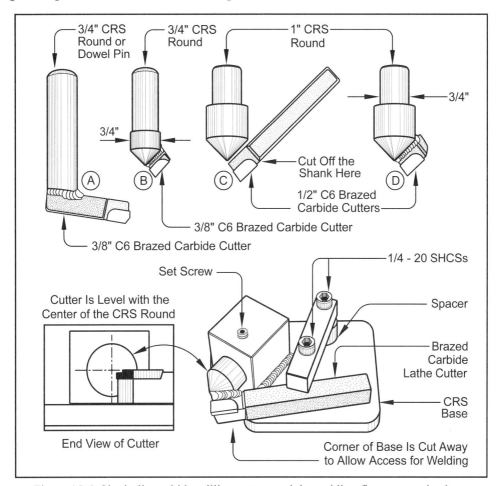

Figure 15-4. Single-lip carbide milling cutters and the welding fixture to make them.

Brass- or Bronze-Jawed Padded Pliers

There are two methods for making the padded-jaw pliers in Figure 15-5. *Method 1* uses a brass insert brazed to the jaws and *Method 2* uses silicon bronze TIG weld filler metal applied to line the inside of the jaws. But, before beginning either approach, the jaws of the pliers need to be ground down to make room for the new jaw material. This step must be done or the pliers will not close properly. At the bottom of Figure 15-5 notice that the edges of the new added jaw metal are slightly rounded so that when the pliers are used to bend materials such as piano wire, high stresses at the bend point are not induced. High stress at a single point can lead to cracking and failure, while a long, gradual bend will not cause stress failures. Padded-jaw pliers can also be used to straighten threaded rods without damaging them.

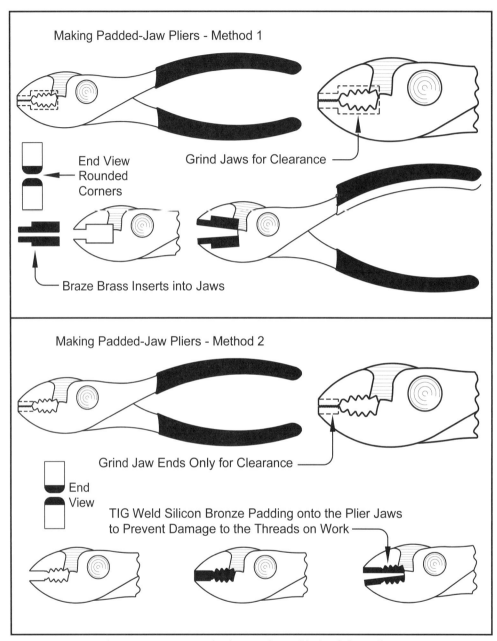

Figure 15-5. Two methods to make padded soft-jaw pliers.

Modifying Vise-Grip-Style Pliers

Vise-Grip-style pliers can be modified to handle long reaches as shown in Figure 15-6. The TIG welded-on adapters can be simple jaw extensions or pairs of telescoping tubes that can reach inside a part to hold it in place while welding.

In the bottom of Figure 15-6, two dowel pins, which touch each other at a right angle, provide smooth, low-friction surfaces for the pliers to pull up on the inside tubing.

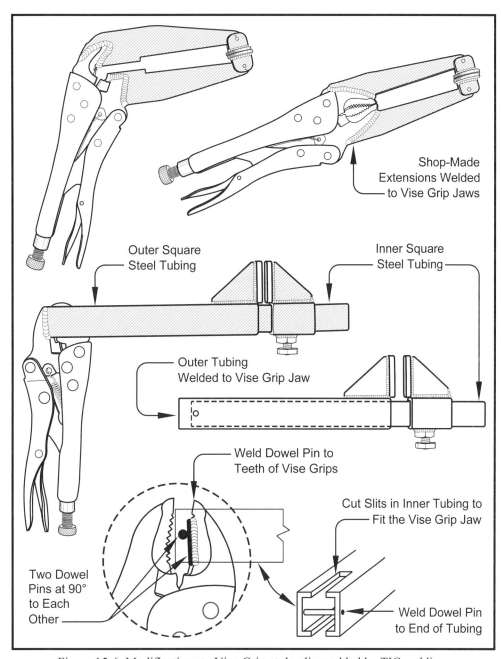

Shop-Made
Extensions Welded
to Vise Grip Jaws

Outer Square
Steel Tubing

Inner Square
Steel Tubing

Outer Tubing
Welded to Vise Grip Jaw

Weld Dowel Pin to
Teeth of Vise Grips

Cut Slits in Inner Tubing to
Fit the Vise Grip Jaw

Two Dowel
Pins at 90°
to Each
Other

Weld Dowel Pin
to End of Tubing

Figure 15-6. Modifications to Vise-Grip-style pliers added by TIG welding.

Mobile Base for a Disc/Belt Grinder

There are four reasons for adding a mobile base to a grinder:

- To allow a 250-pound grinder to be easily moved *outside* the shop to reduce grinding dust *inside* the shop. This mobility provides cleaner breathing air and easier clean-up. The caster-base design in Figure 15-7, which is made from welded angle iron, has a lower center of gravity than if the casters were attached directly to the bottom of the grinder, making this design less tippy. Besides, the flimsy sheet metal base of a typical grinder pedestal is too thin to support casters, or even leveling feet, because the flex in the grinder's base would cause the machine to rock.

- This caster-base design permits easy leveling with the adjustment of one caster to prevent the grinder from rocking on an uneven floor surface.

- Since the base of this pedestal design is open, adding a $^{1}/_{8}$" steel plate to the bottom of the caster base traps dust from the grinding disc *inside* the base instead of allowing it to fall onto the shop floor.

- In a small shop, the grinder can be easily moved out of the way.

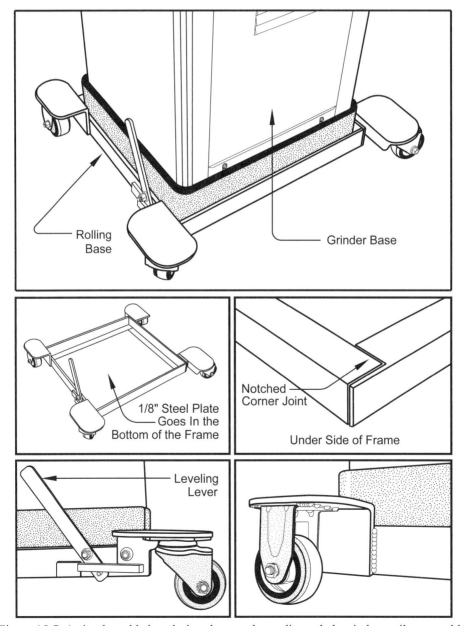

Figure 15-7. A simple welded angle-iron base makes a disc or belt grinder easily moveable.

If the angle iron frame fits too snugly around the base before welding, weld shrinkage will lock the frame to the grinder base. To make the frame fit nicely around the grinder base, yet still be removable, place 2–3 business cards between the frame and the grinder base at 2 inch intervals on each side of the frame. Business cards range from 0.005–0.015 inches in thickness so it is easy—and inexpensive—to attain the proper spacing.

Oxyacetylene Cylinder Carrier

A traditional steel cylinder carrier has two rings, one to hold each cylinder in place as shown in Figure 15-8. All four rings are rolled and welded closed, a simple task, but this design has a major drawback—it allows the cylinders to spin when the cylinder valves are turned, so the welder needs both hands to open or close them, one to turn the valve and one to hold the cylinder to keep it from rotating. It may be traditional, but it is not the best design.

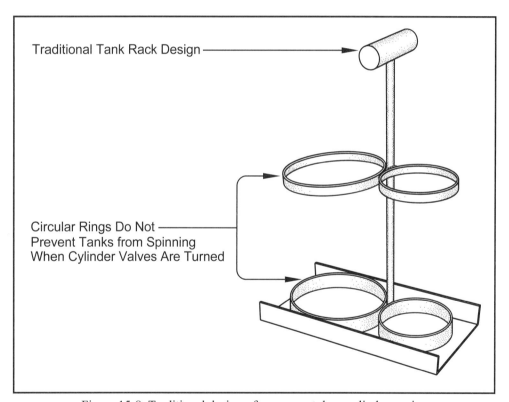

Traditional Tank Rack Design

Circular Rings Do Not Prevent Tanks from Spinning When Cylinder Valves Are Turned

Figure 15-8. Traditional design of an oxyacetylene cylinder carrier.

Figure 15-9 shows a better design which prevents the cylinders from spinning, yet is equally simple, and does not require rolling four rings as the traditional design does. The $1/2$" round CRS handle on this improved design is bent to clear the acetylene regulator, the flashback arrestor and the hose. A great convenience over the older design, yet no more difficult to make.

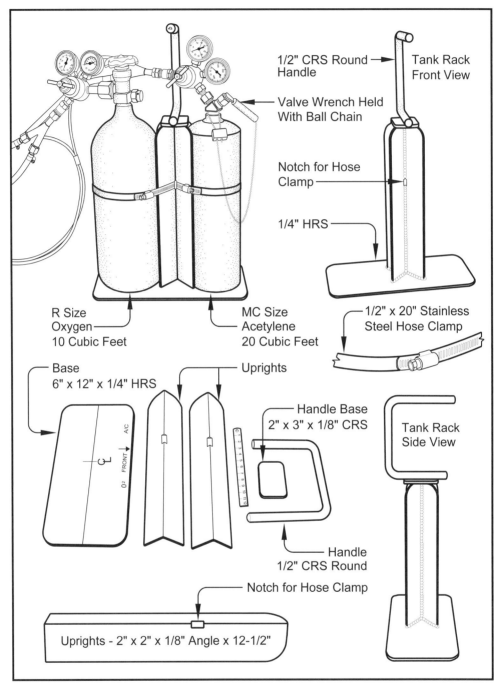

Figure 15-9. Shop-made oxygen and acetylene cylinder carrier prevents the cylinders from spinning when turning the cylinder valves, yet is simple to make. Only fives pieces of steel or aluminum are needed.

Oxyacetylene Circle Cutter Guide

Figure 15-10 shows a shop-made oxyacetylene circle cutter. This guide is easy to adjust and cuts precise discs. Its center pivot point stays in place because it drops into a center-punched hole made in the plate to be cut.

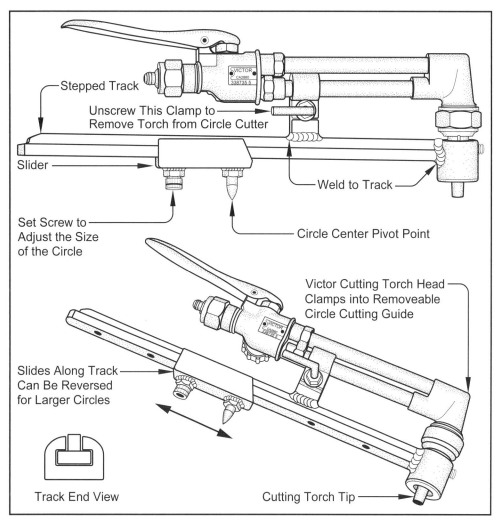

Figure 15-10. Circle cutting guide for an oxyacetylene cutting torch head.

Wrench & Fixture for Rebuilding Victor-Style Regulators

The Victor-style regulators pictured in Figure 15-11 have been in production for more than forty years and are widely copied both in the U.S. and by Asian importers. The design is durable and reliable, but eventually their rubber valve seats harden and cause them to exhibit *creep*. This occurs when either oxygen or acetylene gas leaks at the rubber valve seat and causes gauge pressure to rise, particularly when the torch valves are off. This can be particularly dangerous for acetylene because this gas can spontaneously decompose at pressures above 15 psi causing an explosion.

The problem is not improperly installing the handful of parts from the rebuild kits—they are simple to install—the problem is getting the valve bonnet off without damaging the regulator. This difficulty arises because the body of the valve (or base), and the bonnet (or upper cover), are both round and offer no easy way to hold them so they can be unscrewed.

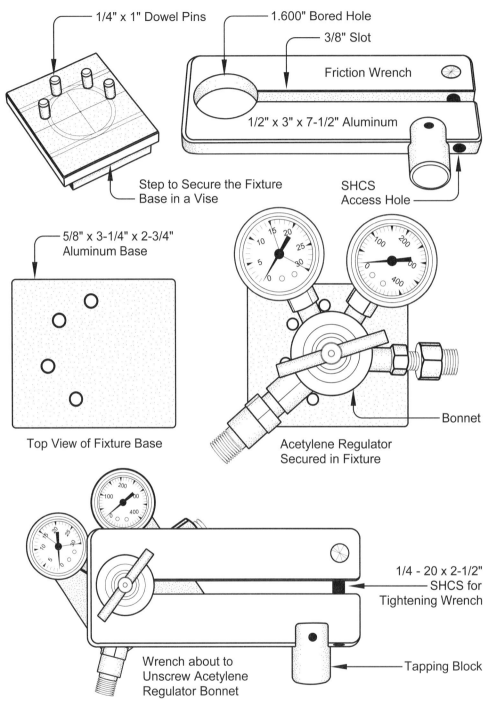

Figure 15-11. Safely opening a Victor-style regulator using a shop-made friction wrench.

The solution to this problem is a shop-made wrench.

Here are the steps:

1. Make the fixture base and friction wrench in Figure 15-11. Aluminum is used in the drawing, but steel can also be used.
2. Secure the fixture base in a vise. The base has a step for this purpose.

3. Place the base of the cylinder regulator in the square fixture base. The gauge stem and low pressure gas outlet fit between the dowel pins. This prevents the regulator base from turning, but does not damage it.

4. Unscrew the pressure adjustment knob from the bonnet.

5. Fit the friction wrench over the bonnet and tighten the SHCS on the side of the wrench.

6. Unscrew the bonnet with the shop-made friction wrench. A few very gentle taps may be needed to break the bonnet threads loose.

7. Now that you have access, follow the instructions in the rebuild kit, then screw the bonnet back on and the regulator is rebuilt.

Pipe Rollers

Figure 15-12 shows a pair of shop-made pipe rollers that greatly simplifies pipe welding. With two pairs of these rollers, the two pipes to be joined are aligned and tacked. Then, while an assistant slowly turns the pipes, the welder can make the entire weld in the flat position without moving his welding rod or torch. See Figure 16-18 for another style of pipe rollers.

Constructed with only five pieces of angle iron, two large and three small, two wheels and two axels, pipe rollers are easy and fast to make. They can be made in a variety of sizes and they are just as good as their commercially-made counterparts and much less expensive.

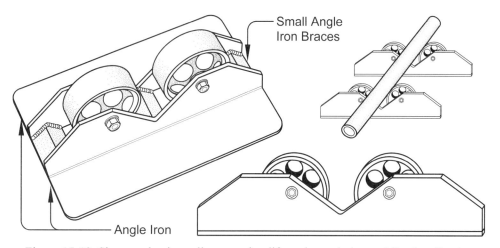

Small Angle Iron Braces

Angle Iron

Figure 15-12. Shop-made pipe rollers can simplify and speed pipe welding by allowing the entire weld circumference to be applied in the flat position.

Randal Rescue Tool

Figure 15-13 shows a tool used by fire departments because of its convenience and versatility when climbing ladders. This tool starts with a pair of commercially available bolt cutters, then an S-7 tool steel hammer face and axe point are TIG welded to the bolt cutter jaws using 312 stainless steel filler metal. S-7 is the tool steel used in making chisels and it provides the shock and impact resistance needed for this tool. A matrix of L-6 weld dots are placed on the face of the hammer and then touched off on a grinder so they are flat and of uniform height. The dots prevent the hammer head from sliding off the item being struck. While L-6 will not hold an edge, it has the highest impact resistance of all tool steels.

Firemen often have to carry bolt cutters up ladders, but now they can add a hammerhead and axe point with very little additional weight.

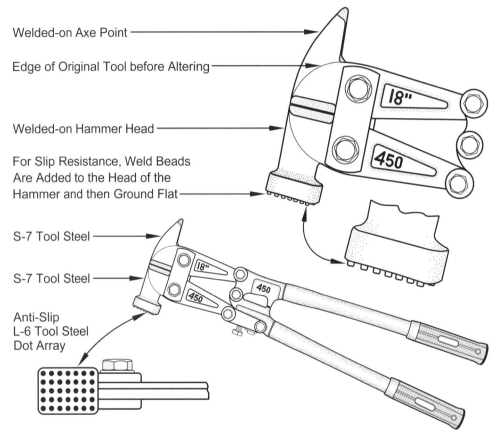

Figure 15-13. GTAW is used to add an axe point and a hammer to a bolt cutter. It is called the Randal Rescue Tool after the name of its designer.

Chain Link Rescue Tool

This shop-modified bolt cutter allows rescuers to rapidly cut through chain-link, also called cyclone, wire fences. Typical fence cutting, particularly in low light levels during a nighttime emergency, is a slow process. The bolt cutter must be withdrawn and pushed over the next wire link below after each cut, and because the jaws of the cutter are rounded, they tend to force themselves out of the fence as the tool is lowered to make the next cut. This does not happen with this shop-modified tool because the top jaw is longer. By starting the cut with the longer jaw on top, the tool makes the cut and drops down and catches the next link, ready for the next cut. The jaw extension is S-7 GTAW welded with 312 stainless steel filler rod. See the rescue tool in Figure 15-14.

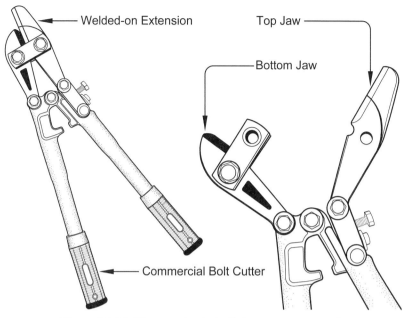

Figure 15-14. Shop-made chain link cutter rescue tool.

Expanded Metal Stretcher

This shop-modified Vice-Grip-style pliers has jaw extensions that pull expanded metal screening tight so it can be welded to a frame or pipe. See Figures 15-15 and 15-16. This tool works well, but can exert so much pull the cumulative effect is to bend the frame. Don't pull the metal too tight.

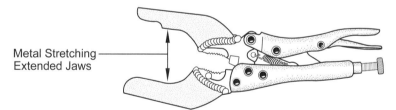

Figure 15-15. Modified Vise-Grip pliers with extended jaws for stretching expanded metal screening prior to welding.

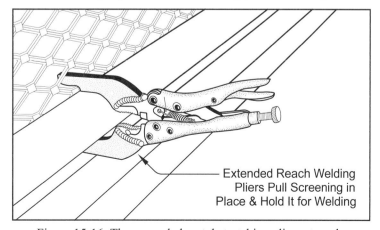

Figure 15-16. The expanded metal stretching pliers at work.

Modified Welding Clamps for Pipe

A Vise-Grip-style welding clamp is designed to hold two flat pieces in position. But by welding an angle iron with a reinforcing rib to the bottom jaws of the pliers, two pieces of pipe can be held in alignment for welding. See the shop-modified welding clamp in Figure 15-17. Fabricate the Y-shaped angle iron section and weld it onto the bottom jaws of the pliers, *then* cut the gap for welding clearance.

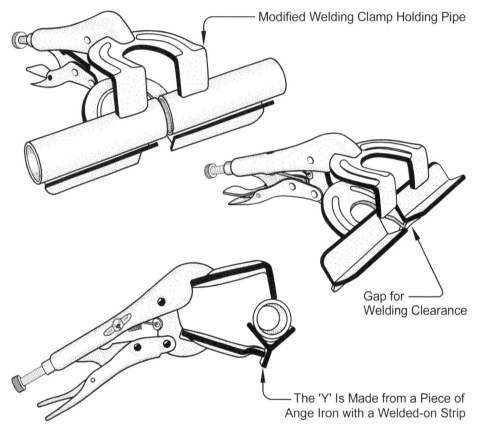

Figure 15-17. A Vise-Grip-style welding clamp
modified to hold two pipe sections in alignment.

Cast Iron Welding

Cast iron culvert covers, like the one shown in Figure 15-18, make very good welding tables so they frequently disappear from city streets and must be replaced.

To secure the new cover in place, standard SMAW rods cannot be used. Cast iron has a high carbon content and welds made using rods for mild steel will crack, but rods specifically designed for welding cast iron will not crack. These rods contain molybdenum which absorbs carbon, yet does not take on its characteristics. These rods are much more expensive than mild steel welding rods, but it takes very little rod to secure a set of theft-proof steel patch plates.

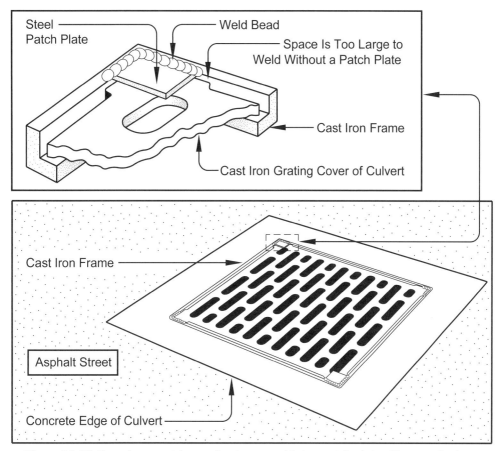

Figure 15-18. Securing a cast iron culvert cover with two patch plates. Four patch plates would be even better. These small plates are essential when the replacement grating has a sloppy fit and cannot be welded at each corner.

Chisel Extension

Figure 15-19 shows how to extend the length of a cold chisel by brazing on an extension. The chisel and its extension are brazed touching each other so, when using the chisel, most of the hammer force is transmitted on the steel-to-steel surface, not through the braze filler metal.

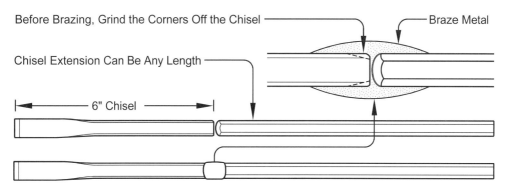

Figure 15-19. A cold chisel lengthened by brazing on an extension. The extension can be CRS or S-7 tool steel. HRS would be too soft.

Shop-Made Tight Quarters Punch

This five-piece around-the-corner punch, made with scrap round and bar stock and a center punch, is designed to provide access to hard-to-reach spots. It is TIG welded of CRS stock and can be scaled up or down as needed. See the punch in Figure 15-20. By grinding a blunt end on the punch, this tool is excellent for dislodging parts stuck in place by time and rust.

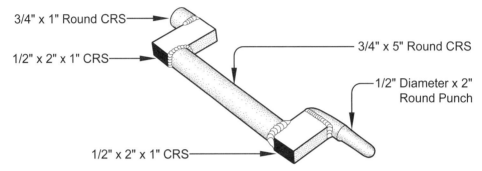

Figure 15-20. Shop-made tight quarters punch.

Simple Shop-Made Welding Jack

This four-piece jack, made with two bolts, a connector nut and a small base plate, is designed for precisely aligning and leveling work before welding. Grinding a small crown on the top of the upper screw reduces the force necessary to turn the bolt under load. Any of the common welding processes can be used to make this tool. See Figure 15-21.

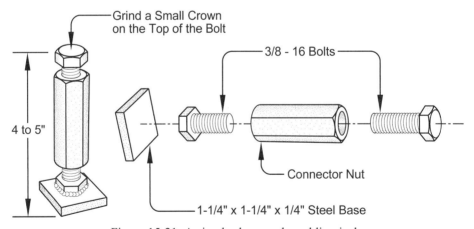

Figure 15-21. A simple shop-made welding jack.

Molds for Lead Pads & Rod Stock

Shops often need to make aluminum molds for casting lead pads and lead rod stock for solder. Since lead does not adhere to aluminum, no release agent is needed to get the lead out of the molds, but the molds must have 1–2° sloping sides, called *draft,* and no undercuts or the rods will not release from the molds. The grooves in the aluminum plate are made using a round-nosed end mill in a milling machine. See Figure 15-22.

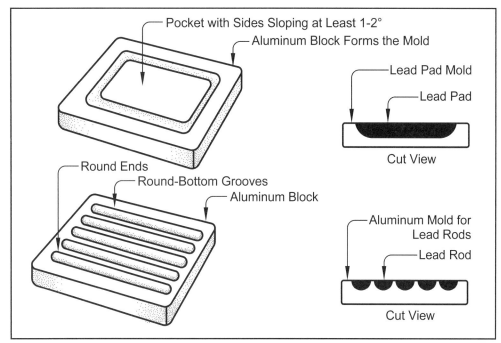

Figure 15-22. Aluminum molds for casting lead pads and lead rod stock.
These molds are normally much longer than those pictured.

Shop-Made V-blocks

V-blocks are handy in the welding shop, but commercially available ones are usually expensive because they are precision ground. Since considerably less accuracy is needed for welding than in machining, these shop-made blocks are fabricated from angle iron and CRS flat stock as shown in Figure 15-23. Welding up a long section of V-block and then cutting it into shorter lengths saves a lot of time.

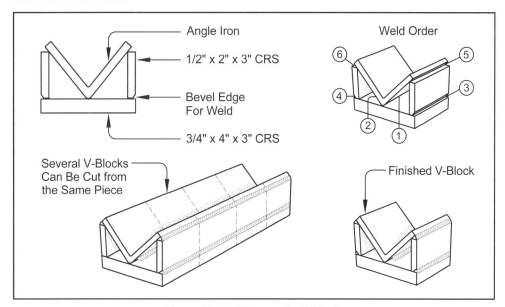

Figure 15-23. Shop-made V-block.

Shop-Made Grinder Tool Rests

Tool rests are both a critical part of a grinder and the one part most often compromised on imported economy grinders. Many of these grinders have durable motors, good bearings, and excellent dynamic balance on the motors themselves, but their flimsy sheet-metal tool rests prevent any serious grinding. And, because they are too small, these rests deflect under load, making them difficult or impossible to adjust. Cheap, cheesy tool rests also prevent the use of diamond wheel dressers.

Figure 15-24 shows a first-class shop-made tool rest to replace the flimsy sheet metal rests on imported grinders.

This tool rest has several advantages:

- Made from $^3/_8$" CRS, the tool rest top surface is extremely rigid and will not deflect under load.

- The edge of the tool rest top surface is *parallel* to the grinder spindle axis, so it provides a guide for a diamond wheel dresser.

- The large area of the tool rest top surface makes it easier to support and rotate work into the grinder wheel. To prevent cut fingers, all edges of the tool rest are rounded.

- Screw slots in the base of the tool rest allow adjustment toward the grinder wheel to compensate for the reduction in wheel diameter with wear.

- Three different versions of this tool rest can be made from the same basic design. The tool rest in Figure 15-24, made for gray and green wheels, is notched to better support the work, not so work can be ground on the side of the wheel, which is a very dangerous practice. The surface of the tool rest is *at* or *slightly above* the wheel center height.

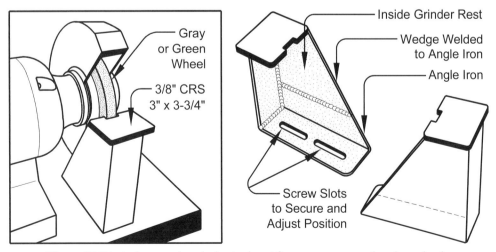

Figure 15-24. A shop-made grinder tool rest for gray or green abrasive wheels.

Figure 15-25 shows all three versions of the shop-made tool rests. The first, for gray and green abrasive wheels, the second, for abrasive cutoff wheels, and the third, for diamond wheels. Diamond wheels grind on their sides, not on their peripheries, so tool rests for these wheels must support work going against the side of the diamond wheel. Tool rests for abrasive cutoff wheels, have a long slot in the tool rest to support work as it moves into the cutoff wheel. Tool rest height will vary with the height of the grinder and will need to be adjusted.

Figure 15-26 shows the parts needed to make the base of the tool rests and the welding sequence. Following this sequence and using proper clamping methods will minimize weld distortion.

Each grinder tool rest requires:

- Two pieces of $2" \times 2" \times \frac{1}{4}"$ angle iron, one piece has screw slots added for adjusting the tool rest in and out with respect to the grinding wheel.

- One $4" \times 4" \times \frac{1}{4}"$ steel gusset plate.

- One $\frac{3}{8}"$ CRS rectangle is needed for the tool rest top surface. For this part, cut a square notch to surround the end of the grinding wheel and remember to round all the edges. Make sure that the front edge of the tool rest is parallel to the motor axle axis because this edge will guide the diamond dresser. Cut a notch to fit the width of the gray and green abrasive wheels with $\frac{1}{16}"$ clearance on each side of the wheel. Cut a slot for the abrasive cutoff wheel and a notch for the diamond wheel as in Figure 15-25.

Worth repeating: Make sure that the front edge of the tool rest is parallel with the motor axis because this edge guides the diamond wheel dresser.

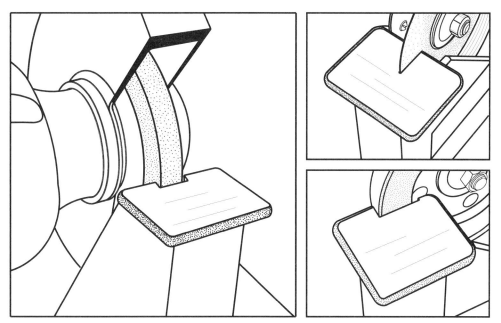

Figure 15-25. Shop-made grinder tool rest surfaces for gray or green wheels (left), for abrasive cutoff wheels (top right), and for diamond wheels (bottom right).

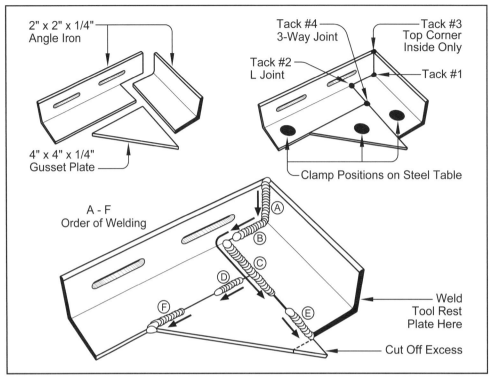

Figure 15-26. Cutting, layout, tacking and welding sequence for the tool rest base. The tool rest top surface is a $^3/_8$" CRS rectangle that is notched to fit the grinder.

Pin Wrench for a Collet Block

Figure 15-27 shows a quick and easy way to fabricate a shop-made pin wrench for tightening a collet block. Although this wrench doesn't look like a commercially made wrench, it works just as well, and because it does not require complex cutting and fitting, it goes together fast.

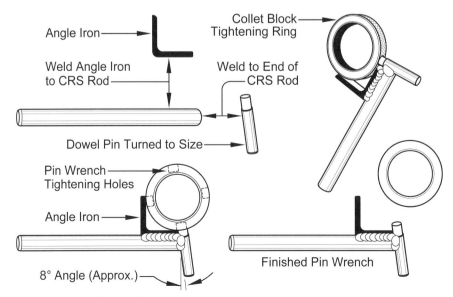

Figure 15-27. Shop-made pin wrench for tightening a collet block.

Ladder Safety Extensions

This safety extension for an A-frame ladder provides a grab bar when the user stands on the last step from the top. Only three lengths of square aluminum tubing and four small plates are required. Five $^3/_{16}$" or $^1/_4$" pop rivets secure each plate to the ladder. See Figure 15-28.

The tubing lengths are joined to each other and to the mounting plates with TIG or MIG welds. Welding cannot be used to secure the plates to aluminum ladders because welding anneals the aluminum ladder leg extrusions, removing much of their strength. Pop rivets can be used on fiberglass ladders as well. Be sure to smooth the ends of the grab bar. The ends of the ladder extension bar should be welded shut or plugged for safety.

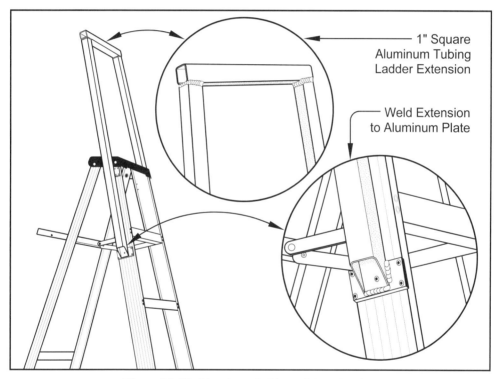

1" Square
Aluminum Tubing
Ladder Extension

Weld Extension
to Aluminum Plate

Figure 15-28. Aluminum ladder safety extension.

Shop-Made Shipyard Drill Press

Figures 15-29 through 15-31 show a shop-made drill press very common in U.S. Navy shipyards. The design is built to support a Milwaukee D-handled electric drill which has a no-load speed of about 500 RPM, draws 7 amps—about one horsepower—and is capable of easily drilling $^1/_2$" holes in steel. This drill press has more output torque, rigidity, axial drill force and mounting versatility than the budget imported drill presses sold in home improvement stores. There is no comparison between their performances.

Although this drill press is not a substitute for the magnetic drill presses typically used for drilling holes over $^1/_2$" diameter, this on-the-spot drill press is invaluable when it comes to saving workers from going back and forth from the worksite to the shop. On board a ship this saves a lot of time and energy. This shop-made drill press is usually tack-welded to the ship deck near the job site and as a result is very stable in use.

In addition, because the drill press table has a removable top plate and a hole in the lower table plate, it can be used to drill holes into work *under* the table much like a magnetic drill press. For these holes, the drill press is tack-welded in place which makes accurate positioning easy. See the drill press table design in Figure 19-31 (top). Chain wrenches can be used to secure the drill press to large pipe for pipe drilling. Also, the vertical column can be removed from the table and rotated 180° to drill holes *behind* the table.

Beside being a step-saver, this drill press has three more advantages:

- Because it is tack welded to the deck, the drill is rigidly held and eliminates the hazard of snapping the operator's wrist if the dill hangs up in the work.

- The lever arm has a 3:1 mechanical advantage and so makes it easy for the operator to apply the high axial force necessary for large diameter drills.

- Unlike a magnetic drill press, if the press is mounted upside down or with the table vertical, the drill press will not fall down if the power fails. This usually happens when someone at a distance from the drilling site kicks out an extension cord.

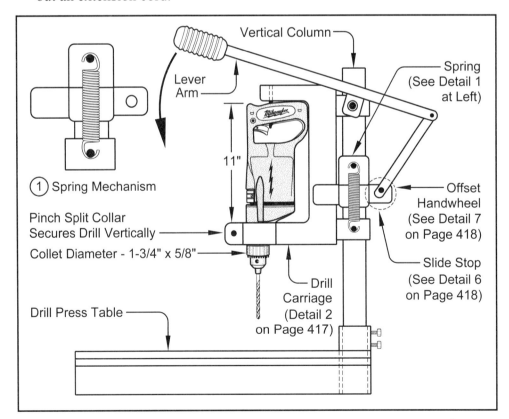

Figure 15-29. Shipyard drill press can be welded in place at the job site and can drill $1/2$" holes in steel. Drilling even larger holes is possible if step-drilling or hole saws are used.

Building this drill press requires only a little machining and intermediate welding skills. Nearly all the steel is commonly found as shop scraps except for the 8–10 inches of $2^{1}/_{2}" \times 2^{1}/_{2}" \times {}^{1}/_{4}"$ square trailer hitch receiver tubing needed to slide on the vertical column. While round tubing or pipe could be used to make the vertical column and its slides, square tubing prevents the side-to-side wobble that a round column would have.

Since trailer hitch receiver tubing is made to slide over the next size smaller tubing and will not have a snug fit on the column, it may be a bit sloppy. Add weld filler metal or braze metal to the inside of the receiver tubing to take up the slack and file the added metal to fit.

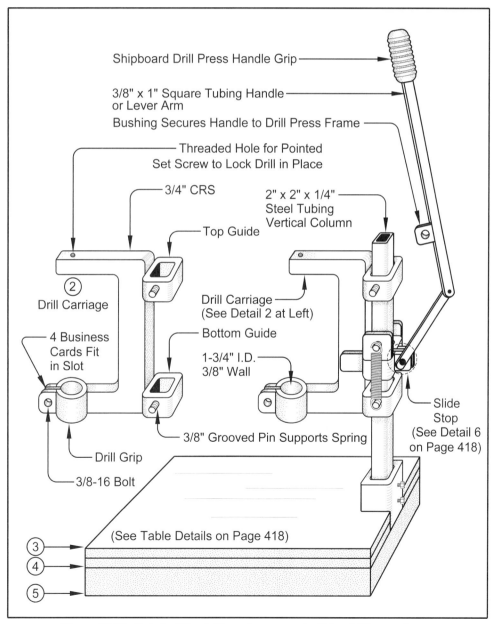

Figure 15-30. Detail of the drill carriage on and off the drill press frame.

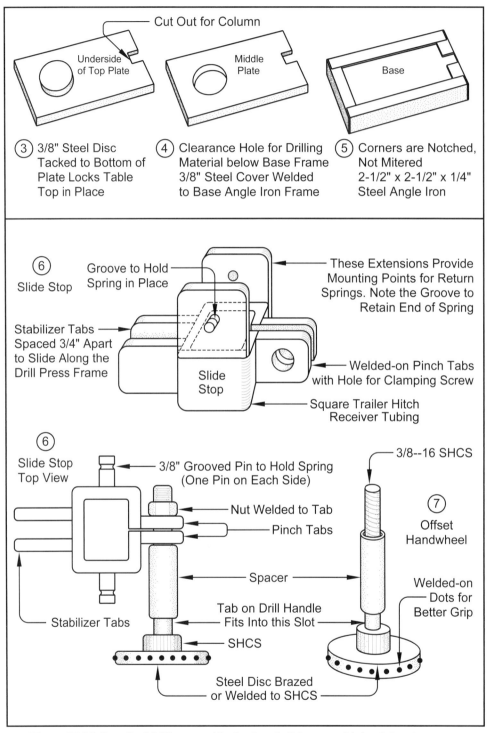

Figure 15-31. Detail of drill press table (top) and slide stop with its tightening screw handwheel (bottom). The removable top steel plate locks into place with the cutout for the column and the steel circle secured underneath it. The middle table plate is welded to the base frame. The spacer on the slide stop screw is required so the drill press handle clears the side of the drill body and the spring support rods. The drill press is ambidextrous, the handle can mount on either the right or left side of the drill body.

Welding Rebar

Figure 15-32 shows the standard techniques for joining rebar by welding.

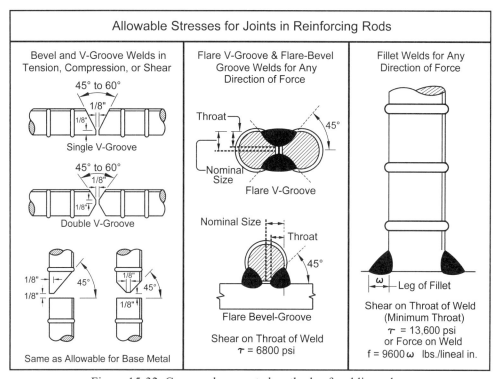

Allowable Stresses for Joints in Reinforcing Rods

Figure 15-32. Commonly accepted methods of welding rebar.

Section II – Splicing Bandsaw Blades

Blade Splicing Methods

There are two methods for splicing bandsaw blades: *electric welding* and *silver brazing*. Each method has its advantages:

*   Welding is much faster than silver brazing, but it requires an electric welder. The good thing about using an electric welder is that once the welding/annealing cycle is determined for a particular blade metal, relatively little skill or technique is needed for good splices.

*   Silver brazing requires an oxyacetylene torch, flux, silver braze-filler metal and a brazing fixture. Although this process does not vary with the blade metal or manufacturer, there is a technique to get a sound silver braze joint which requires some skill. To review how this is done, refer to *Chapter 11 – Brazing & Soldering*, pages 306–309.

Electric Blade Welding Procedure

Bandsaw blade welding is complicated not only because of differences in the blade steel metallurgy and the annealing requirements, but also because of the number of critical steps involved. Also, blade annealing varies not only with manufacturer and type of blade—carbon steel, molybdenum HSS steel or bimetal—but between blade widths. It takes experimentation to determine a satisfactory annealing cycle for a particular blade material and once it has been found, an experienced welder will make note of the cycle on the blade box for the next time this blade material is welded.

Here are the steps for electric blade welding:

1. Always wear heavy-duty leather gloves when handling bandsaw blades, particularly the wider blades. The wider and thicker the blade, the greater the need for gloves.

2. If the blade has been welded before, trim about $1/4$" from each end of the blade. Use a blade shear—usually found on bandsaws that have electric welders—or use an abrasive cutoff wheel.

3. As in Figure 15-33 (top), lay up the two bandsaw blade ends so that the teeth of each blade end point in opposite directions, then adjust the blades so their ends are even, as in Figure 15-33 (middle). Be sure to align the blade edges parallel. This alignment method insures that even if the blade ends are not exactly square, they will fit snugly in the electric welder when butted together.

4. With the blades held as in Figure 15-33 (middle), grind the ends square using the grinding wheel on the electric welder. Unlike the typical pedestal or bench grinder, these wheels grind on the sides of their wheels as well as their edges. Rest the blades on the metal shroud around the grinding wheel and feed the blades into the grinding wheel. Be sure that the trimmed edges are ground so that they both end at a gullet, not at a point. Remove all burrs, then using emery cloth, lightly clean the side face of each blade down to fresh metal for $1/4$" from their ends. With acetone or alcohol, remove all dirt, grease, coatings and oil from the welding area.

5. For the following steps refer to Figures 15-34 and 15-35. Turn the *pressure knob*, sometimes known as the *blade infeed*, to zero. This setting determines the spring force applied between the bandsaw blade ends during the welding cycle. This spring force is applied to one of the electrodes which is in a moveable jaw—usually the right-hand electrode. This spring action forces one blade end into the other during the welding process.

6. Loosen the right- and left-hand blade electrode clamps.

7. Place the A end of the saw blade under the right-hand electrode. Again, make sure the blade is aligned squarely and the teeth are facing towards you, and then tighten the right-hand blade clamp to secure the blade in place. The saw blade end should protrude about $1/4$" out of the clamp, halfway into the space between the two electrodes.

8. Place the B end of the saw blade under the left electrode. Make sure that the blade is aligned squarely, its teeth are facing towards you, and the ends of both blades meet each other. Tighten the left-hand blade clamp to

secure the blade in place. Putting the A and B ends of the band in the right and left electrodes, respectively, is only important if the band has been left threaded through the bandsaw table—and, in some cases, through the workpiece starting hole.

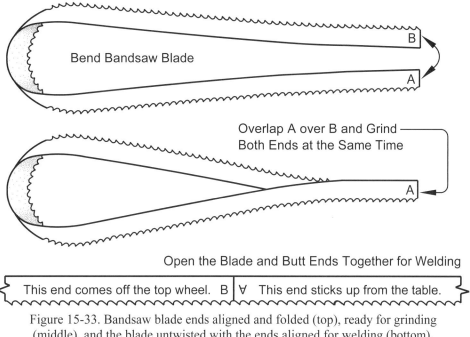

Figure 15-33. Bandsaw blade ends aligned and folded (top), ready for grinding (middle), and the blade untwisted with the ends aligned for welding (bottom).

9. Set the pressure knob for the appropriate blade width. Wider blades need more pressure between their ends during welding, while narrower blades require less pressure.

10. Perform the weld by pushing down the welding switch lever to turn on the welding electricity between the electrodes and apply the spring force between the blade ends. After the ends of the blade meet and fuse, and about $3/16$" on each side of the weld becomes red, release the welding lever. This entire process takes only 1–2 seconds, depending on the blade width and the type of metal. Some blade welders have a push button that starts the welding cycle. Typical blade welders on bandsaws do not have an automatic welding cycle and require the operator to watch carefully and release the weld lever or button after the weld is completed.

11. Allow the weld to cool for 3–5 minutes.

12. Because bandsaw blades are made of O-1 air-hardening steel, welding makes the weld-area steel hard and brittle, so the weld must be annealed to allow it to properly flex in the bandsaw. To do this, open one of the electrode clamps to release the spring compression pressure on the weld and retighten this electrode clamp on the blade in preparation for the application of annealing heat.

13. Gradually heat the weld by pushing the anneal button until the weld turns cherry red—not orange or yellow. A typical $^1/_2$" blade requires 4–5 button pushes to reach red heat—this takes only 2–3 seconds—then another 4–6 button pushes at $^3/_4$-second intervals to anneal the weld zone. Cool the weld slowly by lengthening the time interval between pushes of the anneal button. You may need to shield the weld from ambient light to better see its color during annealing. Some blades require two annealing cycles.

14. Let the saw blade cool for 3–5 minutes, and then remove it from the welder.

15. Use the top edge of the small grinding wheel on the side of the bandsaw to remove the welding flash from the bottom of the weld, and use the bottom edge of the grinding wheel to remove the flash from the top side of the weld. Using both the top and bottom of this grinding wheel avoids the need to flip the blade over to grind its other side. See Figure 15-34.

16. Slide the weld section through the 0.035" gap gauge on the bottom of the welder—see the bottom of Figure 15-35—to verify that the blade has been ground to the proper thickness.

17. Test the weld by bending the blade in an 8–10" radius. If the blade forms a smooth, continuous arc without a crack, the weld is good.

   - If the blade bends into a V-shape at the weld, the blade is too soft and is over-annealed. To fix this, cut off the bad weld, regrind the band ends, and repeat the welding and annealing cycle with longer time intervals between pushes to shorten the annealing time.

   - If the blade snaps at the weld, the weld did not cool slowly enough during annealing. To fix this, cut off the bad weld, regrind the band ends and repeat the welding and annealing cycle, increasing the annealing time.

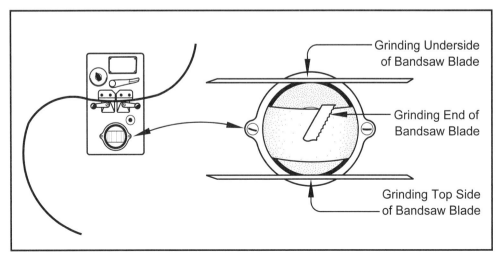

Figure 15-34. Removing welding flash with the bandsaw's own grinding wheel.

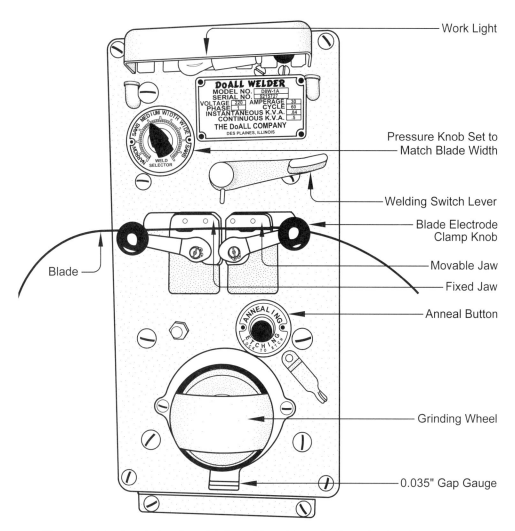

Figure 15-35. Electric bandsaw blade welder with a grinding wheel and a gap gauge.

Blade Welding Troubleshooting

As mentioned earlier, the proper settings of heat and blade infeed are initially found by experimentation. Until you have found the proper settings, here are some welding problems you'll run into and their likely cures:

- Blades that overlap as they weld do not have enough heat and/or too much infeed. When welding be sure that the blades just touch, not overlap. They are friendly, but not that friendly.

- A complete blowout at the weld is the result of too much heat.

- Too little pressure causes a partial weld across the blade. This is from not enough infeed.

- More than $^1/_{16}$" of weld flash on both sides of the blade usually indicates a good weld. Less than $^1/_{16}$" of flash indicates a little too much infeed, and typically, incomplete welds.

Section III – Fixtures

Turnscrew Handle Fixture

Figure 15-36 shows a simple, easy-to-make welding fixture for either GTAW or silver brazing a turning bar onto a SHCS. Use CRS rod stock for the turning bar. Do not use O-1 steel as it will crystallize and fracture under load.

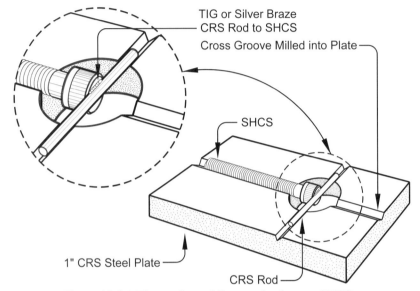

Figure 15-36. Fixture for welding turning bars to SHCSs.

Bracket Welding Fixture

Figure 15-37 (A) shows a Type 304 stainless steel bracket of $^1/_2$" stock for an aerospace welding application. The fixture to make this part has several important features:

- The two vertical dowels on the base of the fixture locate the rectangular base section of the bracket and insure it is parallel to the axis of the L-shaped bent section. See Figure 15-37 (B)

- The step on the right-hand side of the bracket, Figure 15-37 (C), insures that the L-shaped bracket section is accurately positioned along the length of the base.

- The SHCS touching the side of the L-shaped section aligns the bracket side-to-side. See Figure 15-37 (D).

- A SHCS or button head screw holds the base of the bracket in position, Figure 15-37 (E), and the bar clamp holds the L-shaped section in position as in Figure 15-37 (F).

- The opening in the base of the welding fixture provides the welder access to the weld bead under the L-shaped section. See Figure 15-37 (G).

- Because of this rigid fixturing there is no additional machining or bending required after welding to maintain the ±0.010 tolerances on the bracket.

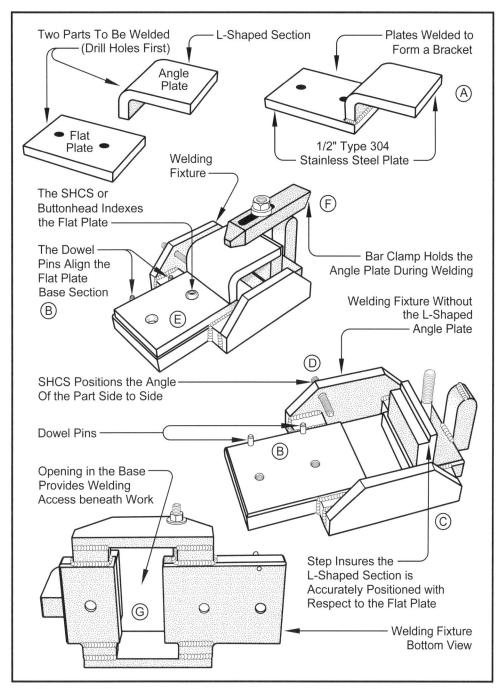

Figure 15-37. How to make a fixture for accurately welding a stainless steel bracket.

Fixture for Welding or Brazing a Pipe or a Rod

The shop-made welding bracket in Figure 15-38 insures that the two parts being joined are held coaxially. This fixture may be used for pipe, tubing, rod stock, or twist drill extensions. There is an additional bail which fits onto the left-hand side of the fixture, but it has been omitted for clarity. The fixture can be made of steel or aluminum.

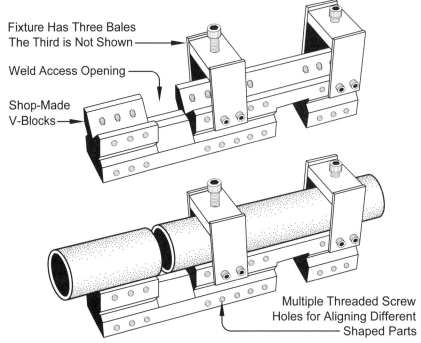

Fixture Has Three Bales
The Third is Not Shown

Weld Access Opening

Shop-Made
V-Blocks

Multiple Threaded Screw
Holes for Aligning Different
Shaped Parts

Figure 15-38. Fixture for welding or brazing pipe,
tubing, rounds, or large twist drill extensions.

Fixture for a Small Right-Angle Part

Figure 15-39 shows a fixture using a toolmaker's grinding vise and a V-block
for holding two parts for welding at a right angle. Though GTAW and brazing
torch heat are hard on precision tools—they can anneal and cause distortion to
hardened tools such as vises and V-blocks—there is no better way to
accurately position parts. Many welders dedicate some older grinding vises
and V-blocks for welding and brazing and mark them *For Welding Only*.

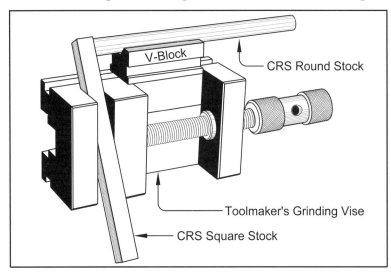

V-Block

CRS Round Stock

Toolmaker's Grinding Vise

CRS Square Stock

Figure 15-39. Using a toolmaker's grinding vise and a V-block
to position parts for a right-angle weld or braze joint.

Securing Work for Brazing or Welding Miters

When a workpiece is either too big or cannot be easily moved, the fixturing methods shown in Figure 15-40 can be used to hold a joint at the precise angle needed. These two positioning methods require no precision tooling and can be assembled in the field.

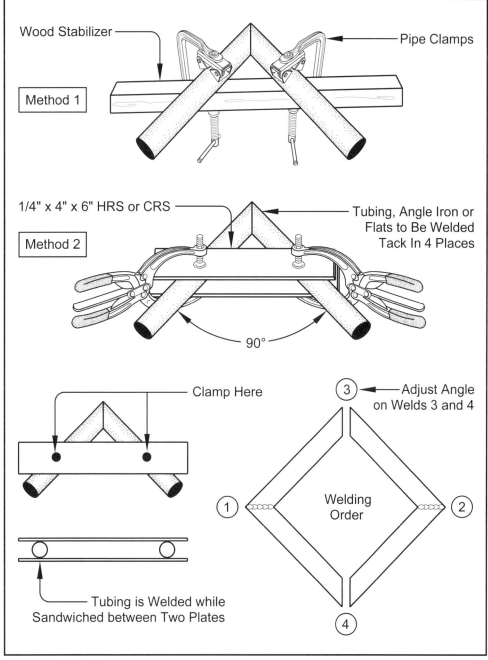

Figure 15-40. Two methods for positioning tubing, angle iron or flats for brazing or welding precise right angles.

Flange Flattening Fixture

Figure 15-41 (top left) shows the part to be made, but weld shrinkage causes the flat bottom plate of the part to dish when it is welded to the threaded flange. Clamping the plate in this simple fixture when welding and as the weld cools keeps the bottom plate flat. The stainless steel washer became dished when it was punched out, but as shown in Figure 15-41 (top right and bottom right) this dishing is used to advantage. In order to put clamping pressure on the plate close to the weld, the washer is placed on the fixture with the dish-shape upward. The notches in the washer can be made with a file, a bandsaw, or with a milling cutter.

A CRS fixture base is threaded to accept four hold-down screws. The flange base of the workpiece is aligned over the threaded holes in the fixture base, then the washer goes on and the workpiece base and washer are screwed tightly to the CRS fixture base. The threaded flange, which fits inside the dished washer, is tack welded and then welded. The CRS fixture base keeps the bottom plate flange of the part flat.

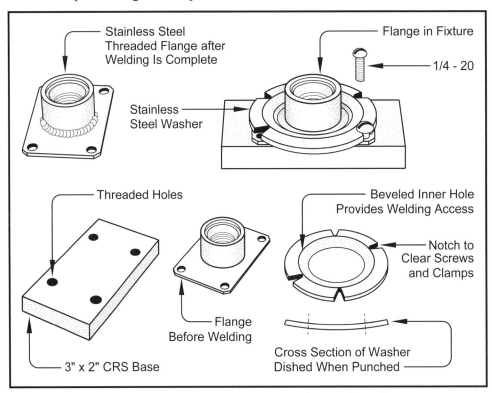

Figure 15-41. Using a welding fixture to keep a flange flat.

Chapter 16

Pipe & Tubing

In theory there is no difference between theory and practice.
But in practice, there is.
—Yogi Berra

Pipe vs. Tubing

The terms pipe and tube are often thought of as interchangeable, but they are not. Pipe usually has much thicker walls than tubing, and these thicker walls allow pipe to accept threads and still have enough metal remaining to provide adequate wall strength to handle fluids under pressure. Tubing, because it has thinner walls, cannot be threaded.

Another difference is that pipe from $^1/_8$–12" diameter is specified by its *Nominal Pipe Size (NPS)* based on a *Standardized Outside Diameter (OD)* and by its *Schedule*, which specifies its wall thickness.

In the 1920s, when the *American Standards Association* standardized this sizing system, the OD was chosen as a baseline so that pipe with a standard OD—and a wall thickness typical of that time—would have an *Inside Diameter (ID)* approximately equal to the nominal pipe size (NPS). Today, though, there is no relationship between existing wall thicknesses, ODs, and nominal pipe sizes. However—just to confuse everyone—these nominal sizes and standard ODs remain in use as the "Standard." Because of this odd system, exact pipe dimensions must be determined from tables.

Since all pipes of the same NPS have the same OD, they all accept the same size threaded fittings regardless of their wall thickness. For a given NPS, the OD stays fixed and the wall thickness varies with increasing schedule numbers. As a result, the ID for a given NPS *decreases* with the increasing schedule size because the wall thickness of the pipe takes up more room. In general, the larger the schedule number, the higher the pressure the pipe can withstand. There are more than a dozen schedule numbers, although not all schedules are available in all pipe sizes. The most commonly used wall thickness is Schedule 40.

Pipe schedule numbers do not indicate pressure capacity because each NPS of the same schedule has a different wall thickness. The schedule must be calculated on the wall thickness for the particular pressure and application. Now, to confuse everyone even more, the terms *Standard (Std.)*, *Extra-Strong (E.S.)*, and *Double Extra-Strong (D.E.S.)* are used to describe wall thickness. Figure 16-1 and Table 16-1 show how these terms fit in with pipe schedules.

Tubing wall thickness is specified in inches or *Manufacturer's Sheet Metal Gauge*. Generally, decimal inches or Sheet Metal Gauge numbers are used for square or rectangular steel tubing for structural or mechanical applications. Decimal inches are also used for round steel and stainless steel tubing designed for fluid transport. Round tubing is usually stocked in outside diameter increments of $^1/_{16}$ inch.

There are more than a dozen different thickness gauge schemes (or tables) listed in engineering handbooks. Some are obsolete, some are not used in the U.S., some apply only to ferrous or only to non-ferrous metals, and others only apply to wire diameter. As you can see, there are many opportunities for confusion. If in doubt which table to use, specify pipe wall thickness in decimal inches.

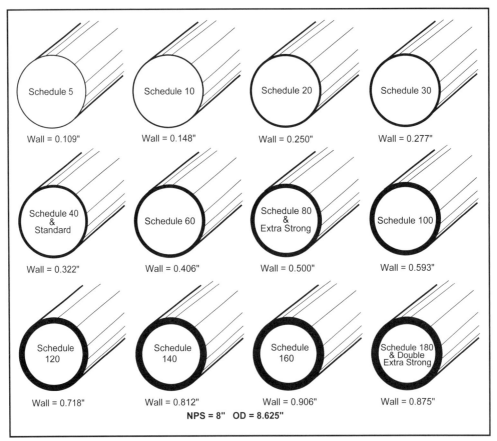

Figure 16-1. Pipe wall thickness comparisons based on schedule number.
Note that all these pipes have the same OD of 8.625 inches, but varying ID with its schedule.

Standard Pipe Sizes

Table 16-1 compares the nominal and actual OD.

Standard Pipe Sizes															
NOMINAL		Actual O.D. (inches)	PIPE SCHEDULES WALL THICKNESS												
NPS (inches)	DN (mm)		5	10	20	30	40 & Std	60	80 & E.S.	100	120	140	160	180 & D.E.S.
1/8	6	.405	.035	.049			.068		.095					
1/4	8	.540	.049	.065			.088		.119					
3/8	10	.675	.049	.065			.091		.126					
1/2	15	.840	.065	.083			.109		.147				.187	.294
3/4	20	1.050	.065	.083			.113		.154				.218	.308
1	25	1.315	.065	.109			.133		.179				.250	.358
1 1/4	32	1.660	.065	.109			.140		.191				.250	.382
1 1/2	40	1.900	.065	.109			.145		.200				.281	.400
2	50	2.375	.065	.109			.154		.218				.343	.436
2 1/2	65	2.875	.083	.120			.203		.276				.375	.552
3	80	3.500	.083	.120			.216		.300				.437	.600
3 1/2	90	4.000	.083	.120			.226		.318					.636
4	100	4.500	.083	.120			.237	.281	.337		.437		.531	.674
4 1/2	115	5.000					.247		.355					.710
5	125	5.563	.109	.134			.258		.375		.500		.625	.750
6	150	6.625	.109	.134			.280		.432		.562		.718	.864
7		7.625					.301		.500					.875
8	200	8.625	.109	.148	.250	.277	.322	.406	.500	.593	.718	.812	.906	.875
9		9.625					.342		.500					
10	250	10.750	.134	.165	.250	.307	.365	.500	.500	.718	.843	1.000	1.125	
11		11.750					.375		.500					
12	300	12.750	.165	.180	.250	.330	.375	.562	.500	.843	1.000	1.125	1.312	
14	350	14.000		.250	.312	.375	.375	.593	.500	.937	1.093	1.250	1.406	
16	400	16.000		.250	.312	.375	.375	.656	.500	1.031	1.218	1.437	1.593	
18	450	18.000		.250	.312	.437	.375	.750	.500	1.156	1.375	1.562	1.781	
20	500	20.000		.250	.375	.500	.375	.812	.500	1.280	1.500	1.750	1.968	
24	600	24.000		.250	.375	.562	.375	.968	.500	1.531	1.812	2.062	2.343	
26		26.000		.312	.500		.375		.500					
28	700	28.000		312	.500	.625	.375							
30	750	30.000		.312	.500	.625	.375		.500					
32	800	32.000		.312	.500	.625	.375		.500					
34		34.00		.312	.500	.625	.375							
36	900	36.000		.312		.625	.375		.500					

Table 16-1. Standard pipe sizes and wall thicknesses.

Tubular Products Overview

Figure 16-2 outlines an overview of the common types of pipe and tubing by application and by name. The *F* beside an application means that the pipe or tubing is for fluid handling and the *S* means it is for structural applications.

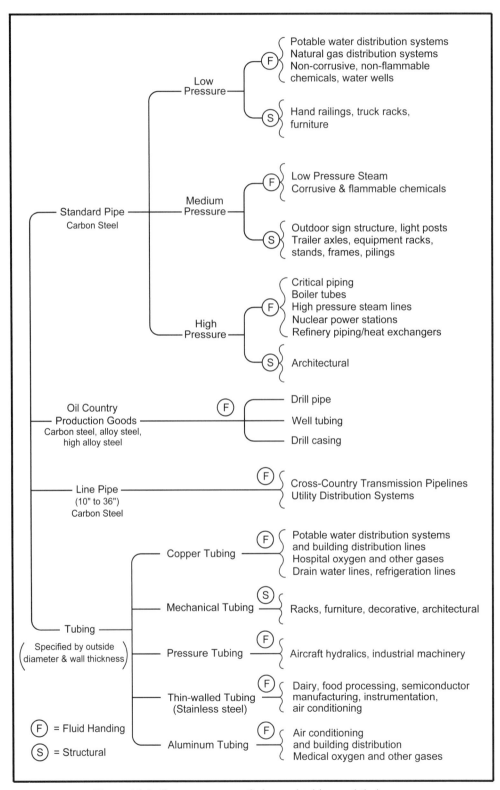

Figure 16-2. Common types of pipe and tubing and their uses.

Manufacturing Processes

The two principal pipe manufacturing processes are *welded seam* and *seamless*. Welded seam pipe manufacturing begins with a roll of flat steel which is cut into strips and then, with the help of heat and a series of rollers, the steel strips are formed into a tubular shape. To complete the pipe, the longitudinal seam is electrically welded closed. See Figure 16-3 (top).

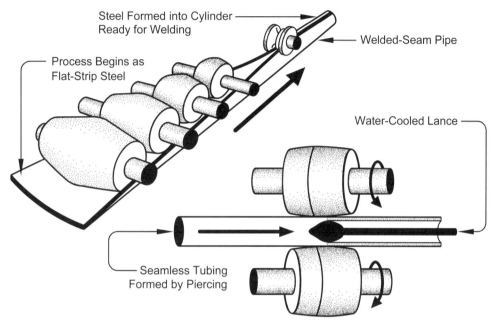

Figure 16-3. Forming a cylinder from strip metal for manufacturing welded-seam pipe (top), and forming seamless tubing by piercing a billet (bottom).

Seamless pipe and tubing manufacturing begins with a billet, or solid cylinder of metal, which is heated and pierced, as illustrated in Figure 16-3 (bottom). The process is then completed by one of two methods:

• Enlarging the resulting cylinder to form a pipe or a tube.

• Extruding the pierced billet through a die to form a tubular shape using heat and hydraulic pressure.

Pipe Welding Advantages

Welding is used for the majority of large-diameter pipe joints since it is more cost effective than using threaded joints. All sizes of pipe and structural pipe joints can be welded. Although the majority of pipe is used for fluid transport, pipe is also widely used for structural and load-carrying applications.

The advantages of pipe welding are:

• Cost savings from eliminating joining fittings and threading pipe.

• Reduction of fluid-flow resistance and turbulence. Welded pipe has smoother interior walls and therefore less turbulence than with threaded-joint pipe. See Figure 16-4.

- Easier to repair than threaded pipe because damaged sections of pipe can be cut out and new sections welded in.

- Higher strength, better vibration resistance, and greater leak-resistance than threaded joints.

- Easier to slide insulation over pipes because there are no protruding joint fittings to get past.

- More welded pipes can be installed in less space than with threaded fittings because with threaded pipe fittings additional "swing" room for wrench-tightening the fittings must be added.

Studies have shown that the labor time to thread or weld $1\frac{1}{4}$" pipe are about the same, but as pipe diameter increases, welding gains a strong cost and time advantage. For example, on a 6" diameter pipe, welding takes only about half the time as threading. In addition, the equipment and personnel needed to move around a pipe length to thread it, align it, and make it up, become more of a problem as pipe diameter increases. Also, with welding, the pipe only needs to be brought into alignment once.

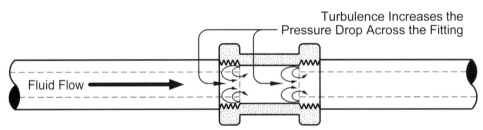

Figure 16-4. Turbulence generated by the step where the pipe meets the fitting.

Welding Procedure Specifications & Welder Qualification

A *Welding Procedure Specification (WPS)* sets down the required welding variables and conditions for a specific application to assure repeatability by properly trained welders. The ultimate objective is to design a WPS and, through testing, prove that the weld produced by the WPS has the characteristics needed to meet the requirements of its specific application and relevant governing code. Some codes include pre-qualified WPSs, so if the welder follows the WPS recipe, welds made with it will meet the code and the welder does not have to qualify the weld design. Some codes do not provide a WPS and state only the testing parameters the weld must pass to be acceptable. This leaves the welder to develop his own WPS for the application. All critical pipe welding requires a WPS. Some of the typical welding variables included in a WPS are:

- Type of base metal.
- Pipe diameter.
- Wall thickness.
- Edge preparation.

- Welding process and its electrical characteristics: polarity, current, voltage, travel speed, wire-feed speed and electrode diameter.
- Filler metal or electrode.
- Preheat conditions.
- Post-weld heat treatment.
- Shielding gas, if any.
- Weld type (groove, fillet, butt or lap).
- Welding position(s).

Only welders who have proven they can make a satisfactory weld following the relevant WPS should be allowed to make critical welds where life and property will be threatened should a weld fail. Such a welder is *qualified* to perform a weld to that *specific* WPS when he has passed a welding test.

Pipe Welding

The typical steps for pipe welding are:

1. Cut the pipe to length.
2. Prepare the pipe ends by cleaning, grinding, wire brushing, or beveling.
3. Preheat the pipe to bring it up to the proper temperature.
4. Insert consumable backing rings and spacers, if any are needed.
5. Position the pipe against the next length of pipe or fitting to which it will be welded so the joint has proper and equal root spacing.
6. When using GTAW and *not* using an insert, protect the backside of the weld from atmospheric contamination with inert gas, usually argon.
7. Apply tack welds to secure the pipes and grind the tack welds.
8. Perform the weld.
9. Perform the post-weld heat treatment, if required.
10. Perform a visual and non-destructive testing (NDT) examination.

Each of these steps will be detailed later.

Pipe Cutting

Table 16-2 lists the methods used to cut carbon steel pipe to length.

Type of Pipe	Cutting Method
Steel pipe 3" diameter or smaller	Manual wheeled pipe cutter, or Wheeled pipe cutter operating in powered threading machine, or Portable bandsaw, or Oxyfuel cutting
Steel pipe over 3" diameter	Oxyfuel cutting, or Abrasive cutoff saw

Table 16-2. Cutting methods for carbon steel pipe.

Cutting Steel Pipe with Oxyacetylene

When cutting small diameter pipe with oxyacetylene, the torch remains in the vertical position at all times. Here are the steps outlined in Figure 16-5:

1. Make a cut from the 12 o'clock to the 9 o'clock position.

2. Make another cut from the 12 o'clock position to the 3 o'clock position.

3. Rotate the pipe a half-turn and make a cut from the 12 o'clock position to the 9 o'clock position.

4. Make the final cut from the 12 o'clock position to the 3 o'clock position.

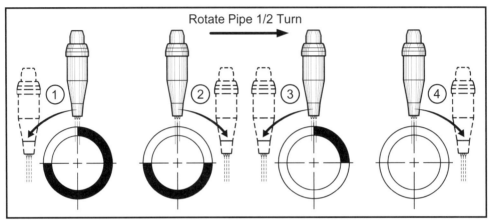

Figure 16-5. Four steps for cutting small diameter pipe with an oxyfuel torch. The torch is held in the vertical position.

Cutting large diameter pipe requires that the torch axis remain pointed at the center of the pipe and angled to make a bevel. Because larger diameter pipes are heavy, the pipe is not rotated, instead the pipe remains stationary and the torch is rotated around the pipe's circumference. See Figure 16-6.

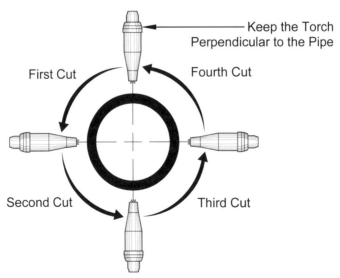

Figure 16-6. Cutting large diameter pipe with an oxyfuel torch. The torch is held at an angle to cut a bevel in the pipe.

Edge Preparation

Edge prep provides access for the welding process to melt and fuse the full depth of the pipe wall, not just the upper portion. Usually the pipe diameter determines what edge prep is required.

- Pipe up to 2" in diameter requires no edge preparation except for squaring and cleaning with an abrasive flap wheel or a wire brush.

- Pipe over 2" in diameter requires edge preparation, which means cleaning, grinding, or brushing, and then beveling.

Common pipe edge preparations are shown in Figure 16-7.

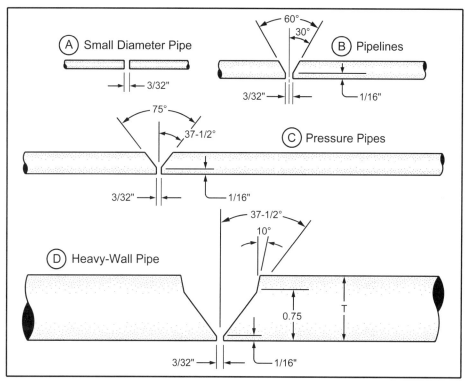

Figure 16-7. Common pipe welding edge preparations. Typical applications are (A) small-diameter pipe, (B) pipelines, (C) pressure pipes, (D) heavy-wall pipe.

Joint Preparation

Additional factors must be considered when choosing the type of joint preparation needed:

- Kind of joint loads—tension, compression, shear, or torsion.
- Level of joint loading and type of loading—static or shock loads.
- Thickness of the pipe and its type metal.
- Welding position.
- Skills of the welders.
- Trade-offs between joint preparation, filler metal, and welding labor costs.
- The applicable WPS and/or governing code will specify joint preparation.

Simple bevels are usually applied with either an oxyacetylene torch or with an air- or motor-driven beveling tool. Many welders prefer to grind the oxyacetylene bevel smooth *before* starting to weld, but applying the entire bevel with a grinder is too slow for production work, so this technique is usually limited to repairs. Although oxyacetylene cutting torches may be hand-held, there are fixtures that clamp onto the pipe end and provide a track to keep the torch in alignment as it rotates around the pipe. These tools may be hand-held or motor-driven. Most large diameter pipe comes with a factory-applied edge preparation.

Pipe Alignment Tools
Figure 16-8 shows several pipe clamps designed to coaxially align and pull together the two sections of pipe to be welded.

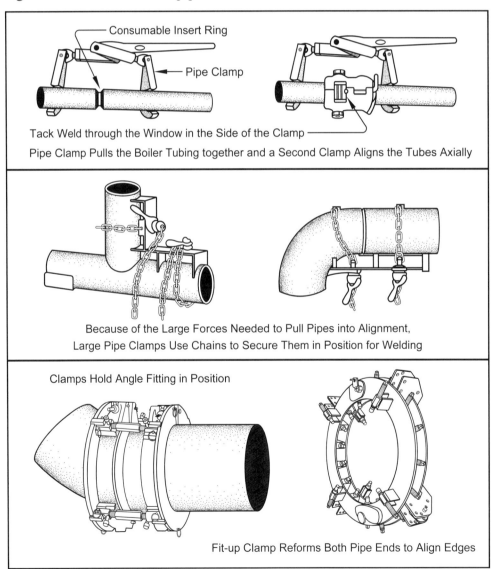

Figure 16-8. Alignment tools for welding pipe.

Some alignment clamps are lever-operated, some have screws, and others are air or hydraulically driven. Most alignment clamps fit over the outside of the pipes, but in pipeline work they may go inside the pipes. Many alignment clamps not only align the pipe ends and correct for root spacing, they also pull the pipe sections together and apply force to the pipes to correct for out-of-roundness.

Consumable Insert Rings

Consumable insert rings are essential when making GTAW welds with both manual and automatic equipment. Used for both piping and tubing, consumable insert rings protect the inside, or backside, of the weld from the atmosphere. They take the place of filling the pipe or tube with inert gas to do the same thing. Because of the cost of inert gas or the difficulty of confining the gas within the section of pipe being welded, particularly in large diameter pipes, weld inserts are a good alternative. Consumable insert rings have two other benefits:

- Aligning the pipe ends and automatically setting the root gap.
- Reducing root bead cracking.

Figure 16-9 shows typical insert ring cross sections, while Figure 16-10 shows a combination insert ring and backing ring.

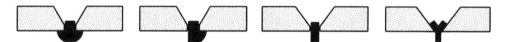

Figure 16-9. Four designs of consumable insert rings in cross section.

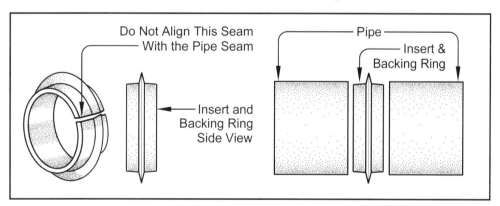

Figure 16-10. Combination insert and backing ring.

Preheating Pipe for Welding

The *preheating* of pipe is done with rosebud oxyfuel torches, but resistance and induction heating methods are also used because they offer more precise temperature control than torches.

Preheating is necessary to assure that heat energy put into the weld is not drawn away to the surrounding cold metal, preventing proper fusion and creating a defective weld. Raising the weld metal and the surrounding metal to 100–300°F *before* welding is usually enough to insure a good weld.

Additionally, because preheating reduces temperature differentials between the weld zone and the surrounding metal, stresses from expansion are reduced, as is the tendency of cracking and distortion. Preheating also helps entrapped gases, especially hydrogen, escape from the weld metal.

The welding process, the electrode used, and the pipe metal will dictate, through the WPS, the preheating temperature needed. Temperature-indicating crayons, portable pyrometers, or thermocouples determine when the metal is at the proper temperature for welding.

Tacking

Tacking is the application of temporary welds in the joint root area. These welds hold the pipes in alignment for welding. For pipe, usually four $^3/_4$–2" welds at 90° intervals are used. When the actual joint welding is performed these tacks are fused into the weld joint.

Tack welds should be placed away from weld bead starts and stops. Place the tacks so the torch will encounter them only *after* the arc has fully stabilized and is generating maximum heat. This insures that the tack weld metal is fully remelted into the main weld bead. Beginning a weld on a tack can lead to discontinuities and weld failure. See where to start the weld in Figure 16-11.

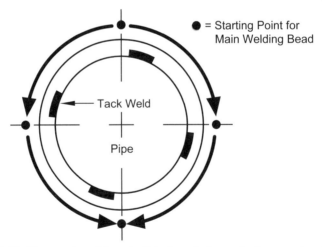

Figure 16-11. Place tack welds out of starts and stops of subsequent weld passes.

Both the start and end of any weld bead is weaker than the weld applied after the arc and the heat flow to the surrounding steel has stabilized. To remove these weaker sections, the root-pass tacks, which are to be remelted into the final weld bead, are ground down, or *feathered*, by grinding their ends away until only the stabilized portions of the bead remains.

In critical welds, each tack weld must be feathered using a narrow grinding wheel that fits inside the weld groove to reach the root. See Figure 16-12. Feathering insures a slag-free weld and complete and uniform remelt of the tack weld with the root-pass weld.

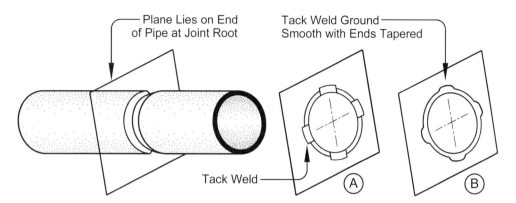

Figure 16-12. Cross-sectional end-view of tack welds:
(A) as welded and (B) after feathering with a grinder.

Types of Weld Passes

There are four different types of weld passes:

- The *initial pass* or *root pass* is done after the tack welds. It provides a solid basis for the remaining weld beads and shields the back of subsequent beads from atmospheric contamination. The size of the root-pass bead must be large enough to sustain shrinkage stresses without cracking.

- The *second pass* is often called the *hot pass*. Its purpose is to get slag inside the root-pass metal to float to the surface of the hot-pass bead so the slag can be removed by grinding or chipping. Also, the hot pass insures complete edge fusion between the root-pass metal and the base metal. Less metal is actually deposited during the hot pass than on subsequent filler passes. To accomplish this, the heat energy (welding current) going into the hot pass is usually set slightly higher than the remaining passes. Note that many welders speak of "burning out the slag" on the hot pass. This statement is not true. The steel of the pipe will burn before the slag will. The hot pass merely makes the slag accessible for removal.

- The *filler passes* or *intermediate passes* are those weld beads applied after the tacks and before the cover pass.

- The *cover pass* is the last welding bead applied and should have a neat appearance and a slight crown of about $^{1}/_{16}$" and not more than $^{1}/_{8}$" to reinforce the weld.

To minimize the accumulation of weak spots, each weld bead should start and stop at a different location from the bead over which it is deposited. See Figure 16-13. When properly done, this sequence of root pass, hot pass, filler passes and cover pass will produce a *full penetration weld* that is just as strong as the pipe itself, possibly stronger. Note that not all pipe joints need this entire weld sequence because either they operate at a relatively low pressure or because their failure is not critical.

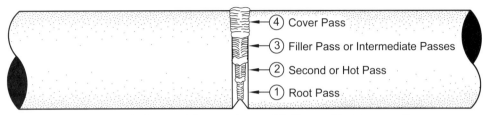

Figure 16-13. Sequential passes in a weld. Pipes with thinner walls,
like Schedule 40 pipes, typically require only a root pass and a cover pass.

Grinding & Chipping

Grinding is done on the root pass to remove slag, reduce the high crown of the
root pass, and to leave a groove. This groove assures that the hot pass will be
performed on sound metal and leave no voids. Do not skip the grinding step;
it is essential to achieve a full penetration weld. See Figure 16-14. Chipping
or wire brushing is also essential and should be done on all remaining passes
to remove flux.

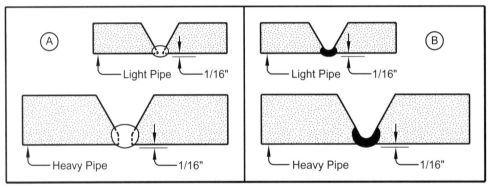

Figure 16-14. Root-pass welds on light and heavy-walled pipe:
Root passes before grinding (A) and after grinding (B).

Excessive Reinforcement of the Cover Pass

Too much of a crown on the cover pass makes the entire weld zone a
constrictor ring and creates excessive stress between the weld and pipe metal
as each responds to temperature changes, a potential cause of failure. Figure
16-15 shows a properly sized cover pass sequence.

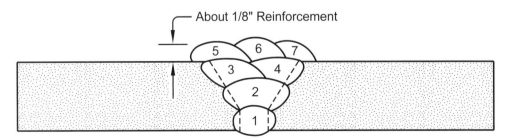

Figure 16-15. Properly sized cover pass reinforcement sequence.
Weld passes numbers 5, 6. and 7 are cover passes.

Maintaining Interpass Temperature

The temperature between weld passes, the *interpass temperature*, should not fall below the preheat temperature. Maintaining interpass temperature is needed to:

- Reduce residual stresses.
- Allow trapped gases to escape.
- Prevent heat from being drawn away into the surrounding cold metal which prevents complete joint fusion.

Besides the interpass temperature required in the WPS, there may also be a maximum temperature requirement. If the heat buildup exceeds this maximum, wait until the temperature falls, and then proceed with the weld.

Typical Pipe Welding Processes

The Welding Procedure Specification (WPS) indicates what weld procedure is required. Table 16-3 shows typical welding processes for carbon steel pipe.

Pipe Diameter (inches)	Wall Thickness	Welding Position(s)	Welding Process
4" or less	Standard	All	OFW
Up to 12"	Standard	All All	SMAW GMAW
4–12"	Standard & Heavy	All	GTAW (root)/SMAW
4" and larger	Thin & Standard	All downhill All up or downhill All up or downhill	SMAW FCAW GMAW
4" and larger	All	All uphill Rolled (1G) Rolled (1G) Rolled (1G)	SMAW GMAW (root) GMAW (root)/FCAW
All sizes	All	All	FCAW GTAW (root)/FCAW GTAW (root)/GMAW

Table 16-3. Typical carbon steel pipe welding processes.

Pipe Welding Tools & Accessories

- *Shop-made double-V base pipe holder* – If you need to align two pipes accurately for welding but do not have a commercial pipe-welding fixture, tack together two lengths of angle iron to form a double V-base as in Figure 16-16. Note that most applications will require either a series of these fixtures or a longer fixture than the one shown.

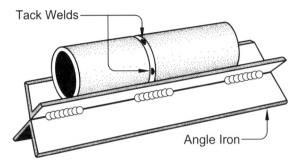

Figure 16-16. Shop-made welding fixture constructed
from angle iron holds pipes in alignment.

- *Pipe jacks* – One of the tools designed for handling pipe which can greatly simplify welding is the *pipe jack.* Used in pairs, pipe jacks support the work at a comfortable height for hand-held bandsawing, for pipe-end weld preparation, and for welding. The screws on the jacks permit the pipe to be easily leveled. Two pairs of pipe jacks can precisely position two lengths of pipe for assembly. See Figure 16-17.

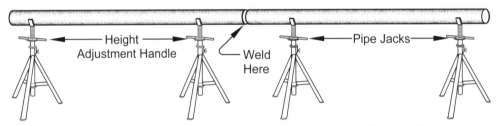

Figure 16-17. Pipe jacks align pipe and get the work off the ground.

- *Pipe rollers* – Another tool that simplifies welding are *pipe rollers,* which are also used in pairs. As shown in Figure 16-18, pipe rollers permit an assistant to rotate the pipe while the welder completes the weld. By slowly turning the pipe, the entire weld can be made in the horizontal rolled position. This method requires less skill and is faster than leaving the pipe in a fixed position and having to weld up, down and upside down.

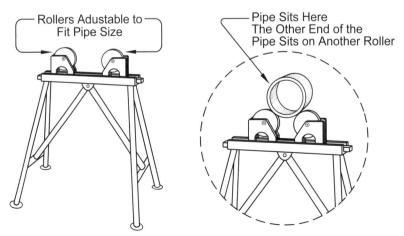

Figure 16-18. Pipe rollers can be shop-made or purchased.

- *The Curv-O-Mark contour tool* – This tool, shown in Figure 16-19 (left), locates any angle on the outside of a pipe just by setting the adjustable scale to the desired angle. To do this, place the tool on the pipe to the *level* position as indicated by the bubble level and strike the built-in center punch to mark the point. Figure 16-19 (right) shows the contour tool locating the exact top, or 0° position, the 60° position, and the 90° position.

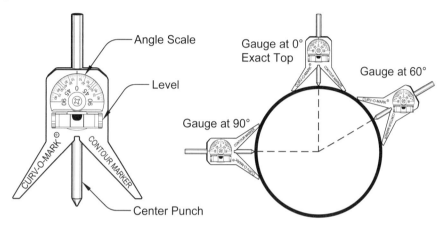

Figure 16-19. Curv-O-Mark contour tool for locating angles around a pipe.

- *Wrap-Arounds* – When cutting a large diameter pipe to length and you need to mark your cut line, use a *wrap-around*. This is a length of thin, flexible material—vinyl, fiber or cardboard—that is wrapped around the pipe $1\frac{1}{2}$ times as shown in Figure 16-20. Adjust the wrap-around so that the second, overlapping layer lies squarely over the first layer, then hold the wrap-around tightly with one hand and mark the cut line with the other. A typical wrap-around is $\frac{1}{16}$" thick by $2\frac{1}{4}$" wide by 48" long.

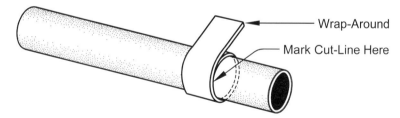

Figure 16-20. Using a wrap-around to mark a square cut line on a pipe.

Fishmouths & Saddles

A *fishmouth* is the shape cut into the *end* of one piece of pipe or tubing so it meets and fits tightly against another pipe to make a strong weld. A *saddle* is the opening cut into the *side* of a pipe to allow fluid from a fishmouthed pipe to flow into the pipe. See Figure 16-21. The saddle opening can be based on a pattern or drawn by hand inside the outline of the fishmouth. The gap between the two pipe or tubing lengths should not exceed the diameter of the electrode wire used to make the weld. Making a fishmouth on tubing is sometimes called *notching*.

Although a saddle can be cut into tubing, most tubing for fluid transfer is joined by fittings and not by using fishmouths and saddles.

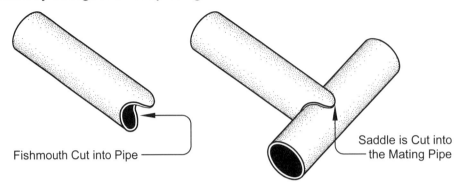

Figure 16-21. A fishmouth on the end of a pipe (left) and a fishmouthed pipe and its mating pipe in place ready for welding (right).

Several common ways to cut a tubing or pipe fishmouth are:

- Hacksawing and hand filing.

- Beginning the saddle on a bench or pedestal grinder and making the final adjustments with a file.

- A hand-operated nibbling tool is another way to make a fishmouth in tubing, although some operator skill is needed. A nibbler cannot be used on pipe because pipe walls are too thick for this tool.

- A hole saw or large end mill in a milling machine also works well on either pipe or tubing.

- Using a dedicated fishmouthing hole-saw, such as the commercial tool shown in Figure 16-22, works well and saves time.

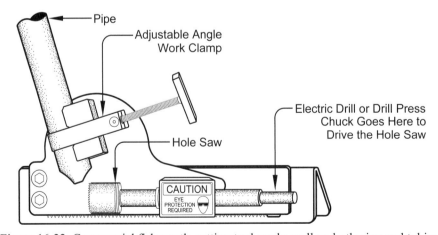

Figure 16-22. Commercial fishmouth-cutting tool works well on both pipe and tubing.

- *Using the Pipemaster tool* – This commercial tool, shown in Figure 16-23, functions much like a miter guide when cutting house molding. The thin rods mounted around its periphery capture the fishmouth shape needed and lock it in place for transfer to the work.

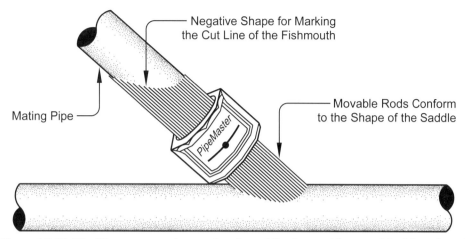

Negative Shape for Marking
the Cut Line of the Fishmouth

Mating Pipe

Movable Rods Conform
to the Shape of the Saddle

Figure 16-23. The Pipemaster tool capturing the saddle shape with moveable thin rods and then the negative of this shape—the fishmouth—is transferred to the mating pipe or tube.

- *Cutting saddle joints* – On pipes too large in diameter to use forged steel fittings, welders can use saddles, Ts, Ys and other similar joints which are fabricated by cutting and joining the pipe material itself rather than using fittings of a separate material. These fabricated fittings, as shown in Figure 16-24, are frequently factory-made, but are sometimes field-made.

The patterns for making the intersection of two or more pipes can be determined using a drafting technique called *descriptive geometry*. Luckily, there are easy-to-use commercial template kits available made of heavy paper, cardboard, plastic or fiber that do the same thing. The welder selects the proper template, positions it on the pipe, and traces the outline onto the pipe. Patterns for both fishmouths and saddles are available.

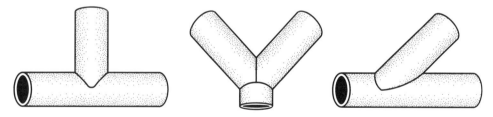

Figure 16-24. Three designs for saddle joints on large diameter pipe.

- *PC programs for cutting fishmouths and saddles* – There are PC programs that are especially useful when a pipe intersection cannot be made using stock fittings. The welder inputs the sizes and angles of the intersecting pipes, and then the program generates a printed pattern and a numerical table to mark the cutting lines. These programs are fast and easy to use and produce cutting patterns for any combination of pipe sizes and intersection angles. Here are the types of patterns this software can easily generate:

  - Pattern for the intersection of two pipes located at any angle as shown in Figure 16-25 (A).

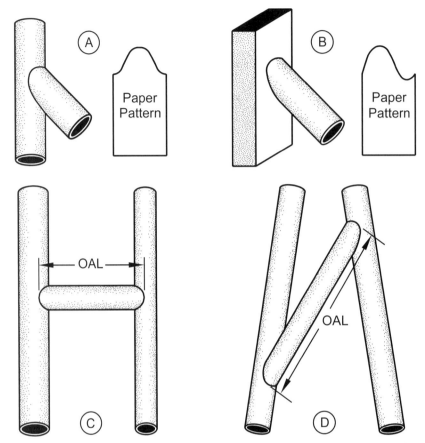

Figure 16-25. PC-based software can generate cutting patterns and related calculations to solve these types of pipe intersection problems.

- Pattern for the intersection of a pipe with a flat surface. This is useful in structural applications as well as pipefitting. See Figure 16-25 (B).

- Overall pipe length (OAL) and cutting pattern for each pipe end for adding a new pipe between two existing parallel pipes of any diameter. See Figure 16-25 (C).

- OAL and cutting pattern for each end for running a pipe between two existing pipes at any angle. See Figure 16-25 (D). This problem is common in structural pipe fabrication.

Holding Tubing in a Vise

Holding thin-walled tubing, especially stainless steel, in a vise when cutting or fishmouthing it with a hacksaw or file distorts the tubing, and the vise jaws damage the smooth sides of the tubing. Here is how to avoid this damage:

1. Insert a tightly-fitting wooden dowel inside the tubing end to prevent the tubing from collapsing in the vise.

2. Then place soft jaws over the steel jaws of the vise to prevent marring the tubing. The soft jaws are usually made of aluminum, copper, lead, or plastic and they can be commercially or shop-made. See Figure 16-26.

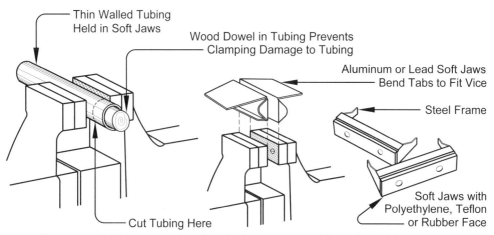

Figure 16-26. Using a wooden dowel when clamping thin-walled tubing prevents crushing the tubing. Also, soft jaws prevent the vise jaws from marring the pipe or tubing.

Pipe Joint Fittings

Smaller pipes are usually joined by using *socketed* or *sleeved* fittings, which are also called *lap-collar* or *sleeve-collar* fitting*s*. Shown in Figures 16-27 and 16-28, both socketed and sleeved fittings use fillet welds. When the pipe is large or when the application has higher pressures than a lap collar or a socketed fitting can handle, forged steel fitting with factory-beveled ends are used as in Figure 16-29. Pipes too large for factory-forged fittings usually have joints fabricated from the pipe material itself.

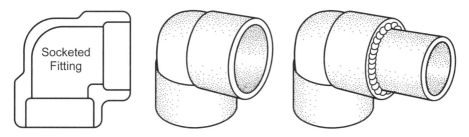

Figure 16-27. Socketed and forged steel 90° elbow in cross section (left), before welding (center), and with fillet weld on pipe (right).

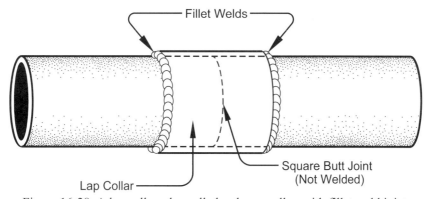

Figure 16-28. A lap collar, also called a sleeve collar, with fillet weld joint.

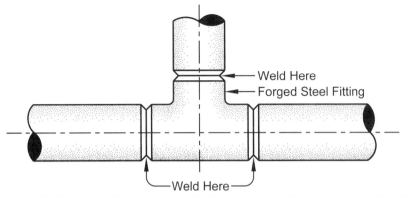

Figure 16-29. Forged steel fitting on beveled pipe ends for high-pressure applications.

Joining Two Equal-Diameter Pipes

In a structural application which will be subjected to torsion, tension or shear, two things are needed: coaxial alignment of the pipes and a strong welded joint. To do this, use an inner alignment pipe as in Figure 16-30 (A) to insure that the pipes are in alignment, and then make a full penetration weld, a weld which is as strong as the pipe itself. Note that the inner pipe in Figure 16-30 (A & B) is for proper axial alignment only, not strength.

In Figure 16-30 (B) a damaged section of pipe is being replaced using an inner alignment pipe. In Figure 16-31, because the pipe is cut with a V-notch and fits snuggly against its mate, no inner alignment pipe is needed. This is a good method to use when the pipes carry fluids and an inner alignment pipe would create additional flow resistance from turbulence around the joint.

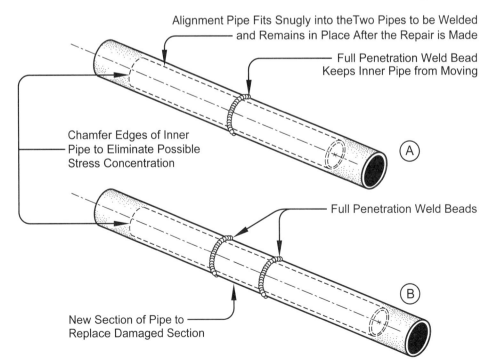

Figure 16-30. Two structural pipe splicing methods which will assure concentric alignment.

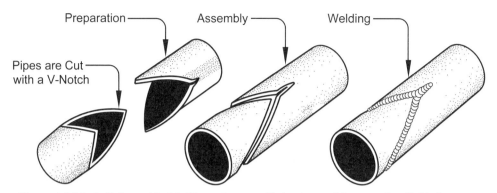

Figure 16-31. Splicing with this V-notch type of joint is good for carrying fluids because there is no inner alignment pipe which could cause flow resistance or turbulence.

Welding One Pipe Inserted into Another

Many times in structural applications, one pipe must be inserted into another and welded in place. Figure 16-32 shows four different methods for doing this from the weakest method to the strongest.

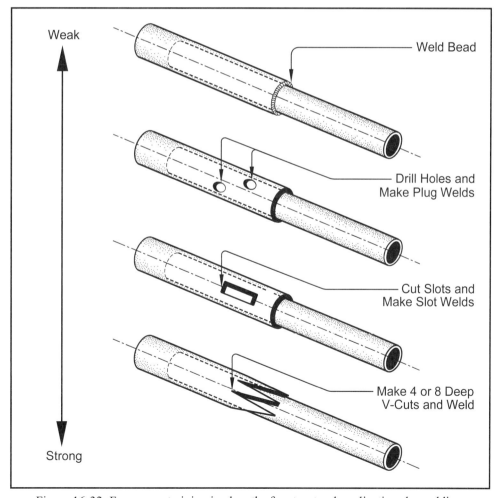

Figure 16-32. Four ways to join pipe lengths for structural applications by welding.

Joining Methods for Tubing

Copper tubing is most often soldered with an air-acetylene, or an air-propane torch using tin-lead or tin-antimony solder. Tubing for potable water *must* use tin-antimony or one of the other lead-free alloy solders. Building and fire codes require that copper tubing carrying medical gases be brazed. Both soldered copper tubing and brazed copper tubing use the same fittings.

Steel and steel-alloy tubing, usually used in high-performance structures such as racing cars and light aircraft rather than for fluid handling, can be oxyacetylene, GMAW, or GTAW welded. Because these applications are structural and load-bearing, careful fitting of the tubing is essential. Gaps should be no larger than the diameter of the electrode used for welding.

Aluminum Tubing Repairs

There are a couple of approaches for repairing punctured aluminum tubing:

- The damaged section can be cut out and a new length spliced in with flared or compression fittings.

- The hole can be covered with a soldered patch as shown in Figure 16-33. First, file the punctured area so it is flush with the rest of the pipe's surface, then clean the aluminum pipe with emery cloth down to clean metal. Using steel wool, solder and a propane torch, tin the aluminum tubing by heating the tubing and scrubbing the steel wool back and forth over the pipe. You will need to hold the steel wool with long-nose pliers.

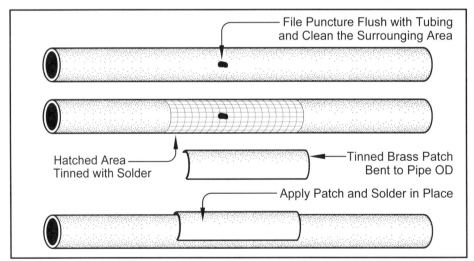

Figure 16-33. Using tin-lead solder to make temporary repairs in punctured aluminum tubing.

After several passes, the aluminum will become tinned or wetted with solder. A 50–50 tin-lead or 60–40 tin-lead alloy works fine. Cut out a brass patch and form it to fit on the pipe. To tin the patch, clean the brass down to fresh, shiny metal, heat the patch with a torch and apply solder. It will quickly become covered with solder, or tinned. To place the patch, heat both the patch and the tubing, and apply the patch over the tinned area of the aluminum tubing. This is only a temporary repair.

Repairing Buried Copper Tubing

If an underground copper tubing water line develops a leak, as in Figure 16-34 (A), and needs to be repaired, the problem is how to install a new section of line and seat it properly when each end of the copper line is firmly embedded in the soil and cannot be moved *horizontally*. Here is how to proceed:

Locate the section of the pipe to be replaced and cut it out, as in Figure 16-34 (B, C & D). Purchase a short length of special diameter patch tubing which is made to just slip *over* the *outside* of the existing tubing. Solder completely around both ends of the patch as in Figure 16-34 (E).

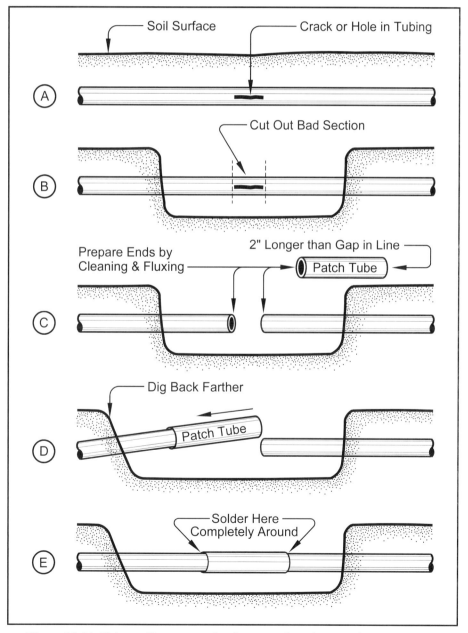

Figure 16-34. Using a slip-over patch tube to repair underground copper tubing.

Avoiding Miters & Fishmouths in Structural Pipe

In many instances we can side step fitting miters and fishmouths by using the method shown in Figure 16-35 (A). In lower stress applications, the method shown in Figure 16-35 (B) works well and saves the trouble of fishmouthing.

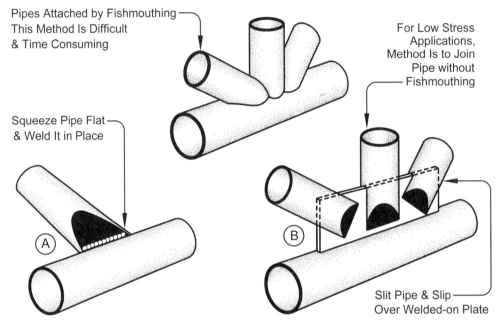

Figure 16-35. The fishmouthing at the top of the figure is difficult and time consuming. The bottom of the figure shows the two methods to avoid fishmouthing.

Chapter 17

Metallurgy

An old error is always more popular than a new truth.
—German Proverb

Introduction

The hardening and softening of metals using heat is essential to making the tools and products of the modern world—everything from kitchen knives to jet engine blades. This chapter focuses on steel because it is the most common metal that is heat-treated and the most used metal in a welding shop.

Metallurgy and heat-treatment is a complex subject. Metallurgists, physicists, and heat-treatment specialists often spend a lifetime in its study, so it is not possible to completely cover this subject in the space of these pages. For critical or complex applications, professional guidance and equipment are essential.

However, this chapter will cover several important heat-treating tasks that can be performed in a welding shop with limited equipment, including the heat treating of several types of tool steels. This chapter explains the advantages and limitations of the equipment needed to perform these processes, along with common heat-treatment problems and their solutions.

Because welding exposes metal to high temperatures, welders need to recognize the importance of metallurgy. Only by examining the crystalline nature of metals and how heat can cause changes in their crystal structure and properties can we understand how metals react to heat and the practical aspects of heating, quenching, tempering and annealing steel. In addition, this chapter explains the iron-carbon diagram, the steel classification systems, the effects of alloying elements, and compares the different types of cast iron. With this background we can then understand how to reduce the negative effects of welding heat on metals.

Section I – Iron-Based Metals

Iron & Iron Alloys

The element iron (Fe) is the most common element on the planet, making up much of the inner and outer core of the earth. Iron makes up all but a few percent of the contents of iron-based metals. These metals have very different properties depending on their carbon content.

Table 17-1 lists the major iron-based metals, their carbon content, characteristics and applications.

Material	Carbon (%)	Characteristics & Applications
Wrought Iron	< 0.008	Very soft material, no longer made commercially. The security bars and window grills described as wrought iron are really mild steel, not wrought iron.
Low-Carbon Steel	< 0.30	Also called *mild steel* or *machine steel*. Does not contain enough carbon to be hardened, but can be case hardened. Used for parts which do not need to be hardened such as nuts, bolts, washers, sheet steel and shafts. Also used in structural steel and machine tool frames.
Medium-Carbon Steel	0.30–0.60	May be hardened. Used where greater tensile strength than low-carbon steel is needed. Used for tools like hammers, wrenches and screwdrivers, which are drop-forged and then hardened.
High-Carbon Steel	0.60–1.7	May be hardened. Also known as *tool steel*. Used for cutting tools, punches, taps, dies, reamers and drills.
High-Speed Steel (HSS M2)	0.85–1.5	May be hardened. Used for lathe and milling machine cutting tools and drills. Retains hardness and cutting edge at red heat. This is the least costly member of the HSS family. See Table 17-2 for details on the alloying elements of all the high-speed steels (HSS).
Cast Iron	> 2.1	Cannot be hardened, but available in several forms with differing properties. Used for machine tool bases and frames, stove grates and many decorative products.

Table 17-1. Carbon content of major iron-containing metals.

Table 17-2 lists the main alloying elements found in the high-speed steels that are most often used in the manufacture of lathe and milling machine cutting tools and drills.

HSS Steel Alloy	Percent					
	Carbon	Chromium	Tungsten	Molybdenum	Vanadium	Cobalt
M2	0.85	4.00	6.00	5.00	2.00	—
M42	1.10	3.75	1.50	9.50	1.15	8.00
T1	0.75	4.00	18.00	—	1.00	—
T15	1.50	4.00	12.00	—	5.00	5.00

Table 17-2. Principal alloying elements of high-speed steels.

Section II – Why Steel Hardens

Structure of Metals

During the hot liquid state metals have no particular structure. There is no orderly, defined or regular organization among their atoms. However, at lower temperatures the atoms have less energy, move less rapidly, and atomic forces arrange them into particular structures or patterns called *crystals*. All metals and alloys are crystalline solids. Figure 17-1 shows the three most common crystal structures in metals and alloys.

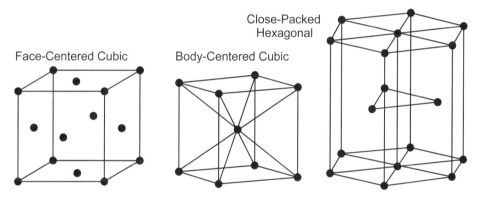

Figure 17-1. The three most common crystal structures in metals and alloys.

Behavior of Pure Iron

As its temperature is gradually increased, the crystalline structure of iron changes, but still remains solid. Here are the crystal structures of pure iron at different temperatures:

- From room temperature to 1670°F, it is *body-centered cubic*.
- From 1670°F to 2535°F, it is *face-centered cubic*.
- From 2535°F to its melting point of 2800°F, it is again *body-centered cubic*.

These changes between different crystalline structures for *pure iron* are not particularly important by themselves. However, if we add as little as one percent carbon by weight to iron, we make the iron-carbon alloy called *steel*. Because of the changes that occur in pure iron's crystalline structure at different temperatures, an entirely new series of microstructures form. These microstructures not only have radically different physical properties from pure iron and from each other, their structures can be modified by applying heating and cooling cycles.

Iron-Carbon Diagram

The best way to visualize the interaction of iron and carbon and the resulting microstructures they form is to study the *iron-carbon diagram*. This diagram shows the microstructures that exist by adding a small percentage of carbon to iron at various temperatures.

Looking at this diagram in Figure 17-2, we can see that:

- Steel exists for iron-carbon alloys with between 0.2 and 2 percent carbon.
- Iron-carbon mixtures with more than 2% carbon are called *cast iron*.
- Depending on its carbon content and temperature, there are six different microstructures as represented by areas on the diagram:
  - Pearlite and ferrite
  - All pearlite
  - Pearlite and cementite
  - Austenite and ferrite
  - All austenite
  - Austenite and cementite

- In the areas showing two microstructures simultaneously, the structure changes from all one microstructure, to a mixture of the two, to all the other microstructures as we move along the bottom axis, which represents the carbon content. For example, in the "pearlite and ferrite" area of the diagram (bottom left), the structure goes from all ferrite at 0.2% carbon, to a mixture of ferrite and pearlite, to all pearlite at 2% carbon. This means that in the areas of two microstructures, both the microstructure and its properties are altered with changes in its carbon content.

- Austenite exists only at a temperature of 1333°F or higher and can contain up to 2% carbon.

Characteristics of Iron

- *Ferrite* is a solid solution of small amounts of carbon (> 0.02%) in iron. It has a body-centered structure and it is magnetic.
- *Cementite* contains about 6.69% carbon. Because our iron-carbon diagram cuts off at about 5% carbon, no region of pure cementite appears. Only structures that contain cementite-pearlite and cementite-austenite mixtures appear.

- *Pearlite* is made up of alternating layers of ferrite and cementite. Pearlite *always* contains 0.77% carbon. Steels and cast irons with more than 0.77% carbon will form mixtures of cementite and pearlite. Steels with pearlite are usually ductile.

- *Austenite* is a solid solution of carbon in gamma iron, which can dissolve up to 2% carbon. Austenite is never stable below 727°F in carbon steel. Above 1418°F it will not be attracted to a magnet.

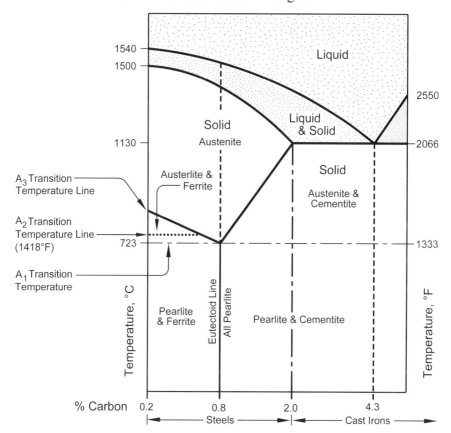

Figure 17-2. Iron-carbon diagram.

This iron-carbon diagram has a special qualification: *it represents only the microstructures that exist at equilibrium.* This means that the diagram shows the structure when the alloy has been allowed to remain at a particular temperature long enough for it to reach its final condition where no further microstructure changes can occur no matter how much longer the alloy is held at this temperature. This equilibrium qualification exists because the changes in crystalline structure do not occur instantly, but take time to complete. Rapid temperature changes can "freeze" a microstructure, so it continues to exist at a lower temperature than it would at equilibrium. This rapid change is the key to hardening steel.

Figures 17-3–17-5 show microphotographs of several of these structures.

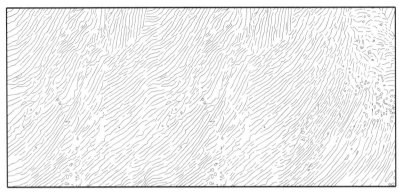

Figure 17-3. Microphotograph at 500 × of Pearlite.

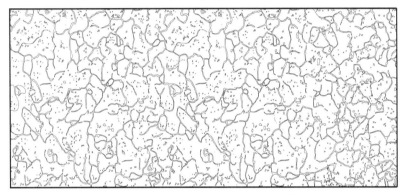

Figure 17-4. Microphotograph at 500 × of Ferrite.

Figure 17-5. Microphotograph at 500 × of Martensite.

Hardening Steel

Martensite is missing from the iron-carbon diagram because it is an entirely new structure. This iron-carbon structure forms if austenite is cooled rapidly, or *quenched*, and the iron-carbon diagram shows only structures that are formed when iron and carbon are cooled slowly. Quenching causes a distorted crystal structure that has the appearance of fine needles. *This martensite is the structure that hardens steel.*

For example, suppose we begin with a steel alloy of 0.77 percent carbon content. The vertical line in the iron-carbon diagram marked "all pearlite" represents this steel alloy. Here is how to form martensite:

Begin by raising the temperature of this alloy above 1333°F, called the alloy's *critical temperature*. Although the alloy remains solid, its microstructure changes from pearlite to austenite. The conversion process from pearlite to austenite is not instantaneous and can take from several seconds to several minutes to complete. In practice, steel is usually raised 100°F above the critical temperature to make sure the conversion to austenite is complete. The black V-shaped area in Figure 17-6 shows the temperature range used for forming austenite. If we slowly lower the temperature of austenite, its previous crystalline structure, pearlite, re-forms and no martensite forms. However, if we *quench* the austenite by lowering its temperature rapidly from above its critical temperature to below 752°F by immersing it in water, brine or oil, an entirely different microstructure called martensite forms.

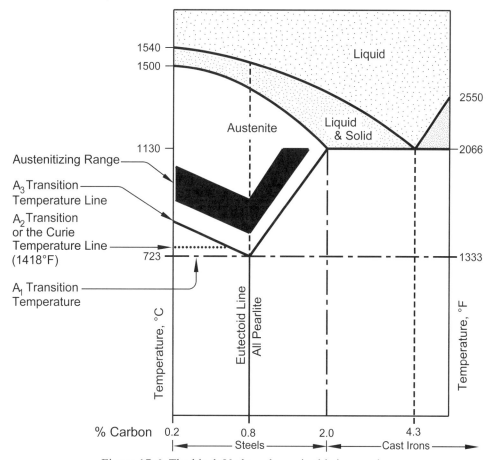

Figure 17-6. The black V-shaped area in this iron-carbon
diagram shows the temperature range used to form austenite.

This occurs because the rapid temperature drop associated with quenching does not give the carbon time to move out of the austenite crystal structure in an orderly fashion to form pearlite. This results in martensite, a new structure that is very hard—much harder and stronger than pearlite. Martensite is also less ductile and is generally too hard and brittle for most engineering applications. But, by tempering martensite, we can restore some ductility without significantly reducing its strength. Martensite is very useful for metal cutting tools, punches, dies and many other applications.

The formation of martensite is what makes the hardening of steel possible. Hardening steel also increases its abrasion resistance, an important factor for many parts subjected to wear. There is no partial transformation associated with martensite, it forms or it doesn't. However, only the parts of a section that cool fast enough will form martensite. In a thick section, it will only form to a certain depth, and if the shape is complex, it may only form in small pockets.

Other Alloying Elements for Steel

Carbon is just one of the alloying elements for steel. Additional alloying elements are manganese, tungsten, cobalt, nickel, vanadium, molybdenum, chromium and silicon. Usually two or more alloying elements are added to further modify the steel's properties. These elements can affect the final hardening, quenching, tempering characteristics, hardness at high temperatures, and nearly all other mechanical properties. All high-performance alloys contain some of the above alloying elements. If we extend the iron-carbon diagram to include other alloying elements, the diagram becomes very complex, but the basic concepts of hardening, tempering, and annealing remain the same.

Section III – Practical Steel Hardening & Tempering

Equipment for Hardening Steel

The two most common methods for hardening steel require the following equipment:

- A metallurgical furnace which is heated by either gas or electricity, and is usually electronically controlled.

- An oxyacetylene torch or gas-air torch. Torches are inexpensive, but have many limitations for heat treatment.

A metallurgical furnace is far superior to a torch. First, it provides excellent control of maximum temperature as well as cooling rate, and second, it allows larger parts to be hardened. Larger parts must soak in the furnace for a considerable length of time at the maximum temperature before the entire part, especially the interior, reaches hardening temperature. Using a torch to heat a part with a varying cross section or sharp corners is difficult and the heating is uneven. Sometimes larger parts must be heated for one hour per inch of thickness to insure that the entire part reaches the same temperature. This is virtually impossible to do with a torch, and certainly not practical. *Larger parts must be sent to a heat treater.*

The largest part that can be hardened using just torch heat is somewhere between the size of a pack of cigarettes and a 1-2-3 block, but success depends on the skill of the operator. The objective is to bring the entire part up to the same temperature without over heating it, which can lead to cracking.

Determining When Steel Has Reached Critical Temperature

There are five methods:

- Electrical instruments, called *pyrometers*, accurately determine the temperature of the steel. Furnaces are usually equipped with pyrometers and hand-held instruments are also available. Using a pyrometer is the most accurate temperature measuring method.

- At about $10 each, a much less expensive alternative is a *temperature-indicating crayon,* as shown in Figure 17-7. The two common brands are Tempilstiks from Tempil, Inc. and Temp Sticks from LA-CO Markal. These crayons are slightly less than $\frac{1}{2}$" in diameter and 5" long. Each crayon melts within one percent of its marked temperature value. Over 100 different temperature crayons spanning temperatures from 100–2500ºF are available and make measuring work surface temperatures quick and easy. The work surface has reached the indicated temperature when the crayon melts and glides along the work. The weakness of this measuring device is that the work can be *above* the indicated temperature and the crayon will still melt and glide, so crayons are best used when approaching the desired temperature from below that temperature.

Figure 17-7. Temperature indicating crayon in its holder with pocket clip.

- Test the work with a magnet to determine when it is no longer magnetic. This assures that the work is at or above the critical temperature. On the left side of Figure 17-6, the horizontal line of small dots indicates this transition from a magnetic to a non-magnetic structure. This is called the *Curie Temperature.* When the steel cools, it will become magnetic again.

- Visually observe that the work is cherry red in subdued light. This is the traditional blacksmith's method and has been used for centuries, even before the hardening process was understood.

- Use a *non-contact temperature probe*. These devices use a red laser pointer to pinpoint the spot where the temperature is measured. Temperature readings are accurate within a few degrees. See Figure 17-8.

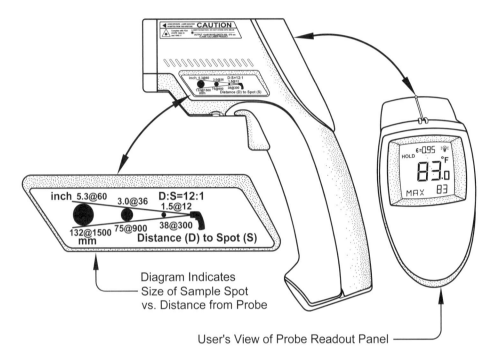

Figure 17-8. Non-contact temperature probe incorporates a laser pointer to indicate the temperature measurement location.

Quenching Steel

The quenching of steel is done by immersing the work in oil, water or brine. Slow cooling in still air is also used.

Different quenching media, also called *quenchants*, have different cooling rates. For a particular steel alloy, too fast a cooling rate will crack or warp the work, too slow a cooling rate and martensite will not form. The quenching media must match the particular steel alloy and the size—heat capacity—of the work.

Each type of steel has its own optimum quenchant. Steels are often designated by their quenchant such as O-1 (oil quench), W-1 (water quench) and A-2 (air quench). As shown in Figure 17-9, cooling in still air is relatively slow, oil is faster, and water and brine are even faster.

Brine cools faster than water because no steam pockets develop around the work. Steam pockets, which form in water, both retard heat transfer and disrupt uniform heat transfer over the part. This can lead to uneven hardening and warping or cracking.

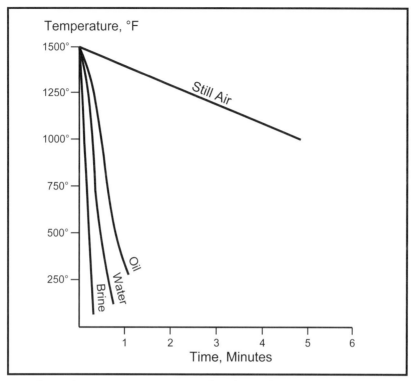

Figure 17-9. Work temperatures versus cooling time using still air, oil, water and brine.

The important interaction between the work and the quenching media is how quickly and evenly heat is transferred from the work to the media. There is no chemical interaction.

Some excellent quenchant choices are:

- Mineral oil.

- Automatic transmission fluid (ATF).

- Synthetic motor oil.

- Commercial quenching oil.

- Johnson & Johnson's Baby Oil, a perfumed mineral oil, will also work fine if you don't mind the scent. Unscented mineral oil is sold over the counter at drug stores as a laxative and is commercially available in 55-gallon drums. Avoid vegetable oil because it can quickly go rancid and cause what machinists and welders call *Monday morning stink*.

Oil Quenching Precautions

- Quench outside or in a well ventilated area so you are not exposed to the resulting fumes.

- Use a steel container, not plastic, which can melt through or catch fire.

- Have a metal cover for the container handy if the oil should catch fire. An even better solution is to have a *hinged* cover on the container to flip shut in case of fire. Also, keep a Class B fire extinguisher close by.

- Monitor the oil temperature and keep it well below its flash point. This flash point temperature is readily obtained from the Manufacturer's Safety Data Sheets (MSDS) or the on the Internet.

- To avoid splashes, use a metal open-mesh basket, rack or screen to lower the part into the oil and to retrieve it later. Such an arrangement also avoids having your face and arms over the oil during the quench.

- If the oil has been heated in a previous use, stir the oil to assure an even temperature distribution before quenching another part.

Quenching Problems & Solutions

- *Uneven hardening* – If a part does not harden evenly when oil quenched, it means that there was not enough oil volume to cool the part uniformly. Cooling rate is determined by the *temperature difference* between the work and the oil. When the quenching oil absorbed heat from the part, the temperature of the oil increased, slowing the cooling rate.

- There are two rules of thumb to determine minimum oil volume:

  - Provide enough quenching oil volume to equal 20 times the volume of the part.

  - Another approach, shown in Figure 17-10, is to provide a large enough oil volume and oil container to leave a space between the side of the part and the side of the oil container equal to 2 times the largest dimension of the part.

  The most even quenching occurs when the work is symmetrical and is dunked up and down vertically in the quenchant, not swirled around in a circle. Swirling cools the front, or leading face, of the part more than the trailing edge, causing warping or cracking. Even if the workpiece is symmetrical, if it has a shape that disturbs the even flow of quenchant around it, the workpiece will not harden evenly. An example of such a part would be a rod with stepped diameters or a cylinder with a larger disc-shaped projection. Regions of the part not cooled fast enough will fail to harden properly. Commercial heat-treat companies have quenching tanks with special spray heads designed to reach these hard-to-cool spots.

- *Not all of the parts hardened* – When several identical parts are individually hardened, the initial ones harden properly, but the later ones do not. This is because the oil, or other quenching medium, was heated up by the initial parts, which slowed the cooling rate for the later parts. To avoid this problem, use a larger volume of quenching medium. The best quenching results are usually obtained when the quenching media is 70–100°F, although some alloys require a higher starting temperature for the quenching fluid. Also, if the temperature of the quenching fluid is too low, it can cause the metal to warp or crack.

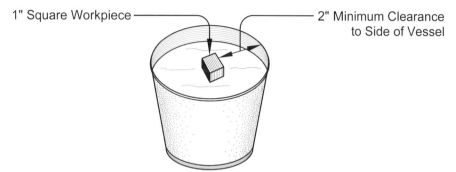

1" Square Workpiece

2" Minimum Clearance to Side of Vessel

Figure 17-10. Quenching container with adequate side clearance to assure proper cooling.

- *Uneven air quenching* – This happens when the work is set on a fire brick to air cool. The upper part of the work hardens, but the bottom does not. This is because the brick prevented the bottom from cooling rapidly enough to form martensite—so it did not harden. The solution is to bend a piece of sheet metal into a Z-shaped cooling stand and use it set on edge to cool the work, as in Figure 17-11. This method allows the top and bottom of the work to cool evenly.

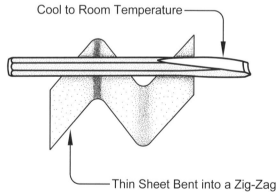

Cool to Room Temperature

Thin Sheet Bent into a Zig-Zag

Figure 17-11. Shop-made Z-shaped sheet metal cooling stand.

Tempering Steel

Tempering, also called *drawing*, reduces the brittleness of hardened steel and removes the internal strains caused by quenching. It is performed by reheating hardened steel to a temperature *below* its critical temperature, and then allowing it to cool to room temperature at a controlled rate. This allows some carbon to escape from inside the martensite structure, reducing its brittleness.

Nearly all hardened steel must be tempered or it will shatter in use. By using different tempering cycles, we can control the balance between hardness and brittleness in the final product.

Tempering temperatures range from 350–1350°F, but most steels are tempered at about 450°F. For a given steel, the higher the peak tempering temperature, the lower the hardness. See the tempering temperature chart in Figure 17-12. Because controlling peak temperature is much more important when tempering than when heating prior to quenching, just using a torch for tempering is crude and not usually satisfactory.

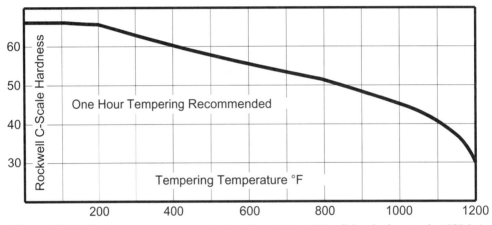

Figure 17-12. Hardness versus tempering for Starrett No. 496, oil-hardening steel, AISI 0-1.

Tempering Methods

There are several ways to temper steel:

- A metallurgical furnace provides the best process control. The work is heated to the tempering temperature and allowed to cool slowly. In some instances, wrapping the work in 0.002-inch thick stainless steel foil and sealing the edges by creasing them is used to prevent oxidation or scaling from forming on the work.

- In commercial heat-treating operations, the work is heated in oil, molten salt or lead baths. Sometimes the work is warmed, or preheated, then placed in the tempering bath. Other times the work is placed in a cold bath and the bath is brought up to tempering temperature. A pyrometer is used to control the bath temperature.

Tempering Colors

Oxides that form on the surface of steel above 420°F are called *tempering colors*. As shown in Table 17-3, specific colors are related to the maximum temperature seen by the metal. A skilled worker can use these oxide colors to determine when the work has reached a specific temperature. This is the same oxide that appears when a drill or lathe bit has been overheated, or *burned*, and a blue oxide appears on its surface. Tempering colors cannot be observed unless the work surface has been cleaned and polished *before* heat is applied.

Tempering Color	Degrees Fahrenheit	Tempering Color	Degrees Fahrenheit
Pale yellow	420	Light purple	530
Very pale yellow	430	Full purple	540
Light yellow	440	Dark purple	550
Pale straw-yellow	450	Full blue	560
Straw-yellow	460	Dark blue	570
Deep straw-yellow	470	Pale blue	590
Dark yellow	480	Light blue	610
Yellow-brown	490	Greenish blue	630
Brown-yellow	500	Light blue	640
Spotted red-brown	510	Steel gray	650
Brown with purple spots	520		

Table 17-3. Tempering colors and their temperatures for carbon steel.

When steel reaches even higher temperatures, the atoms in the steel become so excited they radiate light. For example, at 1652°F steel will glow a cherry red. These colors are used to judge work surface temperature during heating, forging and blacksmith work, but they are *not* oxide colors.

Another instance where colors are referenced in relation to tempering steel is when steel is surface-hardened, called *case hardening*. In case hardening, carbon is absorbed into a thin skin—the case of the work—resulting in beautiful oxide colors. Air is sometimes bubbled through the quenchant to enhance oxide color formation. These colors, such as gun-metal blue, are very desirable on firearm components, but they are relatively fragile and can be destroyed by polishing and by strong light.

Tempering Small Tools & Workpieces

There is a traditional method for tempering small tools and workpieces such as center punches and scribers.

Here is how it's done:

1. Clean and polish the end of the tool to be tempered so the oxides will be visible.
2. Heat a piece of scrap steel plate to red hot. The volume of the plate should be 30–50 times the volume of the work. The greater the volume, the better the results.
3. Remove the steel plate from the heat source and place it on a fire brick.
4. Put the tool to be tempered on the heated steel plate, placing the body of the tool on the plate with the end to be tempered hanging off the plate, as in Figure 17-13.

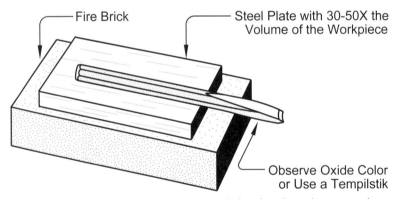

Figure 17-13. Tempering a part on a heated steel plate by observing tempering colors.

5. Heat will transfer from the steel plate to the work. The part of the tool on the plate will heat first, and the heat will gradually work its way out to the end overhanging the plate. Watch the polished portion on the end of the tool. When it reaches the proper oxide color, this indicates the correct tempering temperature has been reached.
6. Quench the part in water to stop the tempering process.

The tempered end of the tool will be harder than the body of the tool that sat on the steel plate. The tip of the tool will be blunted by the tempering process, but do not grind a final sharp point on the tool before the hardening and tempering is complete. The hardening, quenching, and tempering temperature cycle is illustrated in Figure 17-14.

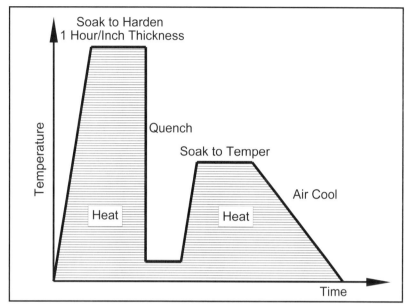

Figure 17-14. Hardening, quenching and tempering temperature cycle for carbon steel.

Hardening and tempering temperature data for different steels can be obtained from a couple of sources:

- The steel company or industrial supply house which sold the metal.
- Tables in *Machinery's Handbook.*
- The Internet.

Case Hardening

Case hardening results from carbon added on the surface gradually migrating deeper and deeper into the steel and increasing the carbon content. Case hardening is a three-step process consisting of (1) adding carbon to the outer skin of the metal, then hardening the portions with this additional carbon by (2) austenitizing the metal and (3) quenching the metal. The result is a hard outer skin around a softer and less brittle core. This hardened skin typically runs from 0.002–0.040" deep.

Here are the advantages of case hardening:

- Low-carbon steel, which cannot be hardened by austenizing and quenching, can be case hardened. In fact, it is the only way to harden low-carbon steel. Medium-carbon steel can also be case hardened, but high-carbon steels and alloys do not benefit from it.
- The depth of the case-hardened skin can be controlled by the carbon-addition cycle time, or when using a product like *Kasenit* the depth is controlled by the number of application cycles.
- A part made of one piece of metal has the benefit of having a hard outer skin and a resilient interior.

- Case hardening is a relatively tolerant process that does not require instrumentation and can be performed under primitive conditions.
- Case hardening is gentle on parts and works well on precision parts with sharp corners.
- Thin layers of colorful oxides, prized by firearms owners, form during case hardening. These oxides are usually just a few molecules thick so, as mentioned before, they are relatively fragile, easily destroyed by light, and cannot be polished without removing them.

Performing Case Hardening

Pack hardening and *Kasenit treatment* are the two types of case hardening variations of most interest to the welder. However, there are many other methods available in a commercial heat-treating operation.

Pack hardening is a traditional case hardening method used long before the actual chemistry of hardening was understood. Here is how it's done:

1. Carefully clean the steel of dirt, scale and fingerprints.
2. Place the workpiece inside a vessel with a source of carbon. Ashes from bone charcoal, leather or walnut shells are favorite carbon sources. Commercial carbon mixes can also be used.
3. With the work and the carbon source in contact with each other, the vessel is sealed to keep air away from the work. The vessel can be an iron box, ceramic or graphite crucible, or can be as simple as an unfired clay pot with a sealing cover.
4. The vessel is brought to a red heat in a fire or furnace for several hours depending on the depth of case wanted. This time and temperature permits carbon atoms to migrate into the outer layers of the work and form *austenite*. The inner work material is not affected because the carbon does not diffuse far inside the work.
5. After allowing the time needed to deposit the carbon and austenize the outer skin, place the entire contents of the vessel into water for quenching. The work may then be tempered if needed.

A widely available product, *Kasenit Surface Hardening Compound*, offers another approach to case hardening using sodium ferrocyanide.

Here is how Kasenit hardening is done:

1. Carefully clean the work of dirt, scale and fingerprints.
2. Heat the workpiece to 1652°F, a light red color. This may be done in a metallurgical furnace or with an oxyacetylene torch.
3. When using a torch, try to support the part so the pliers or tongs holding it do not prevent even distribution of heat. Supporting the work with several loops of soft iron wire may be better than pliers.

4. When the work reaches temperature, dip and roll it in Kasenit powder, which will melt and stick to the work. Make sure the part is completely coated because it is from this powder that the carbon is drawn to harden the work.

5. Heat the work for 2–3 minutes with an oxyacetylene torch, then chill it in water or oil to perform the actual hardening. Make sure your pliers are dry when picking up the work from the Kasenit. *Caution: The coating may flare up briefly when the flame is applied. Also, only use this product in a well-ventilated area.*

6. Repeat Steps 3 and 4 two or more times to increase the depth of the case hardening.

Section IV – Annealing Steel

Annealing vs. Tempering

Annealing is the reverse of hardening. Heating hardened steel *above* its critical temperature converts the martensite to austenite, and then slow cooling reforms pearlite or other soft microstructures leaving the steel in the annealed or softened condition. We can reform either pearlite or martensite as many times as we wish by reheating and adjusting the cooling rate. Fully annealing steel removes all residual stress whether it was induced by cold working, grinding, or by heat-treating operations.

The difference between *tempering* and *annealing* steel is that tempering allows some of the carbon trapped in the martensite to escape the martensite structure. This reduces brittleness, but still leaves the steel hardened and predominantly of martensite. Annealing converts the microstructure to austenite, and by slow cooling, converts all martensite to other softer structures, so no martensite remains.

Practical Annealing

Two major factors limit your ability to anneal steel:

• To completely anneal a workpiece, the entire part must be raised *above* its critical temperature. While this may be done easily with a torch for a part no larger than a cigarette pack, larger parts must be put into an oven or fire to heat thoroughly. Most welding shops do not have an oven.

• Equally critical to successful annealing is the ability to cool the part slowly. Most carbon steel can be annealed either in still air, sand, vermiculite or lime. These last three materials have no chemical interaction with the part, but are merely insulators to retard cooling. High-alloy steels are easy to harden, but hard to anneal. Annealing these alloys requires a very slow cooling rate, approximately 10–40°F per hour. It is difficult to achieve this rate without a metallurgical furnace because the

part must be maintained at temperature for hours for complete transition—
and annealing—to occur.

Annealing Previously Hardened Parts

When annealing a previously hardened part in a metallurgical furnace, sealing
the part in a stainless steel foil pouch will prevent the formation of surface
scale. Parts can be sealed in stainless steel foil or coated with hand soap to
retard surface oxidation. But the most important part of annealing, as
mentioned before, is the cooling rate.

For an example, when you try to anneal $\frac{1}{2}$" diameter ball bearings or other
small high-alloy parts, if the cooling rate is too high, the ball bearings
reharden when cooled. To avoid this problem, increase the mass of heated
material to decrease the cooling rate. This can be done by either heating more
ball bearings at the same time or by heating a larger piece of scrap steel with
the ball bearings. Ideally, the scrap should be more cube- than rod-shaped and
the scrap's volume should be 50–100 times the volume of the bearings.

Section V – Other Heat Applications

Here are some other uses for heat in the welding shop:

- Annealing copper and brass. This may be done in a furnace or an oven by
  heating the metal red hot and then quenching in water or air cooling. This
  process may be done repeatedly after each work-hardening cycle.
- Metal parts "frozen" together by corrosion can often be separated by
  heating the parts red hot and then quenching. The idea is to use heat to
  expand one portion of the assembly against another. Naturally, the heating
  and quenching is likely to destroy the parts' factory heat treatment and
  afterward may need additional heat treatment. Either a torch or a heat gun
  are good heat sources.
- Expanding parts prior to assembly with a torch or heat gun. Sometimes it
  is necessary to *heat* the outer part and *cool* the inner one in a freezer to get
  them to fit together. Do not apply torch heat to bearings or similar
  assemblies. To heat bearings, there are commercial kits that use the
  bearing as the secondary winding of a transformer. The electrical current
  circulating *inside* the bearing metal heats it evenly and safely.
- Heating parts with a torch greatly reduces the force needed for bending,
  especially in steel.

Section VI – Metal Fatigue

Metal fatigue is the development and gradual growth of a crack. After
repeated cyclic stress, this crack suddenly fractures, destroying the part. Metal
fatigue is a phenomenon of crystalline materials. Metal fatigue first became an

issue in the eighteenth century with the advent of the steam engine. Although engineers had enough understanding of physics and materials to design steam engine components to handle the anticipated *static* loads, the *cyclic* loads developed by the steam engine introduced these early engineers to metal fatigue, sometimes with catastrophic results. Even at two hundred revolutions per minute, over time a machine will see over 100 million load cycles. Before steam power, most metal structures were bridges or farm machines which were subject to few load cycles. Suddenly, metal fatigue was an issue.

Today 90% of all "in service" failures are fatigue failures, not stress-overload failures. Proper design prevents fatigue failures. Also, replacing critical parts after a set number of load cycles or hours of service prevents in-service failures. Periodic inspections can spot signs of fatigue failure *before* it occurs.

Most metal fatigue-induced failures occur at one-half to one-quarter of the maximum elastic load the metal can sustain under constant stress. In extreme fatigue cases, as little as one-eighth the maximum elastic load causes failure after enough load cycles. This is why even if a metal part is properly sized to carry its anticipated maximum loads, fatigue failure can eventually occur, causing anything from a minor inconvenience to property damage to loss of life.

How Fatigue Failure Occurs

Even though the result of fatigue failure is a sudden and complete breakage of the part, fatigue failure is a *progressive* failure. After beginning, it may take a very long time to reach complete failure.

Fatigue cracks begin where a geometric irregularity in the part, such as a hole, crack, scratch, sharp corner, or metallic defect, creates a *stress concentration*. Often this increase in stress occurs in a very small area. Although the average unit stress across the entire part cross section may be well below the metal's yield point, a non-uniform distribution of stresses causes the stress to exceed the yield point in some minute area. This results in *plastic deformation* and eventually leads to a small crack. This crack aggravates the already non-uniform stress distribution and leads to further plastic deformation. With repeated load cycles, the crack continues to grow until the cross section of the part can no longer sustain the load. The origin of the crack is on or near the part's surface because that is where stresses are greatest.

Each load cycle works to break the bonds between metal atoms and enlarge the crack. In general, these cracks split the metal's grains, rather than running along grain boundaries. This *intragrain fracturing*, which radiates from the failure's origin, creates a concentric ring pattern called *beach marks* after the pattern left by waves as they retreat from a sandy beach. See Figure 17-15 (left). When the crack becomes large enough that the remaining metal cannot sustain the stress, catastrophic failure occurs. This failure is *intergranular*, or between the grains, and leaves a different kind of pattern between the failed surfaces. The beach mark pattern is caused by uneven crack growth and the rubbing together of the sides of the crack as it develops.

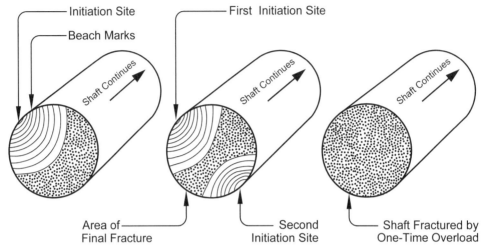

Figure 17-15. End view of a fractured shaft: Beach marks from fatigue crack growth (left), growth of a second fatigue crack (center) and shaft failure by one-time overload (right).

Fracture Interfaces

Because the semicircular-shaped beaching pattern inside the crack radiates from the crack's initiation point, we can determine its point of origin. Sometimes after one crack initiates, a second crack develops on the opposite side of the part as in Figure 17-15 (center). Another clue to understanding what caused a fatigue failure is that the plane of fatigue fracture is always perpendicular to the direction of maximum stress. By examining the ratio of the beaching pattern area versus the intergranular final fracture area, we can see how much margin of safety the part had initially. The greater the area of beaching, the more material the crack had to work through before failure. A failed part with a small beaching area had a smaller margin of safety than a similar part with a larger beaching area. Figure 17-15 (right) shows a failed part without beach marks, which indicates a one-time overload, not a fatigue failure.

Causes of Stress Concentrations

Figure 17-16 (top) shows a metal bar under stress which has no defects or irregularities. The stress trajectories represented by the dotted lines show stress divided evenly across the part so the average stress is the maximum stress. Figure 17-16 (bottom) shows a similar part under stress, but this bar has a notch or crack. The stress trajectories represented by the dotted lines "bunch up" around the tip of the notch. This bunching causes areas of stress concentration resulting in peak stress that is much higher than average stress. As the part is load-cycled, stress concentration in this area will cause a crack. The closer the spacing of stress trajectories, the higher the stress concentration and the higher the likelihood of failure.

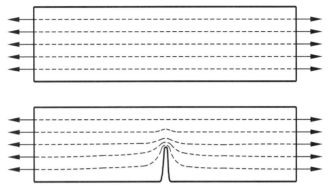

Figure 17-16. Stress trajectories in a flat bar under tension: Bar without defects (top) and a bar with a crack entering its side creating stress concentrations (bottom).

Adding a hole to a part changes the distribution of stress. In Figure 17-17 the peak stress level around the hole increases to 82.5 from the non-hole average of 25, an increase of about 2.5 times.

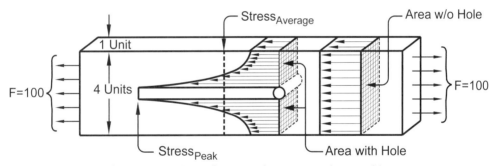

Figure 17-17. Stress increases in a rectangular metal bar under tension caused by the addition of a hole.

When a hole is added, two factors affect the stress levels in the above bar:

- The cross-sectional area of the bar is reduced from 4 area units to 3 area units, so Stress$_{Average}$ increases from 25 to 33.3 units. See Table 17-4.
- The hole disrupts the smooth flow of stress through the bar and produces stress concentrations at the edges of the hole. Unlike sections of the bar without holes, the average stress is no longer peak stress. In fact, the stress around a hole is about 2.5 times the average stress. This is called the *stress concentration factor* or *SCF*. Figure 17-18 shows typical stress concentrators and the modifications needed to reduce stress caused by abrupt shape changes.

Bar Cross Section	Area	Force	Stress$_{Average}$	Stress$_{Peak}$
No Hole	4	100	$\dfrac{F}{A}=\dfrac{100}{4}=25$	Stress$_{Average}=$ Stress$_{Peak}=25$
With Hole	3	100	$\dfrac{F}{A}=\dfrac{100}{3}=33$	Stress$_{Peak}=$ SCF $\times$ Stress$_{Average}=$ $2.5 \times 33.3 = \ \ 82.5$

All units are relative.

Table 17-4. Average and peak stress for cross sections of a bar under tension.

Mechanical engineering handbooks contain charts to estimate stress concentration factors for various part shapes. Usually holes, fillets, steps and sharp corners create stress concentrations from 1.2 to 3 times the average stress at the cross section. The increase of stress above average stress depends on the shape of the specific workpiece and the size, shape and location of the stress raiser.

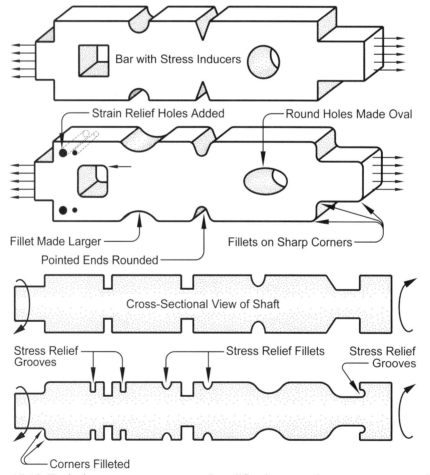

Figure 17-18. Typical stress concentrators and modifications to reduce stress concentrations. The upper two bars are in tension and the lower two shafts are in torsion.

Stress concentrations at the corners of a square hole can be much larger than the average stress, and small cracks and scratches that have sharp points have stress concentration factors between 100 and 1000. Shipbuilders learned about these factors the hard way, hence round port holes. Stress concentrations are more than enough to cause crack growth and fatigue failure.

Fatigue Life Factors

- Sharp corners and abrupt changes in shape create stress points.

- The larger the part, the greater the chance of fatigue cracks. This is because a greater volume of metal is under high stress, which results in a greater chance of residual stress increasing the stress. In calculating fatigue stress, residual stress is added to external stress.

- Type of stress loading—tension, bending or torsion—affects fatigue life.

- Surface finish, particularly scratches, scribe marks, machining tool marks and irregular points along a weld bead add sites of stress concentration. Removing surface scratches by polishing may be helpful, and if possible, place welds in low-stress and low-flex locations.

- Surface irregularities caused by rolling, forging or stamping processes create stress points on the part surface.

- Surface treatments like plating and grinding increase surface stress.

- Fine-grained metals, particularly high-strength steels, are more sensitive to surface finish than larger-grained, lower-strength metals.

- Corrosion attacks the metal surface and causes stress concentrations.

- Exposure to high temperatures usually reduces fatigue life.

- The same steel alloy test specimen exhibits the highest fatigue life when made as a casting, an intermediate life when the sample is rolled stock and stress is applied along the grain or rolling direction, and the lowest fatigue life when it is rolled stock and the stress is applied across the grain.

Predicting Fatigue Life

Plots of stress versus the number of load cycles, called *S-to-N curves* are the most common method of predicting fatigue life. Here is how the data for these curves is determined:

1. Multiple, identical samples are made up for testing and are fatigue tested. Depending on the application, the cyclic testing may be under tensile, flexure, or torsional loads.

2. Some samples are subjected to load cycles at high stress, some at low stress, and some in between. The number of cycles-to-failure is averaged.

3. Then an S-to-N curve is plotted. This curve shows the level of stress

below which the material has infinite life. Ferrous metals display a characteristic leveling off of the S-to-N curve and this point is called the *fatigue limit*. See the upper curve in Figure 17-19, which occurs at about 10^6 load cycles. Non-ferrous metals do not have this distinctive leveling off of the S-to-N curve as ferrous metals do, the stress which will take the part to 5 x 10^8 cycles before failure is taken as the level for infinite life. See the bottom curve in Figure 7-19.

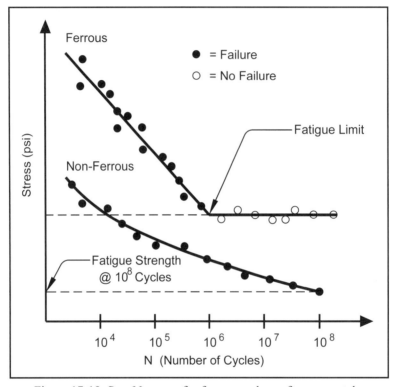

Figure 17-19. S-to-N curves for ferrous and non-ferrous metals.

Fatigue tests do have some important limitations:

- These curves predict fatigue life only for regular, repeated loading of the part and that may not be what the part really sees in service. One way to get around this problem is to specify a maximum number of service hours.

- Because S-to-N curves are specific to a particular stress ratio and surface finish, it may be hard to apply the test results to a particular part.

- S-to-N curves provide only the *average life* and many samples must be run to reach high confidence levels.

- Fatigue data obtained for a simple geometric shape may be hard or impossible to apply to a complex part. The only reliable solution may be to test the actual part in a fatigue machine.

Chapter 18

Power Supplies & Electrical Safety

Trouble is only opportunity in work clothes.

—Henry Kaiser

Introduction

All electrically-based welding processes require a power supply and the electrical characteristics of these power supplies need to match the requirements of each process. To help with this selection, this chapter covers power supply functions, output characteristics, power sources, designs and electrical safety.

Section I – Power Supply Functions

Welding power supplies have five functions:

- *To convert input power* from high voltage at low current to low voltage at high current. The voltage supplied by utility companies, usually 120–575 volts, is too high for welding processes that require voltages in the 20–80 volt range. Welding power supplies reduce utility voltage to within this required range and provide the ability to adjust the power supply's output to the welding process. Trying to weld directly from a power line would cause excessive current to flow, blowing fuses and melting welding cables.

- *To stabilize and regulate the arc with static voltage-vs.-current output characteristics* of the power supply so they match the respective welding process. This means that the arc is maintained even when the arc length changes as the electrode-to-work distance or the electrode wire length fluctuates during welding. If using the wrong output characteristics, small changes in the electrode-to-work distance can extinguish or short out the arc.

- *To adjust the dynamic—or transient—characteristics* of the power supply to rapidly changing arc conditions since big changes in ionization of the arc column occur in as little as a millisecond.

- *To convert 60 Hz AC to direct current, square waves, or to high frequency pulses* to make a specific process possible or to improve its welding properties. In some cases, these waveforms are essential to performing the weld. Older power supply designs merely convert AC to DC, but under microprocessor control many modern power supplies can modify their output nearly instantaneously.

- *To control shielding gas flow on GMAW, GTAW and plasma cutters and to control the wire-feed motor on GMAW and FCAW.* Not only do power supplies control the solenoid gas valve, more sophisticated machines provide both pre-flow and post-flow shielding gas control as set on the machine. Many power supplies also turn on the torch cooling water by energizing an electric valve.

To simplify a complex subject, this chapter examines welding power supplies by dividing them three different ways:

- *Input power sources* – Internal combustion engines or electric utilities.

- *Electrical output characteristics* – Static and dynamic responses.

- *Welding power supply designs* – Engine driven generators and alternators, transformers, SCRs, and transistors.

Section II – Input Power Sources

Internal Combustion Engines

Gasoline or diesel engines drive DC generators or alternators. The simplest arrangement is to have an engine-driven DC generator for SMAW, traditionally the most popular field process. See ❶ in Table 18-1 on page 492.

With the increasing popularity of GMAW and FCAW, constant-voltage engine-driven welding power supplies to support both of these processes became available. See ❷ in Table 18-1.

Older designs for engine-driven welding power supplies did not contain semiconductors, but modern ones do. Adding semiconductor diodes to an alternator provides both AC and DC outputs. For field use, these engine-driven generators are the only choice and are widely used in construction, cross-country pipelining and oil refinery operations.

Progressing from light to heavy duty service, the engines used are: air-cooled gasoline engines, water-cooled gasoline engines, and diesel engines.

Alternators

Alternators, or AC generators, similar to those in autos, contain a set of coils, called *windings*. When the magnetic field cutting through the windings fluctuates as the generator shaft is turned, it induces a voltage in the windings.

Since the field passes through a maximum strength in one direction, through zero strength, and then a maximum strength in the reverse direction, an alternating current is generated. Whether the coil is fixed and the magnetic field rotates, or the magnetic field is fixed and the coil rotates between the magnet's poles, the result is the same: AC voltage appears at the generator's output. See the simplified alternator in Figure 18-1. Practical AC generators have more windings and turns of wire in each winding than pictured in this figure.

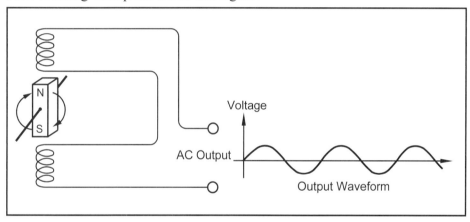

Figure 18-1. Simplified alternator with its output waveform.

DC Generators

In order for a generator to produce DC—which is often more desirable than AC for welding—a rotating mechanical switch called a *commutator* is needed so that the voltage and current flow in the *same* direction even though the magnetic field through the generator coils reverses as the rotor turns. A series of copper bars connected to each generator rotor coil contacts a set of carbon, or graphite, conductive brushes. The commutator connects the coil to the brushes only when the coil is in the proper location to keep current flowing in the same direction. The idea is that adding a commutator to the basic alternator makes it a DC generator.

Figure 18-2 shows a DC generator and its simplified commutator. Practical DC generators have 20–50 coils with many turns of wire on each coil. For each coil there is a pair of *commutator bars*, but the principle remains the same. Also, there are usually some additional means of regulating the generator to stabilize its output with changing loads.

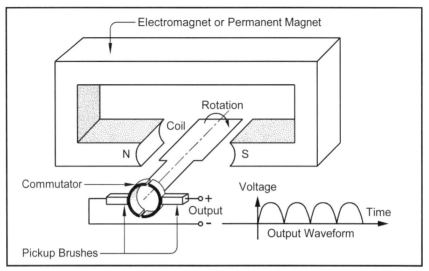

Figure 18-2. Simplified DC generator and its output waveform. The direction of the generator coil rotation changes the polarity of the generator's output.

Power Grid

The utility company supplies electrical power with two types of service:

- *Three-wire single-phase service* is the most common means of supplying power to homes, offices and light industry. This hook-up provides both 110 and 220 volts. See Figure 18-3.

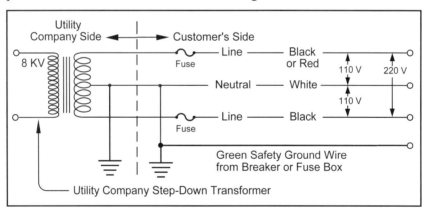

Figure 18-3. Three-wire singe-phase service provides 110 and 220 VAC to homes, offices, and light industry.

- *Three-phase service* is used by industry, especially industrial welding operations, typically 240 or 480 V phase-to-phase. See Figure 18-4.

Both the electric power company and the user enjoy benefits from this three-phase hook-up. In fact, the generators used at the powerhouse and at the electric power distribution system are *themselves* three-phase.

There are lower losses when transmitting three-phase power than with single-phase, both on the distribution system and within the user's facility.

Here are two additional advantages to three-phase power:

- Motors run on three-phase power are more efficient than single-phase motors of the same size on single-phase power. Heavy loads on a single-phase system tend to unbalance the power distribution system, but heavy loads run on three-phase systems do not.

- Most important to welders, three-phase power converted to direct current is a much smoother, more even output with less *ripple,* which is better for welding. This will be covered later in the section called, *Three-Phase Welding Machine Advantages,* starting on page 495.

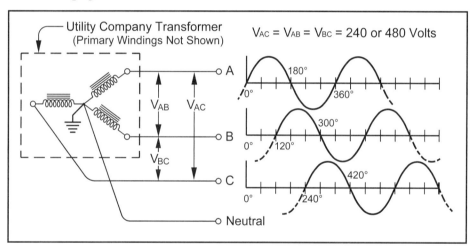

Figure 18-4. Three-phase power is used by industrial customers.

Power Factor

Power factor measures how much of the load is *resistive* and how much is *inductive*. A power factor of *exactly one* means that the load is purely resistive and has no charging currents for inductors—and their inductive losses. A power factor *less than one* indicates that the load has inductive currents. Power factor can be increased, or corrected, by adding capacitors inside the welding machine.

Because power companies penalize industrial customers with low power factors, the power factor of a welding power supply is important economically. To the power company a welding transformer load "looks" like both a resistive and an inductive load. Although inductors do not consume power themselves, the power company must supply the current they use and return on each cycle. Watt-hour meters do not measure this charging current. This current, though, *does* consume energy as it goes to and from the power plant through the power distribution network to the customer's inductive load each half AC cycle. In effect, the power company is supplying a charging current at no cost and must pay for the heat losses incurred in its transmission.

Section III – Electrical Output Characteristics

Static-Output Characteristics

Measuring the output current and voltage under steady-state conditions—when there are no changes in the power-supply load—determines power supply *static output characteristics*. Although supplies are either *constant current* (CC) or *constant voltage (CV)*, many other electrical parameters are needed to define a supply's behavior, such as open-circuit voltage, short-circuit current, and the slope and shape of its characteristic curves.

Determining static characteristics is relatively easy using the test setup in Figure 18-5. The welding machine controls are set for a given current or voltage, then the output voltage and current are measured and recorded as the resistive load goes from an open-circuit to a short-circuit. These changes in resistance are made slowly because it takes the welding machine a second or two to reach steady-state or equilibrium conditions. These voltage and current points define the *static-output characteristic curve* for one power setting of the welding machine. Performing this test across the full range of power settings produces an entire family of characteristic curves, and these describe the machine's *static behavior*.

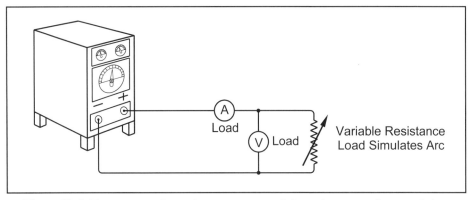

Figure 18-5. Test setup to determine a power supply's static-output characteristics.

Ideal Static-Output Characteristics

Figure 18-6 shows the characteristic voltage-to-current output curves of an ideal constant-current and an ideal constant-voltage power supply.

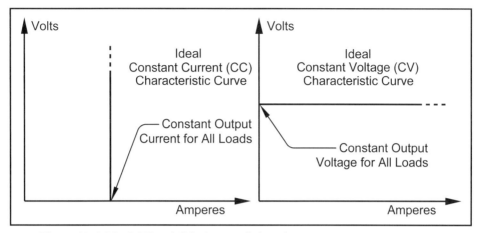

Figure 18-6. Ideal CV and CC characteristic voltage vs. current output curves.

Ideal vs. Practical Power Supply Output Characteristics

Figure 18-7 shows the output curves of *practical* CC and CV welding power supplies. Electrical resistance in the power supply output circuit components—the transformers, inductors, internal wiring and welding cables, as well as the saturation of the magnetic material in the transformers and inductors—cause practical power supplies to differ from ideal power supplies. Also, the inability of any power supply to provide infinite voltage to maintain the current at very high load resistances causes the ideal vertical CC line to become a curve sloping down to the right as in Figure 18-7 (right). For simplicity a single curve is shown. Each graph actually contains a family of curves for different settings of the welding machine.

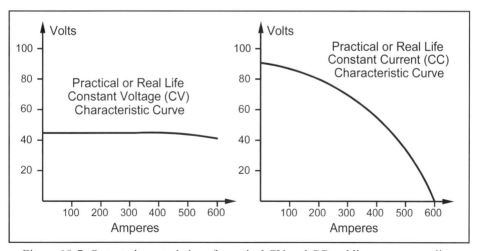

Figure 18-7. Output characteristics of practical CV and CC welding power supplies.

Because the slope of the CV curve is almost flat, as in Figure 18-7 (left), nearly constant voltage is maintained on the arc in spite of big changes in current caused by changing arc length. The real life or practical CV characteristic curve comes very close to the ideal CV curve.

Unlike the CV curves, the CC characteristic curves of the ideal and the practical power supplies differ greatly. However, since the slope of the CC curve is relatively steep, and changes in arc length create much larger changes in voltage for a given change in current, the power supply acts very much like—but not exactly like—a CC power source *within the relatively narrow range of current and voltage where welding occurs.*

Choice of CC or CV Power Supply

Continuous-feed electrode systems, like GMAW, FCAW and plasma cutters, work better with CV supplies which cause the arc length to *self-regulate* when the electrode *stickout* distance changes.

A typical CV characteristic output curve has a slope of –2 volts per 100 amperes. In other words, an increase in output current of 100 amperes causes the output voltage to *drop 2 volts.*

Increasing the stickout distance, also called the *work-to-torch distance*, increases the resistance of the arc as seen by the welding machine. In a GMAW or FCAW process, the electrode wire is fed into the weld at a constant speed. For the arc to be stable, the electrode wire-feed rate must exactly equal the wire burn-off rate. Here is what happens when the arc length *increases* from a stable arc length at a given wire-feed rate:

* When the stickout distance increases, as in Figure 18-8, Point A, the arc resistance seen by the welding machine increases, making the current drop from I_A to I_B and increasing the voltage from V_A to V_B.

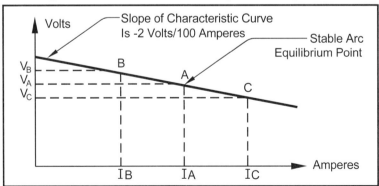

Figure 18-8. GMAW stability with CV power supply.

* A reduced current through the arc slows the wire burn-off rate and allows the constantly-feeding wire electrode to shorten the arc and return to the equilibrium at Point A.

- Therefore, a decrease in stickout distance causes a decrease in arc resistance, and an increase in arc current causes an increase in the wire burn-off rate. This re-establishes the equilibrium condition at Point A. This process is called *self-regulation.*

Welding processes with manual electrode-feed systems, such as SMAW and GTAW, work better with CC power supplies which provide maximum operator control of the weld pool size.

Here's how it works:

As the arc length increases on a CC power supply, the weld current is slightly reduced. This causes the arc to spread out over a greater area and the weld pool freezes more quickly. Conversely, with a shorter arc length, the welding current increases and the weld area is reduced, making the weld pool freeze more slowly, which increases weld penetration. See Figure 18-9. This adjustment of arc length gives the welder control of the weld pool and is especially useful when welding in the vertical and overhead positions. Notice that when the characteristic curve is more steep as a result of a lower open-circuit voltage, the same change in arc length causes a larger change in arc current than when the machine is set for a higher open-circuit voltage. A lower open-circuit voltage gives the welder more control over the weld pool even though the arc current is the same.

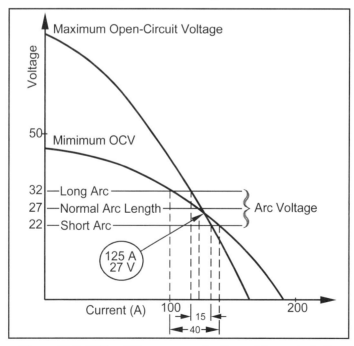

Figure 18-9. With a CC power supply, the welder controls the arc current—and the weld pool size—by adjusting the arc length.

Dynamic Characteristics

Dynamic characteristics affect how the arc reacts to the rapidly changing arc conditions that occur during:

- Striking of the arc.

- Changing the arc length.

- Transfer of metal across the arc.

- In the case of AC, arc extinction and re-ignition at each half cycle.

Although dynamic characteristics are every bit as important as static characteristics, because there is no universally recognized method of measuring them, dynamic characteristics are rarely specified by equipment manufacturers. Dynamic characteristics are usually evaluated by actually using the welding equipment and seeing how it performs.

Static volt-ampere steady-state characteristics have little relation to dynamic characteristics, so knowing one does not lead to knowing the other. However, components added to the output circuit can affect both static and dynamic responses.

Adding a *variable inductor* in the output-current path is the most common method of affecting dynamic characteristics and nearly every welding machine has a fixed or variable inductor in its output circuit. Placing a *capacitor* across the power supply output is another way to affect dynamic characteristics. See Figure 18-10.

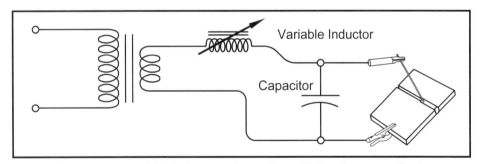

Figure 18-10. Variable inductor and capacitor added to the output circuit.

Constructed like transformers, but with only a primary winding, inductors added to the power supply output circuit resist any change in output current. They do this by storing energy in their magnetic fields and releasing this energy only when needed to prevent changes in output-welding current. If current is not flowing, inductors reduce the rate at which current can increase, and if current is flowing, inductors attempt to maintain the current flow.

Adding *series inductance* in the output circuit of a welding machine results in several changes:

- Modifies the dynamic-output characteristics in order to reduce weld spatter, improve uniformity of metal transfer, and reduce weld-pool turbulence.

- Modifies static-output characteristics and can convert the CV characteristics of a basic transformer power supply to a CC supply, which is essential for SMAW and GTAW. An inductor affects both the shape and position of the static-output characteristic curves. Together with the welding transformer, the inductor actually sets the maximum welding current.

In addition to adding inductors or capacitors, there are two other ways to affect dynamic response:

- Add electronic feedback controls.

- Use waveforms of shape and frequency other than those available from a 60 Hz transformer supply.

Section IV – Welding Power Supply Designs

Early Commercial Designs

The first commercial welding power supplies were motor-generator combinations, sometimes called *M-G sets*. See ❿ in Table 18-1. These were three-phase motors on electric utility power that drove DC generators. M-G sets worked well for SMAW and were widely used, but they are no longer made in the U.S. Most motor-generator sets have been replaced by more efficient transformer-based welding power supplies that have no moving parts other than a fan.

Today, many of these old motor-generator sets are tucked away in maintenance departments where their low electrical-conversion efficiency is not a consideration since they are not in full time use. Yet despite this drawback, motor-generator combinations remain cost effective and useful tools.

Transformer-Based Designs

A transformer-only welding power supply is the least complicated and least expensive design. It provides constant current AC for SMAW, and is used in automotive repairs, farm equipment repairs, and for hobbyist applications.

See Figure 18-11 and ❸ in Table 18-1.

Table 18-1.

	Gasoline or Diesel Engine		Electric Utility Power Lines							
Conversion Starts with:	AC from Alternator	DC from Generator	AC from Utility Lines @ 120/240/480 volts — Single-phase for light & medium welding machines, portable and fixed & Three-phase for heavy industrial, mostly fixed welding machines							AC Motor Drives DC Generator
(conversion device)			Transformer	Transformer + Rectifier		Transformer + Rectifier + SCRs and/or Transistors		Inverter Designs AC/DC/HF Pulses		
Means of Conversion	None Required	None Required								
Output Waveform	AC	DC	AC	AC or DC	DC	AC or DC	DC			DC
Output Characteristics	CC	CC / CV	CC	CC	CV	CC	CV	CC	CV	CC
SMAW	●	●	●	●		●		●		●
GMAW		●			●		●		●	
FCAW		●			●		●		●	
GTAW	●	●	●	●		●		●		
Plasma Arc Cutting				●		●		●		
Column Reference	①	②	③	④	⑤	⑥	⑦	⑧	⑨	⑩

Table 18-1. Welding power supply classification. Welding power supplies have evolved from quite simple to very complex devices. We will follow the path of this development in time as we review the general classes of power supplies. This table provides an overview of welding power supplies. Note the column reference numbers along the bottom row of this table.

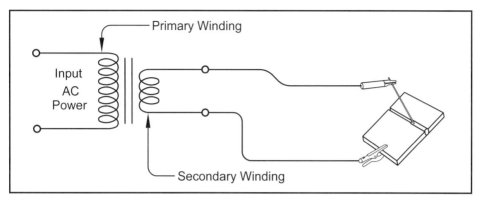

Figure 18-11. Simplified transformer-based constant-current AC welding power supply.

There are many ways to adjust transformer output to match the welding current to the size of the weld. These methods include:

• *Using taps on the welding transformer secondary windings.* Taps are connections to the transformer windings in addition to the two connections at the extreme ends of the winding. Taps effectively change the number of turns on a winding, which changes the turns-ratio between the primary and secondary windings and the output voltage. Taps may be adjusted either by a series of plugs, by a switch as in Figure 18-12 (A), or even by a continuous slider on the exposed secondary winding. In SMAW supplies, taps are on the secondary winding, while in GMAW they can be in the primary winding. The turns-ratio between the primary and secondary winding and the input voltage determine the output voltage.

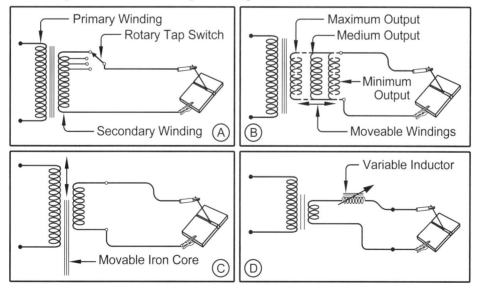

Figure 18-12. Methods of adjusting a transformer's current output.

- *Changing the distance between primary and secondary windings*, usually with a crank or lever, changes the magnetic linkage between them, which in turn changes the output voltage. See Figure 18-12 (B).

- *Altering the iron core* position between the primary and secondary windings to change the magnetic path linking them, Figure 18-12 (C).

- *Adding a tapped or variable inductor* in the transformer's secondary winding controls short-circuit current. See Figure 18-12 (D).

Adding Diodes to a Transformer-Based Power Supply

The next step up in complexity is adding DC capability to SMAW by adding semiconductor diodes which rectify the transformer AC output to DC. See ❹ and ❺ in Table 18-1. Most of these welding power supplies require a 220 VAC or higher service voltage and all of the three-phase power supplies require 220 VAC or higher voltages. The larger versions of these designs, which output 250–350 A and have a 60% or higher duty cycle, are the workhorses of SMAW industrial welding. See Figure 18-13.

Figure 18-14 shows how to extend a single-phase bridge rectifier power supply design to a three-phase supply.

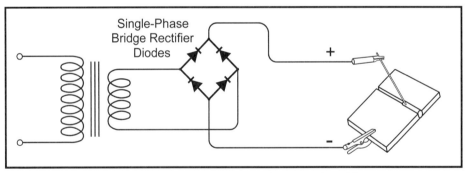

Figure 18-13. Single-phase transformer and rectifier welding power supply provides DC welding power.

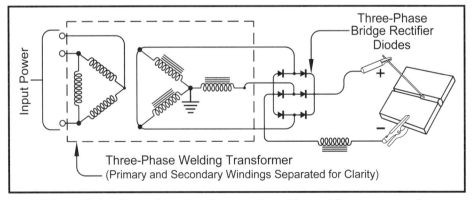

Figure 18-14. Three-phase transformer and rectifier welding power supply.

These three-phase power supplies have a very low ripple which results in a smooth output current that looks like DC to the arc. This is because the arc is sustained and does not extinguish during any part of the AC cycle.

Three-Phase Welding Machine Advantages

- Three-phase input power provides a smoother, more even output which looks more like DC to the arc than the output of a single-phase rectifier. See Figure 18-15.

- The output of the rectifier is a DC voltage with a smaller AC voltage riding on top. Welders will notice that the welding machine rectified voltage output has less *ripple*.

- Three-phase AC power prevents the arc from extinguishing because the output voltage never drops to zero as it does with single-phase AC.

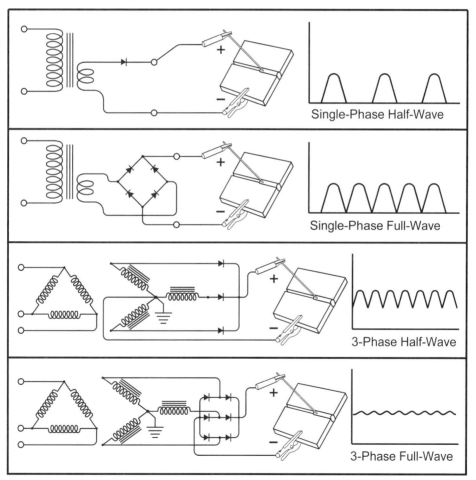

Figure 18-15. Single-phase and three-phase transformer rectifiers and their outputs. The output of a three-phase full-wave rectifier looks very much like the output of a DC supply because it has very low ripple.

Although three-phase power is as near as the closest high voltage step-down transformer, power companies will only supply three-phase power to commercial and industrial facilities, so many welders cannot take advantage of these machines.

Silicon Controlled Rectifier (SCR) Designs

By changing the point on the AC input power cycle when the SCR turns on, or fires, we can control the output of the welding power supply. In fact, we can eliminate many of the tap, moving coil, and variable inductor schemes used to control output. With electronics we can sense the voltage or current to the arc and use semiconductors to control the welding machine's output to maintain either CC or CV characteristics. See ❻ and ❼ in Table 18-1.

With little difficulty, control electronics can incorporate both CC and CV characteristics in a single power supply as in Figure 18-16.

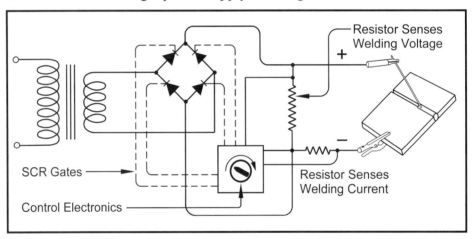

Figure 18-16. SCR-based combination CC & CV power supply. Control electronics senses current, or voltage to load, and adjusts SCR firing to maintain the desired output.

Basic Inverter Design

Figure 18-17 shows a transistor-based inverter design. Depending on the switching frequency, either SCRs (lower frequencies) or transistors (higher frequencies) are used. The incoming AC power feeds a bridge rectifier. The rectifier's output is then "chopped" by a bridge circuit to provide the high-frequency AC to drive the transformer.

This *step-down transformer* reduces the voltage and increases the current output. Its output goes to a second high-frequency rectifier so that all output pulses have the same polarity. The control electronics determines when and how long the transistors turn on. Sensors at the output provide feedback to the electronics and maintain CC or CV output characteristics.

By adding a microprocessor to the control electronics, special waveforms can be added which enhance the welding process.

The advantages of inverter-based welding power supplies over older power supply designs are:

- Reduced weight and volume of up to 70% over 60 Hz transformer-based designs.

- Control electronics provide multi-process capability in a single unit.

- Increased conversion efficiency and higher power factor than 60 Hz transformer designs.

- Increased portability permits shorter welding cables and low cable heat losses, so more power remains available for the welding arc.

- As well as producing special waveforms, microprocessor controls provide rapid adjustment of output to changing conditions at the weld.

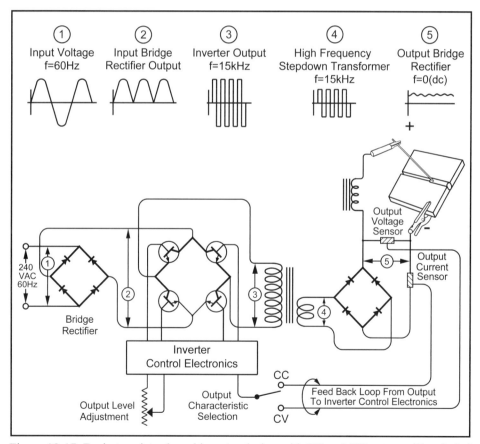

Figure 18-17. Basic transistor-based inverter design with CC and CV outputs. The circled numbers along the top of the figure refer to the shape of the waveforms at the numbered points in the circuit diagram.

Many GTAW power supplies are inverter-based and have even more sophisticated electronics and complex, adjustable waveforms. These waveforms are discussed in *Chapter 7 – Gas Tungsten Arc Welding.*

Current Adjustment

Most transformer/rectifier SMAW or GTAW CC power supplies have one adjustment for arc current which regulates the heat of the arc. As in Figure 18-18, increasing current shifts from Curve A at the low setting through Curve B and Curve C to Curve D at the highest setting. On machines with tapped transformers, each tap point provides a separate current curve. There will be as many curves as there are transformer taps.

Some machines have two controls: a *coarse-current control,* corresponding to the current control described above, and a *fine-current control.* See Figure 18-19. Depending on the machine manufacturer, this control may also be labeled *voltage control* or *slope control.* The fine-current control—a poor choice of label—really controls the open-circuit voltage and moves Point A in Figure 18-20 vertically on the voltage curve.

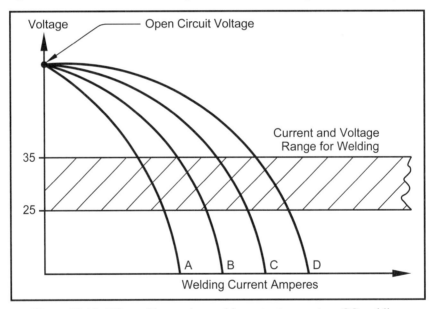

Figure 18-18. Effect of increasing welder output current on CC welding power supply with only one current adjustment.

The coarse-current control moves Point B in Figure 18-20 on the current, or horizontal, axis. Using these two adjustments, we can set an infinite number of characteristics. One of these characteristic curves will put the operating point at the proper current with the proper degree of slope at the operating point to get the desired weld and degree of weld pool control. A steeply sloping curve at the operating point will give the operator the ability to control the weld pool size by arc length adjustment, while a shallow curve, one that provides less change in current with the change in arc length, provides less control. The shallow curve may appeal to the beginner because it is easier to control.

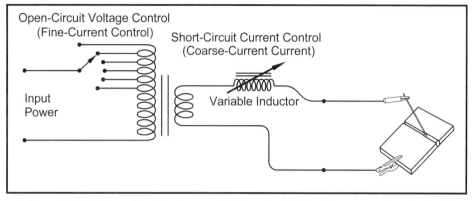

Figure 18-19. Open-circuit voltage control is often labeled *fine-current control* and the short-circuit current control is often labeled *coarse-current control.*

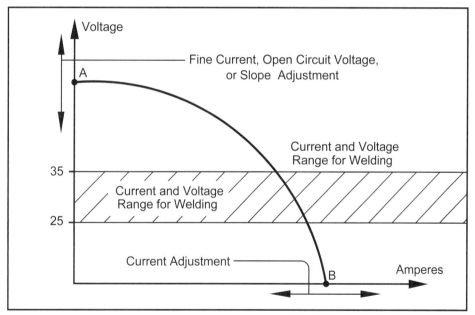

Figure 18-20. The effect of coarse- and fine-current adjustment of a CC SMAW power supply. Using both controls permits the operating point to be set anywhere within the cross-hatched area which is the desirable range of current and voltage for welding.

Duty Cycle & Nameplate Ratings

In the U.S., *duty cycle* is the percent of arc time to total time in any ten-minute period that a welding machine can be operated continually at its rated output. In Europe, a five-minute period is used. For example, a machine delivering 50 amperes for seven of the ten-minute interval would have a 70% duty cycle. Because manual welders do not weld all the time, a 60% duty cycle is typically recommended. The other 40% of the time, manual welders are loading or unloading parts, chipping slag, inspecting work, or changing electrodes. Welding power supplies for automatic welding operations must have 100% duty cycles as they work nearly continuously and may have very long intervals between work stoppages.

The factor that determines the duty cycle is the speed that heat generated inside the power supply can be removed. Heat must be removed from the power supply because high internal temperatures destroy electrical components.

A welding power supply can deliver more output current than its maximum for its rated duty cycle, but only for a shorter time. Charts showing this output current for a particular machine are available from supply manufacturers.

Figure 18-21 shows the output curves for welding machines of three different current ratings. All three machines are rated at a 60% duty cycle. These three curves show that each machine can supply *more* output current for a shorter duty cycle than their nameplate ratings. Each can also supply less current for a longer duty cycle than its nameplate duty cycle.

In general, each machine can provide the combinations of current and duty cycle represented by their duty-cycle curve. The *National Electrical Manufacturers' Association (NEMA)* has established three classes for welding machines based on duty-cycle percentages:

- Class I: Rated output at 60%, 80%, or 100% duty cycle for heavy industrial use.

- Class II: Rated output at 30%, 40%, or 50% duty cycle for automotive and repair shops, not for use in production.

- Class III: Rated output at 20% duty cycle for farm and hobby use.

Welding power sources are specified by the following criteria:

- *Open-circuit voltage* is measured between the electrode and ground when no current is being drawn, typically 50–80 volts for SMAW supplies. Open-circuit voltage is also the voltage on the vertical axis in a voltage-versus-current plot of welding machine characteristics. The higher the open-circuit voltage, the easier it is to strike an arc. But there is also more risk of electric shock.

- *Closed-circuit voltage* or *rated-load voltage,* which is measured across the arc during welding, varies with the type of electrode, polarity, arc length and type of current. Closed-circuit voltage is typically between 17–40 volts.

- *Maximum-output current rating* is the maximum current within the duty cycle.

- *Input voltage* and *current requirements* are single-phase or three-phase. A few welding power supplies can run on either single- or three-phase power, but they usually have lower output current ratings when run on single-phase power.

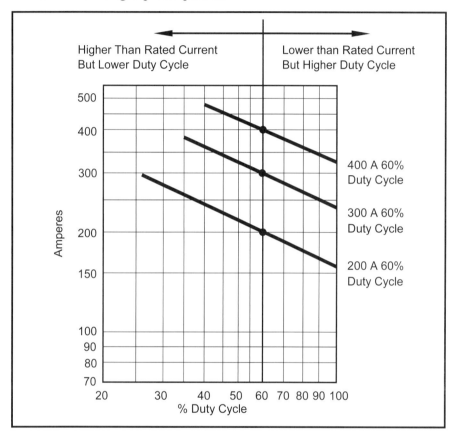

Figure 18-21. Duty cycle vs. output-current curve for three differently rated welding machines.

Section V – Electrical Safety

Electrical Safety
Here are the factors that affect the danger of electrical shock:

- Magnitude of the current flowing through the body.

- Duration of the shock.

- DC or AC, frequency if AC.

- Point in the heart's electrical cycle when shock begins.

- Current path through the body.

- Skin resistance.

Current Level vs. Shock Risk

As more current flows, the severity of the shock and injury increases:

- At about 1 mA, a slight tingling sensation occurs.

- At about 5 mA, a slight shock, which is annoying but not painful.

- At 6–30 mA, a painful shock, loss of muscle control, inability to let go of objects, and possible electrical burns.

- 50–150 mA, severe pain, severe muscle contractions, respiratory arrest, deep burns, injury from shock induced falls, possibly death.

- At 1000–4300 mA, there is strong likelihood of ventricular fibrillation. This is when the heart's electrical rhythm is disrupted and it fires rapidly, but since its chambers pump out of synchronization, it cannot pump blood.

- At 10,000 mA, cardiac arrest, severe burns and death is very probable.

- In addition to shock risk, vaporized copper conductors from high-current shorts can cause loss of vision, severe burns, and death.

Short Circuits

A *short*, or *short circuit*, permits current to flow through the short and diverts the current from flowing through the rest of the circuit where it should flow. This is because the short provides an easier—lower resistance—path between the power source than the rest of the normal load. In welding operations, shorts can be serious, and even fatal if a human *is* in the short-circuit path and the voltage is sufficiently high. Shorts can also blow fuses, ruin equipment, and start fires.

Grounds & Grounding

The National Electrical Code (NEC), which is generally accepted as a guideline for the safe installation of power and power equipment, provides this definition of an electrical ground: It is "a conducting connection, whether intentional or unintentional between an electrical circuit or equipment and the earth or some conducting body that serves in place of the earth." Put another way, the surface of the earth is generally capable of conducting an electrical current from one point to another and the earth serves as a universal reference point from which to measure a voltage. The wire or conductor connecting a device to the earth is called a *ground* or *ground conductor* and the device is said to be *grounded*. The ground conductor keeps the grounded device at zero voltage with respect to the earth.

What Grounding Does

Grounded equipment protects personnel and electrical equipment by:

- Insuring that the electrical equipment remains at ground potential so there is no risk of electrical shock should a person touch an electrical device that has developed an internal short circuit to its housing.

- Blowing fuses or tripping circuit breakers in the power lines, a ground shuts down the equipment, which indicates a short exists and must be corrected. Grounding reduces the risk of fire and equipment damage.

Earth Grounds

There are three common ways to establish a ground at the power panel:

- Drive a copper-plated steel rod into the earth and run a heavy wire from the rod to the grounding connection in the breaker panel. These grounding rods are typically $^5/_8$ inch in diameter and 4–8 feet in length.

- Run a ground conductor from a cold water pipe to the power panel.

- In large buildings, electrical ground is often made by running the ground conductor from the structural steel to the circuit breaker panel.

Grounding on a Single-Phase Load

One side of the power supply line, the *neutral leg*, is connected to the grounding point at the main breaker panel, an NEC requirement. This breaker panel is typically located where utility lines enter the building. The power supply is not grounded yet, only the neutral conductor. The white neutral wire under normal operation carries the same load current as the *hot* or *line* wire, but in the opposite direction. Below is the hazardous situation when the ground pin on a line cord plug is cut off or the safety ground is not connected to the equipment. See Figure 18-22.

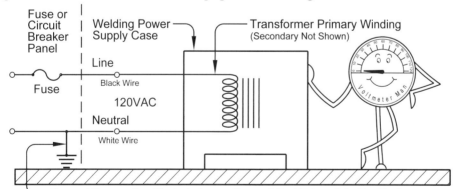

Figure 18-22. A properly fused 120 VAC welding transformer with a grounded neutral gives Voltmeter Man a false sense of security, but an ungrounded and unsafe welding power supply poses a severe hazard.

If a short circuit occurs between the transformer winding or any other component at line voltage inside the power supply, the metal case becomes electrified to line voltage. See Figure 18-23.

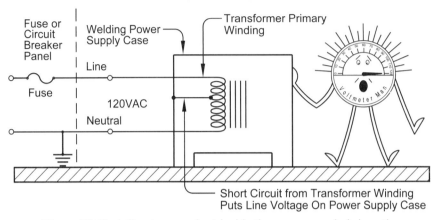

Figure 18-23. A line-to-case short inside the power supply brings the ungrounded metal case to line voltage and can have lethal consequences.

The proper grounding in Figure 18-24 prevents the metal power supply case from reaching the hazardous condition shown above. In addition to the hot and neutral conductors, a third wire called a *grounding wire* or *safety ground* is required by the NEC. This green wire is connected to ground in the power panel and runs along with both the hot and neutral wires to the protected electrical device. However, the safety ground wire connects only to the frame, housing or metallic cover, not to the load. This connection keeps the case at ground potential and provides a current path so that the breaker or fuse blows when a short circuit occurs. Under normal conditions—when no short circuit occurs—this green ground wire does not carry any current; it only carries current during a short.

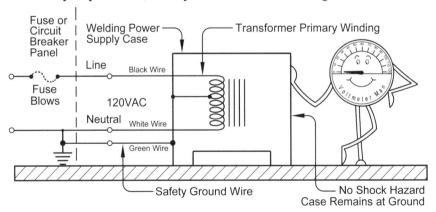

Figure 18-24. Proper grounding protects Voltmeter Man from dangerous line voltages on the welding power supply case and blows a fuse or circuit breaker alerting him to a problem.

Another benefit of proper grounding occurs when a 8 kV high voltage line falls onto the 110/220 volt utility lines during a storm. This high voltage is sure to cause an insulation failure somewhere inside the welding power supply electrifying its metal case. Instead of allowing the case to reach the full 8 kV, proper grounding reduces the maximum voltage and the safety ground provides a good path for the current to flow to ground and blow a fuse or trip a breaker. This prevents the high voltage from remaining on the case awaiting the unsuspecting victim. See Figure 18-25.

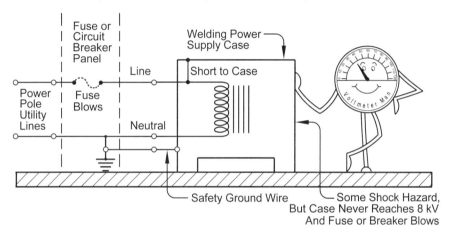

Figure 18-25. Should an 8kV voltage utility line fall onto a 110/220 power line, the electrical insulation within the power supply is likely to break down causing a line-to-case short, putting a high voltage on the case. A properly grounded power supply will reduce the high voltage on the case and blow a fuse or trip a breaker.

Ground Fault Interrupters

Ground Fault Interrupters (GFIs) are an inexpensive way to protect men and equipment on a job site where both the men and equipment may become part of the ground path.

GFIs measure the current entering the equipment through one side of the power line and compare it with the current leaving the equipment on the other side of the power line. If there is a difference between these two currents, the GFI breaks the circuit to the load in just a few milliseconds. The assumption is that current imbalance to and from the load is due to a short to ground. GFIs interrupt power to the load so rapidly that the current through the short to ground does not have a chance to injure or kill. Note that GFIs will *not* protect an ungrounded person who gets *across* the power terminals; there will be no current imbalance and the GFI will not detect the problem. GFIs, good equipment grounding, and proper fusing should all be used to provide maximum protection. Note that in Figure 18-26, even though the welding machine was not properly grounded, the GFI provided protection.

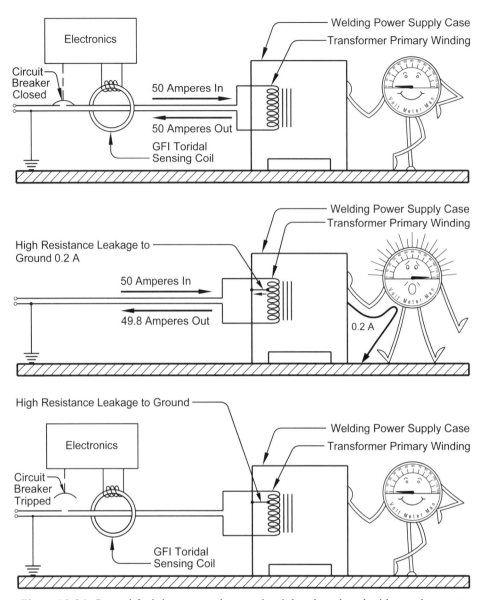

Figure 18-26. Ground fault interrupter leaves circuit breaker closed with equal current into and out of load (top), machine without GFI with high resistance ground to case does not blow fuse, but poses electrocution hazard (middle) and GFI detects small leakage to ground through Voltmeter Man and trips out load before harm is done (bottom).

It is possible to have a high resistance short to ground so that the case or frame of the machine is capable of supplying enough current to electrocute a man *without* enough to blow a fuse. It takes much less current to kill or injure a person than it takes to blow a fuse or circuit breaker. GFIs can detect this high resistance short and shut down the power.

Chapter 19

Bending & Straightening

Experience is the name everyone gives to their mistakes.
—Oscar Wilde

Section I – Bending Equipment Overview

Bending is used in almost every fabricated metal product. Because many times welding cannot be done until the bending operations are complete, the welder is often required to perform bending tasks as part of his job.

Sheet metal and thin plate are bent cold, and often thicker plates are bent cold, but thick rolled plates and rolled sections are frequently heated in ovens, with torches or with induction heaters to reduce the bending forces. Table 19-1 shows common steel products and the methods used to bend them.

	Sheet Metal >3/16" Thick	Plate ≤3/16" Thick	Rods & Bars	Shapes: Ts, Ls, Cs & I-Beams	Wire	Pipe & Tube
Hand Bender	●	–	–	–	–	–
Pin Fixtures and Bending Jigs	–	–	●▲	–	●	●▲
Sheet Metal Brakes	●	–	–	–	–	–
Press Brakes	●	●	●	–	–	–
Roll Brakes	–	●	–	–	–	–
Bending Machines Rotary Mandrel Sand Filling	●	●	●▲	●▲	●	● ● ●
Wrinkle Bending	–	–	–	–	–	▲
Rolls	●	●	●▲	●▲	–	●▲
Flame Bending	–	▲	–	▲	–	▲
Line Heating	–	▲	–	–	–	–
Flame Straightening	–	▲	▲	▲	–	▲
Flame Panel Shrinking	–	▲	–	–	–	–

● = No heat ▲ = Heat used

Table 19-1. Bending methods matched to common steel products.

There are many different styles of bending machines. Here are some of the most common:

- *Sheet metal brakes* come in a variety of sizes from tabletop, hand-powered units to freestanding, hydraulically actuated models. They work by clamping the sheet metal in place, then, using a hinged section of the brake, force is applied at the point of the desired bend. Most of these brakes are limited to 16-gauge steel. See Figure 19-1.

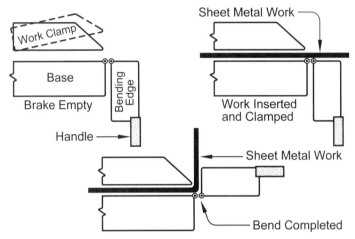

Figure 19-1. Sheet metal brake edge view.

- *Press brakes* are used to bend heavier gauge sheet metal and all thicknesses of plate. Most brakes are hydraulic, but some use an electric motor-driven flywheel. Much higher forces are needed to bend thicker metal and because of this, press brakes use a mating die design instead of the hinged designs of sheet metal brakes. See Figure 19-2 (left). Medium capacity press brakes have 25–100 ton capacities. Shipyards use even larger press brakes with 2,000-ton ratings.

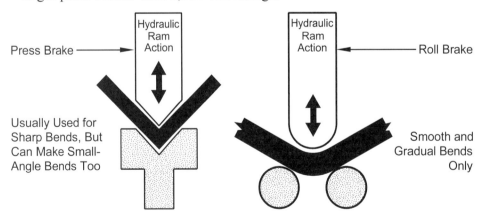

Figure 19-2. Press brake uses matching dies to form sharp bends (left), roll brakes use cylinders or sections of cylinders to form smooth curves (right).

- *Roll brakes* use steel cylinders, or sections of cylinders, to form long-radius bends in thick steel plate for ship hulls. See Figure 19-2 (right).

Roll brakes apply a series of gentle parallel bends to form plate into an arc with constantly changing radii, but they cannot apply compound bends.

Typical Brakes

Figure 19-3 shows an inexpensive vise-insert brake suitable for thin steel and aluminum up to $\frac{1}{16}$" by 1" wide, excellent for making small brackets. Figure 19-4 (left) shows a 50-ton hydraulic press that can bend steel and aluminum up to $\frac{5}{8}$" thick by 12" wide. Figure 19-4 (right) shows a shop-made hydraulic brake based on a 30-ton bottle jack. The insert shows the male and female bending dies for this brake.

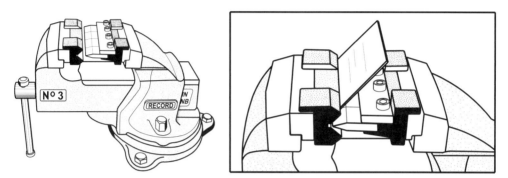

Figure 19-3. A small sheet metal brake used with a vise,
suitable for thin sheet metal, aluminum and brass.

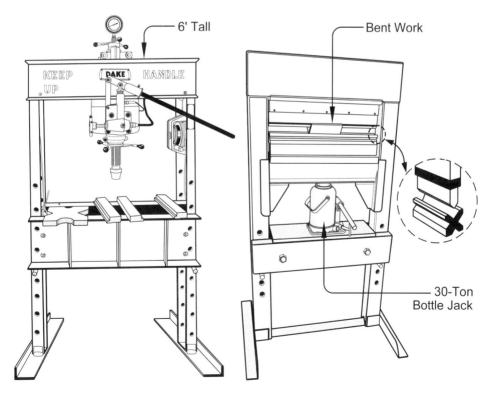

Figure 19-4. Both the commercial hydraulic press (left) and the shop-made hydraulic press based on a bottle jack (right), use steel bending dies (see insert on right).

Section II – Bending Machine Applications

Bending Machine Overview

Bending machines come in dozens of sizes and designs. The smallest are hand- or air-powered and the largest are hydraulic. The principles of these bending machines are basically the same, only the scale and source of bending force differs. The Di-Acro Model 1A, in Figure 19-5, is a small, high quality hand-operated bender that forms round, flat, and square steel, copper, and aluminum stock. With the appropriate dies both tubing and rolled sections can be bent as well.

When bending rolled shapes, pipe, and tubing, the forming dies must fit the work tightly. If the work is not supported and prevented from moving during the bending operations, results will be poor.

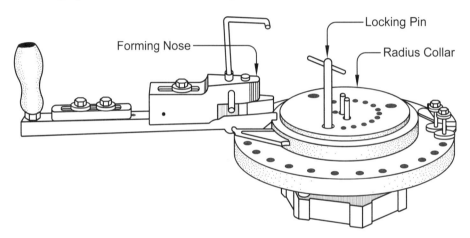

Figure 19-5. Di-Acro bender Model 1A.

Cross-shaped or X-shaped extrusions that cannot be supported and confined by bending dies can be bent by casting the work *inside* a rectangle of a low temperature metal alloy like CerroBend which melts at 158°F. The rectangle with the work inside it is bent with tooling for a rectangular bar, and the low-temperature melting alloy is removed in a hot water bath. The low-melt alloy can be reused indefinitely. See Figure 19-6.

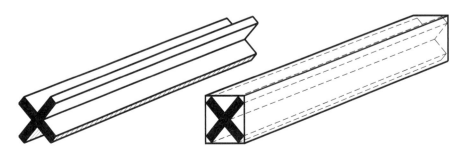

Figure 19-6. Extrusion to be bent (left), and extrusion cast inside a
low-temperature alloy to support the X-shaped part during bending (right).

Figures 19-7 through 19-14 show how to use Di-Acro benders to bend a variety of shapes. Most bending machines use the same principals and only differ in force and scale.

Bending Circles

Circles can easily be formed with benders, but *spring back* must be taken into consideration. Most materials spring back slightly after being bent. To compensate for this, use a radius collar with a smaller diameter than the required circle. Because spring back varies with different materials, actual finished size of the circle is best determined by experiment. Materials should be precut to exact length before forming circles. See Figure 19-7.

Zero Radius Bends

A sharp, zero radius bend can be formed using a *zero radius block* like the one in Figure 19-8, which shows the forming of flat strip stock into a V-shape. This operation, though, can be performed equally as well on round, square, and other solid, ductile materials. When forming heavy materials to a zero radius, their ductile limits must be taken into consideration. Using a small radius on the bending edge of the block will avoid fracturing or marking on the inside of the bend. To increase the forming width capacity, use a built-up nose and mount two or more zero radius blocks on top of each other.

Scroll Bending

Scrolls and other irregular shapes can be formed in rigid materials even though the forming nose of the bender revolves in a perfect circle. This type of forming, as shown in Figure 19-9, is performed by using a collar with the same contour as the shape desired. This is done by adjusting the forming nose so it is located only the thickness of the material away from the 'high point" of the contour collar. Because the material will only bend where the contour collar offers resistance, the forming nose can lead the material around until it contacts the high point and exerts enough pressure to force it into the shape of the radius collar.

Cold Spring & Coil Bending

A spring or coil can be made in all materials by following the method in Figure 19-10. The number of turns in the coil is limited only by the height of the forming nose and the radius pin. Springs and coils can be made to most dimensions depending on the size and ductility of the material. The forming nose must be set so it will clear the end of the material held by the locking pin. The maximum length of this bend is determined by the ductile limits of the material. It must be sufficiently rigid so it will not bow between the forming nose and the radius pin.

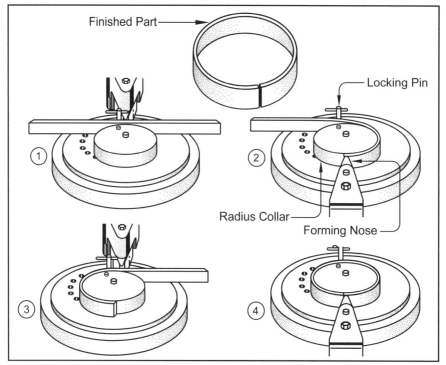

Figure 19-7. Forming a circle: (A) Set forming nose against material and clamp material against radius collar with locking pin, (B) Advance operating arm until forming nose reaches extreme end of material, (C) Relocate material and clamp with locking pin at a point where radius is already formed, (D) Advance operating arm until forming nose again reaches extreme end of material.

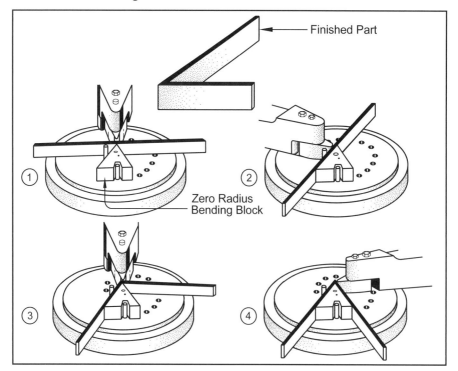

Figure 19-8. Making a zero radius bend.

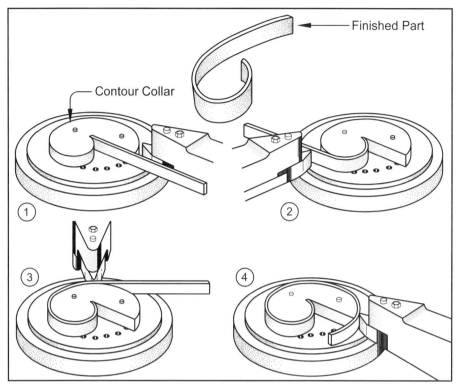

Figure 19-9. Scroll bending.

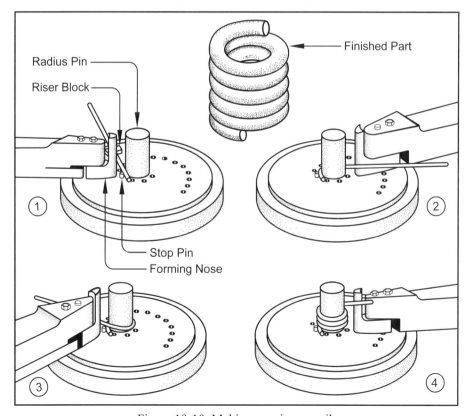

Figure 19-10. Making a spring or coil.

Tube Bending

The *forming-roller method* of tube bending is recommended for all large bends where the centerline radius is at least four times the outside diameter of the tube, as in Figure 19-11. This technique can also be used for bending pipe or heavy-wall tubing to smaller radii and it is the most practical method of bending small diameter tubing. The forming roller and radius collar must be grooved to exactly fit the tube and the tube must not be allowed to slip during the bending operation because any slippage will cause distortion. Nearly all pipe and tube bending methods trap and confine the workpiece in this manner.

Bending Angle Iron

Angle iron with flanges, or *legs out*, can be formed with benders, but this type of bending presents problems because stresses within the material often cause the workpiece to twist out of plane after forming. The twisting is generally more pronounced in fabricated angle than in standard mill-rolled angle. When the flange bent edgewise is less than half the width of the vertical flange, the tendency to twist is greatly reduced. As the dimensions of the angle and the radius of bend vary with almost every job, it is impractical to offer a standard group of accessories for this type of forming. The user must make these parts himself. The flange should be closely confined in the radius collar because as little as 0.002–0.003" variation in clearance can make a great difference in bend quality. Minimizing and controlling clearance is especially important in thinner materials. See Figure 9-12.

Benders can form channels provided the flanges are adequately confined during the bending operation so they will not buckle or distort. See Figure 19-13. Usually the radius of the bend should be three to four times the width of the flange to allow for stretching of the metal. Although this ratio is primarily determined by the thickness and ductility of the material, it can often be reduced considerably. As the different dimensions of the channel shape vary with almost every job, the user must make these parts for his job. Minimizing flange clearance is important in bending channels just as it is in angle bending.

Multi-Sided Zero Radius Bends

Forming zero radius bends around square, rectangular, or other multi-sided blocks employs the same principle used in scroll bending. The forming nose "leads" material between corners of the block. Any number of zero radius bends can be obtained in one operation by this method in all types of solid materials. This type of bending is limited by the size of the square block and the ductility of the material. In general, when squares larger than 1 inch are needed, they should be formed in progressive operations using the zero radius block shown in Figure 19-14.

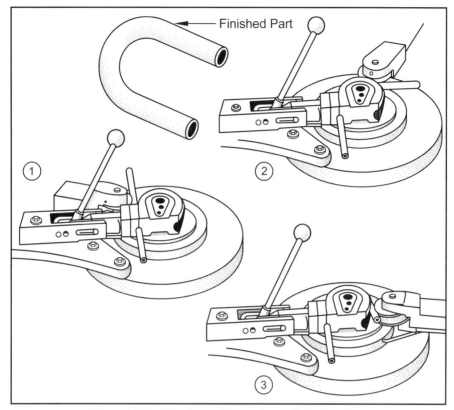

Figure 19-11. Forming-roller method of tube bending.

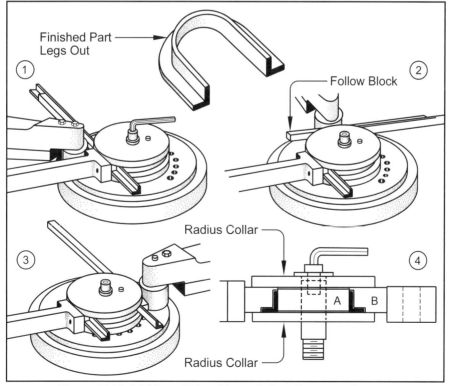

Figure 19-12. Making a U-bend in angle iron flanges, or legs out.

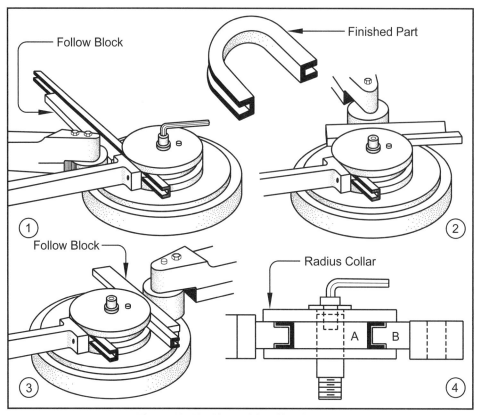

Figure 19-13. Channel bending legs out.

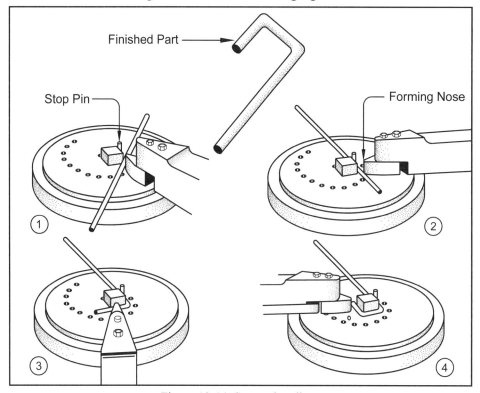

Figure 19-14. Square bending.

Section III – Pipe Bending

Mandrel Bending

Mandrel bending is the term used when a mandrel, or former, actually goes *inside* the pipe or tube being bent. The mandrel is held in place by a mandrel support rod, which shores up the tubing wall to keep it from collapsing. See Figure 19-15. Mandrel bending requires a machine mounted on a longer bed than conventional rotary bending machines, and a frame strong enough to resist the mandrel forces. Lubrication of the inside of the pipe or tube is needed to reduce forces on the mandrel and often requires removal later.

Three advantages of mandrel bending are that it can:

- Create a much tighter bend than bends made without an internal mandrel. Bends as tight as the diameter of the tube are possible versus two to three diameters of the tube for non-mandrel methods.

- Make tight bends without the bending wrinkles common in other methods.

- Maintain the workpiece inside diameter throughout the bend, an important factor in fluid handling applications.

The form of the mandrel will vary with the tubing material, the bend radius, and wall thickness. Mandrel designs vary and may include plugs, a disc, a single ball, or multiple balls.

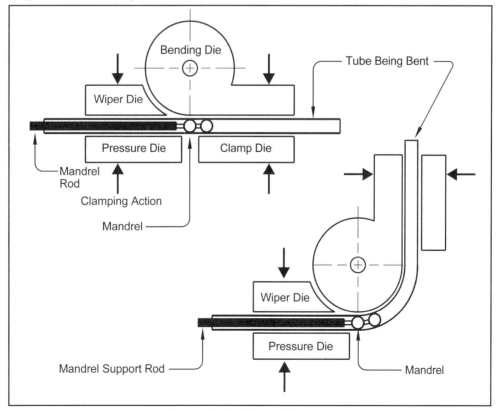

Figure 19-15. Mandrel bending.

Bending Soft Tubing

When bending soft materials, with or without a bending machine, the pipe walls tend to collapse. Filling the pipe or tube interior with dry sand and capping the ends will avoid or reduce this problem. See Figure 19-16. Be sure to leave small holes in the plugs to allow any steam generated by the sand to escape if heat is applied. The sand needs to be well tamped before the ends of the work are capped.

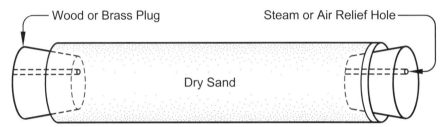

Figure 19-16. Using sand to prevent soft tubing walls from collapsing while bending.

Wrinkle Bending

Wrinkle bending is an old method for bending medium to large steel and copper pipe without using a bending machine. This technique is useful when an elbow fitting of the proper size and angle is unavailable.

Wrinkle bending is performed by heating a band of the pipe about halfway around its circumference on the inside of the desired bend. A rosebud torch tip is essential, and on pipe 8" diameter and larger, two rosebud torches are needed. When the band is dull red, apply a bending force, usually with a come-along. This force will upset the metal on the inside of the bend, forming wrinkles. Each wrinkle should bend the pipe between 9–12 degrees. Nine or more wrinkle bends are needed to make a right angle bend. Because the wrinkle metal also upsets the outside of the pipe, there is very little reduction to the pipe diameter. See Figure 19-17.

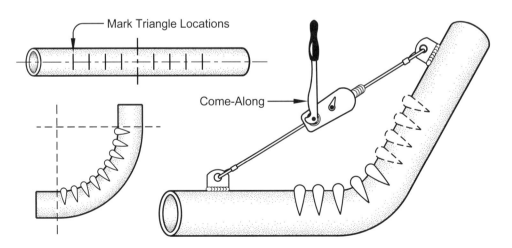

Figure 19-17. Wrinkle bending. Each wrinkle bends the pipe between 9 and 12 degrees.

Flame Straightening Large Pipe

Use flame straightening to remove a kink in a pipe. Alternately, if the pipe is straight and a kink is needed, it can be added with a flame bending operation.

To remove a kink, heat a $3^{1}/_{2}$" diameter area to a dull red and cool, as in Figure 19-18. Repeat if necessary. You can undo any straightening step by heating the opposite side of the pipe.

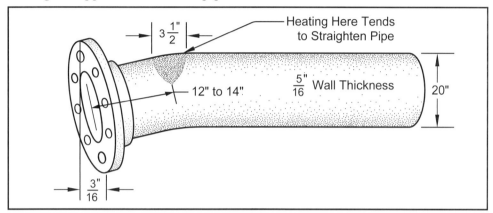

Figure 19-18. Flame straightening a large pipe. The heated section shrinks when cooled.

Section IV – Rolling

Rolls

Rolls are a bending machine design that uses three or more cylindrical rollers to form sheet metal or plate into cylinders or sections of cylinders. Rolls, sometimes called *slip rolls* or *roll benders*, can also form cones or sections of cones. Figure 19-19 shows how rolls work. One end of the roll bender drops out of the way to allow the work to be withdrawn after work is completed.

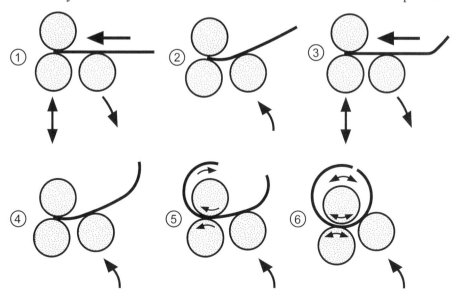

Figure 19-19. Forming a cylinder from a plate with a three-roll bender. After one end is bent upward in Step 2, the work is removed, reversed and the cylinder completed.

Small tabletop, hand-powered versions are widely used for sheet metal bending in HVAC. Factory-installed machines as big as a house and driven by 100 horsepower motors, bend heavy steel plate for water and petroleum storage tanks, boilers, and ship hulls. Roll benders are made in every conceivable size. Figure 19-20 shows a Di-Acro tabletop roll bender.

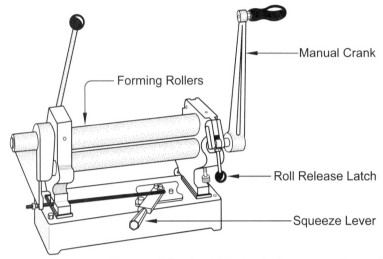

Figure 19-20. Di-Acro tabletop roll bender. This simple design uses three rollers and opens on one end so the work can be removed from around the top forming roller after the cylinder is formed.

Section V – Flame Bending, Straightening & Panel Shrinking

The terms *flame bending*, *flame shrinking*, and *flame straightening* describe three slightly different processes that all use the effects of heat, thermal expansion, partial constraint, and upsetting to permanently change the shape of metal, usually carbon steel.

Flame bending is often used in shipbuilding. It can put curves into steel plate without using a hydraulic press; only an oxyfuel torch and a water source are necessary. One or more curves can be made in a plate and they can be gradual, or severe. The curves can be simple, on just one axis, or complex with changing radii. Flame bending can even form a plate into a concave shape. If too much of a bend has been applied to a plate, flame bending can reduce or remove the bend. In shipyards, flame bending on plate or panels is sometimes called *line heating,* because heat is usually applied along straight or curved lines. Refer to Figure 19-25. Steel fabricators also use flame bending to put camber (vertical curve), or sweep (horizontal curve) into I-beams. Other steel rolled sections, pipe, and tubing can be flame bent too. In fact, any metal can be flame bent. The larger the metal's coefficient of thermal expansion, the better flame bending works.

Flame shrinking, also called *panel shrinking,* uses the same physical processes as flame bending, but accomplishes a different result; it *removes* wrinkles in steel plate panels after welding operations. Wrinkles also form around holes cut in steel panels, and flame shrinking can remove these wrinkles as well. Flame shrinking is a common shipyard activity. Without flame shrinking every hull plate in a ship would carry the outline of the supporting steel ribs behind it.

Flame straightening employs the same techniques as flame bending, but is used to straighten steel members instead of bending them. While flame straightening can be used to remove bends in pipe and small rolled sections, its principal application is the in-place repair of damaged heavy steel sections such as beams, columns, girders, trusses, and crane rails. Flame straightening can repair any steel member. These repairs are often done on bridge beams struck by over-height loads or damaged by over-weight vehicles. Sometimes bridge columns need straightening after being hit by run-away vehicles, loads, or ships. Steel erection mishaps, structural steel fire damage, and cargo container crane boom collapses are also prime candidates for flame straightening. In addition, flame straightening is very useful for straightening railings, racks and other long structures that have been bent by welding shrinkage.

Flame straightening and bending can be performed using only thermal expansion forces to bring the metal into position. Often though, hydraulic jacks, wedges, or come-alongs are used to apply additional external force and to increase the deflection during each heating and cooling cycle.

Advantages of Flame Straightening

- Cost savings of 25% over direct repairs are typical.
- Repairs are usually completed in a few days or a few weeks so there is little or no waiting for the fabrication of new structural elements.
- Equipment required to make the repairs is relatively simple and available in remote areas and third world countries. Repairs made on heavy sections are often completed without the use of additional heavy equipment.
- Strength of the steel is unaffected by flame straightening.

There are a handful of expert flame straightening contractors in the U.S. who perform their skills world-wide and often work twenty-four hour shifts to complete critical repairs.

Principles Behind All Steel-Shaping Operations

To shape steel, four physical events must occur in the following order:

1. Local and rapid heating leading to thermal expansion caused by the application of an oxyfuel torch. More than one torch may be used.

2. Constraint from the cooler and surrounding unheated steel on the hotter metal. This constraint is needed because the cooler metal expands less than the metal in the heated area.

3. Localized upsetting, which happens when the heated metal expands, and if the thermal expansion exceeds the yield point of the metal, plastic

deformation occurs in the *unrestrained* direction. This thickens the metal in the unrestrained sections of the workpiece.

4. When the metal cools, it shrinks in all three directions and causes a geometric change from the original shape.

Changing the shape of steel relies upon rapid thermal expansion because if the entire workpiece were gradually brought up to temperature, it would expand and contract evenly, retaining its shape. To keep the heating and expansion uneven, water or sometimes a compressed air and water mist is applied as soon as the upsetting occurs. Water is applied with a hose or in a mist with the atomizer shown in Figure 19-21. These sprayers may be commercial or shop-made. The advantage of using a mist is that less water ends up in puddles on the floor than when water is applied with a hose.

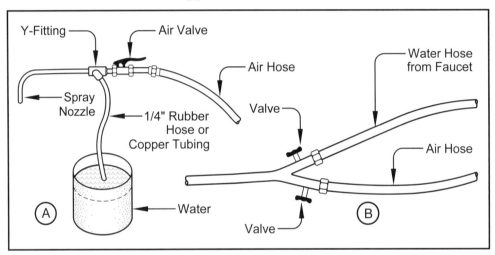

Figure 19-21. Two types of compressed air and water mist sprayers for rapid cooling during flame shrinking.

The heating and cooling cycle is repeated as soon as the metal has cooled to room temperature. In straightening operations, hundreds of cycles may be needed.

Heat may be applied in spots, rings, lines, or triangles to get the required shape changes in the metal. The proper application of heat and cooling can restore previous shapes or create new ones. Today these three processes—flame bending, flame shrinking, and flame straightening—depend on a skilled craftsman's experience and judgment, but development work has begun to automate flame bending for shipyard operations.

Maximum Work Temperature

The American Welding Society codes for bridges and structures limit flame-straightening temperatures to 1200°F because it is generally recognized that below this temperature little or no permanent weakening of the steel occurs. At this maximum allowed temperature, steel is a dull, cherry red in subdued light. To insure that the work is not overheated, temperature indicating crayons, thermocouples or infrared temperature sensor guns must be used when working in bright sunlight.

Flame Bending Bars

As in Figure 19-22, here are the steps to flame bend a rectangular steel bar:

1. Apply heat to the side of the bar you wish to shrink. Here's an easy way to remember this: *The hot side is the short side.*

2. For a rectangular metal bar, maximum bending is usually obtained by heating a 30° triangle that runs from the outside edge of the "short" side seven-eighths of the way down the bar's width, as in Figure 19-22 (top). Use welder's chalk to mark the triangle. The cool, unheated metal in the bottom one-eighth of the bar on the inside of the bend acts as a hinge. Start with a 10° or 15° pie-shaped segment, and work up to wider angles when you see the results.

3. Use a neutral oxyfuel flame and stay within the marked triangle. Move the torch continuously along the heating path to heat the metal to a dull red in subdued light, not direct sunlight.

4. Choose an oxyfuel torch tip that will heat the work quickly, yet stay within the chalked lines. A rosebud tip and two or more torches are needed for large work. Both sides of thick material must be heated.

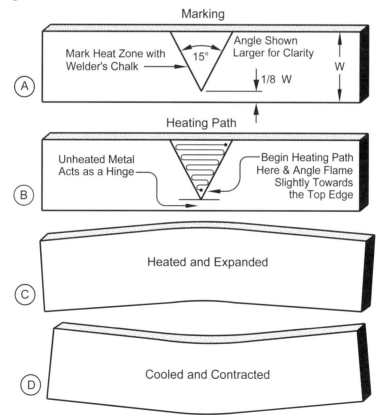

Figure 19-22. Flame bending a rectangular steel bar.

5. Again, because it is impossible to visually regulate metal temperature in bright sunlight, use a temperature-indicating crayon, or a non-contact hand-held electronic pyrometer to keep below the 1200°F temperature.

6. When using water or a compressed air and water spray to cool the work, begin in the area around the heated zone. On smaller jobs, such as this example of a rectangular steel bar, even wet rags can be used for cooling. We want to maintain the maximum temperature differential between the hot and cold zones.

7. When working with higher carbon content alloys, do not apply the cooling spray to the heated zone directly. You run the risk of inducing hardening.

8. Begin with a small trial area of 10–15° to gauge the shrinkage and avoid overshooting the mark. Use V-shapes up to 30° when greater bending is needed. It is much better to perform several small heats than to over-bend and have to use additional heating/cooling cycles to correct your mistake.

Flame Bending Rolled Shapes

Apply torch heat along the paths shown in Figure 19-23, then cool with water or a water and compressed air mist. Do not apply the water or mist directly to the heated metal. Begin by cooling the dark, unheated area around the dull red metal and work inward to the hotter metal. More than one heating and cooling cycle will probably be needed.

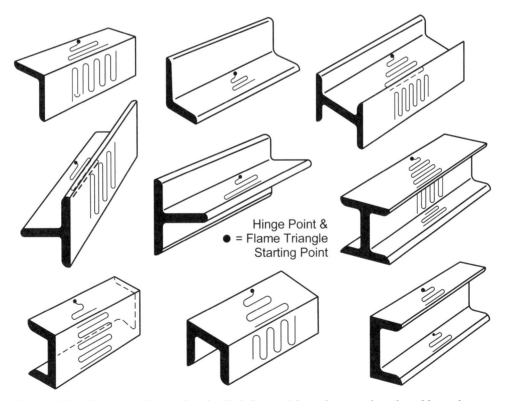

Hinge Point &
● = Flame Triangle
Starting Point

Figure 19-23. Using torch heat to bend rolled shapes. Lines show torch path and heated areas.

Cambering I-Beams

Here are the steps for flame-cambering an I-beam:

1. Sight along the edges of the flanges to see if the beam already has a camber. If camber exists, then plan on increasing the existing camber to the desired arc.

2. Place the beam on horses or other supports so that it is held only on the ends. Place a third horse or support under the beam exactly at the beam's midpoint. The beam and its center support must not touch. Measure the distance between the bottom of the beam and the top of the center support and record this distance on the web of the beam above this point for later reference. See Figure 19-24.

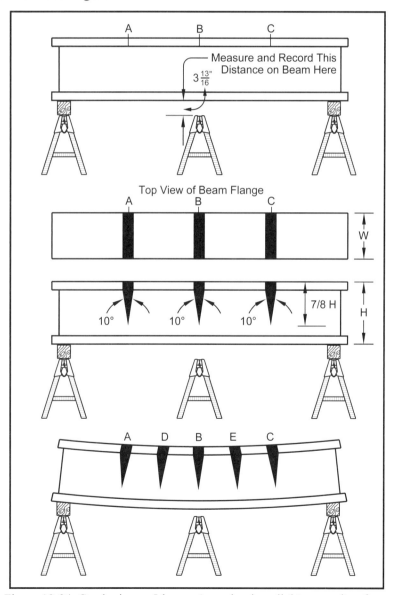

Figure 19-24. Cambering an I-beam. A camber is a slight convexity of arc.

3. Use a tape to divide the beam into quarters, and mark points A, B, and C with welder's chalk.

4. At points A, B, and C, as shown in Figure 19-24 (middle), mark 10° pie-shaped sections running $^7/_8$ of the way across the web and the matching areas on the top of the flange. Although 30° segments produce maximum bending in a single heating and cooling cycle, we begin with 10° segments so as not to over shoot the final bend. As we gain experience we can use wider segments.

5. In subdued light, heat the beam at point B to a dull red with an oxyfuel rosebud tip in the pattern shown in Figure 19-24 (bottom). Start heating at the point of the pie section. Try using two torches, one on each side of the flange working on opposite sides from each other. When the pie shape is heated, apply heat to the upper flange in an area matching the top width of the pie shaped-section. To cool the beam with water, start from the cooler, darker black areas around the heated pie-shape and work into the red-heat zones. When the beam is back at room temperature, measure the camber change at B. If more camber is needed, and it probably will be, mark the pie segment and top web area to be heated and, using the same technique, apply heat at points A and C.

6. After heating and cooling at B and C, check camber at A. If more camber is required, apply heating and cooling at D and E. D is midway between A and B, and E is midway between B and C.

7. If still more camber is needed, repeat at additional intervals midway between previously heated zones. Avoid heating the same areas twice as this will not lead to a smooth, sweeping bend.

Line Heating

Line heating is flame bending performed on steel plate, rather than rolled shapes, pipe, tube, or sheet metal. While line heating can be used in a variety of steel fabrication activities, shipbuilding is its principal use. Steel hull plates vary in size but are typically 6'×21'. Hull plate can run from about $^1/_2$" to several inches in thickness.

In the simplest instance, if oxyfuel torch heat is applied along a line in a plate, the plate will contract into a slight V-shape when it has cooled, as in Figure 19-25 (top). If a series of parallel and evenly spaced heat lines is applied, the plate curves evenly across its width, as in Figure 19-25 (center). Adding more heat lines closer together further increases the bend in the plate, as in Figure 19-25 (bottom).

The unbalanced shrinkage forces between the heated and unheated sides cause the angular distortion just as in other heat bending applications.

For line heat spacing see Table 19-2.

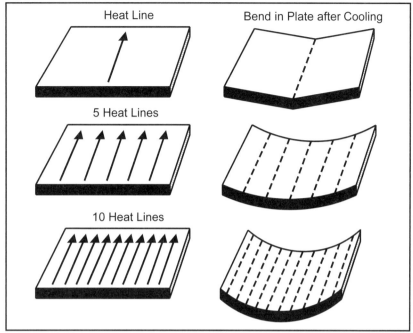

Figure 19-25. Effect of a single heat line on a steel plate (top), effect of multiple heat lines (center), and adding even more heat lines (bottom).

	Heat Line Spacing (inches)
More plate curve	4
↓	6
↓	8
Less plate curve	10

Table 19-2. Typical heat line spacing.

Line Heating Parameters

- *Deflection* – The range of deflection from one heat line on plate steel runs between $3/4$–1 degree for a single heating and cooling cycle.

- *Torch Position* – With the larger, multi-orifice oxyfuel torches used for line heating, a tip-to-plate spacing of between $3/4$–1" will put the hottest part of the flame on the steel and create the maximum bending action.

- *Travel Speed & Flame Path Shape* – There is an optimum line travel speed for maximum deflection. Torch travel that is either too fast or too slow will reduce deflection. Weaving serpentine lines, instead of straight-line travel, increases deflection in a 1" plate by almost 20%. The torch should move rapidly enough that the metal temperature does not exceed 1200°F. Though true that the higher the temperature, the more bending occurs, as mentioned before, we need to limit the maximum temperature to avoid changing the properties of the steel, and for most ship plate steel, this temperature is 1200°F. The exact speed depends on the torch tip, fuel, and oxygen pressures, but $1/2$" steel plate should see a minimum torch speed of 15 inches/minute, and thicker steel, in the 1-2" range, should not fall below 10 inches/minute. Keep in mind that these figures are approximate. When only a small curvature adjustment is needed, line speed may be double the normal speed.

- *Measuring & Regulating Plate Temperature* – Temperature regulating crayons work well to measure maximum metal temperature, but experienced craftsmen tend to watch the color of the steel in subdued light to control temperature. Non-contact, optical pyrometers can also be used.

- *Heat Penetration Depth* – Maximum bending takes place when the line heat penetration reaches the middle of the plate. However, this also causes maximum transverse shrinkage across the plate, perpendicular to the heat lines, so the best compromise between shrinkage and bending is to have line heat penetrate to just short of the center of the plate.

Measuring & Regulating Plate Temperature

Non-contact optical pyrometers are a good way to measure the temperature of the work metal, but these instruments can be pricey and not all shops have them. A good and less expensive method to measure maximum metal temperature is to use *temperature-indicating crayons*. When using temperature indicating crayons, the oxyfuel heating torch is aimed in the direction of torch movement and the crayon is marked on the line-heating path on the steel about 2" behind the torch. If, within two seconds, the plate marking turns color from its initial color as shown in the manufacturer's tables, the calibrated temperature exists on the plate. Tests have shown that, at this two-inch following distance, the steel's temperature falls about 270°F from the under-the-torch temperature. To know the metal temperature directly under the torch we must add back the 270° to the temperature of the crayon.

As mentioned before, many experienced welders simply watch the color of the steel in subdued light to control temperature, but this skill takes time to learn.

Applying Cooling Water

A cooling water stream or a water and compressed air mist is usually applied following the torch along the heat line. This is done for a couple of reasons:

- Cooling maximizes bending by confining the heat to the heat line and maintaining the maximum temperature differential between the heated and the unheated areas.

- The water mist keeps the entire plate at a lower temperature and allows the heat bending cycle to be repeated quickly. However, if only a small bend is needed, cooling water or mist can be omitted.

Controlling Bend

A welder skilled in line heating can match a template to within roughly ± 0.2 inches. Here are some of his methods:

- *Correcting Curves* – If too much curve or bend is applied to a plate, this situation can be reversed by flipping the plate and applying line heat in paths parallel to the initial heat lines.

- *Heat Triangles* – To make a plate concave, or dished, use heat triangles as in Figure 19-26. If two torches are used to apply equal heat to both sides of the plate, balanced contraction occurs. There is no bending, but there is shrinkage after cooling. But, by heating triangular areas on both plate edges at once—this may take more than one torch—shrinkage forms the plate into a concave shape. This is because heat triangles along the edges of the plate will shrink the edges, leaving the center of the plate unshrunk, which makes the plate convex.

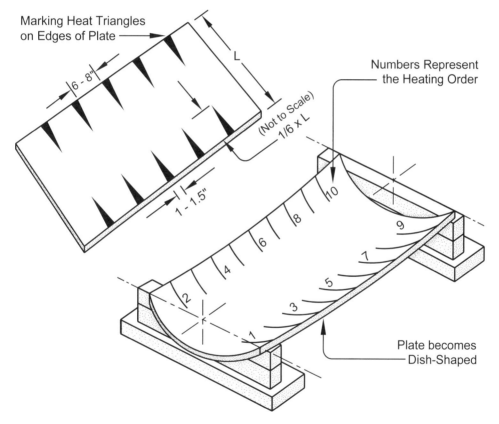

Figure 19-26. Using heat triangles to dish a plate.

- *Using Restraint* – Applying compression stress to the heated side of the plate can double the angular deflection and is a common practice in line heating. This is performed by using wood and steel cleats, which pull the plate up on one side, while dogs are used to hold the plate down against the work surface on the other side. Many times these cleats and dogs are applied at opposite corners to impose twisting forces. See the setup in Figure 19-27. Sometimes a crane is used to apply stress to the work.

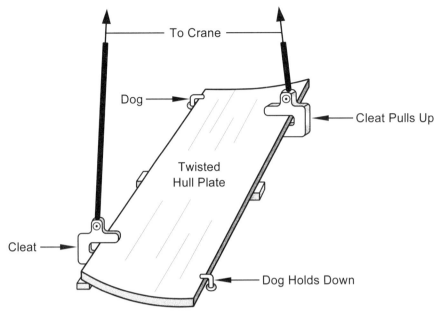

Figure 19-27. When used in combination with line heating, applying restraint and force increases bending. This setup applies twisting forces.

Bending Using Rolls vs. Line Heating

Using bending rolls, also called roll benders, to form plate into a cylinder or sections of a cylinder produces a bend with a *single* constant radius. Using line heating on plates can produce bends with *changing* radii. A gentle bend can transition to a severe bend and there can be several changes in curvature.

Line heating to a great degree can replace roll benders, but roll benders cannot replace line heating. When rolling capacity is limited, line heating can perform the job. Also, it is possible to begin some bending jobs using roll benders and then use line heating to add the final adjustments.

Templates for Checking Curves

Templates are used to insure that the finished plate curves are exactly what are called for in the plans. There are several different template designs:

- *Templates Cut from Plywood* – As in Figure 19-28 (left), plywood patterns with the appropriate curves are placed against the base plate, and if they do not match, additional line heating of the plate is needed. Each template can reproduce only one curve.

- *Curved-Base Templates* – Figure 19-28 (top right) shows a reusable template consisting of a flexible base with attached metal slides, which are secured by wing nuts to a rigid horizontal bar. This reusable template can be configured into many different curves including compound curves.

- *Adjustable-Rod Templates* – This style of template, shown in Figure 19-28 (bottom right), consists of a rigid horizontal bar with holes drilled to accept adjustable rods or posts. This reusable design can be configured for complex, multiple curves.

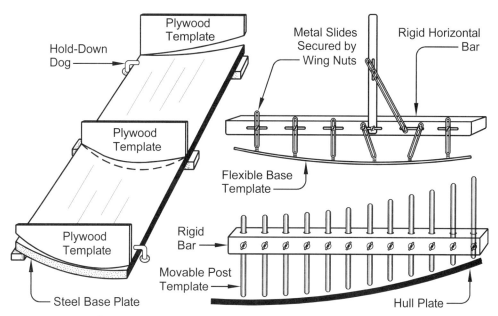

Figure 19-28. Templates used for checking line plate curves.

Section VI – Flame Shrinking Techniques

Flame shrinking can be used to restore metal that has been distorted by cutting or welding heat back to its original shape. For example, when an oxyfuel flame is used to cut a circle from a steel plate, after the plate cools to room temperature, the circle is no longer flat; it bulges in the middle creating a dish shape.

Here is why this dishing occurs: Because the torch heat expands the donut-shaped area around the edges of the circular plate, this outer ring of hot steel is constrained from expanding freely by the cooler metal in the center of the plate. When the thermal forces exceed the yield strength of the steel, this outer donut of steel is stretched to fit the existing cooler inner area. Then, upon cooling, the outer ring shrinks more than the inner—remember, the inner ring is already cool—squeezing the inner excess material into a dish or dome shape as in Figure 19-29 (A).

Here is how to correct this situation: To once more make the circular plate flat, the excess material in the center of the circle must be removed. To do this we simply reverse the heating process. First, apply torch heat to the center of the circle, then let the cool outer material contain the hot inner material. When this center material cools, it will shrink and remove the dome of excess material as in Figure 19-29 (B). Often several heating and cooling cycles are needed to completely eliminate the dome. To speed this process and to prevent the entire disc from getting hot when we want only the center portion to receive heat, the water spray apparatus in Figure 19-21 can be very helpful.

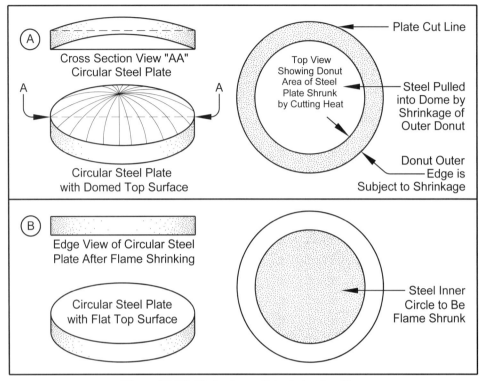

Figure 19-29. Flattening a dished circular disc.

Removing Ripples from a Panel

This problem is just like the excess material in the center of a steel plate. The only difference is the source of the heat causing the distortion is from welding heat, not cutting heat. The solution is the same: Apply oxyfuel heat to the center of the affected panels and shrink them with a water spray. Several heating and cooling cycles are usually required. This ripple-removing procedure is a common shipyard process in which one welder heats the panels with a rosebud tip and another welder follows with a water spray. See the welded panel in Figure 19-30.

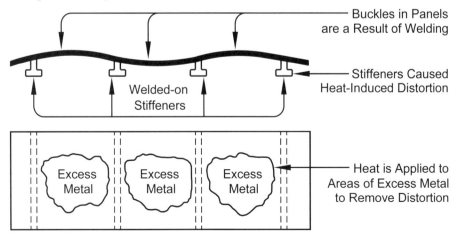

Figure 19-30. Removing ripples in the center of a welded panel.

Removing Distortion from Fences & Railings

Fences and railings made of pipe, tubing or shaped steel are often fabricated by welding the top rail to vertical posts. The problem with this process it that welding shrinkage causes the top rail to deform and pull down on each side of the vertical posts giving the top rail a wavy appearance, as in Figure 19-31.

This problem does have a solution: Flame straightening. To do this, start by applying an oxyfuel flame on top of the rail above the welds. Initially heat an area about 2" long that extends about $\frac{1}{3}$ of the circumference of the pipe or tube above each weld as in the top of Figure 19-31. Several heating cycles will probably be required to flatten the top rail. Until you've gained experience, it is best to perform several small heat cycles than to apply too much heat at once and overshoot the mark with excess correction. No one wants to fix the fix. Always begin flame straightening in smaller areas until you see how much correcting heat is needed.

Here are some other tips for avoiding problems building fences and railings:

- Fit the steel to minimize gaps that must be filled with weld metal. Remember, the more weld metal, the greater the shrinkage.

- Minimize the size of the weld beads themselves.

- For better results, begin welding in the middle and work out toward the ends of the fence.

- To reduce cambering, heat the top of each fence rail over the welds either right before welding or right after.

- Bends in what should be straight fence rails will be noticeable if they exceed $\frac{1}{8}$" in a 2' run.

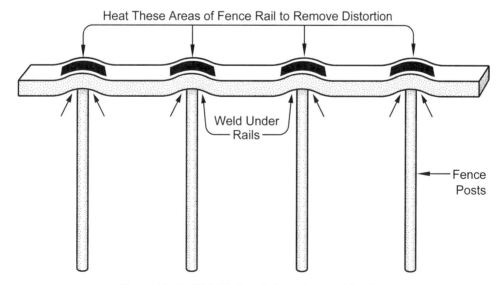

Figure 19-31. Weld-induced distortion resulting in a
wavy fence rail and the solution to the problem.

Section VII – Shop-Made Fixture for Bending Steel Rod into Rings or Links

Figure 19-32 shows how to bend rings around a mandrel.

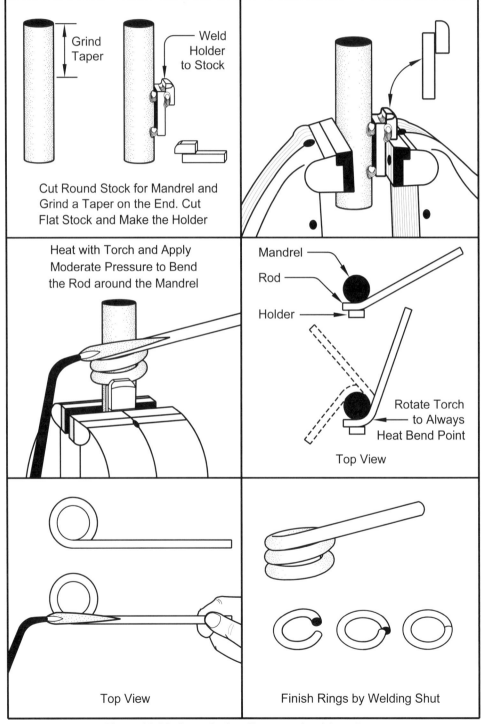

Figure 19-32. Steps for bending a steel rod into rings.

Index

Picture Credits

The author gratefully acknowledges the organizations and individuals who have contributed photographs, illustrations and copyright permissions for this book. These photos and graphics were redrawn and modified by the illustrator to match the style and format of this book.

Aladdin Welding Products, Inc., Figure 11-6.

American Beauty – Assembly Technologies International, Inc., Figures 11-28 & 11-30.

American Welding Society Publications, Figures 3-2, 3-4, 3-5, 3-8, 3-9, 3-16, 3-18, 3-19, 3-20, 3-21, 3-24, 3-25, 3-27, 3-28, 3-29, 5-2, 5-6, 5-7, 5-8, 5-9, 5-10, 5-11, 6-6, 6-7, 6-8, 6-9, 6-10, 6-11, 6-12, 6-13, 6-14, 6-15, 6-16, 6-17, 6-18, 6-19, 6-24, 6-25, 6-26, 7-1, 7-5, 7-7, 7-8, 7-9, 7-10, 7-17, 7-29, 8-19, 9-8, 9-9, 9-10, 9-11, 9-12, 9-13, 9-14, 9-15, 9-20, 9-21, 9-22, 9-26, 10-2, 10-4, 10-5, 10-6, 10-11, 10-12, 10-13, 10-14, 10-21, 10-22, 10-35, 10-36, 10-37, 11-3, 11-4, 11-24, 11-25, 14-31, 15-32, 17-1, 17-3, 17-4, 17-5, 17-9, 17-14, 17-15, 18-8, 18-9, 18-18, 18-20 & 18-2; Tables 5-2, 5-5, 6-5, 6-6, 6-7, 7-5, 7-7, 8-1, 8-3, 8-4 & 10-1.

Applied Home Healthcare Equipment, LLC for Superflash Flame Arresters, Figures 8-23 & 8-24.

Copper Development Association Inc., Figures 11-1, 11-32, 11-33, 11-34, 11-35 & 11-36.

Di-Acro, Incorporated, Figures 19-5, 19-6, 19-7, 19-8, 19-9, 19-10, 19-11, 19-12, 19-13 & 19-14.

ESAB Welding & Cutting Products, Inc., Figures 2-3, 2-4, 8-25, 8-26, 9-5, 9-6 & 9-7.

Industrial Press Inc., Figures 1-5, 1-8, 1-10, 4-1, 4-3, 4-5, 4-6, 4-7, 4-11, 4-14, 4-27, 6-2, 8-3, 8-4, 8-6, 8-8, 8-9, 8-10, 8-11, 8-12, 8-15, 8-18, 8-20, 9-16, 10-3, 10-27, 10-34, 10-41, 11-2, 11-8, 11-9, 11-26, 11-27, 11-31, 11-37, 11-38, 12-1, 12-2, 12-7, 12-8, 12-9, 12-10, 12-11, 12-12, 12-14, 12-15, 12-16, 12-17, 12-19, 12-21, 12-22, 14-1, 14-2, 14-3, 14-5, 14-6, 14-7, 14-8, 14-9, 14-15, 14-19, 14-20, 14-25,14-26, 14-27, 14-28, 14-29, 14-30, 14-41, 14-43, 14-44, 14-45, 14-46, 14-47, 14-48, 14-49, 16-2, 16-3, 16-4, 16-5, 16-6, 16-7, 16-11, 16-13, 16-14, 16-15, 16-16, 16-17, 16-18, 16-19, 16-20, 16-21, 16-22, 16-27, 16-28, 16-29, 16-30, 16-31, 16-32, 16-33, 16-34, 16-35, 18-16, & 18-17; Table 16-3.

James F. Lincoln Arc Welding Foundation, Publisher of *Design of Weldments* and *Design of Welded Structures* by Omar Blodgett, Figures 1-7, 3-23, 9-17, 12-24, 12-26, 12-27, 12-28, 13-1, 13-2, 13-3, 13-5,13-6, 13-7, 13-8, 13-9, 13-10, 13-11, 13-12, 13-13, 13-14, 13-15, 13-16, 13-17, 13-18, 13-19, 13,20, 13-21, 13-22, 13-23, 13-24, 13-25, 14-10, 14-11, 14-12, 14-13, 14-33, 14-34, 14-35, 14-36, 14-37, 14-38 & 14-42.

Lincoln Electric Company, Tables 5-1, 5-3 & 13-1.

The L.S. Starrett Company, Figure 17-12.

Mathey Dearman, Inc., Figure 16-8 (center).

Miller Electric Mfg. Co., Figure 10-23.

David Randal, Figures 1-6, 3-13, 5-12, 7-25, 7-26, 7-27, 7-30, 7-31, 11-10, 11-11, 11-12, 11-13, 11-14, 11-15, 11-16, 11-17, 11-18, 11-19, 11-20, 11-22, 12-3, 12-4, 12-5, 12-6, 12-18, 12-20, 12-23, 12-30, 13-4, 14-14, 14-17, 14-18, 14-22, 14-23, 14-24, 14-40, 14-51, 14-52, 14-53, 15-2, 15-3, 15-4, 15-6, 15-10, 15-12, 15-13, 15-14, 15-15, 15-16, 15-17, 15-19, 15-20, 15-21, 15-22, 15-23, 15-24, 15-25, 15-26, 15-27, 15-28,15-29, 15-30, 15-31, 15-36, 15-29, 15-30, 15-31,15-37, 15-38, 15-38, 15-39, 15-41 & 19-32.

Oxylance Corporation, Figure 10-43 & Table 10-7.

Don Tallman, Figure 15-40.

Thermadyne Industries, Inc., Table 11-2.

Van Sant Enterprises Inc., Figure 16-23.

Vise-Grip – American Tool Companies, Inc., Figures 4-8 & 4-10.

Wallonde Tools, Inc., Figure 16-8 (top & bottom left).

Weldsale Company, Figures 4-20 & 4-21.

The author regrets any omissions from this list, and would appreciate being advised about them so that the records can be corrected.